Fundamentals of Petroleum

Fifth Edition

published by

THE UNIVERSITY OF TEXAS

CONTINUING & INNOVATIVE EDUCATION
PETROLEUM EXTENSION SERVICE

2011

Library of Congress Cataloging-in-Publication Data

Fundamentals of petroleum. — 5th ed.
   p. cm.
 Includes bibliographical references and index.
 ISBN 0-88698-231-6 (alk. paper)
 1. Petroleum.
 TN870.F86 2010
 665.5—dc22

2010044626

Disclaimer

Although all reasonable care has been taken in preparing this publication, the authors, the Petroleum Extension Service (PETEX) of The University of Texas at Austin, and any other individuals and their affiliated groups involved in preparing this content assume no responsibility for the consequences of its use. Each recipient should ensure he or she is properly trained and informed about the unique policies and practices regarding application of the information contained herein. Any recommendations, descriptions, and methods in this book are presented solely for educational purposes.

Catalog No. 1.00050
ISBN 0-88698-231-6
978-0-88698-231-7

*The University of Texas at Austin is an equal opportunity institution.
No state tax funds were used to print this book.*

Editor: Debby Denehy

Graphic Designer: Debbie Caples

Cover Art: E. K. Weaver

Contents

Figures

Tables

Foreword

In the 1970s, the average American realized how oil affected everyday life. Crude oil prices spiked to their highest ever, and Americans had to wait in line for gasoline. The high price of oil spurred new exploration for oil, and producing states like Texas experienced an economic boom. By this time, the Petroleum Extension Service (PETEX®) of the University of Texas had established itself in the oil and gas industry as a quality provider of training books and courses. But even within the industry, there was a growing market niche waiting to be filled.

As the oil and gas industry grew, a large number of new workers flooded the ranks in need of broad, reliable knowledge they could obtain quickly. Many of these new workers had no direct experience with the oil patch but were called upon to understand the processes, equipment, and jargon of the field. Just over 30 years ago, the Association of Desk and Derrick Clubs, a national organization of administrative oil and gas industry workers, approached PETEX about creating a book that gives general workers a basic overview of the entire industry, using an approach that laypeople understand. PETEX agreed, and the first edition of *Fundamentals of Petroleum* was born.

Now in its fifth edition, the book has expanded its reach to address the educational needs of a wide range of industry personnel, from accountants and bankers to insurance agents and executives. Its breadth of coverage provides a valuable reference for all oil industry professionals, some of whom are so specialized that they have limited exposure to other aspects of the industry. As a reference tool, *Fundamentals of Petroleum* has become an industry staple. Throughout its three decades of publication, evolving editions, and increasingly diverse audience, the book has stayed remarkably close to the original concept. Today, the book supports educational programs of many types. Not only is it a supporting text for PETEX classroom courses, it also serves as a textbook for some university petroleum engineering programs and petroleum technology schools.

The book still tells the end-to-end story of petroleum, from geology and exploration all the way through drilling, production, and distribution. It includes new content on cutting-edge technologies, petroleum economics, and alternative energy. Also featured is expanded content on well control and safety and environmental concerns, especially timely inclusions considering the 2010 developments in the Gulf of Mexico. The 2011 edition is available as an e-book and there is also a separate e-assessment tool to test what readers learned.

Oil was headline news in the 1970s and remains so today. Volatile gasoline prices, climate change legislation, speculation about peak oil, and the 2010 incident in the Gulf of Mexico are just a few of the ways oil and gas affects our lives and our futures. More than ever, oil and gas are everyone's business, and with the fifth edition of *Fundamentals of Petroleum*, PETEX hopes to continue explaining the essentials of the industry to an ever-wider audience.

Preface

The world's appetite for energy is expected to increase about 50% in the next twenty years. When you consider our growing industrialized population and the way we consume energy, it is no wonder we have to reach outside usual limits and discover new ways to find and extract the oil and gas we will need. Professionals with advanced expertise are fast developing precision technologies to clearly examine areas beneath the Earth's surface. They are innovating new techniques to maximize yields in existing tracts and drill even deeper to locate and recover resources in areas once considered too problematic.

PETEX® understands these challenges. With the recent economic shifts and Big Crew Change of seasoned skills retiring from the industry, there has never been a time when training has been more important. PETEX is responding to this need by providing this updated fifth edition of an important and highly comprehensive publication that has been an industry staple for decades—*Fundamentals of Petroleum*. The fifth edition has been expanded to deliver current illustrated information to help individuals from all walks of industry understand and perform their jobs better. The book has been enhanced with the help of numerous global industry experts with exact experience in their respective fields, representing major companies, organizations, and independent entities.

Fundamentals of Petroleum travels around the globe functioning in support of training programs, including courses offered by PETEX in Houston and West Texas. It is also used as a training text for large and small companies worldwide and is frequently requested to self-train individuals seeking to enter the oil and gas industry. Several university and high school petroleum engineering and technology programs rely on this material as a textbook for courses offered. The book has proven to be a useful reference tool for generations of petroleum industry personnel. Therefore, I am pleased to present this new edition that is both for and about the industry's Next Generation of petroleum workers.

Dr. A. Lee Hunt, President
International Association of Drilling Contractors (IADC)
Houston, Texas

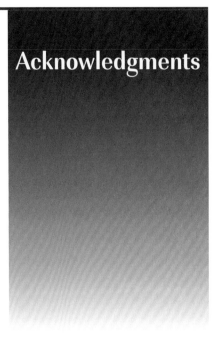

Acknowledgments

The updated content for this fifth edition of *Fundamentals of Petroleum* was graciously and expertly provided by multiple subject-matter experts who are well known and respected in specific fields of expertise. The authors are gratefully acknowledged preceding each of the five parts of this book. In addition to the primary authors, PETEX® appreciates the support of many peer reviewers who helped validate the content and contribute to the completion of this comprehensive edition:

Alan Morgan of Access Exploration
Brian Anderson of SeaBird Exploration
Janet Combes, independent geoscientist consultant
Jane Williams, measurement consultant and PETEX instructor
John Thorogood of Weatherford International
Kevin Lindemer, President of Kevin J. Lindemer, LLC
Mark Mitchell of Weatherford International
Said Boutalbi of Weatherford International
Walter Heitz, refining consultant and PETEX instructor

PETEX also expresses appreciation to the many companies and individuals who loaned photographs, charts, and other graphic images to help demonstrate concepts within this book. Thanks go to the International Association of Drilling Contractors (IADC) for their continued support, and our many loyal customers over the years who continue to use this content in their training programs. PETEX also acknowledges the Association of Desk and Derricks Clubs for inspiring PETEX to create this valuable publication more than 30 years ago.

The new edition of *Fundamentals of Petroleum* would not be possible without the hard work of those who helped refine the text and perform research and production functions. Thank you to Debbie Caples, Graphics Services Manager; Chris Parker and Josh Bauermeister, editors; E.K. Weaver, graphic artist; Sherry Rodriguez and Leah Lehmann, publication assistants; and Fran Kennedy-Ellis, Julia Ruggeri, and Ron Baker—all of whom participated in the process of developing and producing this book.

As an additional note, PETEX acknowledges the long-term assistance of proofreader Doris Dickey who kept a watchful eye over corrections to the various editions of this book over the years. Although she is no longer with us, she remains an integral part of the book's history and spirit.

Debby Denehy, Managing Editor
Petroleum Extension Service (PETEX)
The University of Texas at Austin

Units of Measurement

Throughout the world, two systems of measurement dominate: the English system and the metric system. Today, the United States is one of only a few countries that employ the English system.

The English system uses the pound as the unit of weight, the foot as the unit of length, and the gallon as the unit of capacity. In the English system, for example, 1 foot equals 12 inches, 1 yard equals 36 inches, and 1 mile equals 5,280 feet or 1,760 yards.

The metric system uses the gram as the unit of weight, the metre as the unit of length, and the litre as the unit of capacity. In the metric system, 1 metre equals 10 decimetres, 100 centimetres, or 1,000 millimetres. A kilometre equals 1,000 metres. The metric system, unlike the English system, uses a base of 10; thus, it is easy to convert from one unit to another. To convert from one unit to another in the English system, you must memorize or look up the values.

In the late 1970s, the Eleventh General Conference on Weights and Measures described and adopted the Systeme International (SI) d'Unites. Conference participants based the SI system on the metric system and designed it as an international standard of measurement.

The Rotary Drilling Series gives both English and SI units. And because the SI system employs the British spelling of many of the terms, the book follows those spelling rules as well. The unit of length, for example, is metre, not meter. (Note, however, that the unit of weight is gram, not gramme.)

To aid U.S. readers in making and understanding the conversion system, we include the table on the next page.

English-Units-to-SI-Units Conversion Factors

Quantity or Property	English Units	Multiply English Units By	To Obtain These SI Units
Length, depth, or height	inches (in.)	25.4	millimetres (mm)
		2.54	centimetres (cm)
	feet (ft)	0.3048	metres (m)
	yards (yd)	0.9144	metres (m)
	miles (mi)	1609.344	metres (m)
		1.61	kilometres (km)
Hole and pipe diameters, bit size	inches (in.)	25.4	millimetres (mm)
Drilling rate	feet per hour (ft/h)	0.3048	metres per hour (m/h)
Weight on bit	pounds (lb)	0.445	decanewtons (dN)
Nozzle size	32nds of an inch	0.8	millimetres (mm)
Volume	barrels (bbl)	0.159	cubic metres (m³)
		159	litres (L)
	gallons per stroke (gal/stroke)	0.00379	cubic metres per stroke (m³/stroke)
	ounces (oz)	29.57	millilitres (mL)
	cubic inches (in.³)	16.387	cubic centimetres (cm³)
	cubic feet (ft³)	28.3169	litres (L)
		0.0283	cubic metres (m³)
	quarts (qt)	0.9464	litres (L)
	gallons (gal)	3.7854	litres (L)
	gallons (gal)	0.00379	cubic metres (m³)
	pounds per barrel (lb/bbl)	2.895	kilograms per cubic metre (kg/m³)
	barrels per ton (bbl/tn)	0.175	cubic metres per tonne (m³/t)
Pump output and flow rate	gallons per minute (gpm)	0.00379	cubic metres per minute (m³/min)
	gallons per hour (gph)	0.00379	cubic metres per hour (m³/h)
	barrels per stroke (bbl/stroke)	0.159	cubic metres per stroke (m³/stroke)
	barrels per minute (bbl/min)	0.159	cubic metres per minute (m³/min)
Pressure	pounds per square inch (psi)	6.895	kilopascals (kPa)
		0.006895	megapascals (MPa)
Temperature	degrees Fahrenheit (°F)	$\dfrac{°F - 32}{1.8}$	degrees Celsius (°C)
Mass (weight)	ounces (oz)	28.35	grams (g)
	pounds (lb)	453.59	grams (g)
		0.4536	kilograms (kg)
	tons (tn)	0.9072	tonnes (t)
	pounds per foot (lb/ft)	1.488	kilograms per metre (kg/m)
Mud weight	pounds per gallon (ppg)	119.82	kilograms per cubic metre (kg/m³)
	pounds per cubic foot (lb/ft³)	16.0	kilograms per cubic metre (kg/m³)
Pressure gradient	pounds per square inch per foot (psi/ft)	22.621	kilopascals per metre (kPa/m)
Funnel viscosity	seconds per quart (s/qt)	1.057	seconds per litre (s/L)
Yield point	pounds per 100 square feet (lb/100 ft²)	0.48	pascals (Pa)
Gel strength	pounds per 100 square feet (lb/100 ft²)	0.48	pascals (Pa)
Filter cake thickness	32nds of an inch	0.8	millimetres (mm)
Power	horsepower (hp)	0.75	kilowatts (kW)
Area	square inches (in.²)	6.45	square centimetres (cm²)
	square feet (ft²)	0.0929	square metres (m²)
	square yards (yd²)	0.8361	square metres (m²)
	square miles (mi²)	2.59	square kilometres (km²)
	acre (ac)	0.40	hectare (ha)
Drilling line wear	ton-miles (tn•mi)	14.317	megajoules (MJ)
		1.459	tonne-kilometres (t•km)
Torque	foot-pounds (ft•lb)	1.3558	newton metres (N•m)

HOW TO USE THIS BOOK

It is recommended that this book be read in sequence first to absorb the full end-to-end story of petroleum, beginning with geology and ending with alternative energy sources. It can also be used as an ongoing reference for specific information on topics of interest.

- Chapter objectives, callouts, and summaries help highlight major points for readers.

- Hundreds of color images visually support the text to enhance learning.

- An index is included for convenience in looking up topics.

- Italicized terms are defined in *A Dictionary for the Oil and Gas Industry*, 2nd Edition, available as a separate product.

- Two reading formats are available for reader preference: print and e-book.

- A separate online assessment is also available to test learning comprehension. Readers who successfully complete the assessment will receive a *Certificate of Completion* and Continuing Education Credits (CEUs) that can be useful career advancement tools.

- A companion course aligned with this publication is also offered at the PETEX Houston and West Texas Training Centers and at client locations upon request.

Reader feedback is welcomed so we can continue to refine this publication for the benefit of all users. Please contact us with any corrections or revisions necessary for future editions. As always, PETEX strives to provide quality content to enhance industry workplace performance.

Petroleum Extension Service
The University of Texas at Austin
Global Training Solutions Since 1944
www.utexas.edu/ce/petex
Phone: 800.687.4132
E-mail: petex@www.utexas.edu

THE DEMAND FOR OIL

Oil is used in nearly every aspect of life from fuel for cars, trucks, and planes to plastics, clothing, food additives, and medicines. In fact, it is nearly impossible to find some aspect of modern lives that does not require or depend on oil. Without oil, there would be no global economy. Modern society cannot function without oil.

On average, every person in the world consumes about 195 gallons (738 litres) of oil per year. In the United States, consumption per person is five times that level, while in China it is about half the world average. Although oil is used for nearly everything, it is peoples' need to be mobile and the desire for more freedom of mobility that are the major forces driving oil demand today. As a result, more than half of oil consumption is used for transportation. Demand in developed countries is maturing, while economic growth in developing countries is dependent on oil as transportation systems and wealth grow.

The need for oil continues to increase. Demand has been rising steadily in nearly all regions of the world for the past 25 years. The demand for oil—the collective needs of the oil industry's final customers—drives all other aspects of the oil industry. These needs have changed over time and are expected to continue evolving as consumers and policies change. Changes in oil demand in the short and medium term (one to five years) are largely determined by price movements, economic growth, and weather. Over the longer term, demand is determined by end-user investment decisions and government policy.

In the past few years, growth in oil demand has slowed due to the impact of higher prices, and volume demand has fallen in 2008 and 2009 due to the effects of the global economic recession. But as economies around the world recover, so will oil demand. The rate of growth and the characteristics of demand are likely to change in the post-economic recovery.

Shares of Global Demand

Fuel Type		Regional Oil Demand		Sector Oil Demand	
Coal	26%	North America	30%	Residential/Commercial	12%
Oil	37%	South America	7%	Industry	8%
Gas	23%	Europe	20%	Feedstock	8%
Hydro	6%	Eurasia	5%	Transportation	52%
Nuclear	6%	Middle East	7%	Power Generation	7%
Renewable	1%	Asia	28%	Misc.	12%
		Africa	4%		

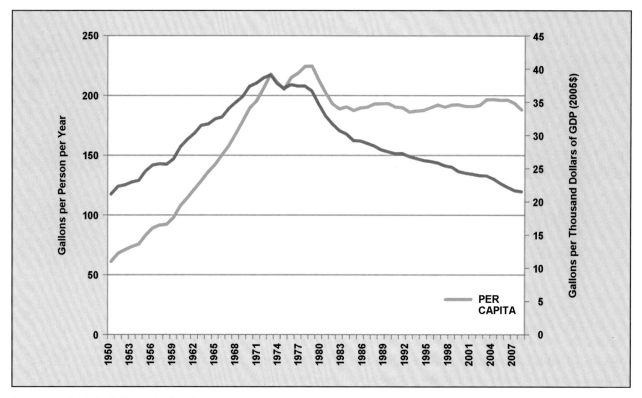

Figure 1. Global oil demand—key drivers

From Past to Present   The history of global oil demand can be divided into three distinct eras (fig. 1):

- **Pre-1973:** Driven by both economic and population growth, world oil demand grew quickly. Rapid industrialization and increasing populations with rising personal incomes combined with cheap abundant oil resulted in a steady rise in global oil demand. The relationships between economic growth, population growth, and oil demand growth were relatively stable.

- **1973 to 1980:** These years were a transition period from the pre-1973 era of cheap oil to a political and price environment characterized by high oil prices, a prevailing view that prices would continue to rise (to safeguard against running out of oil), and policies that would move major economics away from oil.

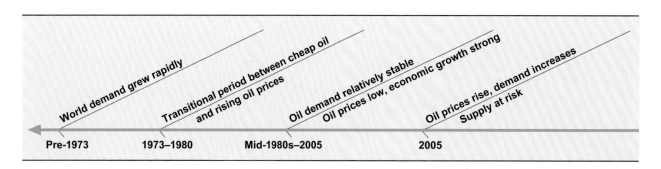

- **Mid-1980s to present:** Since the early to middle 1980s, oil demand had been in a period of relative stability. Oil prices were low and global economic growth was strong. However, the relationships had changed from previous periods. Trends for oil demand per person were flat, and oil demand per dollar of Gross Domestic Product (GDP) fell at a steady rate during this period.

Over the last 25 years, oil's importance to the global economy has been gradually declining:

- Oil use per dollar of GDP has declined at a steady rate, regardless of the rate of economic growth.
- Oil use per person worldwide has been stable for 25 years—between 190 and 200 gallons (719 and 757 litres) per person per year. While rising in some emerging markets, use per person has begun to decline in some major markets such as Japan and Germany.

Regardless of the various changes in oil consumption from one country to another or the rate of economic growth in emerging markets compared to developed economies, the stability in per-capita consumption of oil indicates that on average, world oil demand growth is largely driven by population growth. In some emerging market countries, combined population growth and economic growth are causing oil demand to rise, while demand is maturing and even falling in some developed countries. However, worldwide, the amount of oil needed to create $1,000 of economic growth has been declining steadily since the mid-1980s. In other words, the global economy is becoming more efficient in its use of oil, at a rate of about 1.5% per year. In 2010, it takes about 19 gallons (72 litres) of oil to create $1,000 of economic output. By comparison, it took nearly 40 gallons (151 litres) for the same economic output in the early 1970s.

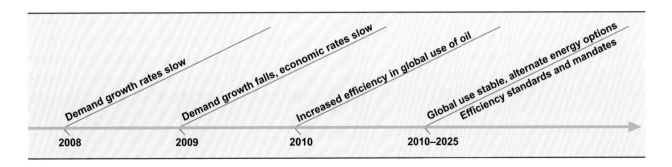

From the early 1980s to about 2005, the price of oil on average was the price needed to work off the spare capacity in the system. This price level encouraged a rise in consumption and, at the same time, discouraged growth in oil production. During this period, events such as hurricanes, cold weather, wars, and accidents that typically impact oil markets had an impact on prices, but these effects were hardly noticed by consumers—at least not in a way that would alter demand patterns in any sustainable manner. Despite relatively low prices and strong economic growth, global oil demand grew at the same rate as population growth.

By 2005, the spare capacity of OPEC—the Organization of Petroleum Exporting Countries—and consequently, the spare capacity of the industry, was essentially zero. Very quickly, oil prices increased to levels unthinkable just a short time before. As demand increased or supply was suddenly perceived to be at risk, prices kept rising. There was no more spare capacity to bring online to meet market demand. As a result, prices shifted to reflect the price level needed to slow down or reduce oil demand. Events, such as hurricanes and political developments, had significant impact on *spot* (immediate) *prices* and consumer prices.

The years 2008 and 2009 might well be one of the rare major turning points in the history of oil demand. By 2008, signs of the impact of high oil prices on demand were beginning to materialize. Countries that subsidized consumer oil prices were raising prices, thereby causing demand growth rates to slow. U.S. consumers began to reduce gasoline consumption and air travel. By 2008, global oil demand growth had slowed to zero, and demand in 2009 fell 2.4 %—the largest fall in oil demand since 1980—as a result of the global economic recession and very high oil prices in 2008.

What Does the Future Hold?

As happened in the late 1970s and early 1980s, the oil industry is experiencing a once-in-a-generation level of change in demand for its products. The global energy picture and that of the United States are being reshaped by prices and politics to a degree not seen since the 1970s. Oil's recent past is unprecedented. Numerous events and developments have occurred in a relatively short period of time. Some individual factors will have significant implications for future oil demand, and taken collectively, impacts could have long-term implications unlike anything experienced in the past. Some examples of recent events and government actions are:

- Hurricanes that severely disrupt U.S. refinery production.
- Oil prices rising to $140 per barrel, causing U.S. retail gasoline prices to exceed $4 per gallon for much of the summer of 2008.
- Vehicle efficiency standards that passed in several of the world's major oil markets, including the United States, the European Union, Japan, and China, which are set to take effect over the next 10 to 15 years.

- Biofuel mandates and targets that displace oil from transportation fuels by 20% or more in the United States, India, the European Union, and Brazil, which are to be established by 2020. Several other countries have much smaller requirements.

- Regulations that reduce carbon emissions and have further implications for oil use.

It could be that oil demand is entering a new, fourth era. Over the next decade and beyond, oil use per dollar of GDP is likely to decline at a faster rate than during the past 25 years, and oil use per capita could begin to decline. As occurred in the 1970s, over the past few years, governments around the world have begun to enact policies to reduce oil demand. Around the world, major oil importing countries are adjusting their energy and environmental policies to guide countries to lower energy intensity, economic growth, and greater energy security. These actions are driven by two major forces: a concern that oil prices will return to the extreme levels of 2006 to 2008 and damage economic recovery and growth, and the need to reduce greenhouse gas emissions to address global warming.

For the first time since the beginning of the oil age, the cost of consuming oil might be higher that the economic benefit of its use. Governments around the world now agree that global climate change poses a real threat to mankind and must be addressed urgently. With transportation the largest single source of carbon dioxide emissions in the United States and second only to coal worldwide, reducing carbon emissions from transportation is a critical component in the effort to reduce greenhouse gas emissions. Reducing greenhouse gas emissions from oil means using less oil, either through higher efficiency or by using substitutes such as biofuels. Countries worldwide are doing both.

Efforts to reduce oil demand through legislation are now unprecedented in the history of oil use. Government initiatives are also supported by tax incentives and mandates that help ensure goals are met. In addition, as these changes gradually begin to impact overall oil demand in the oil-consuming countries of Japan, China, India, Brazil, and the United States, other countries might adopt similar measures, putting additional pressure on oil use around the world.

Pre-1973	1973-1980	Mid-1980s to 2010	2010 and Beyond
Increasing populations	Growth in global demand	Oil demand stabilizing	Unprecedented change
Rapid industrialization	Rising oil prices	Declining oil prices	Global recession
Rising personal incomes	Economic movement from oil	Strong economic growth	Impactful policies and events
Abundant cheap oil	Perceived supply shortage	Emerging energy alternatives	A new era of oil

Past experience is critical in helping us to form the basis for future decisions and plans. The oil industry has an abundance of data and information with which to analyze past oil demand and give insights about the future. But a key question of analysts today remains. Even with good data and analysis available, is the past a good indicator of the future of oil and energy demand? This and other questions will be discussed in the chapters that follow. While future oil demand growth is much less certain now than at nearly any time in the past 25 years, the oil industry and the study of energy markets promises to be more exciting and challenging than it has been in at least a generation.

Kevin J. Lindemer
Independent Energy Research Consultant
Kevin J. Lindemer, LLC

Kevin Lindemer has over twenty-five years of experience in the oil and downstream petroleum industries and is an expert on the global oil industry. He specializes in downstream refining and marketing operations and has worked on consulting and research projects in the energy, biofuels, and downstream oil business worldwide. He holds an MS in Agricultural and Applied Economics and a BS in Plant Pathology with emphasis in economics and chemistry.

PART 1
Exploration

The Authors

GEOLOGY

Christopher Zahm

Bureau of Economic Geology
The University of Texas at Austin

Christopher Zahm is a leading expert in fractured reservoir characterization, including the interpretation of structural folds and faults in seismic. He works with both outcrops and subsurface data to build 3D geologic models used by the petroleum industry. Zahm teaches Petroleum Basin Evaluation and conducts research at the University's Reservoir Characterization Research Laboratory. His research focuses on predicting the distribution of faults and fractures in the subsurface to understand how these features influence fluid flow within petroleum reservoirs. Zahm's career includes key former positions at ConocoPhillips, iReservoir, Colorado School of Mines, and as a consultant to several independent oil and gas companies. He holds a BSC in Geology and Geophysics from the University of Wisconsin, an MS in Geology from The University of Texas at Austin, and a PhD in Geology from the Colorado School of Mines.

EXPLORATION

Christi Gell

Global Business Development,
Earth Modeling
Landmark Graphics, Halliburton

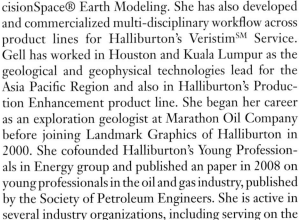

Christi Gell develops and executes sales and growth strategy for DecisionSpace® Earth Modeling. She has also developed and commercialized multi-disciplinary workflow across product lines for Halliburton's Veristim℠ Service. Gell has worked in Houston and Kuala Lumpur as the geological and geophysical technologies lead for the Asia Pacific Region and also in Halliburton's Production Enhancement product line. She began her career as an exploration geologist at Marathon Oil Company before joining Landmark Graphics of Halliburton in 2000. She cofounded Halliburton's Young Professionals in Energy group and published an paper in 2008 on young professionals in the oil and gas industry, published by the Society of Petroleum Engineers. She is active in several industry organizations, including serving on the membership committee of the American Association of Petroleum Geologists. She holds an M.S. in Geology from the University of Houston and a B.S. in Geology from The University of Texas at Austin.

MINERAL RIGHTS AND LEASING

Dan McCue

Director of Land Management
Calera Corporation

Dan McCue is Director of Land Management for Calera Corporation of Los Gatos, California. Additionally, since 1995, McCue has been an instructor at the PETEX Houston Training Center teaching Aspects of Leasing and Joint Venture Partnerships, both onshore the United States and along the Outer Continental Shelf.

Prior to Calera, McCue served Spinnaker Exploration Company as Senior Landman. From 1998 to 2007, McCue was responsible for Spinnaker's lease acquisitions, negotiating commercial deals, drafting operating, farmout, and production handling agreements, and coordinating all competitor analysis for federal lease sales in both shelf and deepwater Gulf of Mexico.

Following the sale of Spinnaker Exploration to Norske Hydro, McCue joined newly formed Beryl Oil and Gas LP as Vice President of Land in 2007. There he was responsible for creating Beryl's Land Department for the integration of newly acquired Gulf of Mexico assets. In 2009, Beryl was sold to Dynamic Offshore Resources.

McCue has a B.B.A. in Petroleum Land Management from The University of Texas at Austin. He then spent 18 years with Amoco Production Company as a Senior Land Negotiator, assigned to various regions of the United States including Alaska.

In this chapter:

- The basic concepts of geology
- The origin of petroleum
- Types of rock and their formations
- The importance of porosity and permeability
- How reservoir pressure influences flow

1.1
Petroleum Geology

The science of geology deals with the origin, history, and physical structure of the Earth and its life, as recorded in rocks. An understanding of the basic principles of geology is essential to the petroleum industry, because most petroleum is found in underground formations made of rock.

Geologists try to answer such questions as: How old is the Earth? Where did the Earth come from? What is the Earth made of? And how has the Earth changed through time? Geologists study the evidence of events occurring millions of years ago, such as earthquakes, volcanoes, and drifting continents and relate these to similar events happening today. They look for evidence of the locations of ancient rivers, deltas, beaches, and oceans and try to decipher how these features shifted position with time. They also research the composition of rocks in the Earth's crust. In their intensive analysis of the Earth, geologists also draw on information from many other sciences, such as astronomy, chemistry, physics, and biology.

The petroleum geologist is primarily concerned with rocks that contain oil and gas, particularly rocks that contain enough petroleum to be commercially valuable. The company that drills for oil wants a reasonable chance of making a profit on its eventual sale, factoring in market price, the amount of recoverable petroleum, the expected production rate, and the cost of drilling and producing the well. Therefore, petroleum geologists actually have two jobs:

- They reconstruct the geologic history of an area to find likely locations for petroleum accumulations.
- They find one of these locations and evaluate it to determine whether it contains enough petroleum to be commercially productive.

Among the general population, there is a common misconception of oil reservoirs. Many people think that an oil reservoir is a large, subterranean cave filled with oil or a buried river flowing with crude oil from bank to bank. Nothing could be further from the truth. Yet it is easy to understand how such ideas come about. Even experienced oilfield workers often refer to a reservoir as an *oil pool*. And because many cities store their drinking water in ponds or lakes also called reservoirs, this term adds to the confusion. In reality, a *petroleum reservoir* is a rock formation that holds oil and gas, somewhat like a sponge holds water.

A petroleum reservoir is a rock formation that holds oil and gas.

A reservoir's size is determined by the amount of oil and gas it contains. An oil reservoir might be broad and shallow, narrow and deep, or a shape in between. The East Texas oilfield covers thousands of acres or hectares but is only 5 to 10 feet (1.5 to 3 metres) thick. The world's largest oilfield is Ghawar field in Saudi Arabia. It is 1.8 million acres in size, 150 miles (250 kilometres) long and 19 miles (30 kilometres) wide, hundreds of feet thick, and currently produces 5 million barrels of oil per day. The largest oilfield in the United States is Prudhoe Bay oilfield on the northern Alaska slope, which covers over 213,000 acres (862 square kilometres) and produces 285,000 barrels of oil per day.[1]

BASIC CONCEPTS OF GEOLOGY

Astronomers and physicists today estimate the Earth might have been formed at least 4.55 billion years ago from a cloud of cosmic dust. As gravity pulled the planet together, the heat of compression and of its radioactive elements caused it to become molten. The heaviest components, mainly iron and nickel, sank to the Earth's center and became the *core*. Geologists believe the core has two parts: an inner, solid core and an outer liquid core (fig. 1-1.1). Both cores are very hot, dense, and under tremendous pressure. Lighter minerals formed a thick, probably solid *mantle* around the outer core. Minerals rich in aluminum, silicon, magnesium, and other light elements solidified into a thin, rocky *crust* above the mantle.

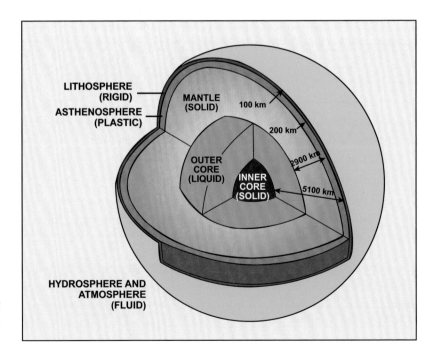

Figure 1-1.1. A cross section of the Earth shows its inner and outer cores, the mantle, and the crust.

[1] "Alaska North Slope production breaks 800,000 bbl/d (127,000 m³/d) barrier." *Petroleum News.* 7 January 2007.

In the past, geologists assumed the continents were always located where they are today. However, numerous lines of evidence, including commonalities between certain fossil plants in Europe and America and a match between the coastlines, has led to the theory that the continents drifted apart over time (fig. 1-1.2). Currently, most geologists think the crust is made up of huge plates that fit together like a jigsaw puzzle; but, unlike a jigsaw puzzle, pieces of the Earth's crust continue to move and change shape. In some places, they slide past one another. In others, they collide with or pull away from each other. The theory that explains these processes is called *plate tectonics*.

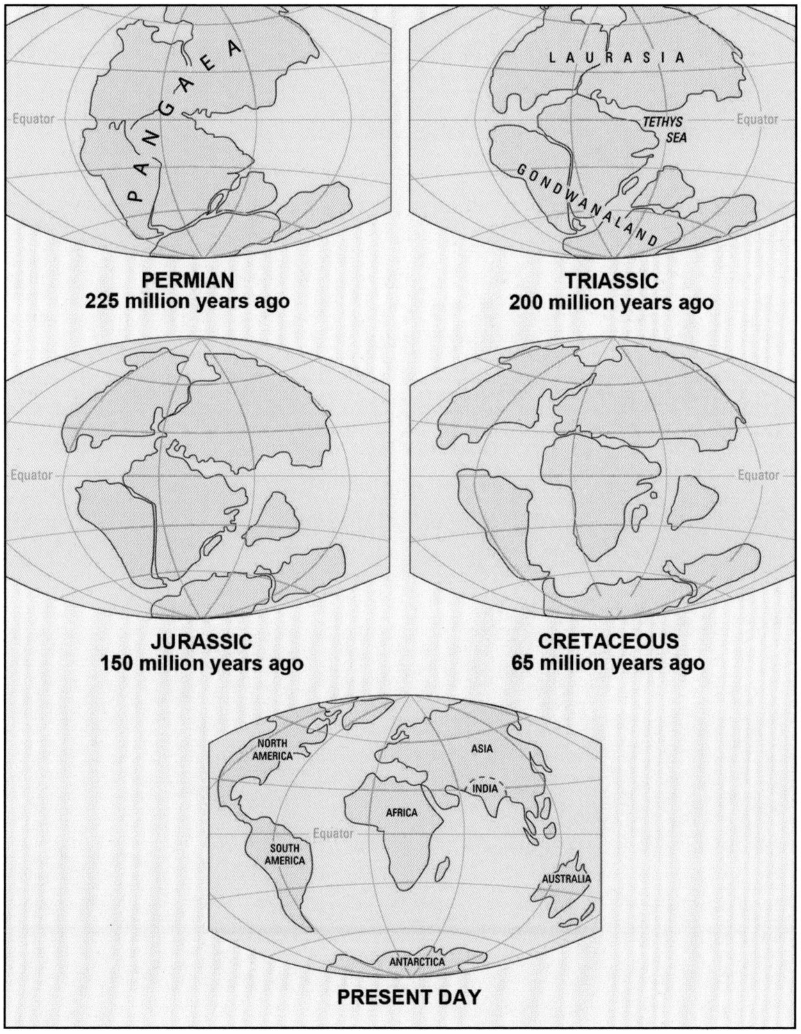

Plate Tectonics

Plate tectonics provide the basis for how continents and formations formed.

Source: U.S. Geological Survey

Figure 1-1.2. The relative positions of the continents as they have changed over the past 225 million years

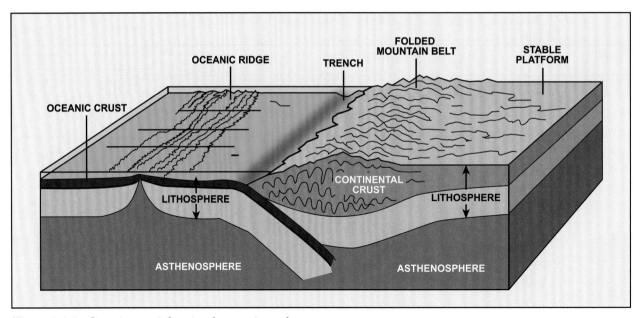

Figure 1-1.3. Oceanic crust is heavier than continental crust.

Crustal Plates   Geologists distinguish between the *oceanic crust* under the ocean and the *continental crust* under the continent surface (fig. 1-1.3). Oceanic crust is thin—about 5 to 7 miles (8 to 11 kilometres)—and is made up primarily of heavy rock that formed when molten rock, called *magma*, cooled. The rock of the continental crust is much thicker—10 to 30 miles (16 to 48 kilometres)—and relatively light. As a result, continents drift like icebergs among heavier oceanic rock and rise high above sea level as mountains where they are thickest (fig. 1-1.4).

Figure 1-1.4. Geologic formations of crust are exposed above the surface as shown in Carbon Creek in Grand Canyon National Park in Arizona (United States).

Photo by Dr. Richard G. Baker. University of Iowa, Department of Geoscience

Some of the best evidence for plate tectonics comes from the bottom of the sea. In the middle of the Atlantic Ocean is a mountain range 10,000 miles (16,100 kilometres) long from Iceland to the southern tip of Africa. It has a deep rift, or trench, along its crest. Investigation of this Mid-Atlantic Ridge suggests it is a place where two great plates are moving apart (fig. 1-1.5). Along the rift is a series of undersea volcanoes. Each time one erupts, the pressure of lava pouring out pushes the sides of the rift farther apart. The lava hardens into rock and becomes new crust between the two plates.

> To understand plate tectonics at work, look at the structural changes taking place under the sea.

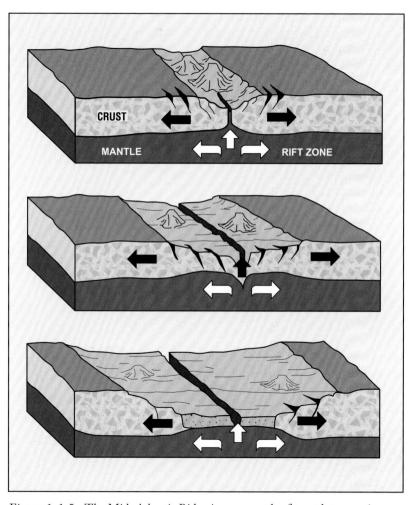

Figure 1-1.5. The Mid-Atlantic Ridge is an example of two plates moving apart, forming new oceanic crust as lava rising from beneath the plates hardens.

Assuming the plates in the Atlantic are moving apart, the Pacific Ocean basin is becoming smaller. Geologists theorize that the westward movement of the North and South American continents (the lighter continental crust) is forcing the Pacific plate (the heavier oceanic crust) downward into the mantle (fig. 1-1.6). This collision of an oceanic and a continental plate accounts for the volcanoes and earthquakes common along this zone.

Geologists also have evidence of what occurs when two continental plates collide. They believe the tallest mountains in the world, the Himalayas, were formed when India collided with Asia. The crustal collision buckled and folded the rocks along the edges of the two plates and pushed them upward. One interesting fact that illustrates the power behind plate tectonics is that the rock on top of Mount Everest is a marine limestone. A rock formed at the bottom of an ocean is now "on top of the world." The Himalayas are still rising by a measurable amount today.

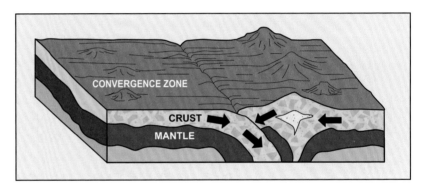

Figure 1-1.6. Along the Pacific coast, the North and South American continental plates are forcing the Pacific plate downward.

Geologic Structures

The continuous movement of the Earth's crust over millions of years has changed the shapes and locations of land masses and oceans. Fossils of marine organisms found in some of the highest mountains and in the deepest oilwells prove that these rocks were once in ancient seas and rose or fell to their present positions.

Geologists describe two basic structures that occur when rocks deform, or change shape, due to tectonic movement:

- Folds
- Faults

At atmospheric temperatures and pressures, rocks near the crust's surface tend to break when subjected to great stresses such as earthquakes. However, much deeper in the crust, the heat rising from the mantle raises the temperature of the rock, and the pressure of overlying rock compresses the rocks below. At higher temperatures and pressures, the deeper rocks become more flexible. They tend to warp or fold rather than break when stressed.

Folds are rock strata that have crumpled and buckled into wavelike structures. Folds are the most common structures in mountain chains, ranging in size from wrinkles of less than an inch to great arches and troughs many miles across. Folds are recognized by rocks that are not flat, but dip or curve (fig. 1-1.7). The arches are called *anticlines*; the troughs are *synclines* (fig. 1-1.8).

Folds

Two basic structures occur when rocks deform:
- Folds
- Faults

Courtesy of Chris Zahm

Figure 1-1.7. This photo of the Sheep Mountain Anticline shows deformation of the Earth's crust by the buckling of layers into folds.

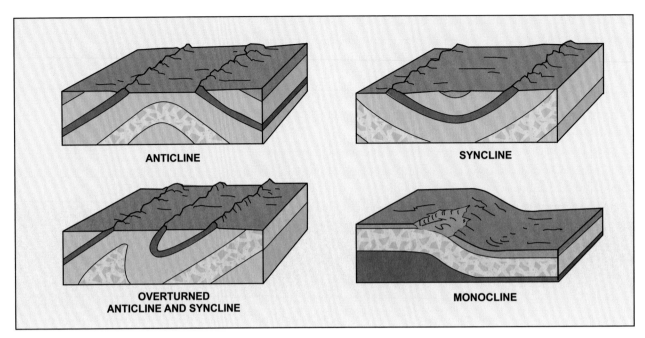

Figure 1-1.8. Geologists group folds into anticlines and synclines.

Geologists further divide anticlines and synclines by how the folds tilt. A circular anticline is sometimes called a dome with dips away in all directions from the high point (figs. 1-1.9 and 1-1.10). Dome shapes are common along the U.S. Gulf Coast in areas where faults, or breaks in the overburden, allow a weak rock called salt to raise into a dome shape. Anticlines or domes are significant structures to petroleum geologists because they often contain petroleum. Broad, regional synclines that dip down toward a common center are called *basins* (fig. 1-1.11).

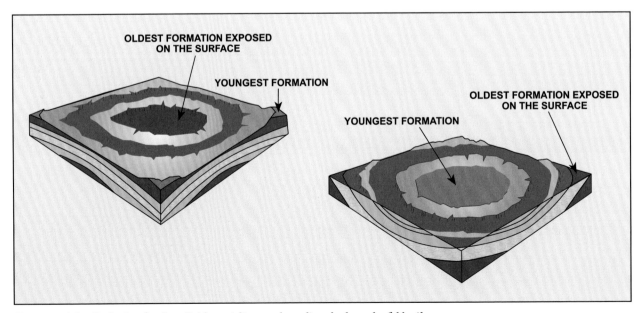

Figure 1-1.9. Geologists further divide anticlines and synclines by how the folds tilt.

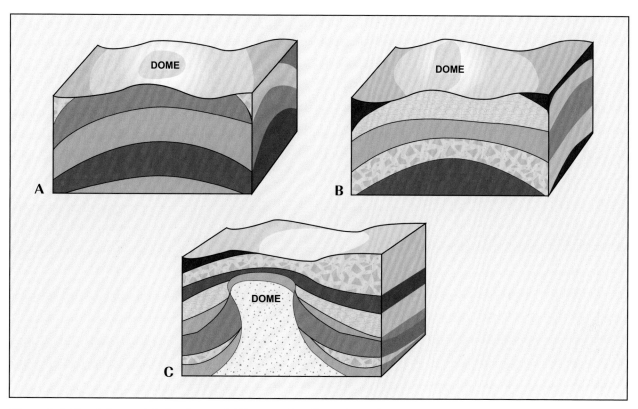

Figure 1-1.10. A dome might be elongated (A) or circular (B) and some have an intrusive core of salt or other type of rock that pushes up the surrounding rock.

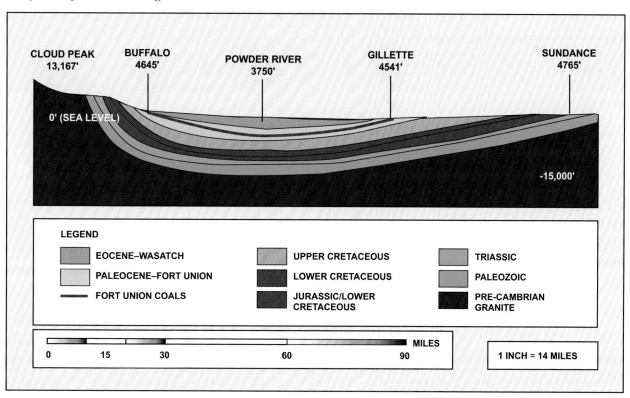

Figure 1-1.11. A basin is a broad inward dipping feature often tens to hundreds of kilometres across. Shown here is a cross section of the Powder River Basin in Wyoming in the United States.

Source: Nova Science Publishers, Inc.

Faults   When rocks near the surface break, the two halves might move in relation to each other, producing a fracture known as a *fault*. The two halves along a fault might move apart a few inches or millimetres, or the two halves might move several yards or metres apart as occurred along the San Andreas Fault in California (fig. 1-1.12). This fracture zone along the west coast of California represents the boundary between the Pacific and North American Plates and is known as the San Andres Fault. During the great San Francisco earthquake of 1906, the ground in the vicinity of the San Andreas Fault moved horizontally 21 feet (6.4 metres).

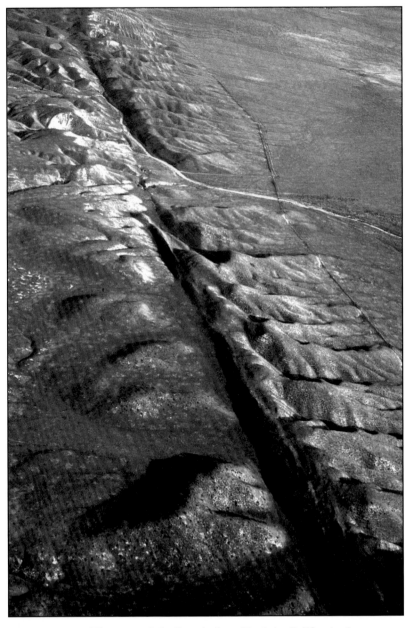

Source: U.S. Geological Survey

Figure 1-1.12. This view of the San Andreas Fault in California shows a distinct fault line.

Faults are generally classified by the direction of their movement. In *normal* and *reverse faults*, movement is primarily vertical, but in *strike-slip or lateral faults* (fig. 1-1.13), movement is horizontal. *Overthrust faults* and *growth faults* have a combination of both horizontal and vertical movement. Faults are important in petroleum geology because their movement creates areas that accumulate oil and gas.

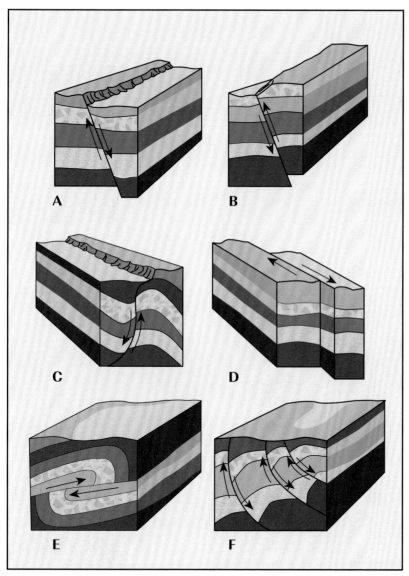

Figure 1-1.13. Several common types of faults are normal dip slip (A), reverse or thrust dip slip (B and C), lateral or strike slip (D), overthrust (E), and growth (F) faults.

Faults are important because their movement creates areas that accumulate oil and gas.

Sometimes faults can produce recognizable surface features (fig. 1-1.14). A *graben* is a long, narrow block of crust between two faults that has sunk relative to the surrounding crust. Conversely, a *horst* is a block of crust that has risen. In the North Sea, oil has accumulated in sediment-filled grabens beneath the ocean floor.

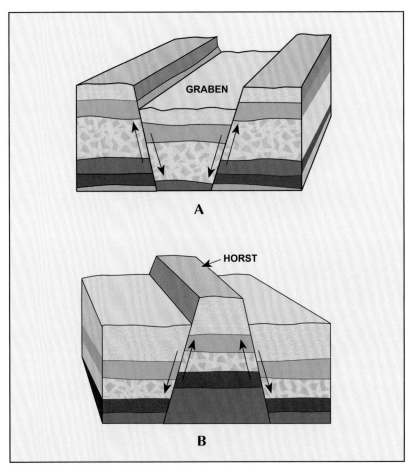

Figure 1-1.14. Two landscape features formed by faults are the graben (A) and the horst (B).

Geologists theorize that about 1 to 1.5 billion years after the Earth formed, simple living organisms appeared in the oceans. More complex forms did not appear in abundance until the beginning of the Cambrian period, only 550 million years ago. Not until the Devonian period, about 350 million years ago, did vegetation become widespread on the Earth. Land animals were relatively rare until much later.

Life has evolved continuously from Precambrian times and the fossil remains of animals and plants followed in a definite order. Geologists have classified rocks in groups based upon this order of succession, as shown in figure 1-1.15. Geologists have determined the lengths of the eras, periods, and epochs by studying radioactive minerals. The presence of life is considered essential to the petroleum story because, according to the prevailing theory, organic matter is necessary for the formation of oil (see *Origin of Petroleum* later in this chapter).

LIFE ON EARTH

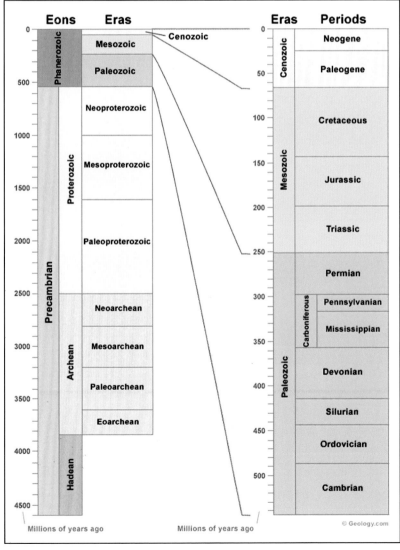

Figure 1-1.15. Geologic time

Categorizing Rocks

The crustal plate material is described as being made of rocks but not all rocks are the same. Different kinds of rock have different minerals and physical properties and were formed in different ways. Geologists group the rocks of the Earth's crust into three types depending on how they were formed:

- Igneous
- Sedimentary
- Metamorphic

Types of Rock

Deep in the Earth's crust, temperatures are high enough to melt rock into *magma*. Magma sometimes erupts to the Earth's surface as lava, or might force its way between other solid underground rock. *Igneous rocks*, such as granite and basalt, are formed when the molten magma cools and solidifies.

Sedimentary rocks are rocks formed from sediments in horizontal layers called *strata*. Water is a crucial ingredient in forming sedimentary rocks. A sediment might be composed of eroded particles of old rock (igneous, sedimentary, or metamorphic) washed downhill into lakes or oceans. Sediment might also be composed of minerals that precipitate out of water. Over thousands of years, the sediment layers become thick and the weight of the layers compact the earlier deposits (fig. 1-1.16). Minerals in the water cement these deposits together into sedimentary rocks. Limestone, sandstone, and shale are typical sedimentary rocks.

> Over thousands of years, layers of sediment thicken and the layers compact under great weight.

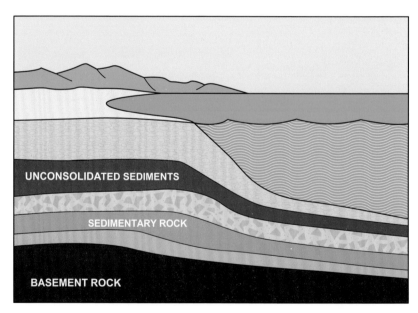

Figure 1-1.16. The weight of overlying sediments and water compacts sediments along with minerals in water creates different cements that alter the rock.

Metamorphic rocks were originally igneous, sedimentary, or other metamorphic rocks that were buried deep in the Earth and subjected to high temperatures and pressures. The word metamorphic comes from the Greek *meta*, meaning after or beyond, and *morph*, meaning to change form or shape. During the metamorphic process, the original rock undergoes physical and chemical changes that greatly alter its composition and appearance (fig. 1-1.17). For example, limestone can be *metamorphosed* into marble, and sandstone can turn into quartzite.

A unit of one type of rock in a layer is known as a *formation*. Formations are stacked on top of one another, deposited in cycles, and then sometimes deformed by folding and faulting.

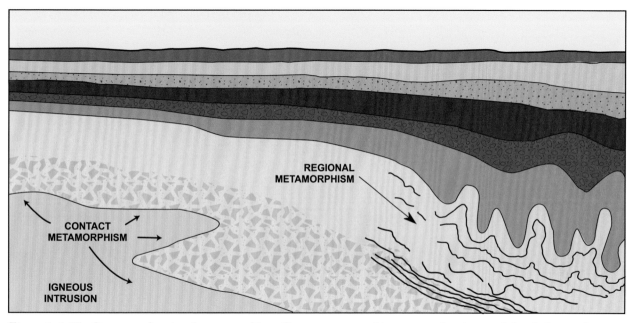

Figure 1-1.17. Contact and regional metamorphism. Contact metamorphism occurs when heat and chemicals come into contact with rock and impose changes. Regional metamorphism is more common and occurs in rock that is buried deep or deformed by tectonic changes.

The Rock Cycle

Faults are important because their movement creates areas that accumulate oil and gas.

Over time, igneous, sedimentary, and metamorphic rocks might be changed into one another. Wind, water, and moving ice erode all types of rock, carrying the particles to the ocean or lakes, and creating new sedimentary rock. The movement of magma into rock creates new igneous rock when it cools and metamorphoses the existing rock with its heat. Tectonic movement raises buried rock to the surface, eroding it, or pushing it deeper into the Earth, where it metamorphoses or becomes magma. Erosion, movement of crustal plates, and movement of molten rock are continuously creating new rocks from the old (fig. 1-1.18).

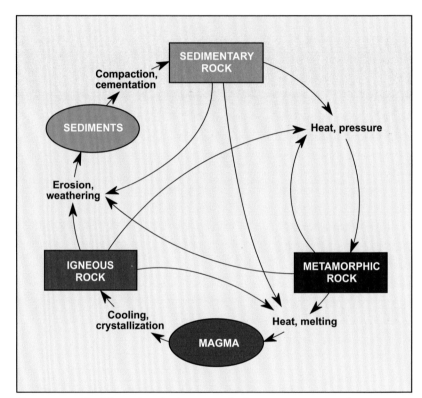

Figure 1-1.18. The rock cycle changes rocks from one type to another.

Petroleum-Bearing Rocks

Petroleum geologists are mainly interested in sedimentary rocks because most oil and gas accumulations occur within sedimentary formations. Most of the world's oil lies in sedimentary rock formed from marine sediments deposited on the edges of continents. This is why many of the largest deposits lie along seacoasts, such as along the Gulf of Mexico and the Persian Gulf. It is uncommon for igneous and metamorphic rocks to contain oil and gas.

The accumulation of hydrocarbons in commercial quantities is a phenomenon resulting from millions of years of geologic activity occurring in exactly the right order. Hydrocarbons must be generated in the subsurface, trapped within reservoir rocks, and remain in place until they are produced. Each of these three steps might take millions of years, and it is this aspect of time that is often the hardest concept to grasp. Geologists must consider the kinds of geologic formations and processes that created favorable conditions for developing large oil reservoirs.

ACCUMULATIONS OF PETROLEUM

Many theories exist about how oil and gas are formed. One well-known perspective—and the most accepted—is the *organic theory*, which states that oil and gas come predominantly from the remains of microscopic plant and small animal organisms. Although large trees and dinosaurs might have been living at the time petroleum formed, it is the smallest organisms that are probably the source of oil and gas. These tiny plants and animals lived in the rivers and seas that covered the Earth's surface millions of years ago (fig. 1-1.19).

Origin of Petroleum

The tiny organisms in rivers were carried along with river silts and mud down to the seas, which were also full of microscopic life. As all these small organisms died, they fell to the ocean floor where they mixed with the silt, sand, and mud. As a result, a rich, organic mixture, called *kerogen*, formed. Kerogen is rich in both carbon and hydrogen. This mixture was cut off from any oxygen dissolved in the water. With no oxygen, the organic material could not decay as it normally would on land. As thousands of years passed, the silt, sand, mud, and organic material continued to build up. Eventually, a thick body of sediments enriched by organic remains accumulated on the bottom of the ocean.

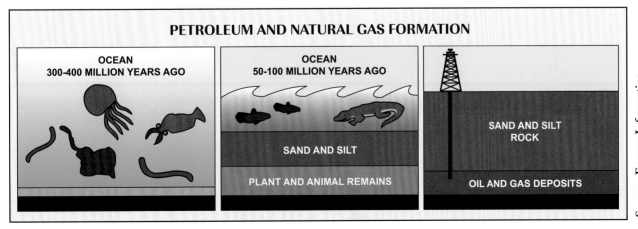

Figure 1-1.19. Abundant sea life helped form petroleum beneath the ocean floor.

Source: Energy Information Administration, U.S. Dept. of Energy

25

> Increasing pressure and temperature cause kerogen and hydrocarbon molecules to recombine to make oil and gas.

As more time passed, sediments continued to be deposited on top until thick beds of sand and mud lay above the sediments containing organic remains. The great weight of the overlying sediments caused changes to occur within the lower layer, turning the loose sediment into rock. Increasing pressure also caused temperatures to increase (fig. 1-1.20). As the rock reached a temperature of 150°Fahrenheit (F) (66°Celsius (C)), the kerogen began recombining with hydrocarbon molecules (fig. 1-1.21). Geologists refer to this recombining of molecules as the critical moment for hydrocarbon development. In this earlier phase of burial, oil is the primary hydrocarbon that develops. From the time the kerogen-rich rocks, often referred to as *source rocks*, are hot enough to generate oil (up to about 300°F (149°C)) they are in a stage called the *oil window*. As the rocks continue to get buried deeper and as temperatures continue to increase to above 300°F (149°C), the heavier, long-chain molecules break into smaller, lighter hydrocarbons such as methane gas. Geologists refer to this stage as the *gas window*. Further addition of *overburden rock* will eventually create temperatures of 500°F (260°C) or more that destroy the hydrocarbons and the source rock.

Figure 1-1.20. Increasing pressure also cause temperatures to increase.

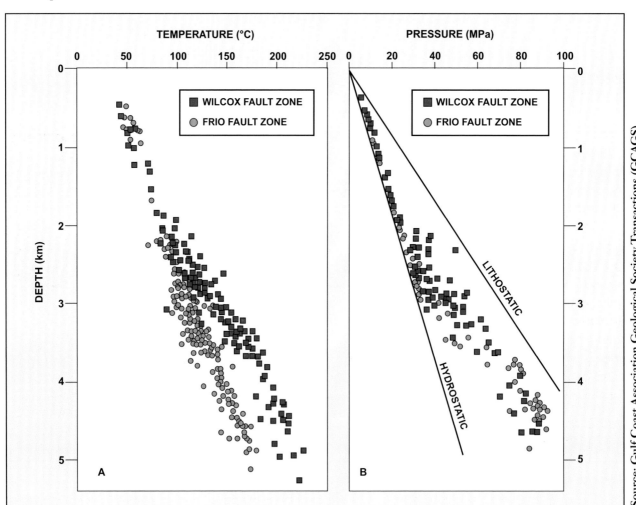

Source: Gulf Coast Association Geological Society Transactions (GCAGS)

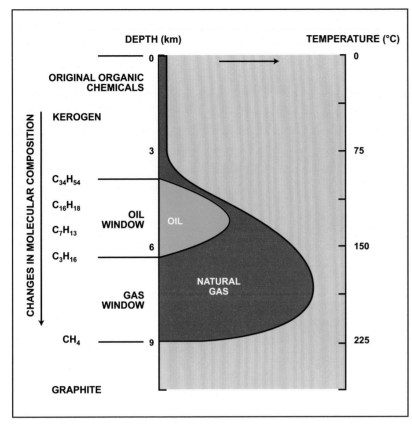

DEPTH (km)   TEMPERATURE (°C)

ORIGINAL ORGANIC CHEMICALS

KEROGEN

CHANGES IN MOLECULAR COMPOSITION

$C_{34}H_{54}$

$C_{16}H_{18}$ OIL WINDOW   OIL

C_7H_{13}

C_3H_{16}

NATURAL GAS

GAS WINDOW

CH_4

GRAPHITE

Courtesy of Professor Stephen Marshak; Publisher: W.W. Norton Company, Inc.

Figure 1-1.21. As the rock reaches a temperature of 150°F (66°C), the kerogen begins recombining with hydrocarbon molecules.

Rock appears solid to the naked eye. However, some rocks have tiny openings, or *pores*, that are visible under magnification (fig. 1-1.22). A rock that has pores is considered to be *porous,* and its *porosity* can be measured. Any oil or gas that exists in the rock is found in these pores, somewhat like the way a sponge holds water.

The greater the porosity of a formation, the more petroleum it can to hold. Porosity might vary from less than 5% in tightly cemented sandstone or carbonate (where the original sediments have been compressed through burial and the grains joined together by minerals precipitated from intra-formational water) to more than 30 percent in unconsolidated sands. To be commercially valuable, most reservoir rock must have a porosity of 10% or more—that is, at least 10% of the rock must have pore space capable of containing petroleum. This number varies based on the rock type and potential changes to the rock such as fracture development, which creates additional pore spaces.

Porosity and Permeability of Oil-Bearing Rocks

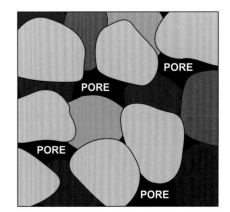

Figure 1-1.22. When reservoir rock is magnified, its porosity can be seen.

Rocks are characterized by:
- Porosity—the volume of pores in rock
- Permeability—the capability of porous rock to permit flow of fluids through the pores

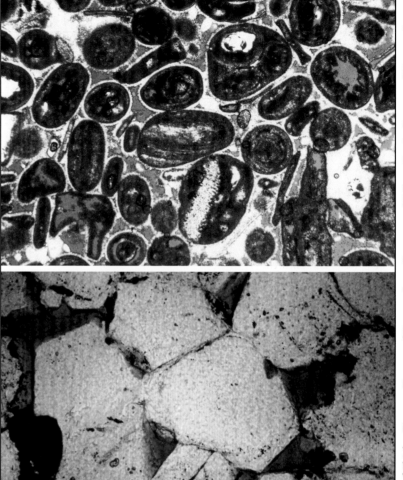

Figure 1-1.23. When reservoir rock is magnified, its porosity can be seen (blue regions between grains). Carbonate grainstone (top), sandstone (bottom).

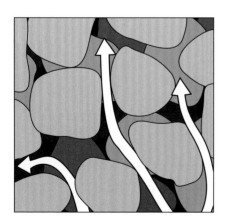

Figure 1-1.24. A rock is permeable when the pores are connected.

A rock is *permeable* when its pores are connected, allowing the oil, gas, and water to move from one pore to another (figs. 1-1.23 and 1-1.24). The unit of measurement of permeability is known as a *darcy*. Most petroleum reservoirs have permeabilities so small that they are measured in thousandths of a darcy, or *millidarcies*. In practical terms, consider that filling a 5-gallon (19-liters) bucket with a garden hose might take 1 to 2 minutes. Under normal conditions, a reservoir that is 30 feet (10 metres) tall by 300 feet (100 metres) wide with 1 darcy permeability would fill the same bucket in about 30 minutes.

Hydrocarbons contained in rock with low permeability have difficulty moving through the rock, and therefore, cannot flow out of the rock and into a well. A porous formation is not necessarily permeable, but highly porous formations are often also highly permeable. Sandstones and carbonates such as limestone and dolomite are generally the most porous and permeable rocks and also are the most common reservoir rocks.

Shale is a rock that has practically no permeability. If it is porous and contains hydrocarbons, it is called *shale oil* or *shale gas*. Shale gas is a product that has recently started production due to advancements in well fracture technology and in horizontal drilling techniques (see later chapters in *Part 2: Drilling*). The western United States, for example, has vast oil shale deposits that will not flow into a well. Advanced mining techniques and other innovative technology is being developed to produce oil from this type of impermeable rock.

The ease with which fluids move through rocks is also a function of the composition of the petroleum. Gas with small hydrocarbon molecules can move through small pores more easily than oil with larger molecule sizes. Very long hydrocarbon molecules are much more restrictive to flow, or *viscous*, and are sometimes referred to as tar, which is an extremely sticky type of oil. Tar holds the individual grains in the reservoir together. If the reservoir is made of sandstone along with significant tar developed, it is referred to as *tar sands*. Like shale oil, tar sands require extensive environmental and technological innovation to recover the hydrocarbons practically and economically. Large tar sand deposits are present in Canada, Venezuela, and Russia.

> Shale oil and tar sands require extensive technological innovation to recover the hydrocarbons economically.

Water is prevalent in the upper crust of the Earth, but because the water contains so many minerals, it cannot be considered fresh. Water throughout the upper crust is essential for petroleum to migrate toward the surface of the Earth. Oil and gas are less dense than water and therefore have a natural buoyancy, or tendency to rise, when mixed with water. Consequently, immediately after hydrocarbons form, they begin to slowly migrate through the permeable rocks toward the Earth's surface, sometimes assisted by cracks or fissures within the rocks.

MIGRATION OF PETROLEUM

Traps   If rock is sufficiently porous and permeable, the petroleum will migrate through it. But, for petroleum to accumulate, something must stop the migration.

A *trap* is an arrangement of rock layers containing an accumulation of hydrocarbons where the formation prevents the hydrocarbons from rising to the surface. The trap consists of an impermeable layer of rock above a porous, permeable layer containing the hydrocarbons. Traps come in all shapes, sizes, and types. The simplest way to group traps is by studying the geologic features that caused them to form. Basic traps are those that formed by folding, faulting, unconformities, changes in permeability within a formation, or some combination of all of these.

Geologists group traps into two types: structural and stratigraphic (fig. 1-1.25). *Structural traps* occur when the reservoir formation deforms in some way. *Stratigraphic traps* are those in which porosity or permeability has changed within a formation or where a nonporous layer seals off the top of a reservoir.

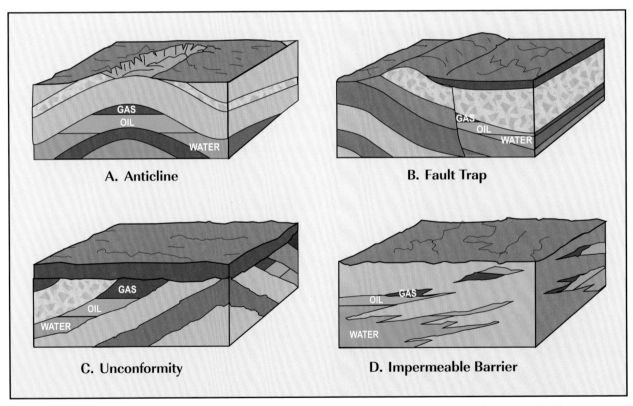

Figure 1-1.25. Basic types of hydrocarbon traps, including (A) anticlinal, (B) fault, (C) unconformity, and (D) impermeable barriers, such as shale surrounding sandstone. A and B are structural traps, whereas C and D are stratigraphic traps.

Structural traps come in various sizes and shapes. Most are formed by the folding or faulting of reservoir rock (fig. 1-1.26). The most common structural traps are anticlinal traps with a four-way closure or combination anticlinal and fault traps, sometimes referred to as a three-way closure with a fault. Emerging unconventional resources such as shale gas or similar resources are located predominantly in stratigraphic traps.

Structural Traps

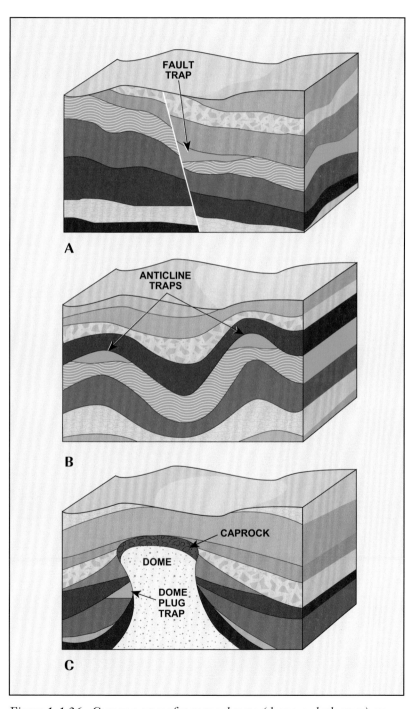

Figure 1-1.26. Common types of structural traps (shown as dark areas) are fault, anticlinal, and dome plug traps.

Anticlinal Traps

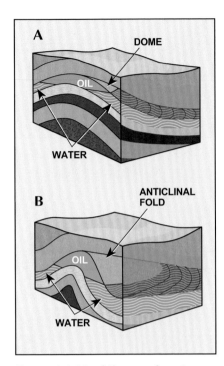

Figure 1-1.27. Oil accumulates in a dome-shaped structure (A) and an anticlinal type of fold structure (B). An anticline is generally long and narrow, while the dome is circular in outline.

Reservoirs formed by folding usually have the shape of anticlines or domes (fig. 1-1.27). In an *anticlinal trap*, the rock layers that were originally formed horizontally are folded upward into an arch or dome. Later, the hydrocarbons migrated from below into one of the porous and permeable beds in the anticline or dome and the hydrocarbons accumulated in the top of the folded porous layer. A *caprock*—a layer of impermeable rock above the reservoir—sealed off the reservoir and stopped further upward movement. Two examples of oilfields with anticlinal traps are the Santa Fe Springs oilfield in California and the Agha Jari oilfield in Iran.

A special type of anticlinal trap is a *plug trap*. A dome with a core of rock, called a *plug*, that has pushed into the other formations can create a plug trap. Usually the plug is made of nonporous salt that has pierced, deformed, or lifted the overlying strata (fig. 1-1.28). Hydrocarbons can migrate into any porous and permeable beds on both sides of the column of salt and be trapped there, unable to flow into the salt. The plug might be somewhat circular, as in a typical salt dome oilfield on the U.S. Gulf Coast or in Germany, or it can be long and narrow, as in the Romanian oilfields.

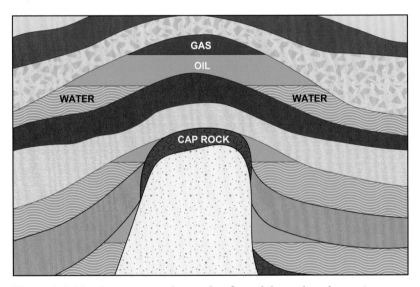

Figure 1-1.28. A nonporous salt mass has formed dome-shaped traps in overlying porous rocks. The formations pierced by the salt plug can form discontinuous traps.

Hydrocarbon accumulations in the traps around the outside of a salt plug are usually not continuous but broken into separate segments by faulting (fig. 1-1.29). This discontinuity can make plug traps difficult to drill successfully.

Geologists are aware of plug traps but cannot always accurately predict precise locations due to the complex geometries caused by the plug intrusion and related faulting. As a result, an oil company might drill many dry holes in attempting to tap reservoirs. Fortunately, recent advances in interpreting exploration data have improved the success rate of tapping a reservoir associated with plugs.

A *fault trap* was formed by movement of rock along a fault line. The reservoir rock is on one side of the fault. In one type of fault trap, the other side is an impermeable layer opposite the reservoir that prevents hydrocarbons from migrating further (fig. 1-1.30). In another type of fault trap, the impermeable material is a rock called *gouge* within the fault zone itself. A fault trap depends on the effectiveness of the seal that the gouge or impermeable layer provides.

A simple fault trap stops hydrocarbon migration with a single fault. However, it is possible for two or even three faults to form a trap (fig. 1-1.31). Petroleum in fault traps tends to accumulate lengthwise, parallel to the fault trend. For example, the accumulations in the many oilfields along the Mexia-Talco fault zone extend all the way from central to northeastern Texas.

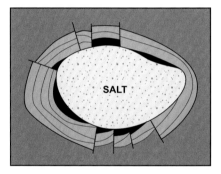

Figure 1-1.29. Discontinuous peripheral traps form around a piercement salt dome.

Fault Traps

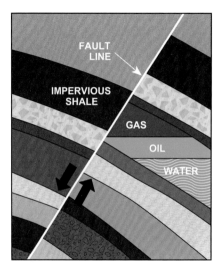

Figure 1-1.30. Gas and oil are trapped in a fault trap–a reservoir resulting from normal faulting or offsetting of strata. The section to the right of the fault line has moved up, leaving impervious shale opposite the hydrocarbon-bearing formation.

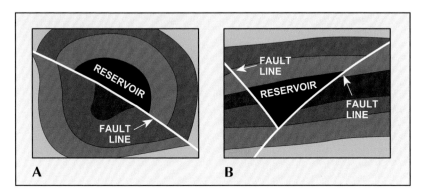

Figure 1-1.31. Structure contour maps show simple (A) and compound (B) faulting.

Stratigraphic Traps

A stratigraphic trap is caused either by a nonporous formation sealing off the top edge of a reservoir bed or by a change of porosity and permeability within the reservoir bed (figs. 1-1.32 and 1-1.33).

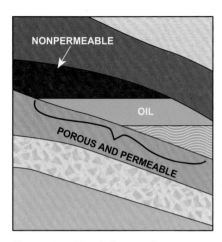

Figure 1-1.32. A change of permeability within a rock layer can form a trap. The lower part of the layer is porous and permeable, but the upper part is not.

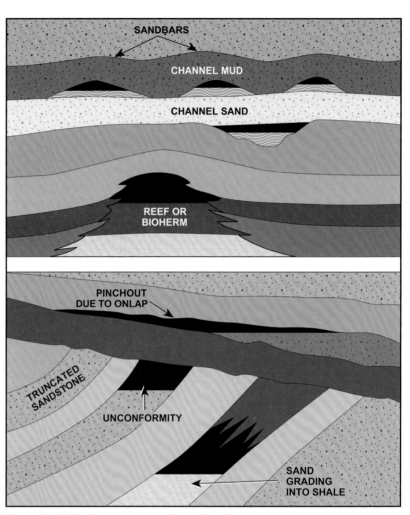

Figure 1-1.33. Common types of stratigraphic traps

In some places in the Earth's crust, a layer of rock formed and then eroded. New sediment was then deposited on top of the existing layer to form a younger layer of rock. The time gap in this geologic record is known as an *unconformity*. Geologists distinguish among three types of unconformities:

- *Nonconformity*—an unconformity where the older, eroded layer of rock is igneous and the newer layer is sedimentary
- *Disconformity*—an unconformity where the old and new rock layers are parallel to each other
- *Angular unconformity*—the older rock below the unconformity that has deformed before the overlying rocks were deposited. This causes the two strata to be tilted relative to each other (fig. 1-1.34).

An unconformity can form a trap if part of a porous bed eroded and was then overlaid with impermeable caprock. An example of a reservoir formed by an angular unconformity is the East Texas oilfield.

A *lenticular trap* is caused by a change of permeability within a rock layer. Abrupt changes in the amount of connected pore space seal off the hydrocarbons in the more permeable part of the bed. These changes might have been caused by an uneven distribution of sand and clay as the sediment was being deposited; for example, in river delta sandbars (fig. 1-1.35).

Unconformity

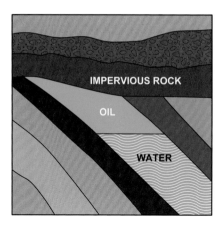

Figure 1-1.34. Oil is trapped under an unconformity.

Lenticular Trap

Basic types of hydrocarbon traps:
- Structural
- Stratigraphic

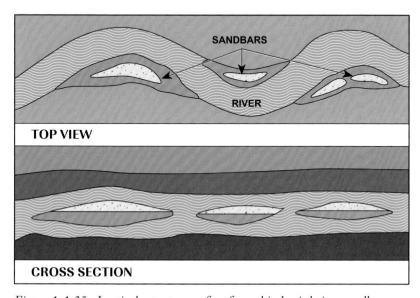

Figure 1-1.35. Lenticular traps are often formed in buried river sandbars.

Combination Traps

It is common for reservoirs to be trapped by a combination of folding, faulting, permeability changes, and other conditions. For example, a reservoir could occur in an anticline that is faulted and associated with an unconformity. The Seeligson oilfield in Southwest Texas and parts of the East Texas oilfield are reservoirs with combination traps.

RESERVOIR FLUIDS

In a hydrocarbon reservoir, fluids are layered:
- Gas (lightest) on top
- Oil (medium) in middle
- Water (heaviest) on bottom

A fluid is any substance that will flow. Reservoir rock usually contains three fluids: oil, gas, and saltwater. Oil and water are fluids as well as liquids. Natural gas is a fluid but not a liquid in its natural state, although it can be liquefied by artificial means.

In a reservoir, the three fluids might be mixed together, layered, or both. When layered, the lightest, gas, is on top; the oil is in the middle; and the heaviest, water, is on the bottom (fig. 1-1.36). Petroleum companies prefer that a reservoir contain all three fluids in layers because the pressure of gas and water can help drive oil out of the rock to the surface, making pumping unnecessary.

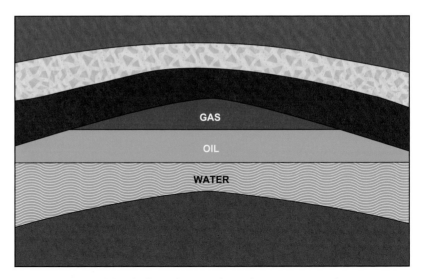

Figure 1-1.36. When hydrocarbons are layered in a reservoir, the water is on the bottom and the gas on the top.

Most oil reservoirs are sedimentary formations that were deposited in or near the sea. These sedimentary beds were originally saturated with saltwater. The forming petroleum displaced some but not all of the saltwater. The saltwater that remains in the formation is called *connate interstitial water*—connate from the Latin meaning "born with," and interstitial because the water is found in the *interstices*, or pores, of the formation. By common usage, this term has been shortened to *connate water* and refers to the water that stayed in the formation when the petroleum reservoir was being formed.

Connate water is distributed throughout the reservoir. Nearly all petroleum reservoirs also have additional water that has accumulated along with the petroleum. It is this *free water* that supplies the energy for a water drive. *Bottom water* occurs beneath the oil accumulation, and *edgewater* is found at the edge of the oil zone (fig. 1-1.37).

Water

Types of connate water in a reservoir:
- Free water
- Bottom water
- Edgewater
- Wetting water

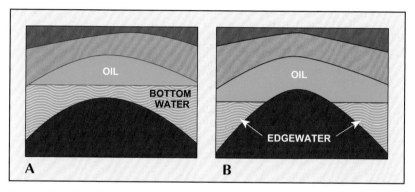

Figure 1-1.37. *Bottom water is below the petroleum in a reservoir (A), and edgewater is at the edge of the oil zone (B).*

Oil, which is lighter and does not readily mix with water, makes room for itself in the pores of reservoir rock by pushing the water downward. However, oil will not displace all the water. A film of water sticks to, or is *adsorbed* by, the solid rock material surrounding the pore spaces (fig. 1-1.38). This film is called *wetting water*. In other words, water is not only in the reservoir below the oil accumulation but also within the pores along with the oil. There are rare exceptions called oil-wet reservoirs that have an oil saturation of 100% of the available porosity and have no film of water lining the pores.

Oil

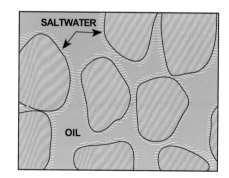

Figure 1-1.38. *Wetting water usually coats the grains of the reservoir rock.*

Natural Gas

Reservoirs usually contain natural gas along with oil. The energy supplied by gas under pressure is probably the most valuable force for pushing oil out of reservoirs. Gas occurs with oil and water in reservoirs in two principal ways: as *solution gas* and as *free gas* in gas caps. The petroleum industry has advanced from the days when it was a general practice to expel, or blow, gas into the atmosphere.

Given proper conditions, such as high pressure and low temperature, natural gas will stay in solution with the oil while in the reservoir (fig. 1-1.39). When the oil comes to the surface and pressure is relieved, the gas comes out of solution, much as a bottle of soda fizzes when you remove the cap. Gas in solution occupies space in a reservoir, and geologists allow for this space when calculating how much oil is in a reservoir.

Free gas—gas not dissolved in oil—tends to accumulate in the highest structural part of a reservoir, where it forms a *gas cap* (fig. 1-1.40). As long as there is free gas in a reservoir gas cap, the oil in the reservoir remains saturated with gas in solution. Dissolved gas lowers the *viscosity* of the oil (its resistance to flow), making the oil easier to move to the wellbore.

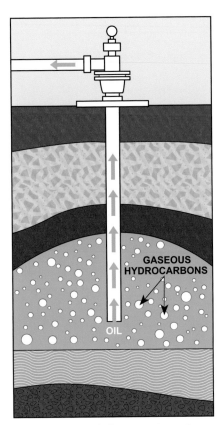

Figure 1-1.39. Solution gas stays in solution until a well is drilled into the reservoir.

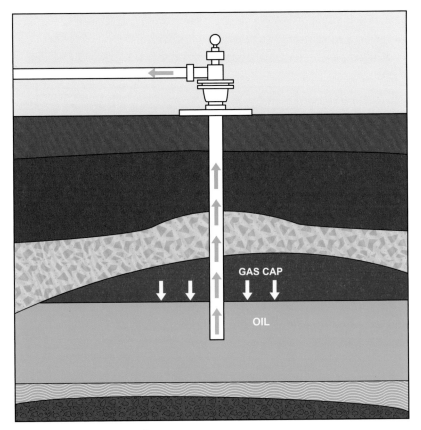

Figure 1-1.40. Free gas forms a gas cap.

Geologists want to find the *oil-water contact line* in the reservoir where layers of oil and water touch. This contact is important because, to get the maximum amount of oil from a reservoir, the oil company does not want to pump up water with the oil. Almost all reservoirs have water in the lowest portions of the formation, with oil just above it. However, the oil-water contact line is usually neither sharp nor horizontal throughout a reservoir. Instead, it is a zone of part water and part oil several feet or metres thick. The same is true for the gas-oil contact, but oil, being much heavier than gas, does not tend to rise as high into the gas zone as water does into the oil zone.

Distribution of the Fluids

All reservoir fluids are under pressure. The weight of the fluid itself creates a normal pressure. Abnormal pressure occurs when the weight of the formations on top of the reservoir adds to the fluid pressure.

RESERVOIR PRESSURE

Fluid pressure in a reservoir is similar to pressure that exists at the bottom of the ocean. Imagine a swimmer in a large swimming pool trying to touch the bottom of the pool. Everything is going well except that the swimmer's ears begin to hurt. The deeper the dive, the more the ears hurt. The reason for the pain is the pressure of the water pressing against the eardrums. The deeper the swimmer goes, the greater the pressure.

Normal Pressure

Normal pressure can be maintained when a direct connection to the surface exists.

Just as water creates pressure in a pool or the ocean, fluids in a reservoir create pressure. When the reservoir has a connection to the surface, the only pressure is usually that caused by fluid in and above it (fig. 1-1.41). As long as this connection to the surface exists, rocks that overlie a reservoir do not create any extra pressure in the reservoir. Even though their weight bears down on the formation, fluids can rise to the surface and escape. Imagine again the swimming pool full of water and dumping a huge load of rocks into it. The rocks do not increase the water pressure. Instead, the water spills out over the sides of the pool.

The same thing happens in a reservoir. Unlike a swimming pool, a reservoir's connection to the surface is usually indirect or meandering. It might outcrop at the surface many miles away or be connected to the surface through porous beds that overlie it. In most cases, as long as the reservoir has an outlet to the surface, the pressure is caused only by the fluids and considered to be normal pressure.

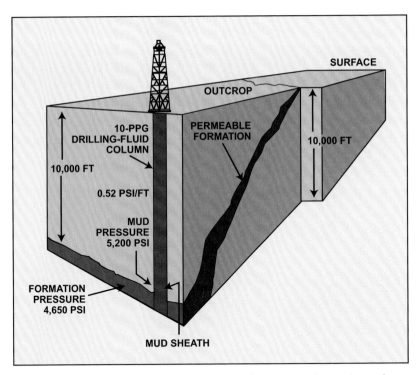

Figure 1-1.41. When the petroleum reservoir has a connection to the surface, the pressure is considered normal.

Reservoirs that do not have a connection with the surface are usually surrounded by impermeable formations. However, the overlying rock formations add to the reservoir pressure because the heavy weight of the overlying beds press down and squeeze the reservoir. Fluids in the reservoir cannot escape to the surface, so the reservoir pressure builds up to abnormally high levels.

If a swimming pool had an airtight lid right on the surface of the water and a huge amount of rocks was dumped on the lid, the weight of the rocks would press down on the water, and the water would have nowhere to escape. The pressure on the water would build and build as more weight was applied.

Abnormally high pressure can also build up due to an *artesian effect* (fig. 1-1.42). Formations surrounding the reservoir will trap the oil and gas but allow the water below the oil to reach up toward the surface some distance away. Because water seeks its own level, when the well provides an outlet for the reservoir, the water under it pushes the hydrocarbons up forcefully.

Abnormal Pressure

An artesian effect occurs when there is a buildup of abnormally high pressure.

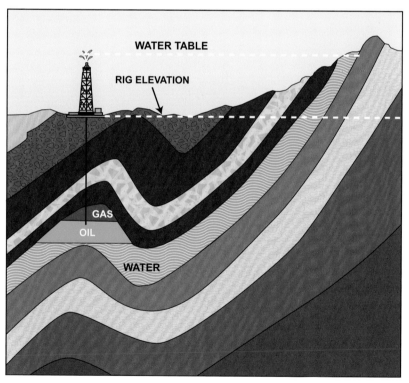

Figure 1-1.42. Abnormal pressure can occur in formations outcropping higher than the rig elevation.

SUMMARY   The science of geology provides the foundation upon which all petroleum geologists operate. Since the Earth was formed at least 4.5 billion years ago, gravity and heat worked together to form the planet and the structures in place today. Petroleum geologists are particularly interested in the interesting and revealing shapes that formed on Earth over time. This reshaping of the Earth's crust has created unique structures in the form of faults and folds that provide perfect traps where oil and gas can accumulate. With the fossil remains of organisms undergoing intense pressure over millions of years, hydrocarbon molecules recombined to make an oily fluid substance—petroleum—that resides within the tiny pores of primarily sedimentary rock. These fluids continue building up pressure within the rock. There they remain until their location is identified by petroleum geoscientists whose job it is to find where the oil reservoirs are located so drillers can tap the resources that lie within.

In this chapter:

- Collecting data using survey tools and databases
- The evolution of seismic surveys and interpretation
- Types of well logs and core samples
- Contour maps and digital computer models

In the past, exploring for petroleum was a matter of good luck and guesswork. Drilling near oil or natural gas seeps where hydrocarbons were present on the surface was the most successful hydrocarbon-finding method in the early days of oil exploration. Today, petroleum explorationists use sophisticated technologies and scientific principles and guidelines to find oil and gas. An *explorationist* is a person with extensive geological training whose job it is to search for new sources of hydrocarbons.

Surface and subsurface geological studies drive the discovery of oil and gas. Seismic data, well log data, aerial photographs, satellite images, gravity and magnetic data, and other geological data provide information that help determine where to drill an exploratory well. Specialists examine rock fragments and core samples brought up while drilling the exploratory well and run special tools into the hole to get more information about the formations underground. Examining, correlating, and interpreting this information make it possible for petroleum explorationists to accurately locate subsurface structures that might contain hydrocarbon accumulations worth exploiting.

In relatively unexplored areas, petroleum explorationists study the *topography*—the natural and manmade features on the surface of the land—to derive a conclusion about the character of underground formations and structures largely from what appears on the surface.

Before choosing a site to study, geologists might contend with an unexplored area covering tens of thousands of square miles or kilometres. To narrow this vast territory down to regions small enough for detailed surface and subsurface analyses, geologists might use a combination of aerial and satellite imaging. A series of landscape features that seem unrelated or insignificant to a ground observer might be interpreted quite differently when seen from the air or on a satellite image.

Previously, aerial photography was the only way to examine the land from the air. Aerial photography had some serious disadvantages.

SURFACE GEOGRAPHICAL STUDIES

Aerial Photographs and Satellite Images

Besides the expense of flying, aerial exploration requires a large number of photographs be taken from varying camera angles and distances. Due to the varying quality of aerial pictures, large-scale geological interpretation was often difficult.

Remote sensing has largely replaced aerial photography. *Remote sensing* uses infrared and other means to map an area. Both satellites and airplanes are used to conduct remote sensing.

Landsat

Landsat data continues to be a primary source of data to help pinpoint commercial deposits.

For over thirty years, National Aeronautics and Space Administration (NASA) *Landsat* satellites have collected information about all of the Earth's landmasses thousands of times since the United States launched the first satellite in 1972. The early purpose of the Landsat Program was to map vegetation and to observe long-term changes on the Earth's surface. Landsat data has evolved, becoming a primary source of data for researching scientific questions. It has become an important resource for decision-makers from many different fields such as agriculture, forestry, land use, water resources, and natural resource exploration.

Geologists use Landsat data to detect the presence of clays often associated with mineral deposits. After sensors from the satellite scan large areas of the Earth, they send images of each location back to Earth. Ground stations pick up the Landsat signals (fig. 1-2.1). When computers process the Landsat images, the Earth's ground features are enhanced and studied. Companies that use Landsat data, however, still need traditional exploration information to pinpoint the location of commercial deposits.

Source: U.S. Geological Survey

Figure 1-2.1. Landsat photos such as this are received by remote sensing systems and processed by computers.

Landsat data can be ordered from the *U.S. Geological Survey (USGS)*. *Orthorectified* Landsat data is available from the USGS free of charge. This type of data has been adjusted to scale, like a map. Explorationists can also buy Landsat data from companies that enhance and interpret the satellite images. Analyzing the raw data can be expensive, although it is less expensive than seismic surveys.

Another type of remote sensing uses radar. Radar devices bounce high-frequency radio waves off land features to a satellite or an airplane. Return echoes are recorded to form a low-resolution relief map that is useful in searching unexplored areas for potential oil-trapping structures and for discerning large-scale terrain features. Imaging radar used in airplanes is called *side-looking airborne radar (SLAR)*.

Radar

Oil and gas *seeps* are obvious signs of a subsurface petroleum source. However, the seepage might be so slow that it is not easy to detect. This is because bacteria and weathering can decompose the oil and gas as soon as it comes to the surface. Chemically testing soil or water can reveal traces of hydrocarbons. Occasionally, plumes of gas rising from seeps on the ocean floor have led to offshore exploration. These seeps can often be seen on two-dimensional and three-dimensional *seismic data*.

Some of the world's great oilfields were discovered because of the presence of oil seeps at the surface. Oil seeps occur either along fractures that pierce the reservoir or at spots where formations rise up to the surface (figs. 1-2.2 and 1-2.3). Seeps at the outcrop of a reservoir are active, meaning that oil or gas is still flowing out slowly, such as at Mene Grande in Venezuela. In other cases, such as at Coalinga Field in California and the Athabasca Tar Sands in Canada, later sediments have buried the

Oil and Gas Seeps

Some of the world's greatest oilfields were discovered from surface oil seeps.

Photo by Simon Nathan

Figure 1-2.3. Oil and gas naturally rise towards the Earth's surface wherever there is a way up as it did in New Zealand (pictured above). If fault lines, fissures or cracks allow, petroleum emerges on the ground as sticky, oily deposits known as seeps.

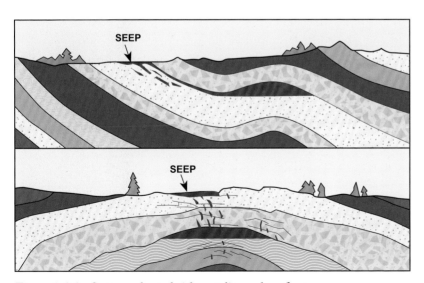

Figure 1-2.2. Seeps are located either updip or along fractures.

part of the reservoir near the surface, sealing it so the seep is no longer active. Seepage from fractures and faults is common and might be oil, gas, or mud as found in the mud volcanoes of Trinidad and Russia.

After the drilling of the famous Drake well in Pennsylvania, United States in 1859 (discussed in *Part 2. Chapter 2.1: Drilling Operations*), it was observed that many newly discovered wells were on anticlines. Explorationists made little practical use of this information until 1885, when geologist I. C. White applied this information to search for gas in Pennsylvania and nearby states. During the latter part of the nineteenth century, geologists were searching for oil in the East Indies and Mexico. By 1897, several U.S. oil companies had even established their own geology departments.

COLLECTING DATA

Much of the data petroleum explorationists need for their work comes from their company files, libraries, and the databases of government agencies and privately operated service companies. Some of the information is proprietary and accessible only to those collecting it, while other information is available for a fee or is in the public domain.

Private Company Libraries

Private companies or geological societies often maintain large collections of drilling and production data, maps, or well logs (data taken from existing wells). Members pay dues for access to the information. The libraries get information from both public agencies and members who contribute their own data. An oil company usually has a data library including all the information it has collected about areas it has explored or developed. The company's geologists will have access to all this information.

Public Agency Records

Oil and gas industry regulatory agencies in the United States collect and file all types of data relating to drilling and production. These files are usually open to the public and accessible to anyone who knows the name of a well, the site of the well, who drilled it, and when it was drilled. Geologists might also get information from a well log or a core sample library, often operated by a public university.

Databases

Both public and private organizations have established computer databases that offer access generally to regional information that is classified by field and reservoir. Most major oil companies subscribe to petroleum databases, and nonsubscribers may request service on a per-search basis. Many government agencies and universities have made data available on their Web sites that is freely accessible.

By 1920, *petroleum explorationists* knew that geological factors besides anticlinal folding controlled oil and gas accumulations. Surface mapping alone could not help in searching for these other factors. Fortunately, geophysical methods of exploration came into existence at this time.

Geophysics is the study of the physics—matter, energy, motion, and force—of the Earth, its oceans, and its atmosphere. Petroleum geologists are mainly interested in the Earth's magnetism, gravity, and especially, seismic vibrations of the Earth. Sensitive instruments can measure variations in one of these physical qualities that might be related to conditions under the surface. These conditions could point to promising oil- or gas-bearing formations. Geophysical study does not guarantee success, but the combination of geophysical information and geological experience reduces the chances of drilling a dry hole (fig. 1-2.4).

GEOPHYSICAL SURVEYS

Some of the world's greatest oilfields were discovered from surface oil seeps.

Courtesy of the Geophysical Institute of Israel

Courtesy of CGGVeritas/Dominique Lecuivre Productions

Figure 1-2.4. Seismic exploration takes geophysicists into the jungles of India (top) and the freezing plains of Alaska (bottom).

Magnetic and Electromagnetic Surveys

Geologists searching for petroleum have applied the knowledge that the Earth has a strong magnetic field. Applying the principle that 'comparable rocks have similar magnetic fields' allows geologists to compare slight differences in the magnetism generated by the minerals in rocks. These magnetic variations can identify the location of different minerals in the rock formations. For example, igneous rock, frequently found as the *basement rock* under sedimentary layers, often contains minerals that are magnetic. Igneous rock seldom contains hydrocarbons, but it sometimes intrudes into the overlying sedimentary rock, creating arches and folds that could serve as hydrocarbon traps. Through magnetic surveys, geophysicists obtain a fairly clear picture of the configuration of the geological formations. A formation out of place with its surroundings can indicate the presence of a fault that might be associated with hydrocarbon deposits.

Magnetometer Surveys

A *magnetometer* is a scientific instrument that detects slight variations in the Earth's magnetic field. These variations indicate how deep magnetized rocks are buried. A magnetometer can be towed behind a ship or an airplane to cover large areas. It collects data that can be analyzed to determine possible locations for exploration.

The development of airborne magnetics is known as the *micromagnetic technique* of oil exploration. An airplane tows a *micromagnetometer* from a low altitude, normally about 300 feet (91 metres) above the ground. It detects micromagnetic *anomalies*, or deviations from the norm. A computer processes the magnetic data from the aircraft. Geologists use these analyses to predict fractures in the *basement* and the characteristics of the overlying sediments. The micromagnetic technique is an efficient exploration method that narrows down relatively small areas for seismic surveys or exploratory drilling.

Magnetotellurics

A *magnetotelluric (MT)* survey operates on the theory that rocks of differing composition have different electrical properties. MT is an electromagnetic geophysical method of imaging formations below the surface of the Earth. Geologists record and measure the naturally occurring flow of electricity between rocks or across saltwater and then analyze and interpret the information to reveal subsurface structures.

Company geologists use magnetotellurics primarily in *reconnaissance* (exploratory) *surveying*, although improved data processing techniques have made it increasingly useful for *development surveys*. The amount of detail this method yields depends on the distance between survey sites. Closely spaced sites result in a detailed survey, which is helpful for deciding where to drill new wells near an area of proven production. Regional surveys provide geologic cross sections or cutaway views of the formations.

Although techniques continue to improve, magnetic and electro-magnetic surveying does not ensure the detection of all traps that contain hydrocarbons. However, these surveys are extremely useful in giving the geologist a better idea of where oil-bearing rocks might be found.

Geophysicists also use the slight variations in the Earth's gravitational field influenced by varying rock weights. Some rocks are denser than others. A square yard (or metre) of dense rock weighs more than a square yard (or metre) of less dense rock, in the same way that a lead ball is denser than a cotton ball.

Very dense rocks near the Earth's surface exert a gravitational force more powerful than a layer of very light rocks. Geophysicists applied gravitational studes during the early days of prospecting off the Gulf Coast of the United States. They could often locate salt domes by gravitational exploration because ordinary domes and anticlines are associated with maximum gravity, whereas salt domes are usually associated with minimum gravity.

First marketed commercially in 1922, the *torsion balance* was one of the earliest gravitational instruments invented. The torsion balance, as well as another early instrument—the pendulum—was rather difficult to use. Today, the most common instrument is the *gravimeter* or gravity meter, a sensitive weighing instrument for measuring variations in the gravitational field of the Earth.

Although the basic principle of the gravitational method remains the same, new technology and instruments continue to improve data collection. A small, portable, highly accurate gravimeter is now available for land work. Also, gravity data can be collected onboard a ship with a great deal of accuracy and with less resolution from the air. Computers are used to help interpret and analyze how gravity variations relate to geology. Gravity maps and models help the geologist examine large areas of development and provide guidelines for planning a seismic exploration program.

Gravity Surveys

Gravity maps and models help geologists examine large areas of development to plan an exploration program.

Seismic Surveys

A seismic survey is usually one of the first pieces of data geoscientists use to map the structure of a prospective area. Unlike the general information from gravity, magnetic, and electromagnetic surveys, seismic surveys give explorationists more precise details on the formations beneath the surface.

Seismology

Seismology works well because the Earth's crust has many layers of differing thicknesses and densities. When energy from the surface, such as an explosion, strikes the layers beneath, part of the energy travels through the layers and part of it is reflected back to the surface. It is similar to bouncing a rubber ball. If the ball is dropped on a concrete sidewalk, its bounce will be quite different than if dropped onto a pile of sand. Similarly, each different layer in the Earth "bounces" seismic energy back to the surface with its own particular characteristics.

Seismic surveys produce artificial earthquakes. Sensors called *geophones* pick up the reflected seismic waves and send them to a recorder. A *seismograph* amplifies and records the waves to produce a *seismogram* (fig. 1-2.5). Seismograms generate a *seismic section*, which is a two-dimensional slice from the Earth's surface downward. Information from a seismic survey indicates the types of rock, their relative depth, and whether a trap is present.

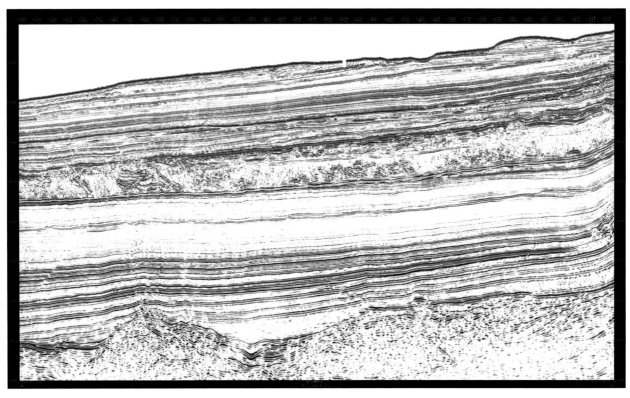

Courtesy of the Moroccan Ministry of Energy and Mines and Vanco Energy provided by the U.T. Bureau of Economic Geology.

Figure 1-2.5. A seismic section indicates boundaries between formations.

The seismic section just described is known in the industry as a 2D (two-dimensional) seismic section. A more modern technique is 3D (three-dimensional) seismic surveying, known simply as *3D seismic*. Computer-based interpretation and display of 3D seismic data allow for a more thorough analysis than *2D seismic* data. In the 3D technique, a company runs many seismic surveys close together to create a series of seismic sections of an area perhaps 2 or 3 miles (3 or 5 kilometres) square. Computer programs compile these sections to form a cubic picture of the area. The advantage of 3D seismic is that an exploration-ist can use computers to slice the cube in any direction—north-south, east-west, horizontally, or on any other plane (fig. 1-2.6). Focusing on an area in this way provides much more reliable information about the geologic structures it contains.

Seismic Data

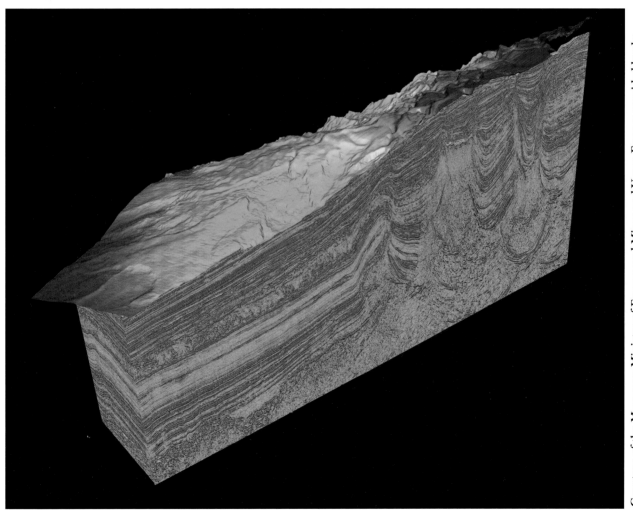

Courtesy of the Moroccan Ministry of Energy and Mines and Vanco Energy provided by the U.T. Bureau of Economic Geology.

Figure 1-2.6. A 3D seismic image is a cube that shows the types of rock, their depths, and whether a trap with hydrocarbons is present.

Seismic surveys:
- 2D—a slice from the surface downward
- 3D—multiple seismic surveys to slice a cube
- 4D—repeated 3D surveys over time
- 4C—multicomponent data from pressure waves offshore

In the Gulf of Mexico where the areas surveyed tend to be larger than on land, 3D seismic is used in offshore exploration. Because it is expensive, an exploration company might use this technique only where it already has other evidence that a large enough oil accumulation exists.

The term *4D seismic* is sometimes referred to in exploration imaging and refers to repeated 3D surveys (through time, as in a fourth dimension) to monitor changes in the formations, primarily in fluid levels.

More recently, *4C seismic* has been used in marine exploration. Marine multicomponent data, known as 4C, is acquired by using traditional air gun sources to generate a pressure wave with four receivers (three geophones and a hydrophone) planted on the seafloor to record both pressure and converted shear waves (fig. 1-2.7).

Photo by Trond Sorem. Courtesy of SeaBed Geophysical. Source: The Norwegian Design Council.

Figure 1-2.7. 4C seismic sensor for deep-water geophysical exploration

The *seismometer*, invented by David Milne, was first used in 1841 to measure and record the vibrations of the ground during earthquakes. A few years later, Luigi Palmieri, an Italian professor, set up a similar instrument on Mount Vesuvius in Italy. Palmieri called his instrument a seismograph. From these simple beginnings seismic exploration evolved.

Dr. Ludger Mintrop, a German scientist, developed one of the first practical uses of seismic data. He invented a portable seismograph machine for German armies to use in locating the positions of Allied guns during World War I. Mintrop set up three seismographs on the battlefield opposite Allied artillery, and when a gun fired, he calculated the precise location. The measurements were usually so accurate that the Germans could often quickly disable Allied artillery. However, the Germans also realized that some miscalculations in distance were due to the variation of seismic vibrations caused by geological formations through which seismograph waves passed. They applied basic geological concepts to correct their computations of the distances.

After World War I, Mintrop reversed the process, setting off an explosion at a known distance from the seismograph and measuring how long it took for the subsurface shock wave reflections to return. Using this information, he estimated the depths of formations. Finding that field exploration confirmed his theories, he put them into practice, forming the first seismic exploration company named Seismos. Soon after Mintrop started the company, Gulf Production Company hired one of the Seismos crews and brought them to the Gulf Coast of Texas, United States. With their arrival, news of seismic exploration spread, and soon rival companies started all over the state.

Two enterprising young brothers—Dabney E. and O. Scott Petty—decided to improve on Dr. Mintrop's methods. They resigned their jobs and spent a year developing a machine much more sensitive than Mintrop's. Their new seismograph used a vacuum tube sensitive enough to register the vibration of a "fly landing on a bar of steel," as Petty explained it. They established the Petty Geophysical Engineering Company, which became one of the early leaders in seismic exploration.

Early Methods

> Seismic exploration based on Mintrop's principles spread after World War I.

Explosive Methods

In the past, the most common method of creating seismic vibrations was to place dynamite (the *shot*) into a shallow hole in the ground and explode it. Geophones embedded in the Earth at various locations around the dynamite picked up the reflected waves. Under certain conditions, dynamite is still used to create seismic waves.

A seismic, or *doodlebug*, crew consists of the *party chief*, geologists or geophysicists to plan the locations of the equipment, surveyors to mark the locations, drillers to drill the holes for the shot, loaders to make up and load the shot, shooters to set it off, and *jug hustlers* to attach the geophones to the recording equipment by means of cables. A *jug* is another name for a geophone.

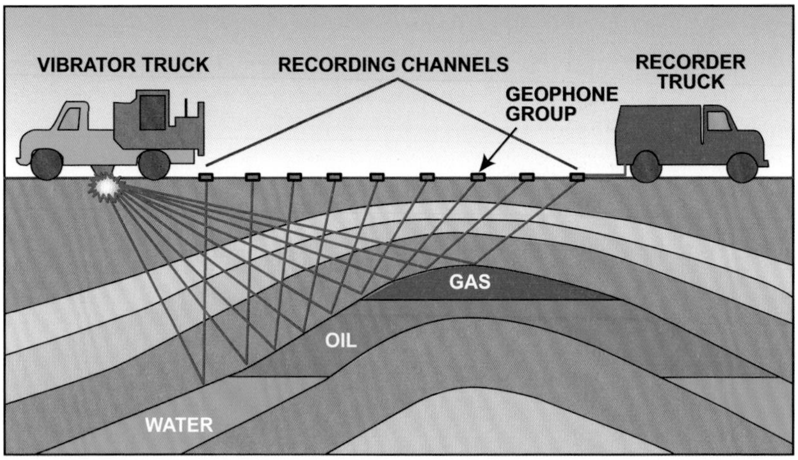

Figure 1-2.8. Engineers have developed mechanical impactors and vibrators to create seismic waves that penetrate down into rock layers to be recorded on the surface.

Source: Cobalt Exploration

Modern Land Methods

Newer methods of creating vibrations in the earth have mostly replaced dynamite. Engineers have developed mechanical *impactors* and vibrators to create seismic waves on the Earth's surface that penetrate down into the rock layers (fig. 1-2.8).

One of the first non-dynamite sources of surface energy is the Thumper, developed by Petty-Ray Geophysical (fig. 1-2.9). This impactor drops a heavy steel slab from as high as 9 feet (2.7 metres) onto the ground to create shock waves. Later, Sinclair Oil and Gas Company developed the Dinoseis, which uses a mixture of propane and oxygen in an expandable chamber to create an explosion.

Figure 1-2.9. The Thumper drops a 6,000 pound steel slab (surrounded by safety chains to warn personnel) 9 feet to strike the earth and create shock waves.

Courtesy of National Energy Technology Laboratory

Courtesy of Industrial Vehicles International, Inc.

Figure 1-2.10. The Vibroseis truck has a vibrator mounted underneath it that creates low-frequency sound waves. Geophones pick up the sonic reflections for recording.

The explosion chamber is mounted under a truck and lowered to the ground for use. The most popular seismic device used today for land exploration is the Vibroseis developed by Conoco (fig. 1-2.10). The Vibroseis generates continuous low-frequency sound waves with reflections that are picked up and changed into electrical impulses by the geophones. These recorded impulses are sent to a computer for analysis and printed as a *seismic reflection profile*. Geologists analyze the profile to determine subsurface structures.

Petroleum explorationists usually use geophones on the surface of the Earth to gather seismic data. They might also use geophones in the borehole of an existing well. In this method, technicians run geophones into a well and attach them to the wall of the hole at intervals of 20 to 100 feet (6 to 30 metres). With the receivers deep in the Earth, surface noise is less likely to distort the signal from the seismic source. Another advantage of this method is it can gather information about the geological structures in the immediate vicinity of the hole.

Figure 1-2.11. Geophysical vessels can log hundreds of thousands of miles of geophysical data.

Marine Seismic Methods

Seismic exploration offshore uses equipment similar to land exploration, except it is used from a ship (fig. 1-2.11). A sound source sends sound waves through the water, and formations beneath the seafloor reflect the seismic waves to *hydrophones*, the marine version of geophones. Commonly, hundreds of hydrophones trail behind the ship on steel cables (fig. 1-2.12). Another method of positioning the hydrophones is a *vertical-cable survey*. In this type of seismic survey, the ship's crew places cables with hydrophones attached in a specific pattern in the ocean. Each cable has an anchor on one end and a strong buoy on the other. Then, the ship sets off the source of seismic waves in a pattern around the cables.

A seismic ship can stay at sea several months if necessary. It has a double crew, one for ship operations and one for seismic operations.

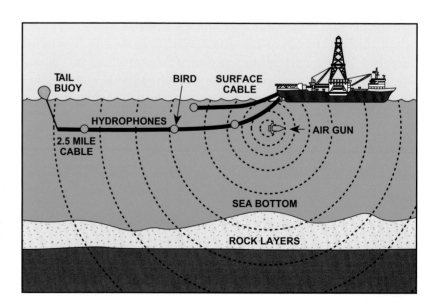

Figure 1-2.12. Seismic operations at sea use sound to create shock waves that have reflections that are picked up by hydrophones.

In some surveys, receivers are laid on the ocean floor rather than towed near the surface. This can be done by laying cables containing receivers or by using a combination of winches and *remotely operated vehicles* (ROVs) to plant individual receivers on the seafloor. This technique is known as *Ocean Bottom Cable*, or *OBC seismic acquisition*. These OBC systems acquire full seismic wave (multicomponent) data from the ocean floor, meaning the image can be of much higher quality than traditional *towed streamer acquisition* techniques. With OBC systems, there is:

- More flexibility exists in the geometry of the data acquisition (for instance, maneuvering around obstructed zones).

- Multiple sensors can be used to remove "ghosting."

- Data noise is reduced (cables are not vibrating due to towing, weather, or currents).

In the early days of marine seismic exploration, explosive charges suspended from floats generated the sound waves. This method is now banned in many parts of the world because of environmental considerations.

Today, an air gun is the most common sound source used on a seismic ship. Air guns contain chambers of compressed gas. As they release the gas under water, it makes loud popping noises, and the rock layers below the ocean floor reflect this sound. Both the "pops" and their reflected echoes are recorded on magnetic tape.

Another sound source used in offshore exploration is steam. An on-deck boiler produces the steam, which is suddenly released from a special chamber into the ocean. The steam hits the cold sea and condenses rapidly, generating the necessary sound. As with the air guns, hydrophones trailing behind the ship pick up the reflected echoes and record them on magnetic tape for future analysis.

Ocean Bottom Cable Systems

Sound Sources

Today, an air gun is the most common sound source used on seismic ships.

Analyzing the Data   Most geophysical ships have computers on board, and the seismic information can be processed at sea (fig. 1-2.13). On other ships, the information is held until reaching shore, where it is sent to a computer for processing. Data collected this way can take longer to gather and interpret. Computers onshore can often handle larger volumes of data. Sometimes, a helicopter might transport the information directly to the operating company's offices to speed up processing.

A satellite system developed by the U.S. government and the oil industry in 1996 can receive data directly from the ship and beam it back to a receiver on land where it is sent immediately to a computer. The computer translates the data into a map that is sent to the exploration company office. There, geoscientists are able to see it in minutes and direct the ship's captain to adjust course to focus on particularly promising formations.

Courtesy of Western Geco

Figure 1-2.13. Onboard computers allow geologists to analyze the seismic data as it comes in.

If all the surface and subsurface information indicates a strong possibility of hydrocarbons, the oil company might drill an *exploratory well* or wells. As drilling progresses, the geologist keeps a watchful eye on the underground rock by means of rock cuttings, core samples, well logs, and test results. Specialists combine all the geological information gathered and recorded as the well is drilled with the surface data and the subsurface findings of the geophysicists. They try to predict whether the reservoir has enough oil or gas to justify completing the exploratory well or drilling additional wells in the reservoir.

Logs are used to record information about the formations through which a well has been drilled (fig. 1-2.14). Exploration companies use several different kinds of logs. Each log gives specific information about the particular well and the formations encountered in it.

RESERVOIR DEVELOPMENT TOOLS

Well Logs

Geophysicists use logs to help predict whether there is enough oil or gas present to justify drilling.

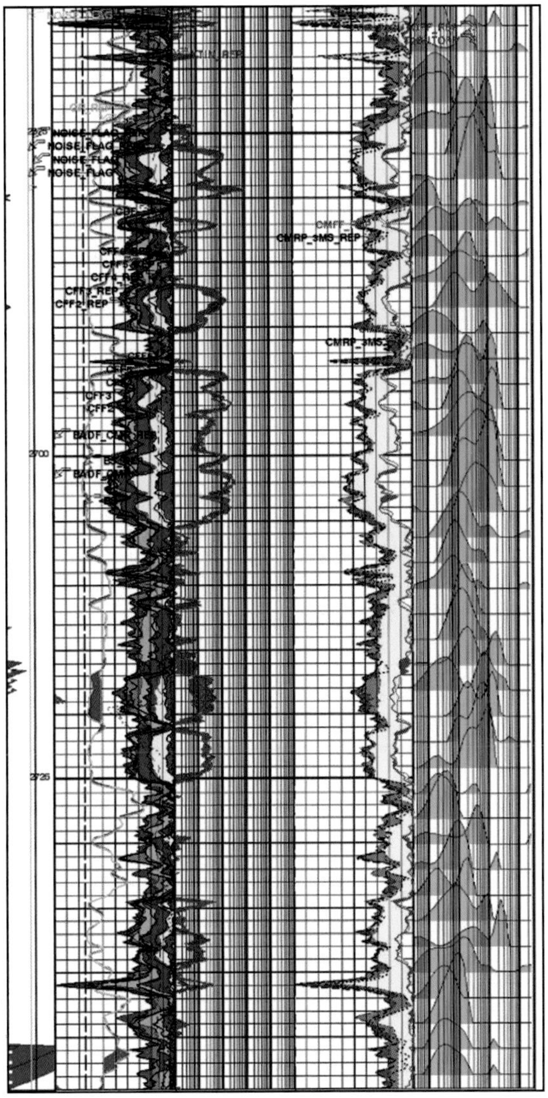

Courtesy of Government of South Australia PIRSA

Figure 1-2.14. A well log is examined for indications of the presence of hydrocarbons and other fluids in a formation.

Driller's Log

The *driller's log* commonly provides basic information to the geologist. The driller is the person in charge of drilling operations. He or she keeps a record of the kinds of rocks and fluids encountered at different depths, along with anything else of interest. Particularly when formations are alternating in soft to hard rock, a driller's log can be a very useful tool for geologists. The driller's log keeps track of exactly how much time it took to drill through a particular formation. This time record is useful to drillers in estimating the drilling time of future wells in similar formations. It also describes the overall characteristics of the well cuttings noted by the drilling crew as a well is drilled. This is useful when a detailed sample log is not available.

Wireline Logs

Geologists use several methods to gather indirect information about the formations down the drilling hole by using *wireline logs*. A *wireline* is a metal line that can be run into the hole with a tool attached to the end. A wireline that can carry electricity to the tool is a *conductor line*, but in oilfield slang, both are often referred to as wireline.

Wireline logging involves complex calculations and interpretation of the information relayed by the tool to the surface. The logging specialist uses a computer to compare, or correlate, data from various surveys. The specialist prints the data as charts or graphs, keeps track of the logging tool depth, and warns of any malfunctions.

Wireline logs gather data differently under varying conditions. The procedure for each log is basically the same. A highly sophisticated electronic instrument called a *sonde* is lowered into the wellbore on a conductor line. The sonde measures and records electrical, radioactive, or acoustic properties of formations that are transmitted up the conductor line as it is raised to the surface at a predetermined speed. At the surface, the wireline unit has computers that translate these signals into graphs for geologists and engineers to interpret. Correlating the information from different types of wireline logs can give the geologist valuable information about rock type, porosity, permeability, and the amount of water and petroleum in a formation (applications of wireline are discussed in *Part 2. Chapter 2.1: Drilling Operations*).

Logs are useful for evaluating exploration wells and planning the best way to produce the oil or gas in a development well. Oil companies are able to get some information from logs run on neighboring wells and will run some logs routinely on every well. Among the most common wireline logs are:

- Electric logs
- Nuclear/radioactivity logs
- Acoustic logs

> Logging methods:
> - A driller's log provides basic information.
> - A wireline log provides complex interpretation.

Two types of electric logs record electrical currents. One type, a *spontaneous potential (SP) log*, records weak electrical currents flowing naturally in the rock next to the wellbore (natural electricity). This shows the boundaries and thickness of each layer of rock. Because the SP log is simple to produce and provides basic information, it is the most commonly used log.

In another technique, a sonde sends an electrical signal through the formation and relays it back to a receiver at the surface (induced electricity). The surface detector might measure either the formation's resistance to the current or how well it conducts the current. A *resistivity log* records resistance, and an *induction log* records conductivity. Because saltwater conducts electricity much better than oil and gas, resistance and induction logs help determine:

- How much water is in the formation
- How freely the water moves (permeability)
- How saturated the formation is with water rather than hydrocarbons

Electric Logs

Just as SP and resistivity logs record natural and induced electrical currents, nuclear logs—also called *radioactivity logs*—record natural and induced radioactivity (fig. 1- 2.15). A *gamma ray log* records gamma particles or gamma rays given off naturally by the formation. A gamma ray log is useful in identifying impermeable formations such as shale and clay-filled sands.

To get a *neutron log*, a sonde sends atomic particles called neutrons through the formation. When the neutrons collide with hydrogen, the hydrogen slows them down. When the log records slow neutrons, it indicates the presence of hydrogen. (Hydrogen is the main component of water and hydrocarbons, but not of rocks.) Therefore, the log shows:

- How much oil, gas, and water might be in the formation
- The type of rock and its porosity
- The salt content

Nuclear Logs

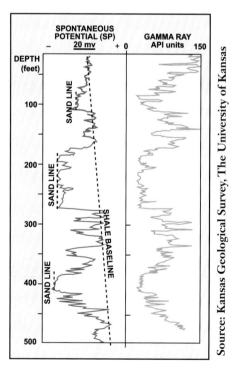

Source: Kansas Geological Survey, The University of Kansas

Figure 1-2.15. SP and resistivity logs record natural and induced electrical currents. Nuclear logs—also called radioactivity logs—record natural and induced radioactivity.

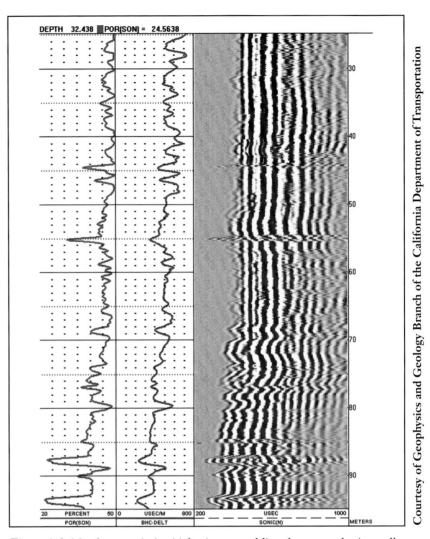

Figure 1-2.16. An acoustic (sonic) log is a curved line that moves horizontally to show the speed of the sound waves and vertically to show the depth.

Courtesy of Geophysics and Geology Branch of the California Department of Transportation

Acoustic Logs

An *acoustic* or *sonic log* is a record of sound waves sent through the rock by an acoustic sonde that transmits and receives a constant ticking sound (fig. 2.16). How quickly sound travels through a rock depends on how dense it is and how much fluid it contains. As rock becomes less porous, the sound waves travel faster.

Sample Logs

Sample logs are logs of physical samples of the underground rock. The two types of physical samples are core samples and cuttings samples.

Core Samples

A core is a slender column of rock that shows the sequence of rocks as they appear within the Earth (fig. 1-2.17). It provides accurate information about the underground formations. To take a core sample, the driller substitutes a hollow center *coring bit* instead of a conventional drill bit (fig. 1-2.18). A core ranges in length from 25 to 60 feet (7.6 to 18.3 metres).

Courtesy of CO2CRC

Figure 1-2.17. This technician is marking the well core to maintain the order in which pieces came out of the ground. Later, they will be sent to a laboratory for analysis.

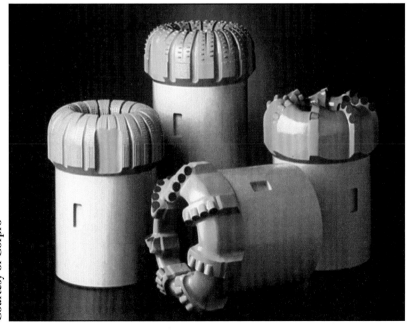

Courtesy of Corpro

Figure 1-2.18. This coring bit drills out a slender column of rock.

When this core sample is brought to the surface, technicians carefully package and send it to a laboratory for analysis of its characteristics. The analysis includes the porosity, permeability, composition, fluid content, and geological age of the core sample. This information helps the geologist determine the oil-bearing potential of the cored beds.

Cutting Samples

When a regular bit drills a hole, it breaks up the rock into pieces called *cuttings*. The cuttings are suspended in the drilling mud and carried up to the surface where geologists use them to analyze the rock being drilled. Because cutting samples are rock fragments and as such, will not form a continuous sample like a core, they are not as useful as cores to the geologist. Cuttings might not all come from the bottom of the hole and could include pieces of formations that have sloughed off closer to the surface. Even with these limitations, cuttings can provide useful data and are regularly examined during drilling.

Drill Stem Test

Like geologic data, test information about a formation accumulates over the life of an oilfield. The more that is known about a reservoir, the easier it is to test a new well quickly and inexpensively. Formation testing provides the oil company with pressure charts or logs made during the test and a report that describes the fluids in the well.

The *drill stem test (DST)* is the principal way to test a formation that has just been drilled. Although somewhat expensive, drill stem testing can bring an oil company a good return on its investment. To run the test, a DST tool is run into the hole. Formation fluids flow into a perforated pipe in the tool. A pressure recorder inside the DST tool and another below the perforated pipe chart the pressure. When the pressure testing is completed, valves in the DST tool close to trap a fluid sample. The DST gives accurate data about a formation's pressure and the composition of fluids the formation contains.

Strat Test

A useful test in reservoir development is the *stratigraphic test*, commonly called a *strat test*. *Stratigraphy* is the study of the origin, composition, distribution, and sequence of rock strata.

> The drill-stem test is the principal way to test a formation that has just been drilled.

A strat test involves drilling a hole mainly to obtain geological information. The borehole exposes complete sections of the formations penetrated, and *stratigraphers* analyze the cuttings taken from the wellbore as it is drilled. The strat test differs from a cuttings sample log. A company only uses a strat test on an exploratory well to examine the cuttings for hydrocarbons. Stratigraphers try to recognize and follow beds of rock from one well to another, going from a well or formation with beds and a rock sequence that have been studied to an untested area they assume to be similar.

Stratigraphic correlation is the process of comparing geologic formations. In oil exploration, stratigraphers compare the geology of a known area with unknown formations in nearby locations to predict the location of new reservoirs. This is done by examining information collected using drillers' logs, sample logs, and electrical logs. The data is used to compare fossils (usually *microfossils*), the composition of formations, and electrical data from one well or area with the same information from another well or area (fig. 1-2.19). Microfossils are very abundant, especially in marine rocks. Using them to compare geologic formation is called *biostratigraphy*. Microfossils are also used in analyzing the environmental aspects of former geologic time periods, known as *paleoenvironmental analysis*. Rock texture and fossil characteristics in formations, particularly those under the oceans, change very slowly. Any sudden changes in the sequence of rock types are geologic signs. Therefore, certain fossils are used as indicators to recognize the continuation of a formation in a new location. If the rock is the same and the fossil markers are the same, the formation is probably a continuation of the previous location.

The sequence, or order, of formations can also be used for correlation. In *sequence stratigraphy*, geologists take the information from seismic surveys and analyze it to understand the existing environment when the rock layer was first formed. For example, geologists can differentiate between sandstone laid down in a river from sandstone formed from a beach. This method works best when drilling closely spaced wells. Stratigraphers can match the formations accurately when they correlate data derived from several wells.

Stratigraphic Correlation

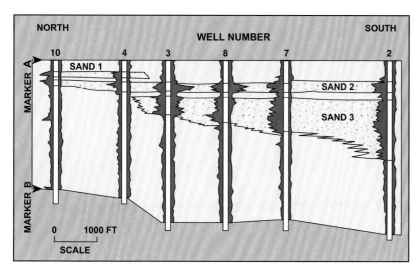

Figure 1-2.19. This stratigraphic cross section shows the presence of sand at various depths over an area of several thousand feet (or metres). The data came from six wells near each other.

Maps

Explorationists use various types of maps throughout the exploration process. Geologists use *base maps* showing existing wells, lease and property lines, roads, buildings, and other manmade surface features to recommend sites for geophysical studies, exploratory drilling, and reservoir development. *Topographic maps* show surface features such as mountains and valleys. Maps can also show information about underground formations gathered from exploration surveys. Gravity survey results are displayed on a *Bouguer gravity map*.

Contour Maps

Petroleum geologists commonly use *contour maps* that show topography, gravity, and other surveys. Contour maps show a series of lines drawn at regular intervals. The points on each line represent equal values, such as depth or thickness. To understand a topographic contour map, imagine looking at a mountain from above. If one would mark a dot every place on the mountain that is 1,000 feet (304.8 metres) high and then connect the dots, it would show a curve going around the mountain. Doing the same at 2,000 feet (609.6 metres), 3,000 feet (914.4 metres), and so on would result in a series of concentric curves. Drawing these curves on a piece of flat paper would create a simple contour map.

Contour maps for exploration might include the geologic structure and thickness of formations. The maps can show the angle of a fault and where it intersects with formations and other faults, as well as where formations taper off or stop abruptly.

One type of contour map is a *structural map*, which shows the subsurface contours of a particular reservoir or formation (fig. 1-2.20). The principle is the same as that used in a topographic map but the structural map clearly shows folds, faults, and other geologic structures below the surface.

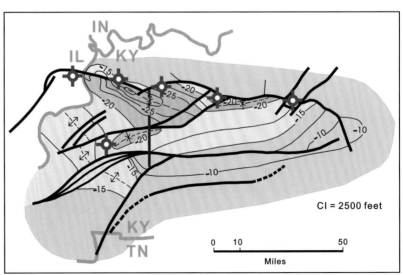

Courtesy of the Kentucky Geological Survey with credit to Jim Drahovzal and Collie Rule.

Figure 1-2.20. A structure contour map shows the depth of a formation from the surface.

The *isopach map* is another type of contour map (fig. 1-2.21). It shows variations in the thickness of a formation. Geologists use isopach maps to calculate how much petroleum remains in a formation and to plan recovery methods, as well as assist in exploration. An *isochore map* is similar to the an isopach map. The isochore map shows the thickness of a layer from top to bottom along a vertical line.

A *lithofacies map* shows the character of the rock itself and how it varies horizontally within the formation. This contour type of map shows the various proportions of sandstone, shale, and other kinds of rocks in the formation. The *biofacies map* is used to show variations in the occurrence of fossil types.

Contour maps include:
- Structural map
- Isopach map
- Isochore map
- Lithofacies map
- Biofacies map

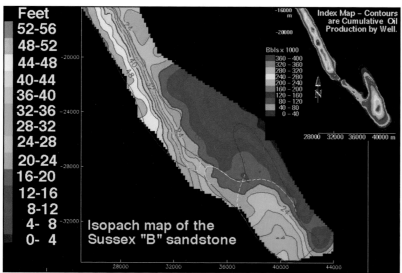

Figure 1-2.21. Isopach maps show the thickness of formations based on microlog surveys.

Vertical Cross Sections

Cross sections reveal anticlinal and fault traps and any horizontal variation in rock.

A vertical *cross section* depicts a portion of the crust as though it were a slice of cake (fig. 1-2.22). It shows structures and fault patterns. Most cross sections show both structural and stratigraphic features together (see *Chapter 1.1: Petroleum Geology*). Cross sections can show possible anticlinal and fault traps or only horizontal variations in type of rock or thickness. The cross sections can also show gravity peculiarities—or anomalies—in a contour form. These depictions have been instrumental in increasing the use of gravity surveys in petroleum exploration.

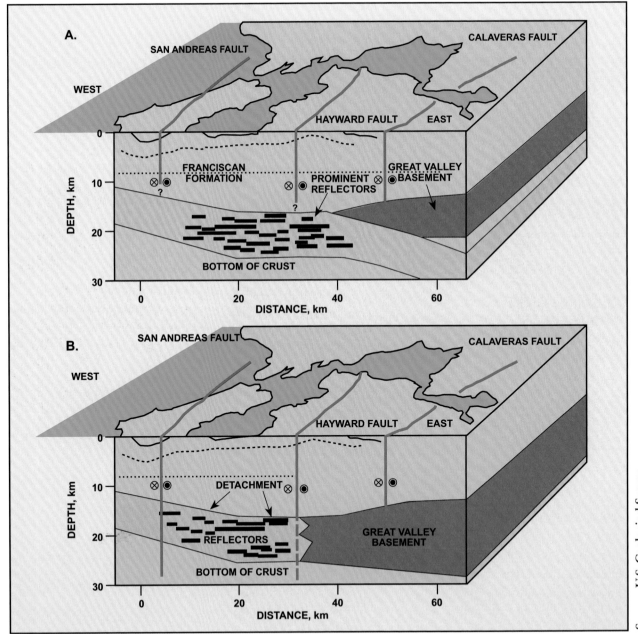

Figure 1-2.22. Vertical cross section

Source: U.S. Geological Survey

Computer technology is essential in exploration. Today, almost all exploration depends on digital data and computers. The enormous amount of data that computers and servers can store and process is invaluable to the petroleum industry (fig. 1-2.23). Geoscientists use many types of software to analyze the data needed (namely, seismic and well data), create maps, create models, and decide where to drill. Often, these software applications are integrated software under a common database, which helps people from different disciplines understand data interpretation, share data, understand a prospect's risk, and make better decisions about which prospects to drill.

Data, Software, and Modeling Technology

Photo by Trond Sørem. Courtesy of SeaBed Geophysical. Source: The Norwegian Design Council

Figure. 1-2.23. Geoscientists rely on computerized images to indicate whether and where to drill.

Most of the data mentioned is collected and stored digitally. For instance, a well log is a Log ASCII Standard (LAS) File and seismic data is collected as a SEG-Y file. Prior to digital logs, it was not uncommon to see dozens of well logs hanging on a geologist's wall for correlation (or laid on a light table). Now, all data is stored in a well file that contains well information such as well header (name, identifying number, location, etc.) data, directional drilling data, production data, perforation data, and so on.

Data

Seismic Interpretation

Analysis of seismic data changed dramatically with the first interactive workstation from Landmark Graphics (now part of Halliburton) in 1984. Thus began the market for 2D and 3D seismic interpretation software. Oil companies load seismic data into an interpretation application and draw, or interpret, the stratigraphy and structure of an area in the application rather than on paper. This was revolutionary because now the subsurface is visible in three dimensions, almost like computer game, and can be scanned through. Geoscientists can look at enormous amounts of data at one time versus one line at a time on paper as was done before. Additionally, seismic interpretation applications include powerful algorithms that can extract data from different attributes of the seismic data that correlate to hydrocarbon presence and rock properties. With this kind of innovative analysis, visualization and automation tools make it easier to spot the even most subtle traps, especially in *nonconventional plays*.

Graphics

Sophisticated computer software makes it possible to collect, generate, interpret, and transmit large volumes of well data.

The results of some types of surveys such as seismic surveys are analyzed by computers. Many graphics laboriously created by draftspersons in the past are now quickly done by computer using sophisticated software. Trained computer operators can generate maps that integrate enormous quantities of data (fig. 1-2.24). For example, they can lay a cross section of a well's path over a seismic section showing the geologic structures or display lease boundaries on top of a porosity map. Computer operators can enhance Landsat, seismic, and other graphics to create three-dimensional images in color to highlight certain features (fig. 1-2.25). Computers can generate a block diagram, which is a perspective drawing of a section of the Earth's crust as it would appear if cut in a block (fig. 1-2.26). A block diagram shows two vertical cross sections with faces at right angles to each other. The top of the block is either a subsurface view or the surface topography. Computers are also used to analyze gravity and magnetic data and combine the results with seismic data to produce a complex three-dimensional image of the geological features being studied.

Courtesy of Shell International Ltd.

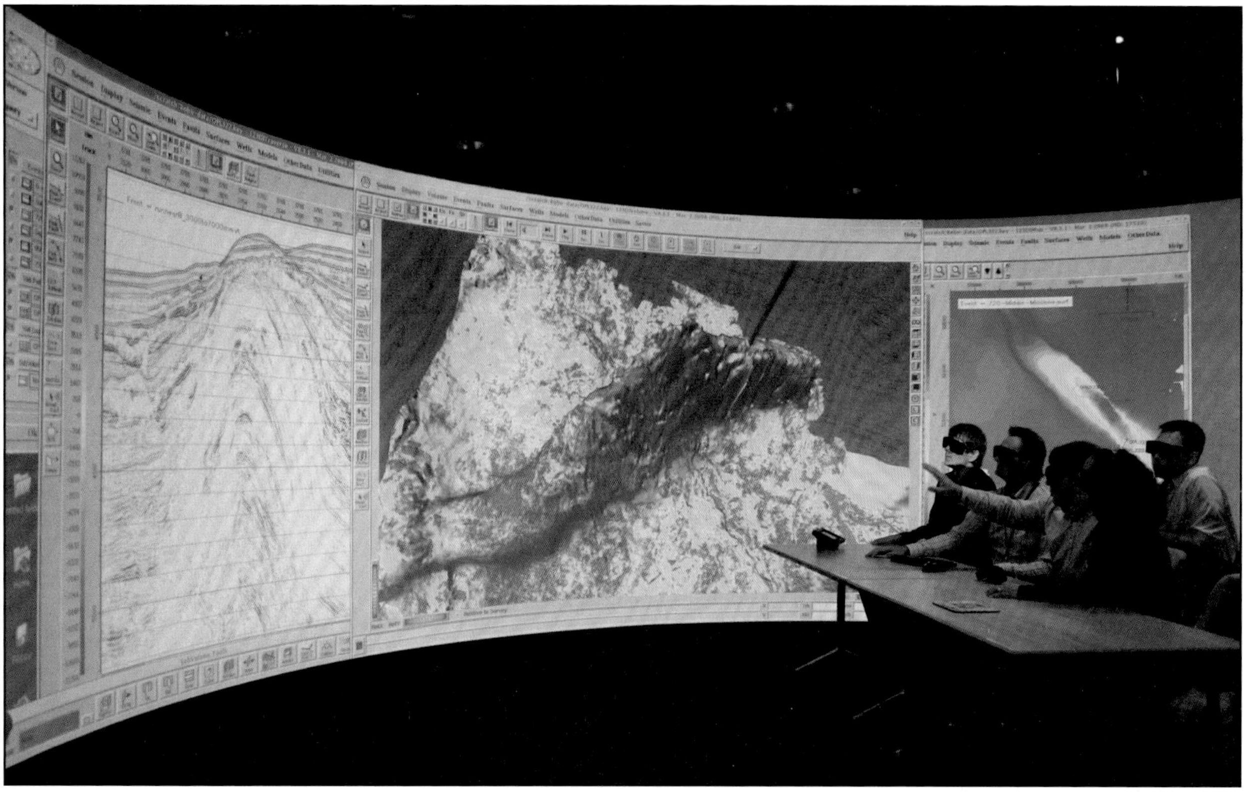

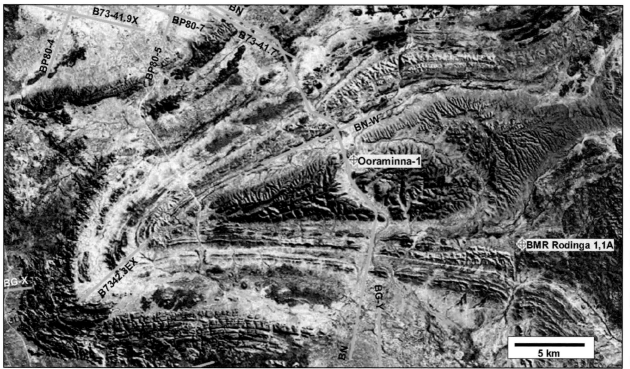

Figure 1-2.24. Maps integrate data to provide clear pictures of geological features. Irregular shapes define porosity and hydrocarbon saturation underground, while the straight lines represent lease boundaries on the surface.

Courtesy of Central Petroleum Ltd.

Figure 1-2.25. Computer operators can enhance Landsat, seismic, and other graphics to create three-dimensional images in color to highlight certain features.

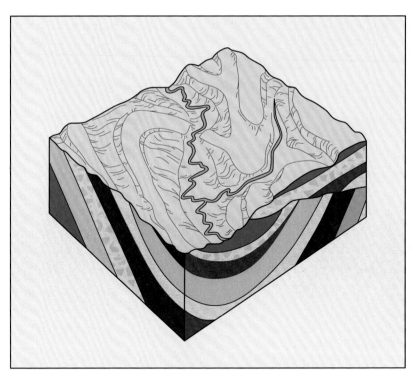

Figure 1-2.26. A block diagram represents a section of the Earth showing subsurface strata and surface topography.

Models

Reservoir modeling helps predict future production of the formation so drilling decisions can be made.

Reservoir modeling is a technique made possible with computer technology. Information is manipulated using a *model*, produced with computer software using a set of parameters, such as the number of wells in a section and the production rates of the wells. The computer operator knows the values of the current parameters and the production history of the reservoir. To predict future production, the operator enters new parameters into the program model in the form of mathematical what-if questions: for example, "What if three wells are added in this area and the production rate is increased by 20 barrels per day?" The computer calculates the new information into the model showing production predictions. This type of analysis is an invaluable aid to decision-makers.

One specific type of model useful in exploration and production is a *geocellular model*. In this case, a 2D or 3D model of the reservoir is constructed and then subdivided into a grid of cells. Those cells are populated with data from wells, such as porosity and permeability, and seismic to determine which specific reservoir properties are away from these known values. Often, this model is passed to a flow simulator application that simulates how hydrocarbons and water will be produced in that field, based on the model.

Geographic information systems (GIS) is a dynamic technology that uses a digital map to display layers of data, which can be shared, analyzed, and evaluated. In petroleum exploration, it is especially useful for reconnaissance surveying. For example, a map could have layers that include many types of data, such as satellite images, geologic maps, lease blocks, locations of pipelines and existing wells, production, location of seismic lines, and so on. The layers can be turned on or off on the map for display. Each of the layers has information associated with the particular data and can be queried and analyzed at a deeper level than just displaying it. For instance, a geoscientist working on a future lease sale can query the GIS to show all leases that will expire within six months. In this case, those leases would be highlighted on the map. The data can be further refined spatially by doing a second query to show leases that will expire within six months in a specific water depth [for instance, between 600 and 1,200 feet (182.9 and 365.8 metres)].

GIS

SUMMARY

Petroleum exploration has expanded dramatically since the early days of drilling. The principles and technologies have morphed from simply looking for hydrocarbons on the surface to developing complex 3D Earth models involving not just geology, but also geophysics, reservoir engineering, petrophysics, paleontology, and drilling techniques. Additionally, the petroleum industry finds itself falling back on sound scientific principles for finding reserves as hydrocarbons get harder and harder to find, Technology will undoubtedly continue to play a substantial role in meeting that challenge.

In this chapter:

- Ownership of mineral resources
- Leasing laws and procedures both onshore and offshore
- Private land rights in the United States
- Lease contract terms and provisions
- Executing a lease and managing agreements

Before a petroleum company can develop oil or gas *reserves*, it must acquire the legal rights to explore, drill, and produce on the site. Acquiring rights differs from country to country. In most oil-producing nations, mineral resources are owned by the national government and petroleum corporations must negotiate with government representatives to secure contracts for mineral development. The complexity, cost, and, in some cases, instability of these arrangements can be significant.

Governments worldwide frequently section their lands into smaller areas called *licenses*, or *leases*. Governments regularly offer licenses or leases to oil companies on certain terms so the companies may begin exploring, developing, and producing oil and gas located under the land. The terms and conditions of these licenses vary widely around the globe (fig. 1-3.1). When the licensing process is government-centered, it can be very bureaucratic and cause delays in parts of the process that can take years to resolve.

In most countries, governments or government rulers own all rights to minerals in the land or under waters (fig. 1-3.2). In other words, the state or national governments own all mineral rights including petroleum. Companies with the capital and expertise will negotiate contracts with representatives of the government. Frequently, the host country retains controlling interest throughout exploration and development. The agreements between a host country and the petroleum companies, many of which are also state or nationally owned, can be extremely complex.

For example, in the United Kingdom, the Queen has rights to extract minerals from all lands in the country, including those located offshore. This means that owners of surface land–whether land under a house or farmland–have no rights regarding mineral ownership.

Although much of the land and mineral wealth belong to state and federal governments in the United States, vast amounts of land—about two-thirds of U.S. onshore territory—belong to private individuals. This means that companies wanting to exploit domestic oil and gas reserves must acquire the rights to do so from private citizens. The legal instrument used to transfer these rights from both private and public ownership to a petroleum company is an *oil and gas lease*, which is another form of a license.

Figure 1-3.1. In most oil-producing nations outside the United States, the mineral rights are owned and controlled by the government.

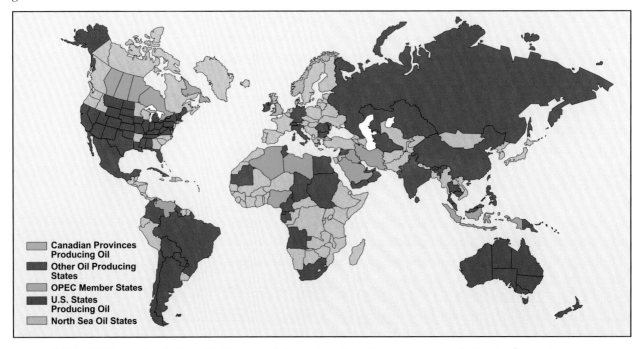

Figure 1-3.2. Of the produced oil worldwide, most rights to the mineral resources are in the hands of central governments.

Most countries do not have extensive private ownership of mineral resources. Even in the United States, most oil and gas is located on state, federal, and Native American lands rather than on privately owned land (fig. 1-3.3).

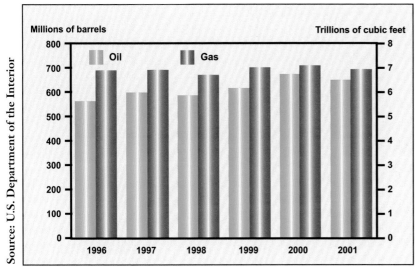

Figure 1-3.3. *Oil and gas production on federally owned land in the United States from 1996-2001*

LEASING OF LANDS

In the United States:
- Most oil and gas is located on state, federal, and Native American land.
- Much of the land is not available for production.
- Leasing of available land is governed by state law.

Each state of the United States has a board or agency that governs the leasing of its lands. The *American Association of Professional Landmen (AAPL)* has a listing of all agencies in all states. In Texas, leasing and managing state-owned minerals is the responsibility of the Texas General Land Office. For example, Texas holds title to lands in various categories such as riverbeds, estuaries, Gulf Coast areas, public school lands, university lands, and park lands. When an oil company wants to lease a tract, it nominates the specific tract or tracts for leasing in anticipation that the Texas General Land Office will make the tract available in an upcoming lease sale. The Texas General Land Office periodically distributes a *notice for bids* offering certain tracts of land and describes procedures and limitations to development.

> To bid on and secure a lease in Texas, applicants must submit a sealed bid to the General Land Office.

Applicants are asked to submit sealed bids. The General Land Office will award the lease to the company bidding the highest bonus (fig.1-3.4).

Most coastal states control submerged lands and *inland waters* within three miles (4.8 kilometres) of their coasts. The exceptions, Texas and Florida, retain ownership of the area 3 leagues—or 10.5 miles (17 kilometres)—from their shores.

State Lease Number
M-
For GLO Use Only

JULY 20, 2010

OIL AND GAS LEASE BID APPLICATION

APPLICANT AGREEMENT I agree, if awarded a lease on the referenced tract, to comply with all terms and conditions of said lease and with all applicable laws that so govern said lease, and as those laws may be amended.

APPLICANT IDENTIFICATION TO APPEAR ON LEASE (type/print)
Name: ____
Address: ____
City: ____ State: ____ Zip: ____ (Include +4 Code)
Telephone: ( ) ____

AREA DESCRIPTION
County(ies): ____ Survey/Area: ____ (If Applicable)
Block/Tsp.: ____ (If Applicable) Section/Tract: ____ Acres: ____

BID SUBMISSION
(A) Bonus Amount ($) ____
(type/print above)
(B) Sales Fee Amount ($) ____
(type/print above)
This Sales Fee is 1½% of the cash bonus as provided in Section 32.110 of the Natural Resources Code as amended.

- - - - - - - - - - - - - - - - - - - -

MGL. NO. ____

APPLICANT NAME ____ (same as above)

BONUS AMOUNT ONLY (A) (**Do Not** include sales fee) ($) ____

STATE OF TEXAS TAX I.D. # ____ (must be an 11-digit number)

SIGNATURE OF AGENT ____ (signature)
____ (type/print name)

Courtesy of the State of Texas General Land Office

Figure 1-3.4. A Texas General Land Office bid application for mineral lease of state land.

In the state of Alaska, only 2% of the land is in private ownership (fig. 3.5). The state's Division of Mineral and Energy Management of the *Department of Natural Resources (DNR)* administers the leasing process.

The DNR evaluates the social, economic, and environmental impact of any development. For example, certain production activities offshore must stop during the annual bowhead whale migration. In some areas, companies wishing to receive a permit to drill might be required to train employees to better understand the local customs, languages, and habits of residents in nearby villages. The DNR approves specific tracts for leasing and informs potential *lessees* of any restrictions and bidding procedures. The highest bidder gets the lease, unless the Commissioner of the Department of Natural Resources rejects the bid as too low.

> The DNR of Alaska closely monitors the state's leases to protect the social, economic, and environmental impact of development.

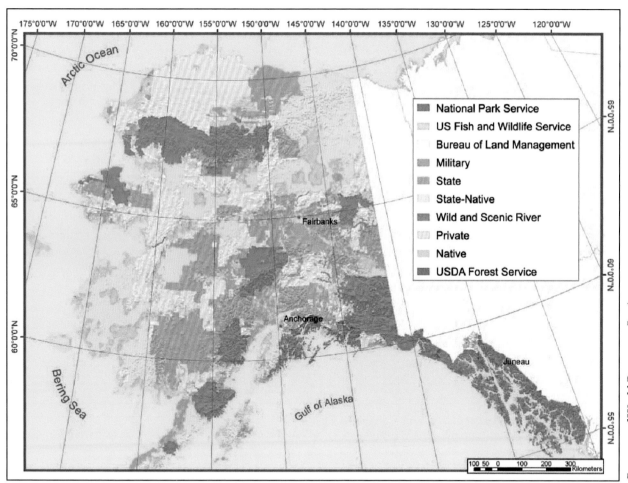

Figure 1-3.5. *Map showing land ownership in the state of Alaska*

Courtesy of World Resources Institute

U.S. Federal Government Land

A large portion of onshore land owned by the U.S. federal government is not available for oil and gas production. Land set aside for military use, national parks, and wildlife refuges, among others, is not generally leased to the petroleum industry. The federal government does lease tracts of public domain land, acquired land, or certain Native American land (fig. 1-3.6).

Public domain land is the federal government originally owned and did not subsequently sell, while *acquired federal lands* were acquired by deeds from earlier owners. Both the mineral and the surface estates of land in the public domain belong to the United States.

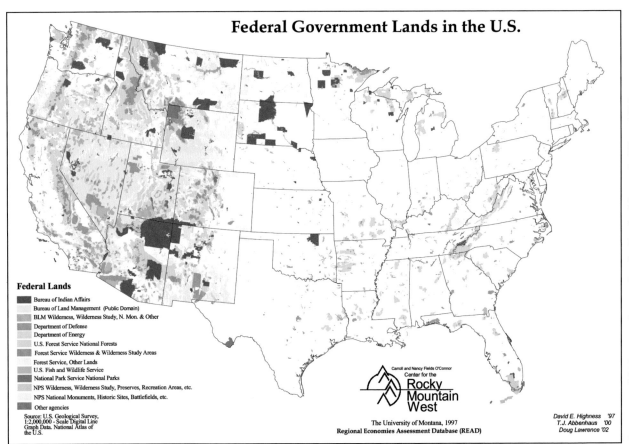

Federal Government Lands in the U.S.

Federal Lands

- Bureau of Indian Affairs
- Bureau of Land Management (Public Domain)
- BLM Wilderness, Wilderness Study, N. Mon. & Other
- Department of Defense
- Department of Energy
- U.S. Forest Service National Forests
- Forest Service Wilderness & Wilderness Study Areas
- Forest Service, Other Lands
- U.S. Fish and Wildlife Service
- National Park Service National Parks
- NPS Wilderness, Wilderness Study, Preserves, Recreation Areas, etc.
- NPS National Monuments, Historic Sites, Battlefields, etc.
- Other agencies

Source: U.S. Geological Survey,
1:2,000,000 - Scale Digital Line
Graph Data. National Atlas of
the U.S.

Carroll and Nancy Fields O'Connor
Center for the
Rocky
Mountain
West

The University of Montana, 1997
Regional Economies Assessment Database (READ)

David E. Highness '97
T.J. Abbenhaus '00
Doug Lawrence '02

Courtesy of O'Connor Center for the Rocky Mountain West, 2002.

Figure 1-3.6. Management of U.S. federal government lands

The Office of the U.S. Secretary of the Interior makes all decisions to open or close federal lands to leasing and may refuse to lease certain lands based on conservation principles or wildlife protection. The *Bureau of Land Management (BLM)* is the bureau of the Department of the Interior responsible for managing the mineral rights of onshore U.S. federal lands and administers leasing and drilling. All BLM public lands and national forests are open to oil and gas leasing, unless prohibited by law or administrative decision. National parks and wildlife refuges are generally excluded. Various federal land management agencies, in particular the U.S. Forest Service, regulate the surface environmental consequences of drilling. These agencies can veto decisions made by BLM. Like leases between landowners and operators, a lease from the U.S. federal government does not transfer the title but simply grants rights to explore, drill, and produce.

The primary term for U.S. federal leases range from 5 to 10 years. The primary term may be extended if drilling has begun or production has been established. Once production ends or if the lease is surrendered, all rights revert back to the government.

Native American tribes in the United States control the leasing of their own lands. The Bureau of Land Management supervises these leases and collects payments, or *royalties*, in exchange for use.

The U.S. federal government controls the area from the states' inland waters to 200 miles (322 kilometres) out or to approximately 8,200 feet (2,500 metres) of water depth (fig. 1-3.7). This region is known as the *Outer Continental Shelf (OCS)*. The OCS leasing is guided by the OCS Lands Act of 1953, which has been amended several times. The *Bureau of Ocean Energy Management, Regulation, and Enforcement (BOEMRE)*, formerly the *Minerals Management Service (MMS)*, is a unit of the U.S. Department of the Interior (DOI) and is responsible for managing the mineral resources offshore of the United States. In 2010, after oil spill, DOI changed name of MMS to the Bureau of Ocean Energy Management, Regulation, and Enforcement (BOEMRE).

Leasing Federal Onshore Lands

Native American tribes In the United States control the leasing of their own lands.

Leasing Federal Offshore Tracts

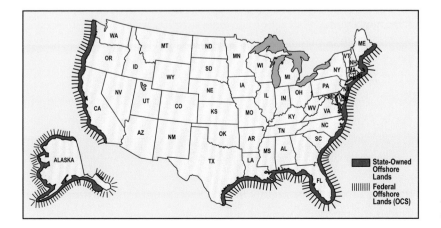

Figure 1-3.7. *Government owned offshore land in the United States*

The U.S. federal government controls land offshore to 200 miles out or about 8,200 feet in depth—a region known as the Outer Continental Shelf.

Unlike the highly regulated onshore leasing system, the DOI has some leeway in leasing U.S. offshore lands. The DOI sets a schedule of lease sales to be conducted in 5-year intervals, called the 5-Year Plan. Each sale follows a series of procedural steps, beginning with a call for information. DOI takes suggestions about which areas should or should not be leased. An *environmental impact statement (EIS)* might be prepared. The DOI then gives public notice of proposed lease sales and allows the affected states to comment on the proposals. Finally, the DOI selects the tracts and the competitive bidding procedures and issues the final notice of sale. Bids are submitted in sealed envelopes and opened on the lease sale day. It is not unusual for a consortium of oil companies to submit a single joint bid on behalf of companies. But companies producing more than 1.6 million barrels of oil per day (equivalent) on a worldwide basis are restricted from bidding with other companies with similar production ownership. This bidding restriction was put in place to reduce fears of companies forming monopolies and eventual price-fixing. These concerns were addressed in 1890 with the passing of the *Sherman Antitrust Act*.

Foreign companies may participate in U.S. federal lease sales where reciprocal agreements allow U.S. nationals to lease in that country. Securing legal rights for resource development is increasingly international and reflects global concerns.

Canadian Land Ownership

With few exceptions, each of the ten Canadian provinces owns and manages its own mineral resources. The Canadian federal government owns and manages the oil and gas of the Northern Territories and offshore lands. The lessee of public lands must deal with a government leasing agency instead of individuals representing their own interests. These government agencies can also provide additional information about leasing from cities, counties, school districts, and other political units within the state or province.

A limited amount of Canadian subsurface minerals are privately owned. In the four western provinces, several companies were granted land with attached mineral rights in exchange for their work in building railroads and opening up the provinces for settlement. Some early settlers of these provinces also acquired mineral rights with their homesteads, which are still in private ownership.

The First Leases

Early leasing agreements between prospectors and landowners were very simple. One lease written in 1853 gave the oil company the right to "dig or make new springs." The cost of digging would be deducted "out of the proceeds of the oil, and the balance, if any, to be equally divided" between the oil company and the landowner. The final statement of this lease revealed uncertainty in the new oil venture by stating that "if profitable," payments will be made.

The length of the 1853 contract is also significant. Both parties agreed that five years was enough time to discover and develop any resources that might be under the surface of the land. Years ago, prospecting was a matter of luck and not science.

It was once believed that, if petroleum was not discovered quickly, then the oil and natural gas would migrate, or move, making further exploration in a specific location unprofitable. Landowners in the United States thought the chances of profiting from an oil or gas lease were diminished if the company did not begin exploration and production immediately after signing the lease. Courts upheld landowners' claims that their lease rights included an *implied covenant* with the lessee. This covenant required the oil operator to develop at once or release the leasehold. Scientists gradually learned more about the natural laws governing the behavior of oil and natural gas. The false ideas about oil migration were eventually disproved.

After hearing continuous litigation about oil and gas migration, the courts decided by 1875 that oil and gas are the property of the first person to capture the resource and reduce it to his or her control. The phrases "capturing" oil and "reducing it to the owner's control" comes from the migratory idea that oil and gas might wander onto one's property and then leave, as animals can. The courts decided they would no longer judge from whose property the oil might have migrated. The person who drilled a well and found oil was the legal owner. Although it seemed like a reasonable decision, the consequences of the court rulings were not entirely beneficial:

- *Rule of Capture*. One consequence of the court decision was the landowner's freedom from liability for draining a common reservoir, even if part of the oil might have been under a neighbor's land. The rule of capture allows the landowner to drill as many wells as he or she can, provided there is no diagonal drilling onto a neighbor's property.

- *Offset Drilling Rule*. The rule resulted from the rule of capture and states that a landowner whose oil and gas reserves are being drained by a neighbor's wells cannot go to court to recover damages or stop the offending operator. The landowner's only option is to drill his or her own wells and produce as fast as possible. If the landowner leases the mineral interest, the person leased to assumes the burden of this rule.

In many older mineral leases, oil and gas were the only listed minerals. However, iron ore, lignite, and other minerals were also mined under these leases to the disadvantage of the surface owner. After several cases, the courts decided that the mineral estate owner did not have the right to "appropriate the soil." Therefore, any minerals whose removal substantially affects the surface belong to the surface owner.

Court Rulings on Oil Migration

In 1875, courts no longer litigated property owner mineral rights. The person who drilled the well was determined the legal owner, resulting in the:
- Rule of Capture
- Offset Drilling Rule

These rulings led to excessive drilling and production.

Government Regulations

In Canada, development is controlled by:
- The Department of Energy, Mines, and Resources
- The regulatory bodies of each province

Both the rule of capture and the offset drilling rule led to excessive drilling and production. There was waste from drilling unnecessary wells, and rapid production reduced reservoir pressures. This altered the natural forces that drive oil and gas to the surface. As a result, the amount of petroleum produced from a reservoir was often less than ideal.

Existing legislation made it impossible to efficiently extract oil and gas and equally distribute the minerals among the owners. In the United States, state governments decided to form regulatory commissions. Conservation or regulatory agencies were established in all oil-producing states. These state agencies have the authority and responsibility to impose and enforce conservation rules such as well-spacing requirements and prorated production rates. State regulatory agencies are also responsible for protecting landowners' correlative rights. *Correlative rights* are given to each person of a group-owned property to produce, without waste, his or her just and equitable share of the oil and gas.

The practice of combining small tracts of land into a single unit or area large enough to meet regulatory agency acreage requirements is called *pooling*. For example, if 640 acres are required for drilling a gas well, four adjacent 160-acre properties can be pooled together, or *unitized*, to meet the drilling permit requirement of the state regulatory agency. All *lessors* will proportionately share royalties from production from any well drilled within the unit, whether or not the well was located on their own property or drilled on another tract within the pooled unit.

Like U.S. state governments, Canadian provinces regularly pass new oil and gas legislation. The laws, administered by various government agencies, control mineral development and leasing practices. In addition to the Department of Energy, Mines, and Resources in Ottawa, Ontario, each Canadian province has its own regulatory agency.

The U.S. federal government also regulates the production of oil and gas through the EPA, BLM, and the MMS of the DOI. Currently, oil and gas production is among the most heavily regulated industries in the United States.

OWNERSHIP IN THE UNITED STATES

Internationally, only the United States permits general land ownership and ownership of mineral rights. A large portion of all oilwells in the world are in the United States, and most mineral rights are owned by private individuals versus government entities.

Ownership of mineral rights is a primary motivator for exploration and extraction. Today, over one million private U.S. landowners have some royalty interests from property. Often, mineral rights are divided many times due to inheritance with each individual owning only a fraction of interest in the property. In the United States, the owner of the surface land might also have the rights to extract minerals from underneath that land, which can be quite profitable.

Because the United States is unique in its ownership complexities, it is important to grasp the basic legal issues, terms, and economic and social dynamics to understand how the petroleum industry leases and develops these domestic mineral reserves.

There are four types of mineral ownership in the United States: private, state or federal government, and Native American tribes (fig. 1-3.8). Each may hold title or established ownership to a piece of land, but only the titleholder may grant rights to develop the resources of the land. The instrument used to grant these rights is called an *oil and gas lease*, or simply, a *lease* (fig. 1-3.9). An oil and gas lease is the most common method of obtaining rights to mineral production.

> The four types of U.S. mineral ownership:
> - Private
> - State
> - Federal
> - Native American

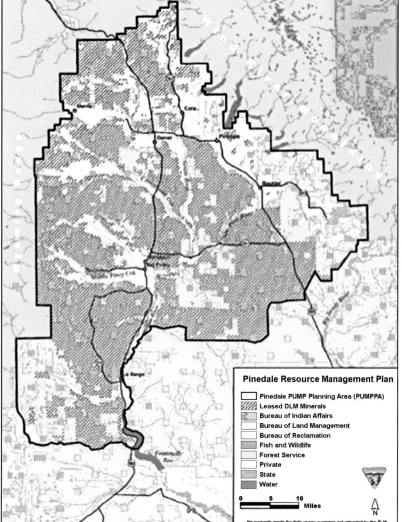

Source: U.S. Bureau of Land Management, August 15, 2002

Figure 1-3.8. Government mineral-ownership map of Pinedale Resource Management site in Pinedale, Wyoming

AAPL FORM 658-85

OIL, GAS AND MINERAL LEASE
TEXAS

THIS AGREEMENT made this _____ day of _____, 20_____, between
_____
_____, Lessor (whether one or more), whose address
is_____, and
_____, Lessee,
whose address is: _____,

1. GRANT. Lessor, in consideration of a cash payment and other good and valuable consideration in hand paid, of the royalties herein provided for, and of the agreements of Lessee herein contained, hereby grant, leases and lets exclusively unto Lessee the land described in paragraph 2 below, hereinafter referred to as leased premises, for the purposes of investigating, exploring, prospecting, drilling and mining for and producing oil, gas (the term "gas" as used herein includes helium, carbon dioxide and other commercial gases, as well as hydrocarbon gases), sulphur, fissionable materials, and all other minerals, conducting exploration, geological and geophysical surveys, core tests, gravity and magnetic surveys, for introducing or injecting fire, air, gas, steam, water, salt water, chemicals, and fluids or substances into any subsurface stratum or strata which is not productive of fresh water for primary, secondary and other enhanced recovery operations.

2. LEASED PREMISES. (Description)

in the County of_____, State of Texas, containing _____ gross acres, more or less, including all riparian rights and any interests therein which Lessor may hereafter acquire by reversion, accretion, prescription or otherwise. In consideration of the aforementioned cash payment, Lessor agrees to execute at Lessee's request any additional or supplemental instruments to effect a more complete or accurate description of the land so covered. For the purpose of determining the amount of any rentals or shut-in payments hereunder, the number of gross acres above specified shall be deemed correct, whether actually more or less.

3. TERM. Subject to the other provisions herein contained, this Lease shall be for a term of _____ years from the date hereof (called "primary term") and as long thereafter as oil, gas, sulphur, fissionable materials or other mineral is produced in paying quantities from the leased premises or land pooled therewith, or this lease is otherwise maintained in force and effect pursuant to other provisions herein contained.

4. RENTAL PAYMENT. Subject to the other provisions herein contained, if operations for drilling or mining are not commenced on said land, or on acreage pooled therewith as hereinafter provided for, on or before one year from the date hereof, this Lease shall terminate as to both parties, unless on or before such date Lessee shall pay or tender, or make a bona fide attempt to pay or tender, to Lessor, or to the credit of Lessor in
_____ at
_____, which depository and its successors shall be Lessor's agents and shall continue as the depository for all rentals payable hereunder regardless of changes in ownership of said land or rentals, the sum of _____Dollars ($_____), hereinafter called rentals, which shall cover the privilege of deferring commencement of drilling or mining operations for a period of twelve (12) months. In like manner and upon like payment or tenders annually the commencement of drilling or mining operations may be further deferred for successive periods of twelve (12) months each during the primary term hereof. All payments or tenders may be made in currency, or by check or by draft, and such payments or tenders to Lessor or to the depository by deposit in the U.S. Mails on or before the rental due date in a stamped envelope addressed to the depository or to the Lessor at the last address known to Lessee shall constitute proper payment. If such depository, or any successor depository, shall fail, liquidate or be succeeded by another depository, or for any other reasons fail or refuse to accept rentals or any other payments, Lessee shall not be held in default for failure to make such payments or tenders until 60 days after Lessee has received from Lessor a proper recordable instrument naming another depository as agent to receive such payments or tenders. If Lessee, in good faith and with reasonable diligence, timely attempts to pay a rental but fails to pay, or incorrectly pays, any portion thereof this lease shall not terminate if Lessee properly pays such rental within thirty (30) days after written notice from Lessor of Lessee's error or failure. Failure to make proper payment shall not affect any other interest under this lease for which proper payment was made. The cash payment is consideration for this Lease according to its terms and shall not be allocated as mere rental for a period. Lessee may at any time or times execute and deliver to Lessor, or to the depository above named, or place of record a release or releases of this lease as to all or any part of the leased premises, or as to any minerals or horizons under all or any part thereof, and thereby be relieved of all obligations as to the land or interest released. If this lease is released as to all minerals and horizons under only a portion of the leased premises, Lessee's obligation to pay or tender rentals and other payments shall be proportionately reduced in accordance with the net acreage interest retained.

5. ROYALTY PAYMENT. The royalties to be paid to the Lessor are: (a) On oil, 1/8th of that produced and saved from said land, the same to be delivered at the wells or to the Lessor's credit into the pipelines to which the wells may be connected. Lessee shall have the continuing right to purchase such production at the wellhead market price then prevailing in the same field (or if there is no such price then prevailing in the same field, then the nearest field in which there is such a prevailing price) for production of similar grade and gravity. Lessee may sell any royalty oil in its possession and pay Lessor the price received by Lessee for such oil computed at the well; (b) For gas (including casinghead gas) and all other substances covered hereby (i) if used off the leased premises or used in the manufacture of gasoline or other products, the market value at the well of one-eighth (1/8) of the gas so used, or (ii) if sold on or off the leased premises, one-eighth (1/8) of the amount realized from such sale, provided the amount realized from the sale of gas on or off the leased premises shall be the price established by the Gas Sales Contract entered into in good faith by Lessee and gas purchaser, provided that on gas sold by Lessee the market value shall not exceed the amount received by Lessee for such gas computed at the mouth of the well; (c) If a well on the leased premises or lands pooled therewith is capable of producing oil or gas or any other substance covered hereby but such well is either shut-in or production therefrom is not being sold or purchased by Lessee or royalties on production therefrom are not otherwise being paid to Lessor, and if this lease is not otherwise maintained in effect, such well shall nevertheless be considered as though it were producing for the purpose of maintaining this lease, whether during or after the primary term, and Lessee shall tender a shut-in payment of One Dollar per acre then covered by this lease, such payment to be made to Lessor or to Lessor's credit in the depository designated above, on or before 90 days after the next ensuing anniversary date of this lease, and thereafter on or before each anniversary date hereof while the well is shut-in or production therefrom is not being sold or purchased by Lessee or royalties on production therefrom are not otherwise being paid to Lessor. This lease shall remain in force so long as such well is capable of producing and Lessee's failure to properly pay shut-in payment shall render Lessee liable for the amount due but shall not operate to terminate this lease. The intermittent production from any well during such year shall not render necessary any new or additional shut-in payments with respect to such well or the acreage ascribed thereto.

Figure 1-3.9. An oil, gas, and mineral lease in Texas (United States)

The Oil and Gas Lease is an essential document in the petroleum industry. Without rights granted in the lease to produce oil and gas, there can be no legal extraction of the resources. Therefore, familiarity with leasing laws and practices and the regulatory agencies involved is critical. In addition, it is important to know the language, or terminology, of leasing to understand the legal aspects. The following are some key terms and their meanings:

- A lease is an agreement between the mineral owner and the petroleum company.

- The mineral owner is called the *lessor*.

- A petroleum company or other party is the *lessee*.

- The lessor grants exclusive rights to the lessee in exchange for *consideration*, usually money, called a *bonus*.

- The lessor also receives a share of the production, known as a *royalty*. The royalty is expressed as a fraction, such as 1/8, and represents a percentage of the revenue received by lessee for the sale of production which is paid to the lessor.

- If there is no drilling, the lessee usually pays a *delay rental* fee each year to prevent automatic lease expiration during a certain time period (the *primary term)*.

- The law requires certain *implied covenants*, or obligations, on the lessee.

- There are specific, *expressed covenants* in the lease for development. Expressed covenants replace implied covenants.

- Historically, the lessee has a 100% *working interest* and is the *operator*.

Many other unique terms are introduced and highlighted in the course of this text.

The Language of Leasing

To understand leasing, one must understand the specific terminology and legal arrangements that are often involved in leasing transactions.

The Mineral Estate

Establishing minerals ownership in the United States can be complicated:
- Two-thirds of U.S. land is privately owned.
- Sometimes, multiple owners exist for one property.
- State laws preside.
- A lease gives the legal right to drill and produce from the land.

Establishing ownership of oil, gas, and mineral resources—called the *mineral estate*—in the United States can be complicated. The mineral estate is considered part of the real estate. Real estate law is *case law*, or *common law*, and is determined by the historical precedents. Much of the United States uses the English system of real property common law, except when contradicted by statute. The state of Louisiana is the exception. In Louisiana, civil law comes from the Napoleonic code rather than from English common law.

Each state of the United States has its own court system. The state court cases set the precedent for state laws regarding petroleum ownership. States that follow the doctrine that oil and gas are owned in place, underground, are sometimes termed *absolute ownership*, or *ownership-in-place* states. The state of Texas is an absolute-ownership state.

If a reservoir lies under two properties, one mineral owner may grant a lease, resulting in a well drilled on the owner's land, while the neighboring mineral owner may not grant a lease. In this case, the non-drilling neighbor might be left with no oil at all. Ownership of the oil underlying both properties shifts to the owner who captured the oil and reduced it to personal property.

In states that follow a *nonownership-in-place* guideline, no one owns the petroleum until it is captured. Title is assumed at the time of production, and the oil and gas become personal property. In either type of ownership, the lease is a legal document granting exclusive rights to explore, drill, and produce.

Regardless of the ownership doctrine, two thirds of onshore lands in the United States are in *private ownership*. Generally, rights to the minerals, oil, and gas below these lands are also privately owned but not necessarily by the same person who owns the surface. An individual or corporation might be a landowner in *fee simple*, a mineral estate owner, a surface estate owner, or an owner of a *royalty interest* in mineral production from the land.

Remaining lands in the United States, both onshore and offshore, are public property that are owned and administered by individual states or by the federal government.

Landowners

Since the Middle Ages and based on English legal heritage, an estate of complete and total ownership in real property is called a *fee*. The owner of *fee simple* property has the right to use the land's wealth, whether it is above, on, or below the surface. And although these landowners have the right to extract oil and gas from their property, they generally do not have the knowledge or capital to do so. Therefore, such a landowner would grant an oil and gas lease to an individual or company who could cause exploration to be conducted.

Landowners can sell the mineral estate or a percentage of it to others through a *mineral deed*. Or, they can sell the surface rights and keep all or part of the mineral estate. A mineral deed differs from a lease in that a mineral deed is generally a perpetual conveyance of an interest in the minerals. A lease grants the lessee the right for a specified period of time to explore for oil and gas, without conveying the mineral rights.

The rights of owners of the mineral estate and the surface estate can vary from state to state. Some states regard the mineral estate as a *possessory estate*—that is, as ownership of the minerals in place. Other states regard the mineral estate as a *servitude estate*, which means it is restricted to a specific use of the minerals by one party, even though the surface is owned by another.

Mineral Estate and Surface Owners

In most states, the mineral estate is the dominant estate. Meaning the surface owner cannot prevent the mineral owner from enjoying its right to use the mineral estate, ie. explore for and produce. The owner of the mineral estate may use as much of the surface as reasonably necessary to recover the oil and gas. The lease usually requires lessee to restore the surface to its original condition and compensate for damages. Petroleum companies are generally fair and attempt to establish a good relationship with surface owners.

Royalty interest in a mineral estate is another type of ownership. A *royalty interest* is a share or percentage of the total oil and gas production. A royalty holder can be a *participating royalty owner* with executive rights or a *nonparticipating royalty interest holder* with no legal rights. A nonparticipating holder only receives a share of the profits from production.

Royalty Interest Holder

Mineral owners can sell their royalty interest or reserve all or part of it for themselves and their heirs. Or, a landowner might keep the property and use a *royalty deed* to sell a percentage of the royalty interest. A landowner can divide the royalty interest into shares and keep a portion and become a co-owner of the royalty interest with several others. Depending on the state laws, conveyances such as this can be perpetual or for fixed periods of time.

LEASING PRIVATELY OWNED LANDS

- A landman is contracted by oil companies to identify and negotiate rights to develop.
- A lease broker is an independent expert in investigating and negotiating acquisition in specific regions.

When a company decides to lease privately owned land, a *landman* becomes involved in the leasing process. Historically, a landman's primary responsibility has been to identify, locate, communicate and negotiate with mineral owners for the acquisition of the rights to drill and explore (fig. 1-3.10).

Most oil and gas companies incorporate landman duties into the corporate structure. The company land department or company landman works closely with the exploration department in understanding the *play* type. Play is a term used to describe geologically similar reservoirs or oilfields with the same source, reservoir, and trap characteristics. Understanding the play type is critical in determining how large an area to consider for lease acquisitions. A one-well play might require only 40 acres. Whereas, a deep exploratory-gas play, where a discovery well can result in numerous subsequent wells and a competitive environment, can require leasing hundreds of thousands of acres.

The company landman might hire an independent landman to research courthouse records to determine if any of the lands of interest have been leased. Later, if it is determined that part of the play is already leased by another company, the independent landman can use the courthouse investigation to understand the lease terms, including the primary term and royalty rates. If the company decides to pursue the play, the independent landman will continue researching court records and pursue lease acquisitions. The company landman might prepare to contact lessees who have previously acquired leases within the play to discuss a joint venture.

An independent landman, sometimes called a *lease broker*, is vital to leasing privately owned minerals. Independent landmen are experts in courthouse investigations and lease negotiations. They are also historically familiar with a specific region of the state or county, increasing the chances of quickly acquiring leases.

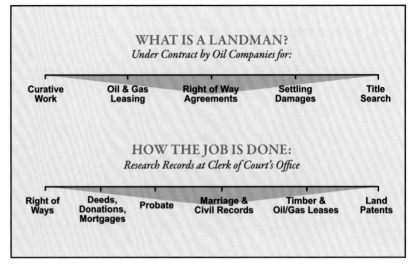

Figure 1-3.10. A landman's job

The landman performs a preliminary check of records to determine ownership of the land and the mineral interests in the land (figs. 1-3.11 and 1-3.12). Every document in the land's history of ownership is investigated and a *runsheet* describing the ownership records is created (fig. 1-3.13). The runsheet will be used later to *clear the title and* establish full legal status of the land before executing the lease (fig. 1-3.14).

Determining Ownership

Figure 1-3.11. Deed records in courthouse establish property ownership.

Source: Bureau of Land Management, U.S. Department of the Interior

Figure 1-3.12. County records show unbroken title chain over time.

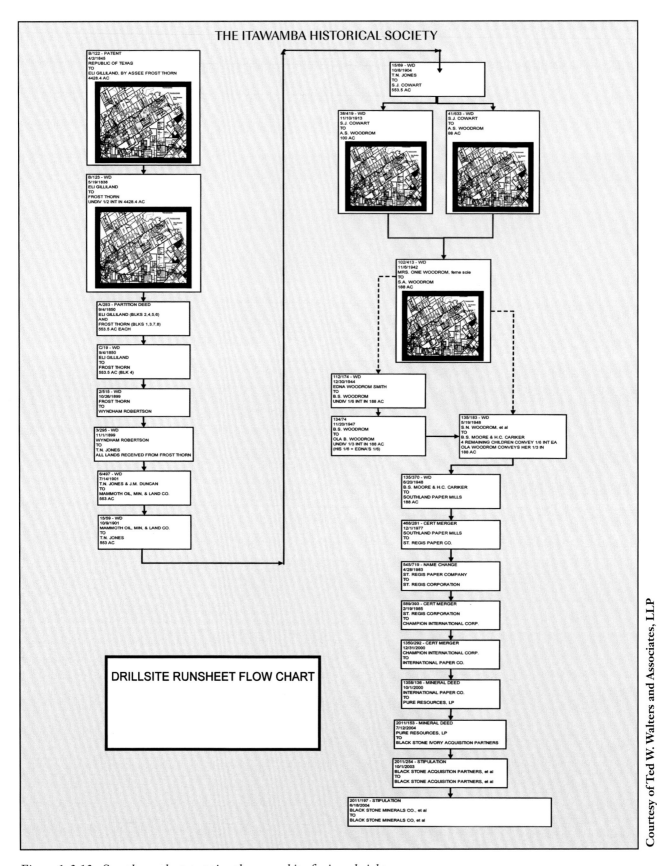

Figure 1-3.13. Sample runsheet mapping the ownership of mineral rights.

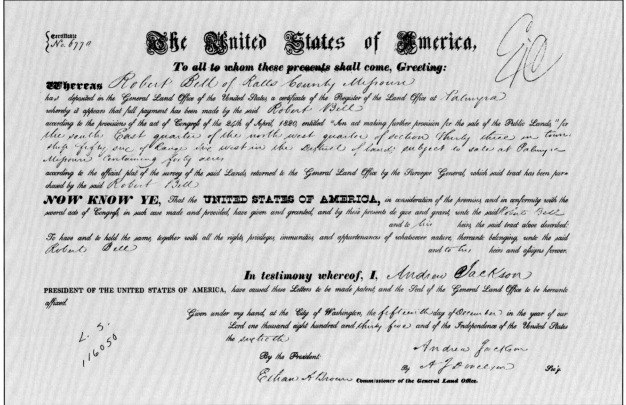

Figure 1-3.14. An 1835 land patent in Ralls County, Missouri, signed by U.S. President Andrew Jackson

Source: Bureau of Land Management, Government Land Office Records

In an ideal situation, the county records show an unbroken chain of title from the *state patent* to the present owner. To minimize the risk of undiscovered claims, the lease purchaser relies on legal advisers to establish facts confirming the chain of title. A title can be cleared by obtaining *title opinions* from a qualified attorney, or *title examiner*, who examines titles to oil and gas properties. Most companies require title opinions before paying bonuses and delay rentals to lessors. Title opinions might depend on abstracts of the property (fig. 1-3.14) or a takeoff. An *abstract* is a collection of all the recorded legal instruments affecting title to a tract of land presented in a shortened form. A *takeoff* is a brief description of relevant title documents concerning a particular property.

Curing a title is legal terminology for solving or repairing problems with the legal title to land. When the chain of title has gaps or other defects, the title examiner might obtain sworn statements or other documents supporting the current occupant's land title, especially by possession and use. Some of these statements, called *affidavits*, are sworn before a notary public and might already be recorded because of past title transfers. The title is not cleared by the affidavits and documents alone. It is cleared by the existence of accurate facts that make the title satisfactory.

Clearing the Title

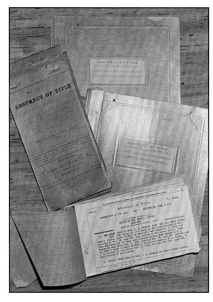

Figure 1-3.15. Abstract of title traces the history of ownership of a property

Establishing the Contract

Because not all owners can grant valid leases, the landman must verify that the lessor has the power to enter into a lease contract. Any person or company interested in obtaining a lease must carefully investigate the legal status and powers of the different types of owners.

The landman and the landowner negotiate a lease through a bargaining process to reach the best deal possible. After negotiation, both parties agree on the primary term, bonus, and royalty. Bonus is generally paid on a per-acre basis. For example, if the company is offering $150 per acre and the lease covers a 100% mineral interest in 160 acres, the bonus to be paid to the lessor would be $24,000. Because real estate law rather than contract law controls leasing, an oil and gas lease must be in writing and should be examined by an attorney prior to execution.

Provisions of the Lease

The provisions essential to a lease—conveyance, term, and royalty—are found in standard lease clauses. *Conveyance* is the granting of interest in the petroleum to a person or company for the purposes of exploring, drilling, and producing. *Term* is the duration of the lease and it is stated in the habendum clause. And royalty is a profit share of production as explained in several royalty clauses dealing with payments from production.

Most leases also contain clauses that deal with the rights of both lessor and lessee when unusual conditions exist. In addition, a lease contains dates, names, and signatures of all parties involved, and the seal and signature of a notary public.

A lease must be dated to avoid disputes about its validity. The controlling date for a lease is the one written in the lease agreement itself, not the date on which it was signed, notarized, or recorded.

Leases might contain various clauses and specifications:

- The *granting clause* transfers the described mineral interest from the lessor to the lessee for a consideration. By accepting the lease, the lessee accepts the covenants, both expressed and implied by the granting clause, such as drilling additional wells, plugging abandoned wells, or treating and marketing the oil and gas.

- Consideration is the benefit to the lessor and is required by some states to make a contract valid. Consideration is a term from contract law. Consideration is often worded as "$10 and other consideration" or similar language. The $10 (U.S.) functions as the consideration for the document. In Texas, no consideration is necessary for the validity of the lease.

- A land description is a legal description of the property. Whether the land is legally measured by metres and bounds by the rectangular survey system or as an urban subdivision, a clear and complete description is essential for the oil and gas lease.

- The *Mother Hubbard clause* allows the lessee to include odd-shaped or small wedges of land inadvertently left out or incorrectly described. A lessor usually limits this coverage to 10% of the described land so as not to include all the that land he or she owns but only that part of interest to both parties.

- The *habendum clause* states the time period of the lessee's interest. A typical habendum clause states the primary term of the lease, showing the amount of time the lessee has to begin drilling a well. If the well is not begun in the specified amount of time, the lease expires.

- *Royalty* is a share of the production profits free of expenses, except for taxes and marketing expenses. The royalty clause details the percentage of production given back to the lessor. The lessor can also receive royalty in money or *in kind*, which means in exchange for money such as in barrels of crude, for example.

- The *shut-in royalty clause* for gas wells allows the lessee to maintain the lease by paying money to the lessor in lieu of royalty on actual production profits when a well is shut in and not producing.

- A *pooling and unitization clause* authorizes the lessee to *cross-convey* interests in oil and gas. To cross-convey means that two or more leases are combined to share interests in return for a proportionate sharing of royalty. The terms pooling and unitization are often used interchangeably but refer to different procedures. *Pooling* is the combining of small or irregular land tracts into a single unit large enough to meet state spacing regulations for drilling. *Unitization* is the combining of leased tracts on a field-wide or reservoir-wide scale so that several tracts may be handled as a single unit for operations such as enhanced recovery projects.

- The *delay rental clause* gives the lessee three choices: drill a well, pay on an annual basis to delay drilling until later but within the primary term, or terminate the lease by neither drilling nor paying delay rental.

> Provisions essential to a lease:
> - Conveyance
> - Term
> - Royalty

Most leases have clauses and specifications to protect the lessor and the lessee.

- Most leases today expire within one year from the lease date unless the lessee begins operations for drilling or makes timely payment of a delay rental. A *paid-up lease* provides for the rental payment to be included in the initial cash bonus. These leases do not require the lessee to take any further action during the primary term.

- A *dry-hole clause* allows a lessee to keep the lease if the first well is unproductive or a dry hole. Then, the lessee has a specific period of time to begin drilling a second well or resume payment of delay rentals.

- If production stops, a *cessation of production statement* allows the operator a certain length of time to restore production, drill a new well, or return to paying delay rentals.

- A *continuous development clause* is designed to keep drilling operations going steadily past the primary term. It allows the operator to develop leased land up to the maximum number of wells permitted by the government.

- An *assignment clause* allows transfer of interest in the lease by either the lessor or the lessee to another party. Most leases change hands frequently before and sometimes after production begins.

- A *damage clause* makes the lessee liable for damages or losses suffered because of drilling or production.

- The *force majeure provision* allows the lease to remain in force if the lessee cannot meet the lease conditions because of delays caused by acts of God. An *act of nature or God* is a legal term for events outside human control, such as sudden floods, hurricanes or other natural disasters, for which no one can be held responsible (fig. 1-3.16).

- Although the *warranty clause* seems to guarantee clear title, the *proportionate reduction clause* covers situations in which an owner might actually own less land than claimed in the property description. If an owner's interest happens to be less than originally claimed, the lessee can proportionately reduce the rentals and royalties paid.

Figure 1-3.16. Hurricane Katrina in the Gulf of Mexico, August 28, 2005, resulted in force majeure delays for the petroleum industry.

Source: United States Department of Commerce, NOAA

Provisions outlining the lessee and lessor's specific rights about the physical operation of the leasehold are included as additions, deletions, or amendments in the final lease. For example, a landowner might want the right to approve placement of drilling equipment, storage facilities, pipelines, and roads. The landowner might insist on a provision that the well site be restored to its original condition or bargain for the right to use gas from a gas-producing well be for heating their home.

The lessee's obligations in terminating a lease agreement are usually explained in the delay rental and habendum clauses. Failure to act in accordance with the terms in these clauses can result in the lessee's *forfeiture* of the lease. The lessee can voluntarily surrender the lease by failure to drill or paying the delay rental. Also, if a well becomes unprofitable, the lessor can demand that the lease be terminated, which would allow lessor to grant a new lease on the property. If the lease contains a *surrender clause*, the lessee must notify the lessor of the intention to surrender the lease. Failure to comply with surrender requirements can result in a penalty or lawsuit for damages.

Executing a Lease

A properly executed oil and gas lease is a written document signed by the mineral owner(s), acknowledged by a notary public or other witnesses, and officially recorded in the records of the county or parish where the property is located.

After signing the lease and receiving consideration, the lessor has no further oil and gas responsibility. The lessee can now further explore and obtain drilling permits, arrange for drilling the well, or negotiate any other agreements to expedite the exploration and development of the leased property.

Division Orders

After signing the lease, the lessee takes responsibility for:
- Exploration of oil and gas
- Obtaining permits to drill wells
- Negotiating agreements for further development

After production begins, either the purchaser or the producer draws up a *division order*, which is a contract of sale for the oil or gas. A division order names all parties who have interest in the well, such as mineral owners, royalty owners, and working interest owners, and their proportionate share of the payments. The written division order is based on the lease terms, the title opinion, and any other agreements affecting ownership of the oil or gas. In addition to warranting title and guaranteeing correct percentages, the division order gives the purchaser certain rights in handling the oil or gas, accounting procedures, and establishing market values.

For oilwells, the purchaser of the oil usually handles the division orders and payments to the operator, royalty owners, and all parties having a guaranteed mineral interests. When gas is sold, the lessee handles the division orders and payments. Whether prepared by the lessee or the purchaser, all division orders must be signed by the operator, the royalty owners, and anyone else having an interest in the production. The division order serves as a contract of sale between the mineral owners and the purchaser.

Support can be offered in the form of money or assigned interest in the leased property in exchange for drilling a well. Generally, a company seeking support money is looking to reduce its capital exposure by asking for funds from another company. Capital exposure is defined as the total dollars required to explore and develop the lease. The supporting company might be willing to contribute cash to the drilling company in exchange for well information useful to the supporting company.

An agreement that trades drilling obligations for an interest in the property is known as a *farmout* to the granting party (the *farmor*) and as a *farm-in* to the receiving party (the *farmee*) (fig.1-3.17). Well information is usually provided only to the company or companies paying for the well. Farmouts are used when one company has leased property that another company wants to acquire through drilling. The company with the leases has decided not to take on the costs and risk of developing the acreage (at least initially) but does not want its leases to expire. The lessee may farmout some or all of its leased acreage to a third party who wants to drill a well on it.

Support Agreements

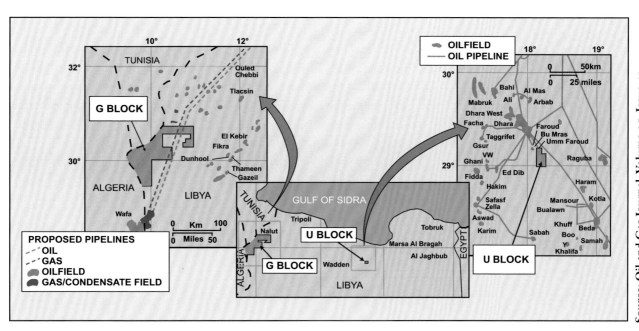

Source: Oil and Gas Journal, Volume 95, Issue 42, October 20, 1997

Figure 1-3.17. A farmout on two blocks of Libyan oil and gas basins was acquired by Canadian Occidental Petroleum Ltd. from Bula Resources (Jersey) Ltd., Dublin.

Acreage Acquisition Agreements

The easiest way to acquire acreage is to purchase the lease. In a lease purchase agreement, one company buys a block of leases from another company that already has files and *plats* or maps of the area. Another common industry transaction is the agreement to acquire acreage with the option to explore and later lease. To do seismic exploration on a property, a company can secure blocks of acreage from one or more landowners by paying a given price per acre. After gathering exploration data, the company usually has the option of leasing promising acreage for an additional fee.

Joint Operating Agreements

Two or more co-owners of the operating rights in a tract of land generally share the exploration costs and possible development by means of a *joint operating agreement*. One of the owners serves as the operator and manages the drilling and related costs. Joint operating agreements explain the rights and restrictions of the operator as well as the nonoperator prior to, during, and after drilling the initial well.

Overriding Royalty Agreements

Overriding royalty is an expense-free share of the production. It is similar to the lessor's royalty, but it is paid out of the working interest rather than the royalty share. For example, a lessee might sell portions of the working interest in the lease to other operators and reserve an override. Because an override does not affect the lessor's interest or royalty, the lease does not provide for it.

In most oil-producing nations, the national government owns its mineral resources. To secure contracts for mineral development, petroleum corporations must negotiate with government representatives. These arrangements can be complex and costly.

Governments worldwide frequently section their lands into smaller areas and regularly offer licenses or leases to oil companies that permit exploring, developing, and producing oil and gas located under the land. The terms and conditions of such agreements can vary widely around the globe.

Before a company develops its oil and gas reserves, it must first acquire rights to explore, drill, and produce on the site. Laws vary from country to country. The United States allows each state to govern its rules and regulations regarding mineral resources. Each state has agencies and organizations that define that state's leasing laws. The American Association of Professional Landmen has a comprehensive list of the agencies in all states.

Federal land in the United States is protected from oil and gas production. The Bureau of Land Management is responsible for managing the federal mineral rights onshore. Offshore, the government controls the inland waters up to 200 miles out or to 8,200 feet of depth. This area is referred to as the Outer Continental Shelf.

When securing a lease, it is important to understand the legal terms used in the specific transactions and agreements that might take place. Without proper rights, there can be no legal extraction of resources. Leasing privately owned land requires the aid of a landman who identifies, locates, communicates, and negotiates the rights to explore, drill, and produce. When production is completed a mineral estate is formed to establish the ownership rights of the oil, gas, and minerals produced. Today, over one million private U.S. landowners have some royalty interests from property. Often, mineral rights are divided many times due to inheritance with each individual owning only a fraction of interest in the property. Ownership can involve either the land or the minerals, or both.

SUMMARY

PART 2
Drilling

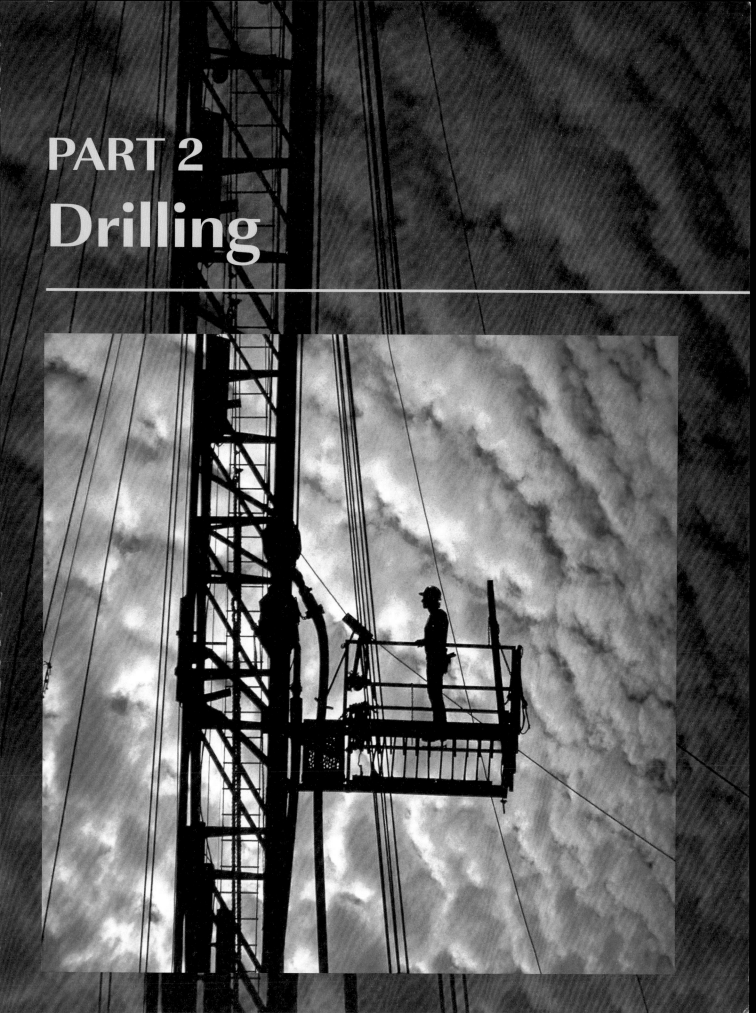

The Authors

DRILLING

Fred Florence

*Product Champion for Drilling
Automation and Optimization
National Oilwell Varco*

Fred Florence has over 30 years of industry experience including managing deepwater semisubmersibles, jackup rigs, and drillships for land, slim-hole, and helicopter operations. He currently leads a team to ensure machine controls are compatible with each other and with newly developed drilling models. Prior to joining NOV, Florence worked for Sedco-Forex, now Transocean, where he held various positions in engineering and operations. He is a member of the Society of Petroleum Engineers and serves on the steering committee of the new Drilling Systems Automation Technical Section formed to promote an industry-wide effort to develop and implement automation tools to improve drilling processes. He holds a B.S. in Electrical Engineering from Southern Methodist University, an M.A. in International Management, and an M.B.A. in Marketing from the University of Texas at Dallas.

MWD AND LWD

John Rasmus

*Advisor, Reservoir Characterization
Schlumberger*

John Rasmus specializes in Schlumberger's logging while drilling (LWD) product line. His current duties include field and client support of LWD interpretation, resistivity and nuclear interpretation support, and special projects. He has held various interpretation development positions, developing new and innovative interpretation techniques for secondary porosity in carbonates, geosteering of horizontal wells, geopressure quantification in undercompacted shales, and downhole motor optimization. Rasmus holds a B.S. in Mechanical Engineering from Iowa State University, and an M.S. in Petroleum Engineering from the University of Houston. He is a member of the Society of Petrophysicists and Well Log Analysts, Society of Petroleum Engineers, American Association of Petroleum Geologists. In addition, he is a registered professional petroleum engineer in Texas as well as a registered professional geoscientist.

METALLURGY

John Hadjioannou

*Laboratory Director,
EPI Testing Group
Engineering Partners, Inc.*

John Hadjioannou specializes in forensic engineering and failure analysis. As a mechanical engineer, Hadijoannou oversees laboratory activities for a broad range of testing, from metallurgical and mechanical testing to failure analysis and corrosion testing. His expertise covers micro and macro fractography to ascertain failure modes and corrosion mechanisms that cause failures of metals and coatings. He has key experience using engineering analyses, such as finite element analysis, to design products and parts when investigating failures. Hadjoannou holds a B.S.M.E. from Southern Methodist University and is a member of American Society of Mechanical Engineers, American Society of Metals International, and American Society for Testing and Materials International. Hadjioannou also serves as an instructor for the Petroleum Extension Service (PETEX) Houston Training Center where he teaches a course on pipeline mainline materials of construction.

Adam Cook

*Mechanical Engineer,
EPI Testing Group
Engineering Partners, Inc.*

Adam Cook is a mechanical engineer trained in forensic engineering, finite element analysis and solid modeling for design and failure analysis. He has experience in the use of scanning electron microscope to evaluate fracture morphologies. At EPI, Cook provides support to principle engineers in forensic and metallurgical projects. Prior to his current position, he served as a certified Operations Engineer for Mission Control Emergency Power Plant at National Aeronautic Space Administration Johnson Space Center. He holds a B.S. in Mechanical Engineering from the University of Kentucky and is a member of the American Society of Mechanical Engineers, the American Society of Materials, and the American Institute of Aeronautics and Astronautics.

CONTROLLED DIRECTIONAL DRILLING

João Luiz Vieira

Global Product Champion for Drilling Tools
Sperry Drilling Services, Halliburton

João Luiz Vieira is responsible for introducing and marketing performance-drilling technology, including promoting a new vertical drilling tool, V-Pilot, and the mud motor-powered rotary steerable Geo-Pilot GXT. He managed directional drilling efforts for 18 years in northeast Brazil and in the Campos Basin in Macae. Vieira came to Houston in 2005 as Business Development Manager for the Latin America Region in charge of introducing new technologies in the region. He has an M.S. in Mechanical Engineering from the Universidade Federal do Espirito Santo and received training at Petrobras Corporate University in Salvadorl. He authored the book, Controlled Directional Drilling, 2nd edition, published by PETEX, and has coauthored a book on directional drilling in Brazil. In addition, Vieira has contributed to numerous papers and articles on directional drilling technologies and is a seasoned instructor, delivering classes on directional drilling to corporate personnel worldwide.

MUD DENSITY

Bill Rehm

Independent Drilling Consultant
Far East Energy

Bill Rehm's expertise focuses on issues surrounding well pressure and improving safety in drilling well control. He began his career at Dresser Industries developing well control and pressure measurement from electric logs. He wrote the first manual on well control accepted by the U.S. Minerals Management Service, and throughout his career, has contributed to some of the most significant technological advancements in recent history including the development of directional drilling, coiled tubing, underbalanced drilling, and high-pressure drilling operations. Rehm was honored in 2009 as recipient of the Legends in Drilling Award presented by the Journal of Petroleum Technology. He has authored several books, including Practical Underbalanced Drilling and Workover, published by PETEX, and has contributed content to other PETEX drilling publications. He is a current member of the PETEX Advisory Board.

SAGD

Jerry Haston

Drilling Engineer
Independent Drilling Consultant

Jerry Haston has more than 35 years of experience in all aspects of drilling and completion activities including mud engineering, drilling engineering, training, well control, supervision, and management in the United States and globally. In 1977, Haston started his consulting business, providing well-site supervision, preparing well plans, and writing and teaching training courses. He began his career with Seis-Tech Exploration and was assigned to Alaska. He then worked as a mud logger for drilling operations in south Texas before joining Sun Oil Company as a geologist locating new drill sites in west Texas. Haston later became a field engineer for Dresser Industries serving Magcobar in the U.S. Rocky Mountains. His roles grew to include management, operations, training, and technical writing. He has a B.S. in Geology from the University of Oklahoma and is an active member of the Society of Petroleum Engineers. Haston also teaches classes on drilling technology for PETEX at its Houston Training Center and for PETEX programs at client sites.

FISHING

Dale Arceneaux

Fishing Tool
Senior Tech Representative
Energy Fishing and Rental Services

Dale Arceneaux has over 45 years of experience working in the oil industry specializing in fishing and downhole intervention. He has held key positions at Tri-State Oil Tools, Wilson Downhole, Petro-Hamco-Enterra/Weatherford, QTS Fishing and Rental, Deltide Fishing and Rental, and Key Energy. He instructs classes on fishing technologies for PETEX at the Houston Training Center.

WELL CONTROL

Steve Vorenkamp

Training Director
Wild Well Control, Inc.

Vorenkamp has 35 years of oil industry experience specializing in pressure detection and target drilling. He currently directs training for Wild Well Control, Inc., a well-established, globally recognized well control company whose training division operates schools for the International Association of Drilling Contractors and the American Petroleum Institute. Vorenkamp's extensive background includes previous positions serving as Manager of WCS Houston for Cudd Pressure Control, President and COO of The Superior Logging Company, Inc.; owner of VOSCON Inc., a directional consulting company, and the Dallas District Manager for Schlumberger. He holds a B.A. in Business Management from Tulane University at New Orleans and a B.S. in Earth Science from the University of New Orleans. Vorenkamp also instructs classes on well control for PETEX at the Houston Training Center and is a member of the PETEX Advisory Board.

DRILLING SAFETY

Jim Johnstone

President and Co-founder
Contek Solutions LLC

Jim Johnstone, a 30-year veteran of the oil and gas business, has worked with various companies to implement management systems and set up exemplary safety programs. He has led process hazard reviews, implemented behavioral-based training programs, conducted safety training, led safety compliance initiatives and investigated incidents. Johnstone began his career with ARCO (now BP) and later became responsible for all its process safety and support of environmental health and safety regulatory compliance for worldwide operations. He has participated in numerous technical committees and authored technical content, including safety publications for the American Petroleum Institute. He holds a B.S. in Mechanical Engineering from Washington State University and a Certified Safety Professional certificate from the Board of Certified Safety Professionals. Johnstone is a member of the Society of Petroleum Engineers, American Society of Safety Engineers, and American Society of Mechanical Engineers.

In this chapter:

- Early drilling methods and operations
- Drilling contracts and drilling personnel
- Rotary drilling systems
- Routine drilling operations
- New drilling technologies
- Offshore drilling units and special operations
- Uses, tools, and techniques of directional drilling
- Fishing, retrieving, and repairing pipe
- Unconventional drilling methods

2.1
Drilling Operations

Once the exploration geologists and geophysicists have obtained and analyzed data for the prospective site, the landman has secured a lease, and drilling permits and other preliminary papers are in order, the company turns its attention to drilling. To understand the complex science and art of drilling for oil and gas, it is important to take a look back at the history of drilling for oil, beginning at the start of the Industrial Revolution.

In the 1800s, workers wanted a better way to illuminate their homes when they returned from labor in factories. In response to this demand, companies began making oil lamps that burned sperm whale oil, which provided a clean, nearly odorless flame that emitted bright light. Unfortunately, the high demand for whale oil resulted in scarcity and near extinction of the whales sacrificed to produce it. Whale oil became so costly that only the wealthy could afford it. An affordable and plentiful replacement for whale oil became necessary. At the same time, factories also demanded reliable lighting as well as good quality lubricants to run steam-powered machines to keep industry churning. Fortunately, an oily substance was noticed seeping from the ground at locations around the world, and the energy landscape changed.

A NEW ERA IN ENERGY

The 1840s

Largely due to high demand for lamp oil, Baku became the world's predominant source for oil in 1872.

The first modern oilwell was drilled in Balakhani, an area of Baku, Azerbaijan in 1846. Since ancient times, the area around Baku had been known to have oil and natural *gas seeps*. The Baku well was drilled to a depth of 69 feet (21 metres). By 1872, due mainly to demand for lamp oil, the Baku area became populated with so many wells that it became known as "Black City." By the beginning of the twentieth century, Baku was responsible for half of the world's produced oil (fig. 2-1.1).

The quest for a better source of lighting and lubricants was also important in the United States. In 1854, New York attorney George Bissell received a sample of an unusual oily liquid from a chemistry professor at Dartmouth College in New Hampshire. The two men wondered if they had discovered a substance that might replace whale oil. The sample was collected from a creek in Pennsylvania that contained a dark-colored substance that easily caught fire. In testing the substance on machinery, it seemed to provide good lubrication. The substance flowed freely from the rocky land and creek near Titusville, Pennsylvania. The settlers called it *rock oil* and named the source Oil Creek.

Courtesy of Brita Asbrink Collection

Figure 2-1.1. Oilwells in Baku, Azerbaijan, in the late 1800s

After examining the oil sample, Bissell was convinced that refined rock oil would burn as cleanly and safely as whale oil and would be a marketable lubricant. Bissell along with James M. Townsend, a Connecticut banker, and several others formed what became the Seneca Oil Company in New Haven, Connecticut.

A problem the company faced was how to best extract the oil from the land. Seneca Oil's goal was to produce large amounts of oil and market it in the populous northeastern United States. Someone at the company came up with the idea of drilling a well to tap the oil. Drilling was not a new concept. People had been drilling saltwater wells in the Titusville area for years. The saltwater was dehydrated to produce salt and, in the time before refrigeration, the *brine* was also used as a food preservative. Many of the saltwater wells also produced oil, which the salt drillers considered a nuisance because the oil contaminated the salt. Townsend hired Colonel Edwin L. Drake to drill a well for Seneca Oil at the Oil Creek site. Drake, a former railroad conductor, used the honorary title of Colonel that Townsend had bestowed on him.

In the spring of 1859, Drake employed William A. Smith to be his *driller*. Smith was a blacksmith and an experienced brine well driller. He showed up at the well site in Titusville with his sons as helpers and his daughter as camp cook. Drake and Smith drove a length of hollow steel *casing pipe* through the soil's soft surface until it reached *bedrock*. The casing prevented loose topsoil from caving into the hole. To this day, drillers still begin wells by placing casing at the top of the hole. Drake and Smith then built a steam-powered *cable-tool drilling* rig, ran drilling tools inside the casing, and drilled the rock (fig. 2-1.2).

Drake and Smith drilled the hole nearly 69 feet deep (21 metres) when Smith noted the bit had suddenly dropped 6 inches (15.24 centimetres). It was almost quitting time on Saturday, so he shut the operation down. The next day on Sunday, August 27, 1859, Smith decided to check on the well. Overnight, oil from a *formation* 69½ feet (21.18 metres) below the surface had flowed into the well casing and filled it to the top, indicating drilling was a success.

Although not verified, the well was said to have produced around 300 to 400 gallons (about 1,135 to 1,514 litres) per day, far more than the gallon or so collected from seeps in the creek. The success of Drake's well demonstrated that a drilled well in the United States could yield marketable amounts of oil.

Drake's well was the first in the United States drilled for the sole purpose of finding and producing oil. News of the accomplishment spread rapidly and, because a ready market existed for refined rock oil, dozens of new rigs sprang up in the area to take advantage of demand. Saltwater drillers, formerly reluctant to drill oilwells, quickly changed their minds.

Colonel Drake's well in Titusville marked the beginning of the *petroleum* era in the United States. Refined rock oil became the primary lamp oil in homes and businesses. As industrial machines became more common, refined rock oil also became an important commercial lubricant.

The 1850s

Courtesy of the Drake Well Museum, Pennsylvania Historical and Museum Commission

Figure 2-1.2. Edwin L. Drake (right) and his friend Peter Wilson in front of the Drake well in 1861

Colonel Edwin Drake drilled the first well in the United States for the Seneca Oil Company.

The Late 1800s

The first successful well drilled at Rancho Ojai in California prompted further drilling that provided most of California's energy.

Reports of oil drilling in Pennsylvania rapidly reached all parts of the United States, Canada, and abroad. Interest in oilwell drilling was particularly high in California, where the population was growing fast. Unlike the northeastern United States, which had plenty of coal for heating and firing industrial boilers and machinery, California had none. But California had many oil and gas seeps similar to those in Pennsylvania.

Enterprising Californians applied drilling technology to the oil seeps in California. The first successful well was drilled in 1866 at Rancho Ojai near Ventura, California, and the Sulphur Mountain oil seeps. It was 550 feet (168 metres) deep and produced 15 to 20 barrels (about 2 to 3 cubic metres) a day; it was considered a great success. This prompted the drilling of many more wells, providing much of California's energy.

Other Parts of the World

Titusville, Pennsylvania, is often credited as being the birthplace of the modern oil industry. While that is certainly true for the history of the United States, many developments in oil exploration also occurred before, during, and after the Drake well in many other parts of the world. The Azerbaijanis, Polish, Romanians, Dutch, and finally, the British, can all claim "firsts" in the history of the modern oil industry.

Poland

Records from the early 1500s show that oil seeps could be found along the Carpathian Mountains of Poland. During the 1850s, scientist Ignacy Lukasiewicz experimented with the distillation techniques first performed by Canadian scientist Dr. Abraham Gesner. Lukasiewicz wanted to produce kerosene from the seep oil. In 1853, he registered his distillation process in Vienna, which at that time was the seat of the Austro-Hungarian Empire. The Gorlice region of the Carpathian Mountains, approximately 50 miles (80.5 kilometres) west of the Polish town of Bóbrka, was the site of primitive, hand-dug wells. These wells supplied Lukasiewicz with the crude oil he needed for his kerosene business. Soon, more wells were dug at greater depths, from 98 to 492 feet (30 to 150 metres) deep. The deeper wells provided a much better quality of crude.

Ploiesti, Romania, was the site of the first commercial refinery in the world, built in 1856 by Marin Mehedinteanu and his brothers. The refinery was the first of its kind to use a primitive method of distillation, producing lamp oil to be used for street lighting. By 1857, Romania could boast that Bucharest was the first city to use kerosene to provide public lighting and that Bend, a city north of Bucharest, was the site of its first commercial oilwell. Four years later, boasting another first, wooden rods and auger-type bits were used to dig another well to a depth of 492 feet (150 metres). By 1900, Romania became the third largest oil-producing region in the world. Annual production was at 1.9 million barrels (302,076 cubic metres) of oil.

Romania

Drilling and distillation became worldwide efforts in the late 1850s.

Oil was discovered in Burma in 1854 in the Magwe Division, specifically in the areas in and around the cities of Yenangyaung, Chauk, and Minbu. A separate area of development was the Arakan fields, although the crude obtained proved to be limited in supply and therefore not commercially viable. The Burmah Oil Company was a company founded by David Sime Cargill in Glasgow, Scotland, in 1886 after Burma became a British colony. The Burmah Company was the single explorer/developer of oil interests in British Burma until 1901, when Rockefeller's Standard Oil began operations. The Rangoon Oil Company, which was eventually absorbed into Burmah Oil Company, had been founded earlier to refine and process oil that had been gathered from the primitively hand-dug wells in Upper Burma. The Burmah Oil Company was also an innovator. At its oilfields, it introduced new technologies like mechanical drilling. At its refineries in Yangon, there was continuous distillation of crude.

Burma (Myanmar)

Indian oil exploration began around 1886. The McKillop Stewart Company found oil in upper Assam, near the city of Jeypore. A few years later, more oil was discovered in 1889 by the Assame Railway and Trading Company (ARTC), marking the beginnings of the Indian oil industry. As Rockefeller's Standard Oil continued to gain dominance in the U.S. industry, international companies took steps to compete. On the Indian subcontinent, Asiatic Petroleum was formed to market petroleum products in South Asia. Asiatic Petroleum was a joint venture of British Petroleum, Royal Dutch Shell, and the Rothschilds companies. In 1928 came the formation of Burmah-Shell Oil Storage and Distributing Company of India Limited, a joint venture between the Burmah Oil Company and the Asiatic Petroleum group.

India

The Dutch East Indies

The Dutch took great interest in finding oil in their colony, the Dutch East Indies, which today is the country of Indonesia. It had long been known that geological formations along the islands of Borneo, Sumatra, and Java hinted at the possibility of the presence of oil. Dutch geologists had identified more than fifty potential sites for oilwells by 1869. These sites, which had oil seeping out to the surface, were at first concentrated on the island of Java. Drilling operations began in 1872. Five years later, the Dordrecht Oil Company set up operations to become the first oil company in the colony. In 1890, in the northern area of Sumatra, the Royal Dutch Oil Company found great success with drilling for oil. Almost thirty years later, Royal Dutch would merge with a British company and form the Royal Dutch Shell Group, or simply, Shell. By 1925, the total daily output of oil being pumped out of the Dutch Indies was at 23.1 million barrels (3.7 million cubic metres) of oil.

Lake Maracaibo, Venezuela

Oil seepages were reported in what is now Venezuela as early as the 1500s. Long before the Spanish colonized Venezuela, the natives knew of the oil seepages and used the oil for medicinal purposes. In 1852, Hermann Karstwen's report in the Bulletin of the German Geological Society confirmed the presence of oil springs in and around Lake Maracaibo. In 1878, Compañia Nacional Minera Petrólia del Táchira was the first oil company to be incorporated in Venezuela. The late 1800s and early 1900s saw much exploration and production for oil. Venezuela would later become known as having the second largest proven oil reserves in the world after the Middle East.

> Oil seepages were found in Venezuela as early as the 1500s. Venezuela became known as having the second largest oil reserve in the world.

William Knox D'Arcy, a British entrepreneur, is often credited as starting the modern oil industry in Persia, known today as Iran. In 1901, he and other partners negotiated with the shah of Persia to explore Persia and search for oil and other minerals. They made an offer of £20,000 for a sixty-year concession for exploration. The agreement called for a land area covering 480,000 square miles (1,200,000 square kilometres). Entitling D'Arcy to all the oil rights of Persia except for five provinces in the north, the agreement has come to be known as the D'Arcy Oil Concession. Although the Iranian government would receive 16% of oil profits, it would later become clear that this was an ill-advised decision that would affect the country's economic welfare in the latter half of the century. The site of the drilling was at first in southern Persia at Shardin until 1907; drilling was then moved to Maidan-i-Naftun. After not locating any commercially viable wells during the first several months of exploration, the drillers finally struck oil on May 26, 1908, at a depth of 1,180 feet (360 metres). The quantity discovered made it viable for commercial sale. The Anglo-Persian Oil Company (APOC) was soon founded in 1909. APOC would eventually become British Petroleum.

Persia (Iran)

Standard Oil of California (Socal) won a concession from the Saudi Arabian government in 1933 to search for oil in Saudi Arabia. The Arabian American Oil Company (Aramco) was thus formed. It would be about five years later, after many unsuccessful drills, when oil would finally be found in Dammam. Known as Dammam Number 7, because it was the seventh hole drilled, the well was able to produce 1,500 barrels per day (240 cubic metres per day). The Ras Tanura refinery, which would eventually become the world's largest, began operations in 1945. With growing political tension and the threat of nationalization of the oil industry, the Saudi government continued to increase its share of Aramco from 25% to 60%, and finally, in 1980, to 100%. The name was formally changed to Saudi Aramco in 1988.

Saudi Arabia

Oil was discovered in Iraq in 1938 by the Iraq Petroleum Company, which was jointly owned by U.S., British, French, and Dutch oil companies. In 1927, the Iraq Petroleum Company had won a concession from the Iraqi government to search for oil in Kirkuk. Prior to this, there had not been any exploration for oil in Iraq. Soon after the discovery in Kirkuk, the government nationalized the oil industry, seizing control of the Iraq Petroleum Company in the process.

Iraq

The 1900s and Spindletop

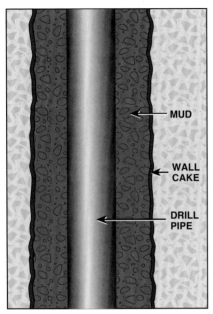

Figure 2-1.3. Wall cake stabilizes the drilling hole.

The United States grew increasingly dependent on oil as a plentiful and inexpensive source of energy. Individuals and companies were drilling wells all over the country. In the late nineteenth century in Beaumont, Texas, located in flat, coastal-plain country, there existed a dome called *Spindletop* rising about 15 feet (4.5 metres) above the surrounding plain. Gas seeping out of the dome could be ignited easily with a lighted match.

A real estate speculator and self-taught geologist named Patillo Higgins was particularly interested in Spindletop and was convinced that oil and gas lay about 1,000 feet (305 metres) below it. Around 1890, he purchased land on top of the dome and partnered with others to drill two unsuccessful wells. These wells encountered thick, loose sand that caved into the drilled hole, preventing further drilling. The formation was so thick it collapsed before it could be drilled or *cased*. Discouraged but certain that oil lay below Spindletop, Higgins offered to lease the property to anyone willing to drill a 1,000-foot (305-metre) well.

An Austrian mining engineer named Anthony Lucas accepted the challenge. After another frustrating and costly failure, Lucas finally *spudded* (began drilling) a new well at Spindletop on October 27, 1900. He hired the Hamil Brothers of Corsicana, Texas, to drill the well using a *rotary drilling rig* while most drillers used *cable-tool rigs*. Unlike cable-tool rigs, *rotary rigs* required *drilling fluid* to operate. The drilling fluid contains particles to prevent formations from caving in. To manage the troublesome sand, the Hamils closely monitored the mix of drilling fluid.

Using the rotary rig, drilling fluid, also called *mud*, was sent down the hole. The fluid picked up the rock *cuttings* made by the bit and carried them back to the surface for disposal. The Hamils used a mud mixture of water and special particles to achieve a higher density than water to exert a force against the side of the hole to reduce caving. The particles in the mud also formed a strong sheath, or *wall cake*, on the sides of the hole, much like plaster on walls of a room. Because the well was kept full of drilling fluid and the fluid formed a wall cake, the sand was stabilized and prevented from caving in (fig. 2-1.3).

By January 1901, the new well reached about 1,000 feet (305 metres). On January 10, the crew lowered a new bit, resulting in *drilling mud* gushing from the well. A geyser of oil soon followed, shooting up 200 feet (60 metres) above the 60-foot-high (18-metre-high) derrick (fig. 2-1.4).

As Lucas watched the *gusher* from a safe distance, he estimated it flowed at least 2 million gallons (nearly 7,570 cubic metres) of oil per day. In oilfield terms, that is about 48,000 barrels of oil per day. One *barrel* of oil is equal to 42 U.S. gallons (159 litres). Spindletop flowed unparalleled amounts of oil, demonstrating the effectiveness of rotary-type rigs over cable-tool rigs.

Many nations outside the United States were also using oil for fuel, lamp oil, and lubricants. World industrial production relied mainly on coal until fuel oil use became prevalent. Fuel oil had several advantages over coal. The major advantage was that fuel oil had higher energy content (Btu) than coal and was easier to ship and store. In 1911, the British began powering the ships of the Royal Navy with fuel oil rather than coal, making refueling at sea possible. The United States followed Britain's lead in converting its own Navy to using fuel oil. The use of fuel oil greatly reduced the time and manpower needed to refuel, supplied a more powerful fuel, and reduced the expense and problems of providing coaling stations around the world.

The United States had plentiful supplies of oil while Britain did not. The British encouraged the formation of the Anglo-Persian Oil Company—the forerunner of British Petroleum. After exploring Persia (now Iran) and making agreements with the Persians, the Anglo-Persian Oil Company discovered a large oilfield with a well at Masjed Soleiman, Iran, in 1908. This was the first major oil discovery in the Middle East. Soon the Anglo-Persian Oil Company was the largest oil producing company in the world.

Just as the Lucas well demonstrated success in the United States, the great Middle East oilfields showed that large volumes of oil could be developed on a global scale.

Photo by John Trost

Figure 2-1.4. The 1901 Lucas well is estimated to have flowed about 2 million gallons (7,570 cubic metres) of oil per day.

Use of fuel oil:
- Reduced U.S. Navy time and manpower needed to refuel vessels
- Provided more power
- Reduced the expense of worldwide coaling stations

The Power of Cable-Tool Drilling

Many of the world's first wells were drilled using the cable-tool method.

A common method of drilling used by Colonel Drake and many who followed is *cable-tool drilling*. This equipment uses a drilling rope or *wireline* (cable) fastened to a mechanism on the surface to provide an up-and-down motion to dig a hole. Drake used a steam-powered cable-tool rig to drill the Titusville well. The rig's steam engine turned large pulleys and belts powering a large wooden *walking beam* to move up and down (fig. 2-1.5). A drill bit hung from the end of a rope or cable was attached to the front of the walking beam. The crew lowered the bit into the hole with the cable and set the walking beam in motion. As the beam rocked up and down, the bit rose and dropped repeatedly. Each time the bit dropped to the bottom, it pierced the rock and deepened the hole.

Photo by Carla Jensen, Odessa, TX

Figure 2-1.5. Cable-tool rig

Cable-tool drilling is effective in hard rock formations. The hole is made by the impact action of the bit suspended from steel drilling cable. The chisel has a small split in the middle of the *cutting face* and its edge is slightly bent, creating a small rotation at every impact, helping to split the rock (fig. 2-1.6). The fractured rock creates loose pieces of rock, or *rock cuttings*. Drilling stops when it becomes necessary to *bail*, or remove, the cuttings from the hole.

Cable-tool drilling is less expensive to operate and it can perform some operations faster than other methods, but its disadvantages are twofold:

- The driller must frequently stop drilling and pull the bit out of the hole to bail out the rock cuttings the bit chips away. If not removed, the cuttings will impede the bit's ability to drill ahead.

- This method is not useful in soft rock formations because the rock fragments tend to close in around the bit and wedge it in the hole.

Although cable-tool rigs are no longer common, they once drilled a large number of wells. Rigs with the characteristic pyramid-shaped wooden derricks were a frequent sight from the 1860s to the 1920s (fig. 2-1.7). Later, portable cable-tool rigs that were smaller and contained many steel components became standard. By the late 1950s, the few remaining cable-tool rigs were completely replaced by more efficient rotary drilling rigs.

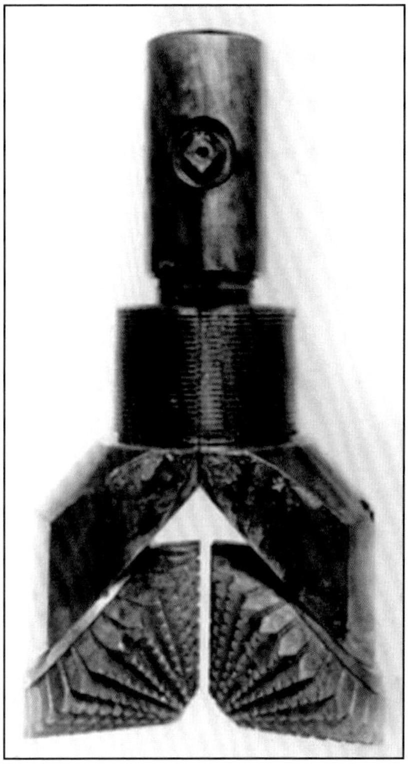

Courtesy of Baker Hughes Incorporated

Figure 2-1.6. A drill bit

Photo by Walter Eskridge

Figure 2-1.7. Cable-tool drilling rig and derrick

117

The Success of Rotary Drilling

Rotary drilling became standard after drilling at Spindletop proved successful.

The first rotary drilling rig was developed in France in the 1860s for the mining industry. Variations of the rig appeared in the United States. It was unpopular at first, because drilling companies mistakenly believed that most petroleum lay in hard rock formations and therefore thought they could drill effectively using cable-tool rigs. But in the 1880s, two brothers named M.C. and C.E. Baker drilled successful water wells in soft formations of the Great Plains of the United States with a rotary unit and fluid-circulating system. The rotary technique proved equally successful in the soft rocks of the Corsicana oilfield in Texas, which was accidentally discovered by drillers searching for water. When Anthony Lucas finally succeeded in drilling the Lucas well at Spindletop using rotary drilling, the method spread in the developing industry (fig. 2-1.8).

Fig. 2-1.8. Rotary drilling at Spindletop revolutionized the drilling industry.

Figure 2-1.9. A typical 1920 oilfield of drilling and production operations

Before long, oilwells were springing up in great numbers (fig. 2-1.9).

In rotary drilling, the teeth of the bit are forced into the rock at the bottom of the hole and rotated. While the bit is rotating, *drilling fluid*—usually a mixture of clay and water referred to as drilling mud—jets out of nozzles in the bit at high velocity (fig. 2-1.10). These jets of mud fluid move cuttings away from the bit teeth to continuously expose fresh, uncut rock for the bit to drill. The mud lifts the cuttings off the bottom and carries them up the hole to the surface for disposal. Because the drilling fluid continuously removes the cuttings from the hole, there is no need to stop drilling to remove cuttings.

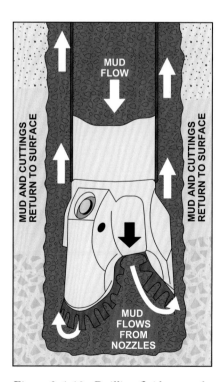

Figure 2-1.10. Drilling fluid, or mud, circulates down through the pipe, out through the bit, and back up the hole.

DRILLING TODAY

Making hole is an industry term for drilling holes to reach formations.

A modern drilling rig is a kind of mobile factory that contains essential components to drill holes to considerable depths. The industry refers to this as *making hole*.

A rotary rig is the most common type used today (fig. 2-1.11). Most land rotary rigs are mobile. A drilling company can easily move the rig and erect it at a desired location to perform drilling. When the well is finished, the rig can be taken down and moved to another location. Most mobile rigs are moved by truck. Rigs can also be specially outfitted for transport by helicopter to mountainous or jungle locations, or they can be built to cross desert sands or sit atop man-made ice islands.

Fig. 2-1.11. A rotary rig

The discovery of oil offshore has led to the development of several different types of rotary rigs for use at sea. Some are mobile and towed by tugboats to the drill site, used there, and then towed to the next location. Some offshore rigs are self-propelled to move independently. And some are erected on the site and left there throughout the life of the oilfield. Drilling in arctic regions has led to the development of specialized rotary rigs that can withstand extreme cold and movement of *pack ice*.

Early oil entrepreneurs faced many obstacles in getting oil out of the ground. As they drilled in new areas and encountered problems, they responded with innovative drilling methods to overcome their challenges. Today, engineers continue to develop smart tools and techniques to solve the drilling problems they encounter, especially in challenging regions and terrain.

One engineering decision involves selecting the proper materials to drill, depending on the dynamics of the formation to be encountered. Drilling equipment and components are largely made of metal and can be changed by drilling environments under and above ground. It is therefore necessary to understand the interactions of metals with minerals underground and the effects of the forces of pressure and temperature as well as weather. These factors point to the complex discipline of metallurgy, described next.

Oilfield Metallurgy

Among the engineering tasks associated with drilling is considering the properties of metals to be used in operations. The science of *metallurgy* in oilfields is a broad discipline that studies the design, formation, and analysis of metals used in the oil and natural gas production industry. Steel has classically been the predominant material used due to its strength, formability, and cost. However, as new techniques are put into practice and increasingly harsh environments are encountered, the necessity of more specialized materials becomes readily apparent.

> Metallurgy is the design, formation, and analysis of metals used in the oil and natural gas industry.

To gain a basic understanding of metallurgy and how it affects drilling operations, it is helpful to break the topic into three primary areas of consideration:

- The metal's microscopic crystalline arrangement—how it is structured
- The metal's mechanical properties—how it performs
- The metal's chemical composition—what gives the metal its properties

Examining Metals   When examining metals at their most basic level—the atomic level—the metals used in oilfield operations fall into one of two categories: *body-centered cubic (bcc)* or *face-centered cubic (fcc)* lattice (patterned) structures. Solid metals are made up of regularly arranged *crystal lattices* (crystals arranged in a particular pattern) that heavily influence the physical properties of metals, for instance, strength. These properties influence a metal's usefulness.

Steel *alloys* are formed from two or more chemical elements with at least one being a metal (fig. 2-1.12). They are defined as a fusion of iron and carbon with additional elements added to achieve desired physical properties, such as hardness and resistance to breaking and corrosion. Steel alloys are broken down into two groups: *low-alloy steels* and *high-alloy steels*. Low-alloy steels are usually used to achieve increased *hardenability*, which in turn, improves their other mechanical properties. High-alloy steels are typically stainless steels and are resistant to corrosion.

Steel at room temperature begins with a body-centered cubic atomic structure. Once heated past 1,360 degrees Fahrenheit (°F) (738 degrees Celsius (°C)), its structure begins to change. Low-carbon content steel can be further heated to approximately 2,700°F (1,482°C), at which point the atomic structure shifts again. Further increase of applied heat will begin melting the solid iron to a liquid.

Treating steel with heat is a method used to achieve a wide variety of mechanical properties, especially when using steel of the same chemical composition. After being heated, the method of cooling is a significant factor in the resulting steel structure and properties. Slow cooling of the steel causes atomic structure and grain structure changes in the reverse order.

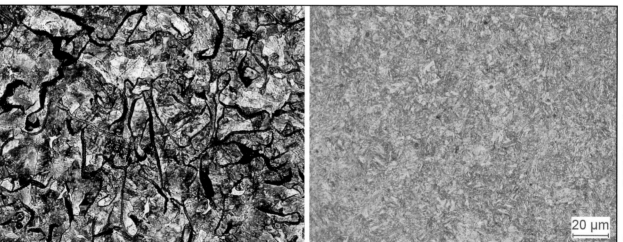

Courtesy of EPI Materials Testing Group

Figure 2-1.12. Closeup of metals taken with a high-powered microscope: etched cast iron microstructure (left) and alloy steel 4140 quenched and tempered martensite (right)

A metal's physical properties determine which metal to use for oilfield operations. In the oil and gas drilling industry, the three most commonly referenced mechanical properties of metals are:

- *Yield and tensile strength*:
  - Yield strength—the point at which, when exceeded, a material will no longer completely return to its original shape after removing the applied load
  - Tensile strength—the point at which, when exceeded, the material will break
- *Toughness*—a material's inherent resistance to cracking, measured as the amount of energy a sample can absorb before rupturing
- *Hardness*—a material's resistance to indention, machining, or abrasion

Choosing Metals for Oilfield Use

Common mechanical properties of metal:
- Yield and tensile strength
- Toughness
- Hardness

It is important to test a material's mechanical properties before use in oilfield operations. This helps determine safety factors for designed parts and provides a known maximum for the load the material can handle (fig. 2-1.13). The mechanical properties of metals can be quantified by mechanical testing. Typical tests include tensile testing, impact toughness, hardness, corrosion, and fatigue.

Tensile test—the most common test to determine mechanical properties. In this test, a piece of the material is pulled in line on an axis. Stress and strain are calculated as an increased load is applied. In figure 2-1.13, the graph reveals the yield and ultimate tensile points for a given tested material. Notice the straight line from zero to the yield point. The material is deformed at the yield point and will no longer snap back to its original shape. At the failure point, the material's tensile strength is exceeded and it will break.

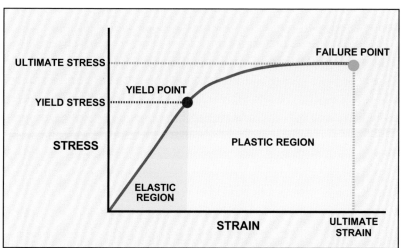

Figure 2-1.13. Example of a stress vs. strain curve

Charpy impact test—measures the amount of energy a material can absorb before rupturing. In this test, a V- or U-notch of specified size is cut into the material and placed in a testing chamber, then struck with a striker on a pendulum. The amount of energy absorbed is calculated after impact.

Hardness tests—determines a material's resistance to indentation, machining, and abrasion. Multiple types of hardness tests and scales are used but all operate using a common method. A hard object of known weight is punched or pressed on the surface of the material, and the resulting notch is measured. Hardness charts help to compare different hardness values according to hardness scales.

Hardness can also be used to estimate the tensile strength of a material. Once a hardness value is obtained, it can be converted to an equivalent Brinell hardness and multiplied by 500 to obtain an approximate ultimate tensile strength.

Chemistry Considerations

Impurities that weaken mechanical properties:
- Nitrogen
- Oxygen
- Sulfur
- Phosphorus

There are several commonly found elements in steel besides carbon that affect the end result. Generally referred to as impurities, the elements that typically lessen the mechanical properties of a material are nitrogen, oxygen, sulfur, and phosphorus. Additional elements can be added to steel to reduce or overcome these deficiencies:

- *Molybdenum*—significantly increases high-temperature strength and hardenability
- *Nickel*— added to increase toughness and resist cracking
- *Chromium*—improves hardenability and resistance to oxidation and corrosion

A common type of steel encountered is cast iron, frequently used for valves, pumps, and compressors. Cast irons are primarily a combination of iron, carbon, and silicon. Other alloy elements commonly used are manganese, phosphorus, nickel, cerium, and magnesium.

Another common form of steel is low-alloy steels, which represents a broad group of steels with multiple applications. Low-alloy steels can usually become harder and alter their properties with heat treatment. There is a subclass of low-alloy steel that uses a lower carbon content to improve welding and forming capabilities while retaining strength. These are known as high-strength, low-alloy steels. Low-alloy steels are used for drill pipe, line pipe, drill collars, wellheads, and even platforms and drilling rig structures. Because corrosion is a frequent and troubling problem in oilfield operations, some stainless steels are widely used for their strength and corrosion resistance.

Corrosion is the disintegration of a material due to chemical reactions with its surroundings. In the most general terms, this refers to a loss of electrons when metals react with water and oxygen, commonly known as rusting on iron.

Corrosion is a natural process that has always created problems for oilfield operations. Water—especially saltwater in and around formations—is problematic when it enters areas where iron-based metals are used, such as pipe (figs. 2-1.14). As water or an acid contacts the metal, an electrochemical reaction causes corrosion. When this occurs over time, it damages and weakens the metal. As oilfields get older, more and more water is produced from them, and increased water production means increased corrosion problems.

Fundamentals of Corrosion

When water contacts metal, an electrochemical reaction causes corrosion. Inhibitors and cathodic protection slow down corrosion.

Courtesy of EPI Materials Testing Group

Figure 2-1.14. Corroded pipe (A) and magnified corrosion pits (B)

Fighting corrosion is an ongoing battle. Whenever metal pipe is placed in the ground, corrosion starts in places along the outside surface of the pipe. All metals tend to oxidize under certain conditions with some metals more susceptible than others. Iron, in the form of steel, is the metal of major concern in pipe and in drilling equipment.

The process of corrosion cannot be stopped but progress can be slowed. Engineers can fight corrosion with *cathodic protection*, which uses a bar of metal, such as magnesium or zinc, attached to the pipe to cause preferential corrosion of the magnesium or zinc instead of the pipe. Special chemicals added inside of pipes, called *inhibitors*, are also helpful in reducing the corrosion rate of metal. For certain installations, specialized electrical systems are also used instead of sacrificial bars of metal.

One of the best defenses against the adverse effects of corrosion in oilfield operations is the use of steel alloys composed of various metals that naturally resist corrosion. Therefore, selecting the right metals for pipe and equipment and monitoring their stability in service are critical activities of managing oilfield operations.

Overall, material selection and heat-treating processes serve a wide range and variety of needs for steel that serve specific purposes in drilling, producing, and transporting oil and gas from reservoirs to market. Through the years, additional applications and harsh conditions have called for increasingly specialized materials. Oilfield metallurgy enables the oil industry to consider environmental and application factors in great detail to design the most effective materials for oil and gas recovery and delivery.

The companies and people involved in engineering and drilling tasks play a vital role in ensuring that drilling is accomplished according to plan. Oilwell drilling and production operations are carried out by companies that employ experienced, skilled personnel supported by a number of expert specialist subcontractors (fig. 2-1.15).

A lease is generally owned by a group of companies with one partner designated as the *operator*. The operator's job is to manage all the activity on the lease to carry out the partner's joint decisions.

Because the operator holds the rights to the oil and gas on the lease and is responsible for producing it, the operator sets the specifications for the well. The operator:

- Plans the well
- Obtains drilling permits
- Requests competitive bids for a rig
- Hires the expert crew and any additional services

The operator negotiates an agreement with a *drilling contractor* with drilling rigs and access to crews needed to drill the wells. Then, the contractor often hires subcontractors to supply the additional expertise and equipment needed for the drilling program. Once this is accomplished, the contractor will drill the well according to the operator's specifications.

The operator might also hire other *service companies* that specialize in services needed for parts of the drilling program. Generally, the operator has a person on site at all times, called the *company representative*. This individual works closely with the contractor's manager to ensure the contractor drills the well to specifications.

Drilling Personnel and Contracts

The operator manages the drilling process. The drill site team includes:
- Toolpusher
- Driller
- Derrickhand
- Rotary helpers
- Roustabouts

Courtesy of Texas A&M University—Integrated Ocean Drilling Program

Figure 2-1.15. It takes a well-trained, highly skilled crew to run a drilling operation.

Contractors   A drilling contractor owns and operates the drilling rig. To do this, the drilling contractor maintains a crew to perform work on the rig. A typical crew on a land rig consists of the following positions:

- Toolpusher
- Driller
- Derrickhand
- Two or three rotary helpers (floorhands/roughnecks)
- Lease hands

Offshore, the contractor also hires:

- Several roustabouts
- Maintenance staff
- Marine crew

The *toolpusher* is the contractor's top manager on the drill site, responsible for the rig's overall operations and performance. The toolpusher makes sure the crew drills the well to the operator's specifications. It is customary in some areas to refer to the toolpusher as the rig superintendent or rig manager.

The *driller* is subordinate only to the toolpusher and is the person who operates the drilling machinery. The driller also manages the day-to-day activities of the derrickhand and rotary helpers.

The *derrickhand* has two jobs. First, the derrickhand looks after the mud pumps and sometimes monitors and records the condition of the drilling mud. Second, when the drill pipe is removed from or put into the hole, the derrickhand handles the top of the pipe from a small platform high in the derrick, or mast, of the rig.

Rotary helpers, *floorhands*, or *roughnecks* handle the bottom of the pipe on the rig floor when pipe is removed from or put into the hole. At other times, rotary helpers maintain and repair the tools and equipment on the rig.

Offshore, *roustabouts* assist in loading and unloading equipment and supplies delivered by boat to the rig. They are also responsible for keeping the entire rig painted, cleaned, and repaired. Sometimes on land rigs, roustabouts are called *lease hands*. Offshore rigs have crews trained in both drilling and marine operations. They also employ electricians, mechanics, and welders. The person in charge of the offshore rig is called the *offshore installation manager*. This manager has overall responsibility for the safety of all personnel onboard the rig.

The process of well drilling begins with a *drilling bid proposal*. The operator commonly sends the bid proposal in the form of a document to several drilling contractors located in the area of the proposed operation. The drilling contractor responds with a price to provide equipment and crew necessary to comply with specifications and achieve a profit. Often, the operator selects the contractor with the lowest bid. However, the operator also considers a contractor's safety record, past performance, and proven drilling capabilities to ensure safe, reliable, and quality services.

When the operator accepts a contractor's bid, both parties sign the bid and it becomes a *contract*. The contract is an agreement between the operator and the contractor that spells out what each is expected to do and provide to drill the well to specifications. The contract contains clauses that address items such as location of the well, the date drilling will begin, the well's depth, timeline, amounts payable to the contractor, and other stipulations.

An important part of a contract is the operator's specifications for the well. The contract states details such as diameter and depth of each part of the hole, the drilling mud, and the equipment and services each party will supply.

Operators and contractors use one of four basic types of contracts, depending on assignment of financial risks and local market conditions. Contract options are:

- Footage contract
- Daywork contract
- Turnkey contract
- Combination agreement

The operator and the contractor are always concerned about time needed to complete the job. All types of contracts focus on personnel safety, preserving the environment, correct operation and maintenance of equipment, and protection of property throughout operations.

Bid Proposals and Specifications

A contract is an agreement between the operator and the contractor that outlines job duties and drilling specifications.

Footage Contract

In a *footage contract* (or *meterage contract*), the operator agrees to pay the contractor a certain amount for each foot (or metre) of hole drilled. A footage contract is riskier for the contractor than for the operator because the operator pays the contractor the same amount regardless of how long it takes to drill the well. If something happens outside the contractor's control making it impossible to drill the well, the contractor loses money. If all goes well, the contractor might receive more money with a footage contract than with a daywork contract. Generally, these contracts are only used in areas with well-known geology, where well designs are standard, and drilling conditions are predictable.

Daywork Contract

The most common contract is a *daywork contract*. The operator pays the contractor an amount per day to use the rig, regardless of work the rig is performing. The contractor is paid by the hour instead of by the foot or metre. Usually, daywork contracts have different pay rates depending on rig operation. For instance, one rate might apply while the rig is actually drilling, and another rate might apply while the rig is capable of drilling but is shut down while waiting for operator orders or for third-party services. Other rates might apply if the rig is shut down due to equipment problems or harsh weather.

Operators use daywork contracts when the well to be drilled is in a high-risk area—one in which the formations are difficult to drill. Such formations can present unusual delays and risks that the operator must address. Under such conditions, it is unreasonable for the contractor to bear the financial risk of dealing with geological uncertainties. A daywork contract is usually used when the operator is drilling a *wildcat well* in an area not previously drilled. Daywork contracts are also used on routine wells where it is commercially attractive to both the operator and contractor.

In a daywork contract, the operator compensates the contractor by paying a *day rate* for rent of the rig and crew. In addition, the operator pays the costs of all third-party services. The total of both the dayrate and additional costs is called a *spreadrate*. Generally, the spreadrate is about twice the dayrate.

Turnkey Contract

A *turnkey contract* requires the operator to pay the drilling contractor an agreed amount when the well is finished. This type of contract states the contractor will furnish all the equipment, materials, and people needed to drill the well. The contractor also controls the entire drilling operation with minimum onsite supervision by the operator and assumes all financial risk, adjusting the price to reflect the risks. The operator benefits by not having to assume risk and eliminates accounting expenses by receiving a single bill for the entire operation. Sometimes turnkey contracts are awarded to contractors in a location with which they are especially familiar and where they have considerable experience drilling. In this respect, turnkey contracts are simply a variation of the footage contract as previously described.

Combination Agreement

A *combination agreement* combines payment methods. For example, the operator might pay footage (meterage) rates to a certain depth and pay daywork rates for any drilling below that depth. Another way to structure a combination agreement is to include clauses that provide for a daywork rate for particular operations. For instance, a *standby time rate* compensates the contractor for days when the rig and crew are on the site and able to drill, but for reasons beyond their control, cannot drill.

This situation can occur, for example, when the contractor is waiting for operator permission to start testing operations, for equipment or materials to arrive, for muddy roads to become passable, or other such obstacles. Most footage (meterage) contracts contain clauses concerning daywork rates, which makes them combination agreements.

Drilling a hole to depths of 30,000 to 40,000 feet (9,144 to 12,192 metres) is a considerable task and requires a high-powered *rotary drilling rig* to perform the job (fig. 2-1.16, 2-1.17, and 2-1.18). The basic steps of drilling a well on land or offshore are as follows:

- The rig drills a hole with a rotating bit and flushes the cuttings back to the surface with the drilling mud.

DRILLING SYSTEMS

Drilling systems include:
- Hoisting
- Rotating
- Circulating
- Power

Figure 2-1.16. Modern land rig

Figure 2-1.17. Modern offshore rig

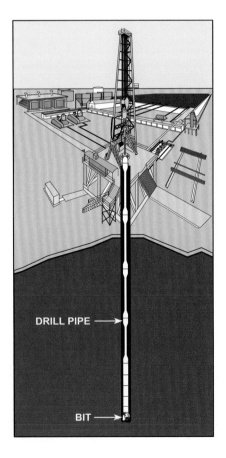

- Sections of *drill pipe* above the bit are screwed together in a *drill string* that connects equipment in the hole to equipment on the surface.

- The drilling crew adds more lengths of drill pipe as needed to drill a deeper hole.

- Periodically, drilling is stopped and steel pipes called casing are lowered into the well and cemented in place to line the borehole.

- Drilling continues in the smaller size hole beneath the casing.

- Drilling and casing are continued in sequence until the target formations are reached.

To do this job, several major pieces of equipment and machinery are required. These key components are divided into four main systems:

- Hoisting
- Rotating
- Circulating
- Power

Figure 2-1.18. Schematic of rotary land rig with drill stem and bit on the bottom of the drilling hole.

The *hoisting system* hoists the drill pipe in and out of the hole and supports the drill pipe, keeping it in tension. The system works like a *winch*, where the *drum*—or *spool*—sits horizontally between two posts with a hoisting rope attached. Turning the drum with a crank arm winds the rope around the drum and lifts the object attached (fig. 2-1.19).

The hoisting system of a rotary drilling rig is similar. It consists of the derrick or mast (the posts), the drawworks (the spool and crank), and the drilling line (the rope). Because the loads are heavy, a *block* and *tackle* are added. The *crown block* (or *crown sheaves*) is fixed atop the derrick or mast. The crown block is stationary, but the *traveling block* moves up and down. Heavy loads are attached to the drilling hook underneath the travelling block (fig. 2-1.20).

The Hoisting System

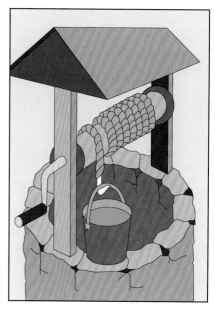

Figure 2-1.19. Similar to the action of a drilling winch, a windlass hoists a bucket with water from a well.

Hoisting systems include:
- Derrick
- Drawworks
- Drilling line

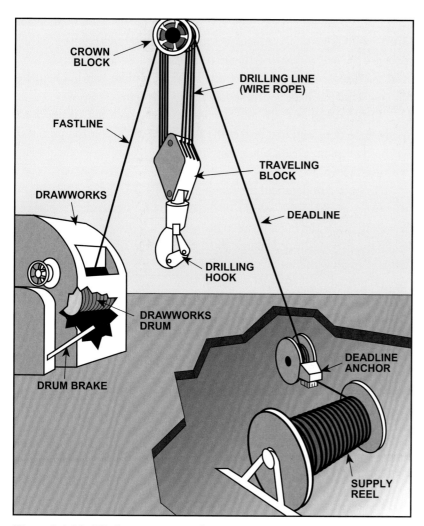

Figure 2-1.20. The hoisting system of a rotary rig is shown without the derrick.

As the drill pipe is lowered into the hole, the travelling block and hook support the entire weight of the drill string and bit. When the bit touches bottom, some of the load is transferred to the bottom of the well. As the drill string is lowered more, the weight increases. The transfer of weight must be carefully controlled, because too much weight can damage the bit, and too little weight can slow the *drilling rate*.

The drill string consists of many joints of drill pipe and the *bottom hole assembly (BHA)*, consisting of the bit, special steel tools, and thick-walled pipe called drill collars. The bit engages the rock to cut the hole. The special tools help keep the bit drilling along a straight line, or steer it along a desired course, called the wellbore trajectory. The drill collars are used for weight. The driller controls the hoisting and lowering of the drill string, transferring only part of the weight of the drill collars to the bit. The rest of the weight is used to keep the drill pipe in tension, to reduce buckling loads that could cause it to fail. Because the drill pipe is rotating and constantly bending back and forth with each revolution, it will eventually break, similar to what happens to a paper clip if bent continuously back and forth.

Drill collars are stiff and do not buckle under the compressive loads. The steel wall of a drill collar is also much thicker than the wall of the drill pipe. Drill collars can survive much higher cyclical loads without failing.

To better understand the concept of weight transfer, think about the forces at play. The weight of the drill string suspended below the traveling block and hook is called the *hook load*. Consider a vertical well: when the bit is a short distance above the bottom of the well, the hook load is equal to the weight of the drill string. For example, this might be 200,000 pounds (91 metric tons). When the driller lowers the drill string and the bit just touches the bottom of the hole, the hook load is still 200,000 pounds (91 metric tons). As the driller continues to lower the drill string, the hook load will be reduced to a value of, say, 180,000 pounds (82 metric tons). The 20,000 pounds (9 metric tons) transferred to the bottom of the hole is called *weight on bit*. If the drill collars with BHA weigh 50,000 pounds (23 metric tons), the point of equilibrium is located somewhere along the BHA and there is still 30,000 pounds (14 metric tons) hanging below the drill pipe, keeping it in tension. If the driller lowers the load until the weight on bit is 60,000 pounds (27 metric tons) —50,000 pounds (23 metric tons) of BHA and 10,000 pounds (5 metric tons) of drill pipe—the point of equilibrium will be in the drill pipe, which can lead to pipe failure. The driller controls the load to make sure the point of equilibrium, or zero tension/compression, is always within the drill collars.

The derrick and mast are universally recognized symbols of oilwell drilling. They look similar and do the same job but are used at different drill sites. Both are basically a steel tower as high as 120 feet (36 metres) or higher above the rig floor. Derricks and masts support the traveling and crown blocks and the enormous weight of the *drill stem*. They also support the drill pipe and drill collars as they are pulled out of the hole and set back away from the wellbore. The major differences between derricks and masts are:

- *Derrick*: a permanent A-frame structure with legs that sit on the corners of the rig floor (fig. 2-1.21). It must be disassembled to move it from the site. Offshore rigs often use derricks because the entire rig containing the derrick moves, so no reassembly is necessary.

- *Mast*: a portable A-frame structure that sits on the rig floor or on the ground. It can be folded or collapsed to transport it to another site. Most land rigs use masts because they are easy to move (fig. 2-1.22).

Derricks and Masts

Figure 2-1.21. A derrick has four distinct legs.

A derrick is a permanent frame.
A mast is a portable unit.

Courtesy of National Oilwell Varco

Figure 2-1.22. A mast being transported

More recent designs of some deepwater offshore rigs include *dual-activity derricks* with two sets of crown sheaves and traveling blocks to enable simultaneous operations, such as drilling the surface hole while *making up* surface casing (fig. 2-1.23). With this system, surface casing can be lowered into the water using an *auxiliary hoist* while drilling occurs with the main hoist. When the surface hole is complete, the drill string is pulled up until the bit clears the ocean floor. Then the rig is moved to align the casing with the hole. The casing is lowered on the auxiliary hoist while the drill string is retrieved using the main hoist. Simultaneous operations eliminate *flat time*, or nonproductive time, and improve overall drilling efficiency.

Courtesy of Transocean

Figure 2-1.23. Transocean's Discoverer Spirit drillship with dual-activity derricks

The *crown block* and the *traveling block* each comprise a set of pulleys, or *sheaves*. The crown block sits at the top of the derrick or mast (the crown) and never moves. The traveling block moves up and down in the center of the derrick or mast. A *drilling hook* extends from the bottom of the traveling block. The swivel or top drive, which is connected to the drill stem, hangs from the hook when drilling. Sometimes the top drive is connected directly to the traveling block to shorten the equipment suspended in the derrick.

The *drilling line* is made of wound steel wire ranging in diameter from ⁷/₈ to about 3.5 inches (about 23 to 89 millimetres). It comes on a spool called a *supply reel* (fig. 2-1.24). This reel can be quite large, sometimes 6 feet (almost 2 metres) in diameter, depending on the length of line wrapped on it. The drilling line functions as follows:

- The line runs from the supply reel to the crown block and passes through one sheave (fig. 2-1.25).

- It goes down to the traveling block and wraps around it through one of its sheaves and heads back up to the crown block.

- To increase the strength of the hoisting system, the crew threads, or *reeves*, the line back and forth several times between the two blocks to reinforce the system. Although the line is one continuous piece, its strength is that of several lines.

- The end of the line from the traveling block goes to the *drawworks drum* and is anchored there.

Blocks and Drilling Line

The drilling line is spooled around a supply reel.
The deadline runs from the crown block to the supply reel.
The fastline moves rapidly on and off of the drum.

Figure 2-1.24. This supply reel mounted on the derrick floor supplies wire rope for the rig.

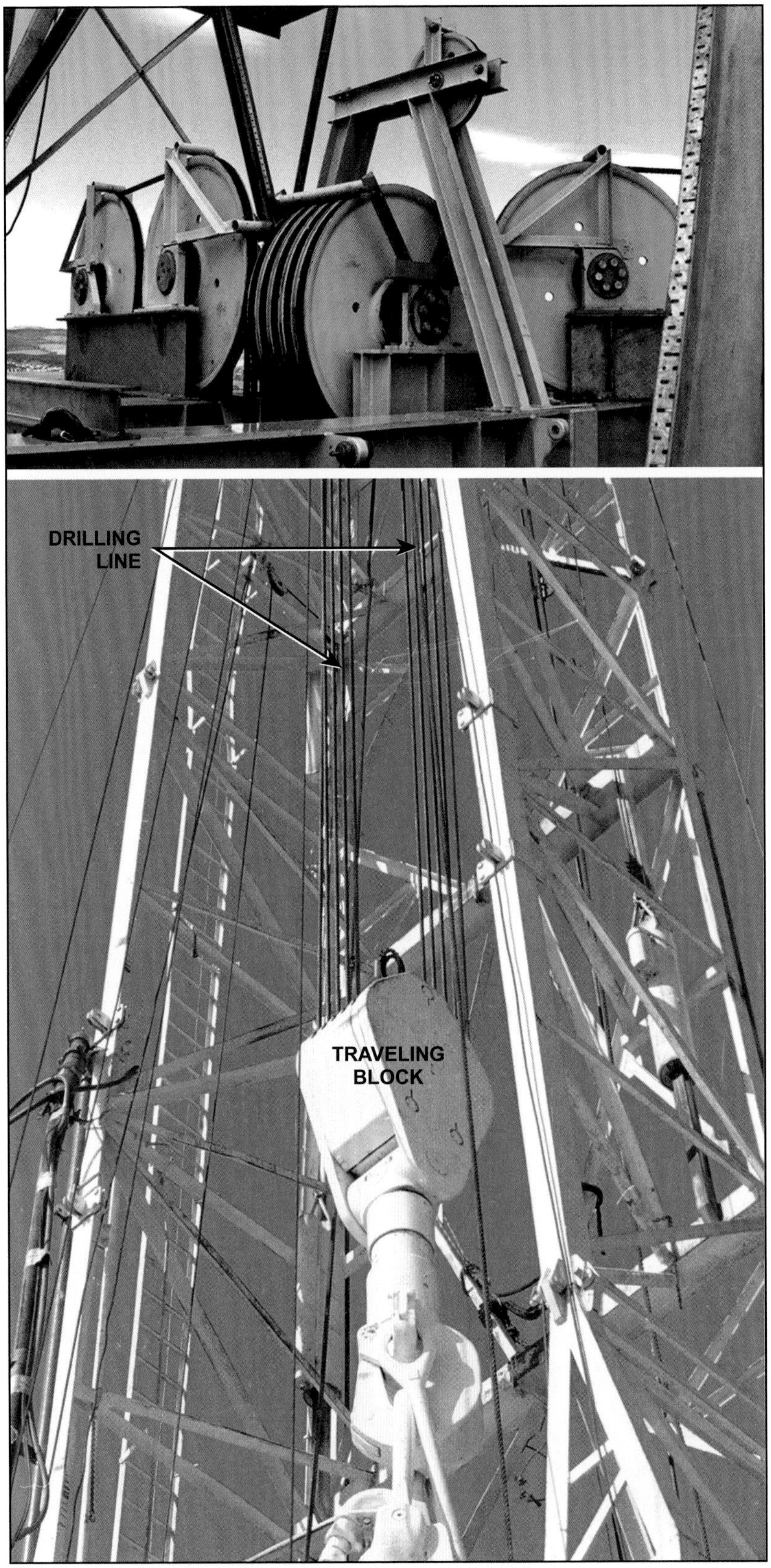

Courtesy of National Oilwell Varco

Figure 2-1.25. Drilling line passes through the sheaves (top) and the traveling block (bottom).

The part of the drilling line that runs from the drum through the traveling block and the crown block is called the *fastline* because it moves rapidly on and off the drum. The part of the drilling line from the crown block to the supply reel is the *deadline*. It does not move at all during hoisting or lowering. In fact, a special anchor usually fastened to the rig's substructure secures the deadline (fig. 2-1.26). The drum spools the line in or out, lifting or lowering the traveling block. The drawworks on the rig floor contains the drum and other equipment in a steel housing unit (fig. 2-1.27)

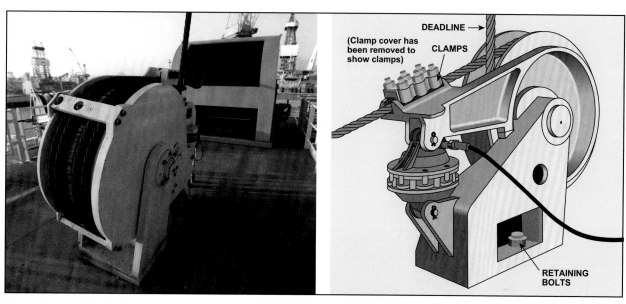

Courtesy of National Oilwell Varco

DEADLINE

(Clamp cover has been removed to show clamps)

CLAMPS

RETAINING BOLTS

Figure 2-1.26. A deadline anchor on the rig's substructure holds the deadline in place.

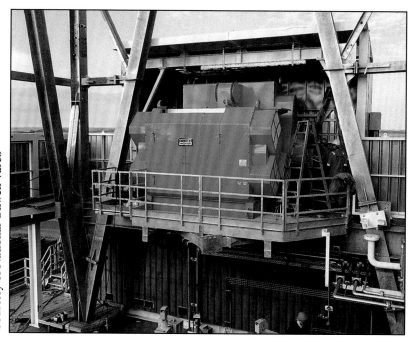

Courtesy of National Oilwell Varco

Figure 2-1.27. The drawworks on the rig floor contains the drum and other equipment in a steel housing unit.

The drilling line is stored as one continuous length of around 2,200 feet (671 metres) of wire rope on the supply reel. To perform scheduled *slip-and-cut* maintenance programs, the anchor is loosened and a small amount of wire is allowed to slide through the clamps. A slip-and-cut program changes the locations of wear and stress by slipping the line through the system at prescribed intervals so it wears evenly. After several slips the drum would be too full, so the worn line is cut and the line re-anchored to the drum. When the line has moved one ton of load over the distance of one mile, it is said to have given a *ton-mile* of service. The metric unit for this measurement is a *megajoule*. (One ton-mile equals 14.317 megajoules.) The driller carefully keeps ton-mile records to plan the slip-and-cut programs on the drilling line.

Drawworks

> The drawworks is the largest and heaviest component on the rig. It houses the drum and drilling line.

The drawworks is one of the largest and heaviest pieces of equipment on a drilling rig. It houses the drum around which the drilling line is wrapped (fig. 2-1.28). As the drum rotates, the drilling line spools on or off the drum. This raises or lowers the traveling block and the drill stem hanging from it.

Courtesy of National Oilwell Varco

Figure 2-1.28. The drilling line on the drawworks

The driller operates the drawworks at the *driller's console* on the front left side of the drawworks. On some rigs, the driller is located inside a control cabin and can operate the drawworks using a joystick, much like one used with video games (fig. 2-1.29).

The controls include brakes, clutches, and a transmission. A pair of brakes located on each end of the drum holds the load stationary and supports the weight of the traveling block, rotating equipment, and drill string. By releasing the brake, the driller can use gravity to lower the drill string, and by applying power to the drum, raise the drill string.

On traditional drilling rigs, the drawworks are set up as follows:

- Extending out of each end of the drawworks above the drum is a powered shaft called a *catshaft*.

- On each end of the catshaft is a spool-shaped *cathead*.

- Breakout catheads loosen joints.
- Makeup catheads tighten joints.

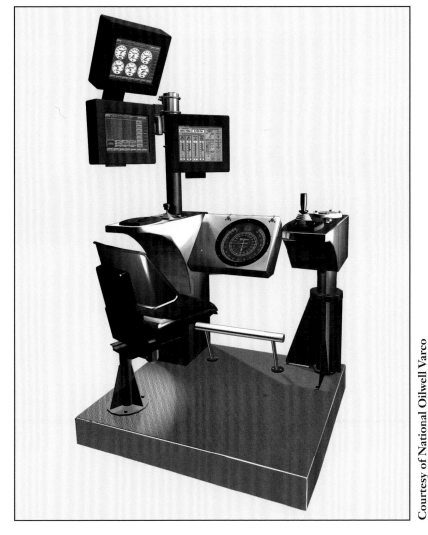

Courtesy of National Oilwell Varco

Figure 2-1.29. The driller's console controls the power, transmission, and brakes of the hoisting system.

Figure 2-1.30. Makeup cathead attached to a catshaft

- On one side of the drawworks is the *makeup cathead*, and on the other side is the *breakout cathead*.
- The crew uses the makeup cathead to apply tightening force to large wrenches called *tongs* (figs. 2-1.30 and 2-1.31). The tongs are used to *make up*, or screw together, and tighten joints of drill pipe and drill collars.
- A chain runs from the end of the tongs to the makeup cathead.
- When the driller rotates the cathead, the chain is pulled tight. Pulling in the chain pulls on the tongs and causes them to tighten the pipe on which the tongs are latched.
- The breakout cathead is used to apply loosening force to *break out*, or unscrew, joints of pipe. A wire rope runs from the end of the tongs to the breakout cathead, loosening the pipe as the cathead rotates. The makeup and breakout catheads are often called *mechanical catheads*.
- Next to each mechanical cathead is a small spool also attached to the catshaft.
- The spool forms a *friction cathead* around which large cloth-fiber rope, or *soft line*, can be wrapped.

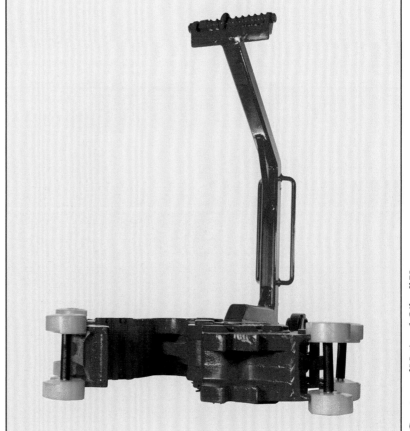

Figure 2-1.31. Tongs

- With a friction cathead and soft line, a crewmember can move heavy items of equipment on the rig floor. Because using friction catheads is dangerous, many contractors install small, pneumatically or hydraulically operated hoists called *air hoists*, or *tuggers*, to perform many of the lighter hoisting tasks on the rig floor formerly done with friction catheads (fig. 2-1.32).

Some newer rigs have drawworks without catheads. A separate cathead, usually using hydraulic cylinders instead of a catshaft, is used for the makeup and breakout tongs (see fig. 2-1.30). Because the catheads are separate from the drawworks, there is more flexibility in positioning them on the rig floor in a location for optimum pipe-handling efficiency.

Figure 2-1.32. An air hoist moves heavy equipment around the rig floor.

Automated roughnecks are machines designed with jaws that grip and spin tool joints.

However, the manual operation of making up and operating drill pipes is hazardous, and in many areas of the world, considered to be extremely dangerous. Now the process is mechanized to improve safety and efficiency. *Automated roughnecks* have been developed to make and break the connections for drill pipe, drill collars, and casing. These are machines that run on tracks embedded in the drill floor, or hang on supports on the drill floor or from lines suspended from the derrick. Automated roughnecks retract from the well center while pipe is raised and lowered. Then, they are driven forward to spin the pipe and tighten the connections.

Some drawworks have an *autodriller*, which is a special control attached to the brake or brake control circuitry, similar to cruise control on a car. The driller can choose appropriate settings and the autodriller controls the *payout* of the drill line, gradually lowering the drill string to maintain constant weight on the bit, drilling speed, torque on pipe, or differential pressure. The autodriller is used only for drilling, not for *tripping in* or *out* of the hole.

There are also special control systems to control speed when tripping in or out. These computer-based controllers adjust the braking force, depending on weight of load hanging on the hook and the speed of travel. This is similar to the automatic braking system used on cars.

Automation

Autodrillers and speed controllers use surface measurements to control the drawworks and brake. On some wells, downhole measurements are combined with the surface information and fed into computer models that calculate the optimal drilling parameters. The computer output is used as a suggestion to the driller to adjust throttle settings for improved performance. In some cases, the models describe a safe operating envelope, beyond which, drilling efficiency begins to deteriorate. These models might be in real-time or used on the next bit or the next well to achieve continual process improvement.

The industry is looking ahead for ways to connect the downhole and surface measurements in real-time to automatically control the downhole drilling process. Some companies have modified the rig control network to allow a computer interface to adjust throttle settings to the primary drilling machinery. In addition, some of the service companies have developed real-time predictive computer models for various aspects of drilling, including models of problems such as excessive drill string vibration, poor hole cleaning, and too much or too little wellbore pressure when tripping, among other issues. The model computes the proper throttle set point that feeds directly into the machine. The driller monitors the process, much like a lathe operator monitors the work being done in a machine shop. As this technology develops, expect to see more real-time automatic drilling for many of the processes that are done manually today.

A conventional rotating system includes all the equipment that turns the bit. The primary element of a rotating system is the top drive or the rotary table.

On smaller rigs, a rotating system generally used is a powerful machine called a *rotary table* (fig. 2-1.33). Located on the rig floor, the rotary table creates a strong rotating force, or *torque*. The bit at the bottom of a hole can be thousands of feet (metres) deep, connected to the rotary table on the surface by the drill string. Additional equipment helps transmit torque from the table to the bit.

On rigs that use a rotary table, the rotating equipment from the surface to the bottom of the hole consists of a swivel, kelly, rotary table, drill pipe, drill collars, and bit. The kelly, the drill pipe, and the drill collars are collectively called the drill stem. A drilling crew often refers to the entire drill stem as the *drill string*. A description of each component of this system follows.

The Rotating System

Rotary Table

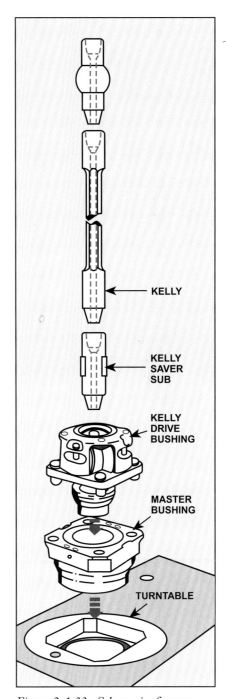

Figure 2-1.33. Schematic of rotary table equipment from the surface to the bottom of the hole

Swivel   The *swivel* hangs from the drilling hook on the bottom of the traveling block by means of a large *bail*, or handle (fig. 2-1.34) The outside of the swivel does not rotate, but the inside does. The swivel supports the drill string and is a conduit for drilling fluid, allowing everything below it to rotate.

Courtesy of National Oilwell Varco

Figure 2-1.34. The hook on the bottom of the traveling block is about to be latched onto the bail of the swivel.

Kelly

| The kelly is a square or hexagonal-shaped pipe that rotates the stem and bit. |

Attached to a threaded connection on the bottom of the swivel is the *kelly*. This is a special section of pipe in lengths of 40 and 54 feet (about 12 and 16 metres). The kelly is not round like most pipes but has flattened sides, giving it a square or hexagon shape. It looks like a big Allen wrench and operates as follows:

- The four- or six-sided kelly fits inside a corresponding square or hexagonal opening in a device called the *kelly bushing* (fig. 2-1.35).

- The kelly bushing fits into a part of the rotary table called the *master bushing*.

- Powerful gears in the rotary table rotate the master bushing.

- As the master bushing rotates, the kelly bushing also rotates. The square or hexagonal opening in the kelly bushing fits against the square or hexagonal kelly and causes the kelly to turn. The flat sides of the kelly and kelly bushing act like the head of a bolt and a wrench that can grip and turn it.

Copyright © The University of Texas at Austin—PETEX

Rotating equipment
components:
- Swivel
- Kelly
- Rotary table
- Drill pipe
- Drill collars
- Bit

Figure 2-1.35. The kelly passes through the kelly bushing, which fits into the master bushing of the rotary table.

- The turning kelly rotates the drill stem and the bit. Because the kelly slides through the opening in the kelly bushing, the kelly can move down as the bit drills the hole deeper.

With its master bushing and kelly bushing, the rotary table supplies the necessary torque to turn the drill stem. When the crew removes the kelly and kelly bushing, the hole left in the master bushing accommodates a special set of gripping devices called *slips*.

A slip is placed on the pipe to prevent it from falling into the hole.

Slips have teeth-like gripping elements called *dies* that fit around the drill pipe to keep it from falling into the hole when the kelly is disconnected (fig. 2-1.36). The driller can lock the rotary table to keep it from turning when necessary, such as when installing a new bit.

On a rig that uses a rotary table and kelly, the driller picks up the kelly and swivel out of the *rathole* by sliding the open hook on the traveling block through the bail of the swivel. The kelly is stored in the rathole. The new joint of drill pipe is put into the mousehole before it is added to the drill string at a connection. The rathole is larger than the mousehole. Crewmembers stab and *make up* the bottom of the kelly onto the top joint of drill pipe that sticks up out of the rotary table. The slips suspend this joint and the entire drill string in the rotary table. With the kelly made up, the driller starts the mud pump, the crew pulls the slips, and the driller lowers the kelly drive bushing to engage the master bushing.

The driller starts the rotary table to rotate the drill stem and bit. Then the driller gradually releases the drawworks brake, and the rotating bit touches bottom and begins making hole.

Courtesy of National Oilwell Varco

Figure 2-1.36. Various designs of slips have gripping dies that keep pipe and casing from falling into the hole.

SLIPS

BOWL

On large rigs, the conventional swivel and rotary table arrangement are replaced with a powered swivel called a *top drive*. The top drive hangs from the traveling block and has its own heavy-duty motor (fig. 2-1.37). The motor turns a threaded drive shaft that connects directly to the top of the drill stem to turn it. Rigs with top drives do not need a kelly, kelly bushing. The swivel and bail are built into the top drive. They do have a rotary table to hold the drill stem in place with the slips. Some newer rigs use a low-speed, hydraulic *rotary support table* for backup in case the top drive malfunctions.

On rigs with a top drive:

- The crew stabs and makes up the top joint of drill pipe (singles or stand) onto the drive stem of the top drive. (A stand is a set of single joints assembled as one unit.)

- Then, the driller starts the mud pump to circulate mud and starts the motor in the top drive.

- The string and bit begin to rotate, the bit is lowered to the bottom of the hole, and drilling begins.

Top Drive

On rigs with a top drive:
- The crew stabs and makes up the top joint of drill pipe onto the drive stem.
- The driller starts the mud pump and the motor.
- The string and bit rotate.
- The bit is lowered to the bottom of the hole.
- Drilling begins.

Figure 2-1.37. With the drill string in the slips, the top drive is hoisted into position to pick up a new stand of pipe.

Kelly versus Top Drive

On rigs with a rotary table and kelly, crewmembers say the "kelly is drilled down" when the bit has made sufficient hole and the top of the kelly is near the kelly drive bushing. At this point, a new joint of drill pipe must be added to the drill string before the hole can be drilled deeper. Rigs equipped with a kelly can add only a single joint at a time to keep drilling. Rigs with a top drive can drill with a stand of two or three pipes.

On both kelly and top drive rigs, the crew pulls the pipe out of the hole to change out a worn bit. Instead of unscrewing every joint of drill pipe, the crewmembers pull out pipe two at time on a *doubles rig* and three at a time on a *triples rig*. They arrange these assemblies in the derrick in units, or *stand*s (fig. 2-1.38). Handling them in stands is faster than handling them individually. Similarly, with a top drive rig, at *kelly down* the crew can add a stand and resume drilling. This saves time by eliminating about one-half or two-thirds of the connections.

Figure 2-1.38. Floorhands set the lower end of the stand of pipe off to one side of the rig floor.

On rigs equipped with a top drive, the driller stops rotating, hoists the drill pipe off bottom, and sets the slips supporting the drill string. The driller stops the mud pump and the floorhands *make a connection* by adding (connecting) a new stand of drill pipe to the drill string so the hole can be drilled deeper. The top drive has a pipe handler that can screw into the top of the stand about 60 to 90 feet (18 to 27 metres) above the drill floor. The motor of the top drive provides the *makeup torque*, instead of a makeup cathead. With a rotary table system with kelly, joints of pipe must be added one at a time as the hole deepens rather than the top drive allowing connection of an entire stand. Fewer connections helps increase the overall drilling rate.

Consider this summary of advantages and disadvantages of today's top drive systems:

- *Advantages*
    - Safer—no need to move out of the way when tripping
    - Faster—one connection per stand instead of one connection per single joint
    - Assists directional drilling—fewer connections means less time needed to reorient the drill string after connections
    - More efficient—can rotate and pull up at the same time (*backreaming*)
- *Disadvantages*
    - Too expensive to use on smaller rigs
    - Requires a tall derrick or mast

Manufacturers have developed a portable top drive for use on smaller rigs. These are sometimes rented to drill a difficult section of the hole or to drill directionally (drill at an angle; see section on Directional Drilling later in this chapter). A top drive also offers a huge advantage during directional drilling because it enables backreaming, meaning the top drive lets a driller rotate the pipe while pulling out of the hole, which cannot be done with a rotary table system.

Making a Connection

To make a connection on a rig with a rotary table and kelly, the driller picks up the drill string high enough for the kelly to clear the rotary table and to expose the last tool joint above the floor. Floorhands set the slips around the joint of drill pipe, and the driller slacks off the drill string weight to suspend the drill string in the slips. Workers latch the two big wrenches called *tongs* on the kelly joint and tool joint of drill pipe. The tongs act as mechanical hands similar to the way a person screws or unscrews a bolt and a nut. A chain or wire-rope pull line runs from the end of the tongs to the breakout cathead on the drawworks.

In figure 2-1.39, *breakout tongs* are shown on top around the end of the kelly. The driller engages the cathead. It pulls with enough force to break the connection and begin unscrewing the kelly from the top drill pipe tool joint. To prevent the drill string from turning below the kelly when the breakout tongs are being pulled, a second set of tongs, called backup tongs, is placed around the tool joint of the top joint of drill pipe. The backup tongs are secured by a wire rope called a *snubbing line* to one of the derrick legs or a special post on the drill floor (tong post). After the tongs are placed on the drill pipe and kelly, and before the driller pulls on the breakout tongs with the automatic cathead, the crew stands away from the arc of the tongs. This is to prevent any crewmember from being struck in the unlikely event the snubbing line or the pull line breaks.

Figure 2-1.39. Crewmembers latch onto drill pipe with breakout tongs.

Once the joint is loosened, the driller engages a *kelly spinner*, which is an air or hydraulic motor mounted near the top of the kelly. The kelly spinner rapidly spins the kelly to back it out (unscrew) from the drill pipe tool joint.

Once the kelly is backed out of the tool joint, crewmembers swing the kelly over to the *mousehole* where the next joint of drill pipe has been placed. The mousehole is a small circular opening in the drill floor with a piece of pipe designed to support a single joint of drill pipe, much like a scabbard holds a sword. Workers stab the kelly into the joint in the mousehole, and the driller spins up the kelly into the joint using the kelly spinner. The crew grabs the tongs, latches them onto the kelly and pipe, and tightens the joint to the correct torque. To tighten a connection, the tongs are used in reverse of the positions described for breaking out a connection. The breakout tongs will be used as backup when tightening the connection in the mousehole. Next, the driller picks up the kelly and the new joint of pipe. The lower end of the new joint is screwed into the pipe string hanging in the slips. The driller engages the kelly spinner to screw the two pipes together, then they are tightened to the specified torque using tongs.

For a rig with a top drive, the process is a little different. The driller will continue drilling until the bottom of the top drive is near the drill floor. The load is hoisted to lift the bit off bottom and the slips are set to support the drill string. The top drive pipe handler breaks the connection between the top joint of pipe and the top drive. There is no need for tongs for this operation because the pipe handler has built-in tongs. The driller hoists the top drive above the next stand of drill pipe. A derrickhand passes the top of the stand to an *elevator*, a special hinged tool hanging below the top drive. An elevator has handles that wrap around the tool joint of drill pipe and casing to help lift or lower it singly or as an entire string. The stand is lifted off the floor as the floorhands guide the bottom of the stand to well center. The driller lowers the stand as the floorhands align it with the pipe in the slips to stab the two pieces together. The driller lowers the top drive, stabbing it into the top of the stand, and the top drive motor spins the two together, so there is no need for a kelly spinner. In fact, this screws together both the top and bottom connection of the new stand at the same time. A backup tong is used to keep the drill string from turning in the slips, but there is no need for makeup tongs, because the top drive provides sufficient makeup torque.

Drilling Assembly

The drilling assembly consists of *drill pipe*, *drill collars*, and the *drill bit*. The bit is screwed onto the bottom of perhaps 15 to 30 drill collars (or fewer in some highly deviated directional wells). The bit and drill collars, and perhaps some additional components making up the bottomhole assembly, are lowered to the bottom of the hole on lengths of drill pipe. Many sections of drill pipe are added for the bit to reach the bottom of the hole.

Drill Pipe and Drill Collars

Drill pipe and drill collars are comprised of steel tubes through which drilling mud flows to the bottom of the hole. Drill pipe and drill collars come in sections, or *joints*, about 30 feet (9 metres) long (fig. 2-1.40). Important pipe dimensions are the inside and outside diameter and wall thickness, which affect the weight of each joint. The greater the column of steel is, the greater the weight.

Drill pipe is available in various diameters. The most common diameters used on land rigs are 3½, 4½, and 5 inches (8.9, 11.4, and 12.7 centimetres). Offshore rigs might use pipe up to 6⅝ inches (16.8 centimetres) and 7-inch (17.8 centimetres) pipe is being used on some ultra-deepwater rigs. The weight of drill pipe varies with its diameter and wall thickness. To provide perspective, the commonly used 4½-inch (11.4-centimetre) drill pipe weighs 16.6 pounds per foot (6.9 kilograms per metre). Thus, a 30-foot (9-metre) joint of such drill pipe weighs 498 pounds (226 kilograms), plus a little extra for the tool joints.

As described earlier, drill collars are used to put the weight on the bit to drill. They are larger in diameter than drill pipe and have thicker walls. For example, one available type of drill collar joint is 7 inches (18 centimetres) in diameter and weighs 125 pounds per foot (186 kilograms per metre). Thus, a 30-foot (9-metre) joint of a drill collar weighs 3,750 pounds (1,701 kilograms), significantly more than 1 ton (1 tonne).

Figure 2-1.40. Drill collars racked in front of drill pipe on the rig floor

Drill pipe and drill collars are joined together, or *made up*, using threaded connections on each end. These threaded connections are called *tool joints* (fig. 2-1.41). One tool joint is a pin (male) connection, and the other is a box (female) connection (fig. 2-1.42). Each joint of drill pipe will have a male tool joint on one end and a female joint on the other end. The pin of one joint fits into the box of another joint, allowing the crew to make up long strings of pipe. The tool joint is thicker than the drill pipe, making it strong enough to handle the twisting, turning, and stretching forces from drilling.

Drill collars do not need tool joints because the walls are thick enough for the pin and box connection threads to be directly manufactured into the steel wall. The connections use metal-to-metal seals strong enough to contain the high-pressure mud inside the drill string. The ability to seal relies on high torque from the tongs or automated roughnecks. The threads are lubricated with special alloy grease, called *pipe dope*, to ensure the torque applied to the joint is efficiently translated into load on the sealing faces.

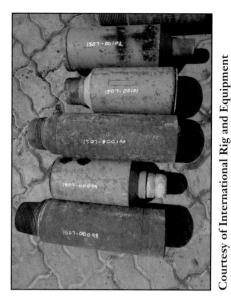

Courtesy of International Rig and Equipment

Figure 2-1.41. Tool joints are threaded connections like the pin-ends in this photo.

Courtesy of MSI Oilfield Products

Figure 2-1.42. Tool joints have a pin connection and a box connection. To prevent damage, thread protectors are often used.

The Bit

At the bottom of the drill stem is the *bit*, which drills the formation rock, dislodging it so the drilling fluid can circulate the fragmented material and bring it back up to the surface. Generally, the driller chooses a bit based on the hardness of the formation to be drilled. The most common types of bits are roller cone bits and diamond bits (fig. 2-1.43A and B). They range in size from 3 inches (7.6 centimetres) to 26 inches (66 centimetres) or larger in diameter. Some commonly used sizes are 17½, 12¼, 7⅞, and 6½ inches (44, 31, 20, and 17 centimetres).

> **Three main types of bits:**
> • Roller cone
> • Diamond
> • Hybrid

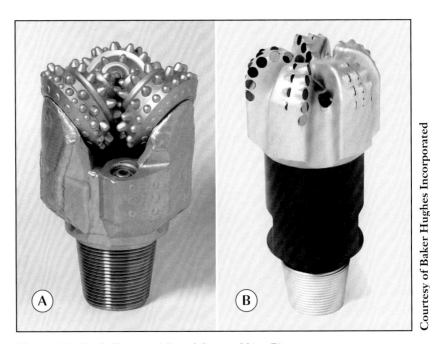

Figure 2-1.43. Roller cone (A) and diamond bits (B)

Courtesy of Baker Hughes Incorporated

Roller Cone Bits

Roller cone bits usually have three (and sometimes two or four) cone-shaped steel devices that turn as the bit rotates (figs. 2-1.44). Several rows of teeth, or cutters, on each cone scrape, gouge, or crush the formation as the teeth roll over it. The cutters might be machined from the cone's steel alloy, or they might be hard pellets of tungsten carbide, called inserts, placed into holes drilled into the cones.

The cones rotate on bearings. Some bits use ball and roller bearings (fig. 2-1.45A). Others use journal, or plain, bearings. And some use a combination of both types of bearings (fig. 2-1.45B).

Journal bearing bits do not wear out as quickly as ball and roller bearing bits but are more expensive. Bearings can be sealed or unsealed. In unsealed bits, drilling mud provides the only lubrication to bearings. Sealed bits include some ball and roller bearing bits and all journal bearing bits. The seals keep drilling mud away from the bearings, protecting them from abrasion. These bits have a small pool of grease built in for lubrication, because drilling mud cannot lubricate sealed bearings.

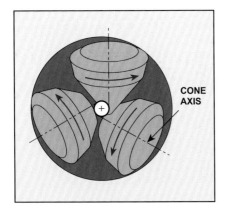

Figure 2-1.44. Each cone of a roller cone bit rotates on its axis.

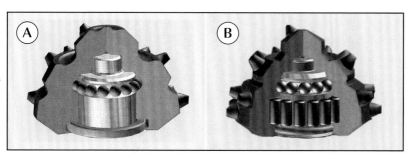

Figure 2-1.45. Each cone rotates on ball and roller bearings (A) or journal bearings (B) or both.

Most roller cone bits are *jet bits*. The drilling fluid exits from the bit through nozzles between the cones. The nozzles on the bit create high-velocity jets of mud, which hit the bottom of the hole and lift cuttings away from the bit so they will not obstruct drilling.

Diamond Bits

Diamond bits do not have roller cones. Instead, small industrial diamond cutters are embedded in the sides and bottom of a single *fixed head* that rotates as one piece with the drill string (see fig. 2-1.43B). Diamond bits work by shearing, or slicing, the formation, rather than gouging and crushing it like roller cone bits. They are used for drilling soft, medium, and hard formations. The initial cost is higher than that of roller cone bits, largely because diamond bits generally do not dull as quickly as roller cone bits and therefore last longer in service.

The diamonds in this type bit can be natural or man-made. The rarity and expense of mining natural diamonds led scientists to create, or synthesize, diamonds from carbon. Unfortunately, synthetic diamonds are even more expensive to manufacture than natural diamonds are to mine. However, an advantage of synthetics is that manufacturers can control the size and shape. They can be made larger than natural diamonds and cylindrical or triangular.

There are two types of synthetic diamonds:

• *Polycrystalline diamond compact* (PDC)
• *Thermally stable polycrystalline* (TSP)

The main disadvantages of diamonds are they can be damaged by high temperatures during drilling and by interrupted circulation of drilling mud.

Hybrid Bits

Hybrid bits combine natural and synthetic diamonds and sometimes tungsten carbide inserts on a fixed-head bit. The diamonds are sometimes placed as individual cutters or used in a pad made by heating grit-sized diamonds with tungsten carbide powder. Bit designers place the different types of cutters on different parts of the hybrid bit according to where each will work best and last longest. Hybrid bits are often used in hard formations or where thin layers of particularly hard, abrasive layers or *stringers*, are expected.

The Circulating System

The circulating system pumps drilling fluid down the hole through a series of pipes. Then it pumps the drilling fluid, or mud, out the bit at the end of pipe at the bottom of the hole, then all the way back to the surface (fig. 2-1.46).

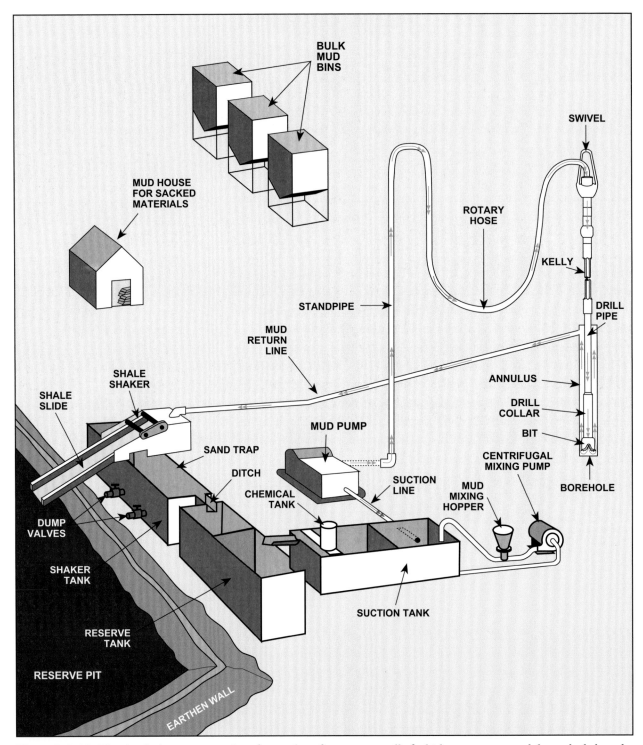

Figure 2-1.46. The circulating system consists of a number of components, all of which serve to get mud down the hole and back to the surface.

Large, heavy-duty *mud pumps* are the heart of the circulating system (fig. 2-1.47). Most rigs have additional pumps to serve as backup if one pump needs repair. But if drilling requires a large volume of mud, such as with a large-diameter hole, or high pressure and high flow rates in an extremely deep, horizontal well, the driller can use two, three, or four pumps together to increase pump capacity.

Circulating Equipment

Figure 2-1.47. The mud pump pumps drilling fluid into the hole.

The pumps take mud from steel tanks, or *mud pits*, in which the mud is stored. As the mud passes through the pumps, it is pressurized before sending the mud through a standpipe and rotary hose (fig. 2-1.48):

- The *standpipe* is a rigid pipe that conducts mud from the pump up one leg of the derrick to the rotary hose.

- The *rotary hose*, or kelly hose, is connected between the standpipe and the swivel or top drive. The rotary hose is flexible because it must move downward as the hole is drilled deeper and the swivel moves closer to the rig floor. It must also move upward for the crew to add sections of pipe to the drill string.

- The *swivel* has a high-pressure rotating seal called a *washpipe* to conduct fluid from the rotary hose to the rotating drill pipe.

STANDPIPE

MOUSEHOLE

Courtesy of Dr. Tom Dunkley Jones

Figure 2-1.48. Drilling rig floor

- The mud goes into the swivel and down the kelly or top drive and enters the drill pipe connected just below. It then goes down the drill string, through the drill collars, and out the bit nozzles.
- When the mud shoots out the rotating bit, it lifts cuttings from the bottom and returns them to the surface with the mud.
- The mud moves back up the hole to the surface through the *annulus*, or annular space, between the outside of the drill collars and drill string and the inside of the hole.
- The mud is then cleaned and reused in a continuous process.

> The mud return or flow line returns the mud and cuttings to the shaker where the cuttings are separated from the mud.

On the surface, the mud and cuttings leave the well through a pipe called the *mud return line* or *flow line*. The mud and cuttings flow out the return line and onto a vibrating screen called the *shale shaker* (fig. 2-1.49). The cuttings rest on the screen, but the mud falls through the screen and back into the mud pits to be cleaned and reused. Then the mud pumps pick up the clean mud and send it back down the hole. Normally, mud circulation continues as long as the bit is *on bottom* and drilling. Sometimes, the mud is circulated with the bit just off bottom to clean the wellbore of any excess cuttings.

The cuttings on the shaker screen vibrate off and move down a slanted trough called the *shale slide* into a pit dug in the earth. This earthen-walled pit, often lined with plastic to protect the surrounding ground, is called the *reserve pit*. It is basically a large temporary holding area for drill waste material that will be transported later to a disposal site.

Courtesy of ICDP, GFZ Potsdam

Figure 2-1.49. A shale shaker removes cuttings carried to the surface by the mud.

During drilling, the mud contains tiny particles of rock, called *solids*, along with larger cuttings. These solids cannot be removed by the shale shakers and therefore, require special equipment, namely a *desander* or *desilter*, to clean the mud (fig. 2-1.50). Additional solids removal can be obtained using a mud *centrifuge*. If the mud contains gas, the circulating system could include a *degasser* to remove it.

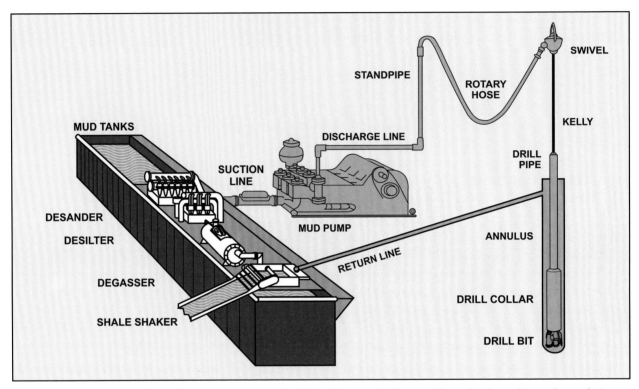

Figure 2-1.50. Additional circulating equipment can include a degasser, desilter, and desander, located over the mud pits downstream from the shaker.

Drilling Fluid Compensation

Drilling fluid, also called drilling mud, is a mixture of water, clay, and specific minerals and chemicals added to help perform tasks. Drilling fluid is different from completion fluids and formation fluids. Drilling fluid has barite and looks like dirty water in a puddle, so it is called mud. In comparison, completion fluids are usually clear, and formation fluids could be saltwater, oil, gas, or any combination of these.

Besides removing cuttings from the hole, the mud cools and lubricates the bit as it drills. Mud also exerts hydrostatic pressure inside the hole, which prevents fluids in the formation from entering the hole and escaping to the surface. Pressure in the hole forces solid clay particles in the mud to stick to the sides of the hole as the mud circulates upward to the surface, forming a thin, impermeable wall cake (see fig. 2-1.3). This wall cake plasters the hole and reduces the amount of liquid in the mud that naturally seeps into the formation penetrated. Wall cake stabilizes the hole to help prevent caving in.

A *mud engineer* is responsible for monitoring the physical and chemical properties of the mud. The mud engineer formulates the right mud for the job in a particular well. Once the correct formula is achieved, the mud engineer must maintain the mud's properties as necessary during drilling. Some of the mud properties an engineer closely monitors are:

- *Viscosity*, or resistance to flow, which affects the mud's ability to carry cuttings. Water is a low viscosity fluid; syrup has a higher viscosity.

- Weight, or *density*, which affects the mud's ability to prevent formation fluids from entering the wellbore or the formations from becoming unstable. Water weighs about 8.3 pounds per gallon (specific gravity of 1.0). Weight material can be added to double the density, and more.

- *Filtration* rate, or water-loss properties, which affects the mud's ability to build an effective wall cake

- Solids content, which affects mud density and bit penetration rate. Too high a solids content can lead to drilling problems.

> Mud engineers monitor the mud:
> - Viscosity
> - Weight
> - Filtration rate
> - Solids content

The drilling fluid in the wellbore can react with the clay formations through which the well is drilled. Depending on the age and composition of the clay, it can absorb water from the mud and swell or collapse into the well. This caving can cause the well to become blocked with rock cuttings and, if this is not corrected, the drill string can become stuck in the well. It is the mud engineer's job to anticipate these problems and include additives, such as *inhibitors*, to prevent chemical reactions. In severe cases, it might be necessary, instead of a water-based fluid, to use emulsion made of nontoxic biodegradable synthetic oils. Although costly, the synthetic oils can almost entirely inhibit clay swelling. New "designer muds" are available using nanotechnology.

The solids content of mud is important because it affects the rate of bit penetration. The more solids in the mud, the slower the penetration rate because solids add weight to the mud and thereby, increase mud pressure on bottom. This action presses against the formation, compressing the rock, making it harder, and slower to drill. Lower weight muds allow the crushed rock under the cutters of the drill bit to break free and move up the hole.

The Power System

A drilling rig needs power to run the circulating, rotating, and hoisting systems. Usually, this power comes from internal combustion engines known as *prime movers*. The rig also needs some way to transfer power from the engines to a particular component, such as the mud pumps, drawworks, or rotary table.

Engines

A rig's power needs are large enough to require several engines. Most rigs, depending on well depth and rig design, need two or more engines to provide an excess of 1,000 horsepower (hp) (fig. 2-1.51). Shallow or moderate-depth drilling rigs need from 500 to 1,000 hp for hoisting and circulation. Many are in the 1,500 hp range for hoisting alone. Heavy-duty rigs for deep, 20,000-foot (6,100-metre) holes are usually in the 3,000-hp class. New rigs are now available for 40,000-foot (12-kilometre) wells with a 1,250 hp top drive and a 3,000 hp drawworks, plus four mud pumps. Auxiliary power for lights and other needs might be 100 to 500 hp on land rigs and several times this amount on larger offshore rigs.

Floating rigs used in deepwater operations have 2,000 and 3,000 hp *thrusters* to keep the rig positioned over the well against the forces of wind, waves, and ocean currents. Total power needs of such a vessel might exceed 46,000 hp.

Today, the most common source of energy is diesel engines, specifically, *compression-ignition engines*. They do not use spark plugs to ignite the fuel-air mixture in the engine cylinders. Rather, diesel engines compress the fuel-air mixture, which generates heat and ignites the mixture. Natural gas and liquefied petroleum gas (LPG) engines are *spark-ignition engines* and use spark plugs. Diesel engines have become more popular than gas or LPG engines because diesel fuel is easier and safer to transport than gas or LPG.

Figure 2-1.51. Three diesel engines power this rig.

In some cases, rigs are powered directly from public electrical distribution systems on offshore platforms connected to power ashore. Some platforms use the gas produced from their wells to power gas turbine generators.

Power Transmission

The two primary methods of transmitting power from an engine to the rig component requiring power are by *mechanical drive* and *electric drive*. Each one has advantages and disadvantages. The choice of type is largely a matter of preference and cost. With either method, the driller controls the amount of power and where it goes.

Mechanical Drive

In a mechanical-drive rig, a collection of pulleys, belts, or chains connect each diesel or gas engine to the rig components requiring power (fig. 2-1.52). This collection is called the *compound*.

With compounded engines, the driller can use one, two, or all of them at once. An auxiliary compound can be used to transmit power to a *mud pump* on the ground. Although good in theory, this method takes power away from the main rig engines at times when it might be needed. For this reason, auxiliary equipment is not powered by the main rig engines, except on smaller rigs. The auxiliary components, such as the generators and the pumps, are driven directly by independent engines on most mechanical rigs. This allows the engines on the rig to provide power to the hoisting and the *rotating components*.

Two primary transmission methods:
- Mechanical drive
- Electric drive

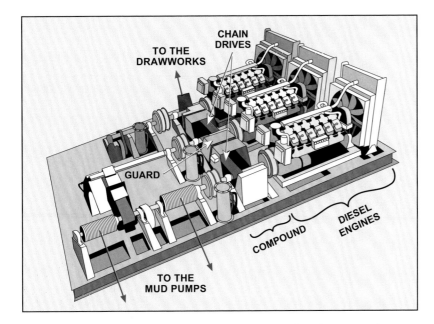

Figure 2-1.52. Three diesel engines and the compound send power to the drawworks and mud pumps.

Electrical Drive
Diesel engines drive large electric generators on electric *silicon-controlled rectifier (SCR)* rigs (fig. 2-1.53). The generators produce *alternating current (AC)* electricity that flows through cables to a control house called an SCR house (fig. 2-1.54). In the SCR house, the AC current is converted to *direct current (DC)* and transformed to the correct voltage required by every electric component on the rig (fig. 2-1.55).

Figure 2-1.53. This diesel engine drives an alternating current electric generator. This engine-generator set is one of three on this rig.

Figure 2-1.54. Controls in the SCR house where AC electricity is converted to the correct DC voltage for the many DC motors powering this rig

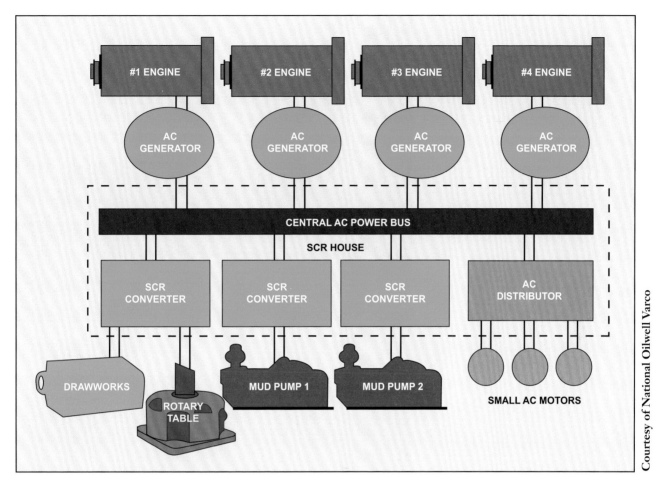

Figure 2-1.55. SCR electrical power system diagram

From the SCR house, electricity goes through more cables to electric motors. DC traction motors of varying horsepower are attached to the equipment to be driven; for example, the drawworks and the mud pumps (figs. 2-1.56 and 2-1.57).

The SCR system has several advantages over the mechanical system. The electric system eliminates the heavy and complicated machinery that make up the compound. Because an *electric rig* does not require a compound, crewmembers do not spend time lining up and connecting the compound with the engines and drawworks. Motors have a much higher initial torque than engines, which improves torque-intensive operations such as hoisting and rotating.

Figure 2-1.56. Motor-driven drawworks

Figure 2-1.57. Powerful electric DC traction motors driving the drawworks

On an SCR rig, the engines are placed at a distance from the rig floor making the operation much quieter. An SCR rig could be hooked up to a commercial electric power *transmission* line and run without the diesel generators. This might be done when a rig is located in a city where the engine noise is prohibited or restricted. The major disadvantage of the SCR rig is that skilled electrical technicians are required to maintain the electrical system.

After the operating company has acquired the leases, signed the contracts, and addressed all other aspects of approval, the company must determine exactly where to drill the well and prepare the site to begin drilling.

DRILL SITE PROCEDURES

The drill site must provide sufficient space for the drilling rig and the collection of equipment needed to drill. In addition to physical space, the drill site must accommodate the special handling of materials, including the waste materials generated during drilling operations.

For drilling onshore, the operator or a contractor might need to clear and level the land, build access roads, and dig reserve pits. Operators must comply with federal and local government laws and regulations regarding environmental protection and make efforts to preserve the surface area of the drill site as required. For example, the company might not be permitted to dig reserve pits and instead, might be required to place large steel bins on the site to receive the cuttings and other materials normally dumped into pits. The company would then arrange to transport these bins from the site and properly dispose of the materials. Even in areas where the law permits reserve pits, the operator often lines the pits with thick plastic sheeting to prevent any contaminated water or other materials from seeping into the ground (fig. 2-1.58). Because a source of fresh water is needed for the drilling mud and for other purposes, the operator might drill a well to provide water before moving the rig onto location. Otherwise, water might have to be piped or trucked to the site.

Preparing the Drill Site

A drill site must:
- Have ample space
- Comply with laws
- Have an adequate water supply

Figure 2-1.58. Reserve pit

A cellar creates room beneath the rig for installation of drilling equipment.

When a well is drilled on land, the rig crew or contractor digs a rectangular pit called a *cellar* or drives an underground channel of pipe into the ground called *conductor pipe* at the drill site. The crew lines the cellar with boards or builds forms and pours concrete to make cellar walls. The cellar provides room beneath the rig to install drilling equipment such as the well control equipment and wellhead.

On land, the top of the well starts in the middle of the cellar (fig. 2-1.59). Sometimes the crew uses a small truck-mounted rig to begin making hole. The initial hole is called the *conductor hole*. It is generally as large as 36 inches (91 centimetres) or more, about 20 to 100 feet (6 to 30 metres) deep, and is lined with pipe called *conductor casing* or conductor pipe to keep the ground from caving in. If the topsoil is soft, crewmembers might drive the conductor pipe into the ground using a pile driver instead of using a separate small rig. However, in some cases, the main rig drills the conductor hole. Conductor pipe conducts drilling mud back to the surface from the bottom when drilling begins.

Next to the cellar, the crew usually digs another hole, much smaller in diameter than the conductor hole, and then lines it with pipe (fig. 2-1.60). This is called the *rathole*, and it is where the kelly is stored when not in use. On small rigs, the crew sometimes digs a third hole—a *mousehole*—also lined with pipe. This hole extends upward through the rig floor and holds a joint of pipe ready for making up. It is not necessary to dig a mousehole on large rigs because the rig floor is high enough aboveground to hang a joint through a hole in the floor.

Figure 2-1.59. A concrete pad to support the substructure surrounds this cellar. The conductor casing protrudes from the middle of the cellar. Some blowout preventers are shown to the right of the cellar.

When drilling offshore, federal, state, and regional laws and regulations apply to operations according to the location of the well. Drilling plans must comply with environmental codes. Material to be disposed of must be collected and transported properly as stated by law. If fresh water or other supplies are needed, they must be transported by supply boat, and any waste must be transported away.

A cellar is not required offshore. Instead, conductor pipe is driven into the seabed to provide structural support for the well control equipment. In soft seabed sediments, the conductor might be jetted, much like pushing a flowing garden hose into the dirt.

Additional activities required for an offshore well might include a video survey of the seabed to ensure there is no debris or obstruction that could interfere with drilling. More information about drilling offshore can be found later in this chapter.

Figure 2-1.60. This rathole is storing the kelly when it is not being used. At right, a joint of pipe rests in the mousehole.

Rigging Up

Once the site is prepared, the drilling contractor moves the rig and related equipment onto location (figs. 2-1.61 and 2-1.62). Whether on land or offshore, the process is called *rigging up* and proceeds as follows:

- First, the base of the rig—the *substructure*—is centered over the conductor pipe in the cellar. The substructure supports the derrick or mast, the pipe, the drawworks, and sometimes, the engines.

- If the rig uses a mast, the crew raises the mast within the substructure from a horizontal position, hoisting it upright. If the rig uses a derrick, the crew assembles it piece by piece on the substructure.

- Other drilling equipment such as the mud pumps are moved into place and prepared for drilling.

New rig technologies make this process relatively quick and efficient. Other rigging-up operations include:

- Erecting stairways, handrails, and guardrails

- Installing auxiliary equipment to supply electricity, compressed air, and water

- Setting up storage facilities and living quarters for the toolpusher, company representative, and others

- Bringing the drill pipe, drill collars, mud supplies, and many pieces of equipment and supplies to the site to make hole (usually done by a contractor)

- Rigging up is installing the rig on the drill site.
- Once complete, the hole is ready for spudding in.

Figure 2-1.61. A mast is raised to the upright position using the drawworks.

Figure 2-1.62. This heavy-lift vessel is transporting this rig to its offshore location. Most offshore rigs are moved fully assembled then stabilized with supports or anchors on the ocean floor.

Drilling begins when all preparations are complete. In oilfield language, the hole is ready for *spudding in*, which proceeds as follows:

Spudding In

- The crew takes a large bit, about 17.5 inches (444 millimetres) in diameter for land operations and 36 inches or more (914 millimetres) in diameter for offshore operations, and attaches it to the first drill collar.

- Then, the crew lowers the bit into the conductor pipe by adding drill collars and drill pipe one joint or stand at a time until the bit reaches the bottom.

- If a rotary system is used, the driller continues with the kelly attached to the top joint of pipe and begins making hole. He or she starts the pump to circulate mud and engages the rotary table. If a top drive is used, no kelly is present and the top drive system is engaged.

- Whether a rotary table or top drive, the crew uses the drawworks to lower the drill string to apply weight on the bit.

- When the bit is on bottom and making hole, the phrase "on bottom and turning to the right" indicates that drilling is proceeding. This comes from using a rotary table that traditionally turns to the right.

Using a Rotary Table   When using a rotary table system, the kelly moves downward through the kelly bushing as the bit drills. Because the ground near the surface land is usually soft, the kelly is soon *drilled down*. This means that its entire length reaches a point just above the bushing.

To drill the hole deeper:

1. The crew must add more pipe to the string to lengthen it.

2. The driller uses the hoisting system to add pipe by picking up the kelly and attached drill string off bottom.

3. When the tool joint of the topmost joint of pipe clears the rotary—meaning it passes through the opening in the rotary table to a point just above the rig floor—the crew sets the slips around the pipe and into the opening in the master bushing. The slips grip the pipe and keep it from falling back into the hole while the crew *breaks out*, or unscrews, the kelly from the drill string.

4. When the kelly spins out of the drill pipe and releases, the crew moves it over to a 30-foot (9-metre) single joint of drill pipe resting in the mousehole.

5. Then crewmembers stab the pin of the kelly into the box of the new joint and screw the two together to make them up.

6. The crew latches backup tongs onto the joint of pipe in the mousehole to keep it from turning as the kelly spinner turns the kelly into the joint.

7. The crew latches the makeup tongs to tighten the kelly to the top of the new joint.

Once the kelly is made up tightly to the new joint:

1. The driller picks up and moves the single joint from the mousehole over the rotary table (fig. 2-1.63).

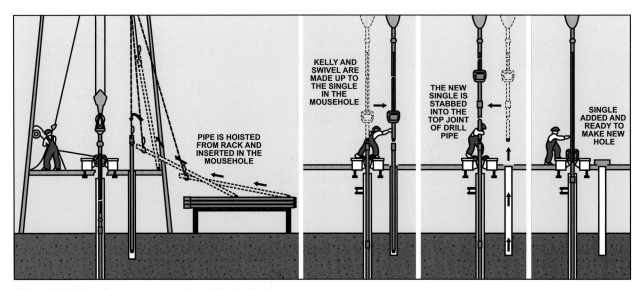

Figure 2-1.63. Making a connection with a kelly

Copyright © The University of Texas at Austin—PETEX

2. The crew stabs the bottom of the new joint of pipe into the top of the joint of pipe coming out of the borehole and again uses the kelly spinner to make up the joint.

3. The crew latches the tongs to apply full torque to the connection.

4. With the new joint made up, the crew pulls the slips, and the driller lowers the pipe until the bit nears the bottom.

5. Then the driller starts the pumps, begins rotation, applies weight to the bit, and drills the next joint of pipe approximately 30 feet (9 metres) or more, depending on the length of the kelly.

The crew repeats this process each time the kelly is drilled down.

Using a Top Drive

When the rig uses a top drive, the crew follows essentially the same procedures to make up the drill string, often making up two, three, or four joints at a time instead of one (fig. 2-1.64). The multiple made-up joints, called a *stand*, sit in a rack on the rig floor to the side of the mast or derrick. The top drive can be used to drill with singles just like the kelly, or the crew can make up stands ahead of time and drill with stands.

With a top drive, there is no need for a rathole, because there is no kelly. The top drive has auxiliary equipment to latch onto the new single or stand so it can be lifted over the well center. The motor of the top drive replaces the kelly spinner, screwing in both the top and bottom connections of the new pipe. The crew uses the backup tongs to hold the pipe in the slips. Makeup tongs are not required because the top drive has enough power to apply full torque to the connections.

Sometimes the rig is equipped with an *automatic roughneck* that routinely replaces the tongs. See fig. 2-1.76 later in this chapter.

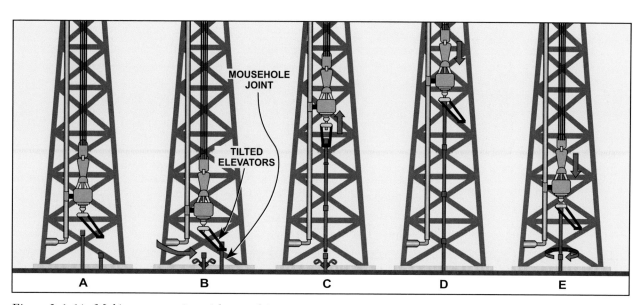

Figure 2-1.64. Making a connection with a top drive

The Surface Hole

At a determined depth of possibly hundreds of feet or metres to a few thousand feet or metres, drilling will stop temporarily so the crew can pull the drill stem from the hole. The first part of the hole is known as the *surface hole*. Even though the formation containing hydrocarbons might lay many thousands of feet or metres below this point, the toolpusher stops drilling to take steps to protect and seal off the formations close to the surface. For example, drilling mud could contaminate zones containing freshwater used for drinking by nearby towns. To protect such zones, the crew runs special pipe called *surface casing* into the hole and cements it in place.

Tripping Out

The first step in running casing is to pull the drill stem and bit out of the hole. Pulling the drill stem and bit out to run casing, change bits, or perform some other operation in the borehole is called *tripping out*.

Using a Rotary Table

Tripping out includes:
- Removing the stem and bit
- Running casing
- Changing bits

When tripping out with a rotary table system, the driller stops rotation and circulation and uses controls on the drawworks to raise the drill stem off bottom until the top joint of drill pipe clears the rotary table and holds it there. The rotary helpers then set the slips around the drill pipe to suspend it in the hole. Using tongs, the rotary helpers break the kelly out of the drill string and put it into the rathole (fig. 2-1.65). Because the crew leaves the swivel and the rotary hose on the kelly when placing it in the rathole, the area above the rotary where the top of the drill string protrudes from the hole is clear. Only the traveling block hangs above the drill pipe suspended in the hole.

Attached to the traveling block and hook are a set of drill pipe lifting devices called *elevators*. The elevators might remain attached to the hook at all times and swing downward into position when the crew removes the swivel from the hook. Elevators are clamps that can latch onto the tool joints of the drill pipe (fig. 2-1.66). The crew latches the elevators around the drill pipe, and the driller raises the traveling block to pull the pipe upward. The pipe is usually removed from the hole in stands of three joints. When the third joint of pipe clears the rotary table, the rotary helpers set the slips and use the tongs to break out the pipe. The crew guides the stand to the rack on the rig floor, often called the *setback area* or simply, the *setback*.

Once the bottom of the stand of pipe is set down on the rig floor, the derrickhand takes action. The derrickhand stands on a small platform called the *monkeyboard* about 90 feet (27 metres) high in the mast or derrick and is secured by safety belts and harnesses. The derrickhand unlatches the elevators from the top of the stand and guides the stand back into the *fingerboard*, which is the rack that supports the tops of the stands (fig. 2-1.67). Working as a close-knit team, the driller, rotary helpers, and derrickhand continue tripping out until all the drill pipe, drill collars, and the bit are out of the hole.

BAIL

SWIVEL

KELLY SPINNER

TOP OF KELLY

RATHOLE

Figure 2-1.65. While tripping out with a rotary table system, the kelly and related equipment rest in the rathole.

Figure 2-1.66. The open elevator has a latch and comes in several sizes and weight ratings.

Figure 2-1.67. Standing on the monkeyboard high in the mast, the derrickhand guides a stand of pipe into the fingerboard.

Using a Top Drive

If a top drive is used, the driller can lift, rotate, and pump all at the same time, if necessary. The top drive and drill string are hoisted using the drawworks. The crew sets the slips just below the top joint. The top drive has its own set of tongs, called a *pipe handler*, to break the connection beneath the top drive. Instead of a kelly spinner, the top drive motor spins out. The top drive elevators hang from the top drive just like the hook in a kelly system. However, if hole conditions require the driller to rotate and pump and pull, or *backream*, the top drive can be reengaged at any point during the trip.

Pipe Racking

> The bottomhole assembly is much heavier than drill pipe and must be housed in a fortified rack.

On a land rig, the pipe is moved from location to location using trucks, because it is too heavy to move it while inside the derrick. To do this, the pipe must be transferred to horizontal pipe racks near the ground away from the drill floor, where it is staged for loading onto trucks. After the rig move, the trucked pipe is placed back on the pipe racks. As work begins on the new well, these joints of pipe can be picked up one at a time for the crew to drill with singles, as described earlier. When the first casing point is reached and the drilling temporarily halted to trip out of the hole, it is more efficient to *rack the pipe* vertically in the derrick in stands instead of laying down and picking up each joint of pipe.

The height of the derrick and the strength of the setback section of the drill floor (meaning, the setback capacity) determine whether the rig can rack pipe in doubles or triples. However, the same process is used to rack the stands, regardless of their length.

For manual operations:

1. The bottom of the stand is pushed to the setback area by the rotary helpers and guided manually into position as the driller slowly lowers the stand to the floor.

2. At the top, the derrickhand disconnects the elevator from the stand and uses a rope to pull the stand to the monkeyboard to guide the stand into position in the fingerboard.

3. The derrickhand then latches one of the *fingers* to keep the stand in place.

4. Meanwhile, the driller lowers the empty elevators to the floor, where the rotary helpers latch them to the top of the next stand.

This process is repeated until all the drill pipe is out of the hole.

Because the components of the bottomhole assembly are much heavier than drill pipe, these tubular components are racked in a separate part of the setback area specially strengthened for the extra weight. The floor crew and derrickhand often use air or hydraulic hoists, sometimes called *tuggers*, to help pull the heavy equipment into position.

In recent years, a number of machines were developed to mechanize this process to make it easier and safer. These *pipe-racker machines* move drill pipe and bottomhole assembly components between the well center and the setback. The fingers of the fingerboards can be opened and closed remotely. This means the derrickhand is not needed at the top because the pipe is positioned, racked, and secured semi-automatically. There are also other types of machines that can pick up the pipe from the horizontal pipe racks, move them to the drill floor, and hand them off to the pipe-racking machines.

When drilling with a top drive, the operation is more efficient if the stands are made up ahead of time. Some rigs, mostly those offshore, are equipped for *off-line stand building*. The drill floor is arranged where the pipe racker and the automatic roughneck can be used to make up stands while the top drive is drilling ahead. An inventory of stands is racked in the setback, and one stand at a time is added to the drill string to lengthen the string while drilling.

More recently, companies have developed rigs designed to enable one person to make an efficient connection. This type of rig integrates the pipe handling between the horizontal pipe racks and the top drive so it can rapidly pick up and lay down singles. This allows the derrick and drill floor to be built without a setback. These rigs are smaller and as such, are easier and faster to move between locations.

Some newer rigs have sophisticated pipe-racking systems that can rack casing and even marine risers. Others allow for dual-activity operations. New automated pipe-handling systems are continually being developed.

Running Surface Casing

After tripping out, the only thing in the hole is the drilling mud that was pumped into the hole as the pipe was tripped out to prevent the walls from caving in or formation fluids from entering the wellbore. After the drill stem is out, a special casing crew often is engaged to run the surface casing.

Casing is large-diameter steel pipe used to line or case the wellbore. The crew runs the casing into the hole using special heavy-duty casing slips, tongs, and elevators. Casing accessories include centralizers, scratchers, a casing or guide shoe, and a float collar, described as follows:

- *Centralizers* keep the casing in the center of the hole so the cement distributes evenly around the outside of the casing.

- *Scratchers* help remove wall cake from the side of the hole so the cement can form a stronger bond (fig. 2-1.68).

- The *float collar* is a special coupling located one or two joints above the bottom of the casing string and contains a valve that lets fluids pass down the string but prevents them from flowing up.

- A *casing shoe*, or *guide shoe*, fits onto the end of the bottom joint (fig. 2-1.69). The casing shoe is a short, heavy, cylindrical section of steel filled with concrete and rounded on the bottom. It prevents the casing from snagging on irregularities in the borehole as it is lowered. The cement can later be drilled out using the next bit. The shoe has an opening in its center out of which cement can exit the casing. Like the float collar, there might be a flapper valve or a ball valve built into the casing shoe to prevent reverse flow while running casing or when cementing, because cement hardening inside the drill string is not desirable.

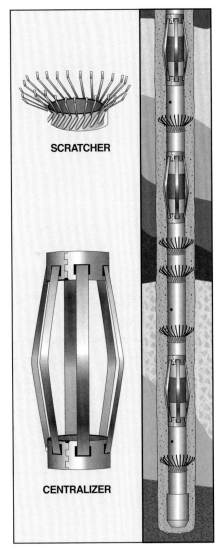

SCRATCHER

CENTRALIZER

Figure 2-1.68. Several centralizers and scratchers are installed on the casing to aid in cementing.

Figure 2-1.69. The guide shoe is made up on the bottom of the first joint of casing to go into the hole.

The casing crew and drilling crew run the surface casing into the hole one joint at a time (fig. 2-1.70 and 2-1.71). Like drill pipe, casing is available in joints. The lengths come in standard ranges: range 1 casing varies from 16 to 25 feet (5 to 8 metres), range 2 is 25 to 34 feet (8 to 10 metres), and range 3 is 34 to 38 feet (10 to 12 metres). Instead of tool joints, the threaded casing connection is called a *casing collar*. Joints are spun-in using a *casing spinner* and tightened using *casing tongs*. After the hole is lined from bottom to top with casing, the casing is suspended in a *casing hanger* and cemented in place.

Figure 2-1.70. Casing stacked for use in this drilling operation

Figure 2-1.71. The crew runs surface casing into the hole.

Cementing the Casing

A specialized service company usually performs cementing using cement made for oilwells. Although not very different from the cement used as a component in ordinary concrete, oilwell cement can adhere under extreme conditions and need not be exposed to air to harden. This type of cement is referred to as *portland cement* and usually contains special additives tailored to the particular well. For example, if the temperature in the well is high, the cement sets (hardens) faster than normal. Adding a retarder slows down hardening so that high-temperature wells can be cemented successfully.

Cementing service companies stock various types of cement and use trucks on land or supply boats offshore to transport the cement in bulk to the well site. Bulk cement storage and handling at the rig location make it possible to mix large quantities in a short time period. The cementing crew mixes dry cement with water, often using a recirculating cement mixer. This device thoroughly mixes the water and cement by recirculating previously mixed liquid cement, called *slurry*, with dry cement and more water.

Powerful cementing pumps move the slurry through pipe to a special valve made up on the topmost joint of casing (fig. 2-1.72). This valve is called a *cementing head* or *plug container*. The cementing head is a crossover connection from the large-diameter casing to the small high-pressure cement line. A plug container, or *retainer*, holds rubber plugs used to separate the mud and cement. Next:

1. As the cement slurry arrives, the crew releases the bottom plug from the cementing head, which precedes the slurry down the inside of the casing. The bottom plug keeps any mud inside the casing from contaminating the cement slurry where the two liquids meet. The plug also wipes off mud that adheres to the inside wall of the casing and prevents it from contaminating the cement.

2. The plug travels ahead of the cement until it reaches the float collar where it stops. Continued pump pressure breaks a seal in the top of the plug and allows the slurry to pass through.

3. The slurry flows out through the float collar and guide shoe and starts up the annulus between the outside of the casing and the wall of the hole until the annulus is filled with cement.

4. When enough cement has entered the casing, the crew releases a top plug from the cementing head and pumps a liquid, called *displacement fluid*, behind the top plug. The plug and this liquid, usually a cushion of fresh water followed by mud, chase the cement and fill the casing. The top plug keeps the displacement fluid from contaminating the cement slurry. It also wipes most of the cement clinging to the wall of the casing.

5. When the top plug comes to rest on the bottom plug in the float collar, the crew shuts down the pumps and allows the slurry to harden.

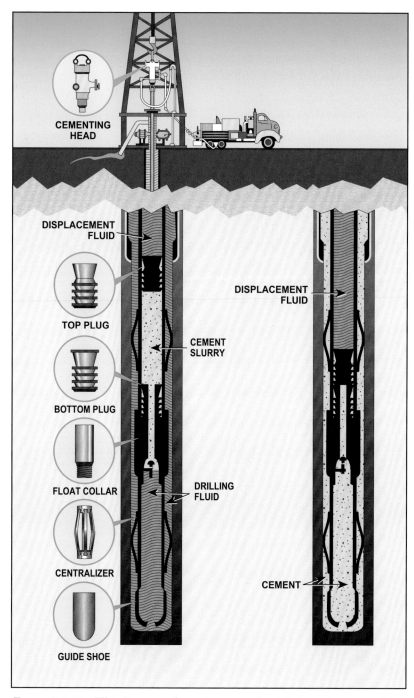

CEMENTING HEAD

DISPLACEMENT FLUID

TOP PLUG

BOTTOM PLUG

FLOAT COLLAR

CENTRALIZER

GUIDE SHOE

CEMENT SLURRY

DRILLING FLUID

DISPLACEMENT FLUID

CEMENT

Waiting on cement is the time allotted to harden the cement. After the hardened cement is tested, crewmembers use a smaller bit to trip in.

Figure 2-1.72. This diagram of a casing cementing job shows the route of the slurry as well as the role played by the various cementing accessories.

Allowing time for the cement to harden is known as *waiting on cement*. Hardening can take a few hours or more than 24 hours, depending on well conditions. Allowing adequate waiting time is important for the cement to set properly and bond the casing firmly to the wall of the hole. After the cement hardens and tests indicate the cement has bonded with no voids between the casing and hole, then drilling resumes (fig. 2-1.73).

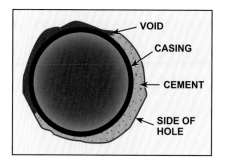

VOID

CASING

CEMENT

SIDE OF HOLE

Figure 2-1.73. After the cement hardens, tests indicate whether the cement has bonded with no voids between the casing and hole.

The casing and cement provide a strong structural barrier between the formation and inside of the casing. It is important to isolate the weak surface formations from the high-pressure zones that will be encountered as the well is drilled deeper.

Tripping In

To start drilling again, the crew trips a smaller bit that fits inside the surface casing. Crewmembers first make up the bit on the bottommost drill collar. Then, working together, the driller, the rotary helpers, and the derrickhand make up the stands of drill collars and drill pipe and trip them back into the hole.

When using a rotary table system to make up a stand of pipe, the rotary helpers set the slips around the pipe in the hole (fig. 2-1.74).

Figure 2-1.74. Crewmembers making a connection

The derrickhand then latches the elevators to a stand in the setback. As the driller picks up the stand, the rotary helpers swing it over to the pipe in the hole and stab it. Next, they latch the backup tongs around the pipe in the hole and spin up the new stand. If the rig has a top drive, the process is similar, but only the backup tongs are needed (fig. 2-1.75).

Figure 2-1.75. Using a top drive, the crew stabs and makes up the joint of drill pipe and the motor turns the drill stem and the bit.

Some rigs are equipped with an *Iron Roughneck*™ (automated rough-neck) to replace the drill pipe tongs and *spinning wrench* when tripping in and tripping out. The drill crew positions the stand over the rotary table, and the roughneck machine spins in the pipe and torques it using integral spinners and tongs (fig. 2-1.76). In this manner, crewmembers are not exposed to the hazards of the spinning wrench and tong lines, and makeup torque is applied more consistently for every connection.

When the drill bit reaches bottom, the driller resumes circulation and rotation. The bit drills through the small amount of cement left in the casing, plugs, and guide shoe and into the new formation below the cemented casing. As drilling progresses deeper, formations tend to become harder. As a result, the crew usually needs to make several *round trips* (trips in and out of the hole) to replace worn bits.

Sometimes, formation pressures at the bit exceed the strength of the *uncased hole* (open hole) above. In such cases, intermediate casing is run and cemented to isolate these formations.

Figure 2-1.76. An Iron Roughneck™ *spins and bucks up joints with built-in equipment.*

While drilling the next section of hole, and during all phases of drilling, the drilling crew must take steps to prevent an influx of fluids into the well. Left uncontrolled, an influx can lead to a *blowout*, which is an uncontrolled flow of fluids—oil, gas, water, or all three—from a formation that the hole has penetrated. Uncontrolled influxes are quite rare events and can be prevented with careful monitoring of the well and proper control of fluid density. These procedures are so important that a later section on *The Use of Mud Density* discusses formation pressures in more detail and a separate chapter is devoted to *Well Control* (Chapter 2.2).

Controlling Formation Pressure

At a predetermined depth, drilling stops again to run another string of casing. This string of casing might be the final one or an intermediate one, depending on the depth of the hydrocarbon reservoir. Generally, wells in relatively shallow reservoirs—for example, 10,000 feet (3,048 metres) or less—only require one additional casing string. Wells in deep reservoirs—for example, up to 20,000 feet (6,096 metres) or more—usually need at least one intermediate casing string. Intermediate casing is smaller than surface casing because it fits inside the surface casing to the bottom of the intermediate hole (fig. 2-1.77). The crew runs and cements it in much the same way as surface casing.

Other reasons for running intermediate casing in a well are to seal off *troublesome formations*. These formations could cause a blowout due to abnormal pressure or lost circulation. Troublesome formations are also those that contain shale that sloughs off the walls of the hole and fills the hole. *Lost circulation* is a condition where quantities of mud are lost to a formation that contains caverns or fissures or is coarsely permeable. Loss of mud lowers pressure in the hole, which can allow the formation pressure to exceed the *backpressure* of the column of mud (hydrostatic pressure). Operators can successfully drill troublesome formations by carefully controlling the properties of the drilling mud. However, the crew must *case off* and cement troublesome zones so they do not cause problems when drilling the well to its final depth.

Intermediate Casing

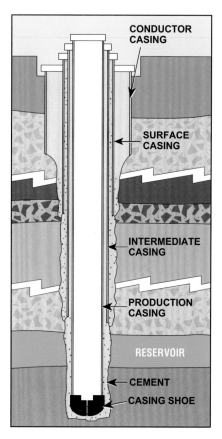

Figure 2-1.77. Intermediate casing fits inside the surface casing, and the production casing fits inside the intermediate casing.

Expandable Casing

A new technology is emerging using *expandable casing*. After the casing is run, a special plug is pulled or pumped to enlarge the inside diameter of the casing so a larger bit can be used to drill the next section of the hole. In this way, a larger diameter hole can be made to the reservoir, allowing greater rates of production.

Drilling to Final Depth

Once the well is drilled, tests determine whether to proceed or abandon the well.

The crew drills the next part of the hole using a smaller bit that fits inside the intermediate casing. Often, this part of the hole is the final section, unless the well needs more than one intermediate casing string. Crewmembers trip in the bit and drill stem, drill out the intermediate casing shoe, and resume drilling to reach the *pay zone*. The pay zone is a formation capable of producing enough gas or oil to make it profitable enough for the operating company to complete the well.

When drilling occurs in an existing oilfield, the company already knows whether the well is a *producer*. But if the well is a *wildcat*—a well drilled in an area where no oil or gas is known to exist—the company must determine whether the well has struck oil or gas in sufficient quantities to make additional investment economical. To make this determination, the operator orders tests to evaluate the well. The tests indicate conditions that help to decide whether to proceed or abandon the well.

Evaluating Formations

There are several techniques to assist an operator in deciding whether to set a final string of casing or abandon the well. First, a geologist thoroughly examines the cuttings to determine whether the formation contains hydrocarbons to continue drilling. The geologist works closely with a mud logger to examine cuttings from the shale shaker and analyze them in a portable laboratory at the well site. A *mud logger* is a technician who monitors and records information brought to the surface by the drilling mud as the hole penetrates the formation (fig. 2-1.78).

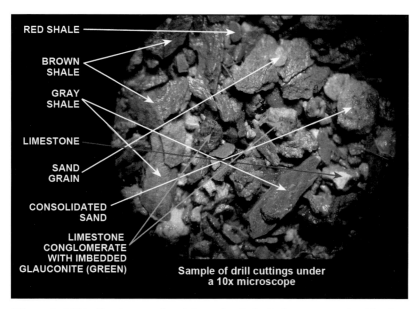

RED SHALE
BROWN SHALE
GRAY SHALE
LIMESTONE
SAND GRAIN
CONSOLIDATED SAND
LIMESTONE CONGLOMERATE WITH IMBEDDED GLAUCONITE (GREEN)

Sample of drill cuttings under a 10x microscope

Figure 2-1.78. Cuttings retrieved from the shale shaker are examined by the mud logger.

Wireline logging, also called electric logging, is a valuable method of analyzing downhole formations. Using a mobile laboratory, well loggers lower sensitive tools to the bottom of the well on wireline and pull them back up the hole (fig. 2-1.79). As they pass up and down the hole, the special tools measure and record the formation properties and any fluids (oil, gas, and water) that might be present. Loggers can generate many types of logs, as explained in Part 1 devoted to exploration.

Wireline Logging

Figure 2-1.79. Drillers running wireline to measure formation properties and record, or log.

Transmission of formation data:
- Wireline logging
- Logging while drilling
- Measurement while drilling

Experienced geoscientists and engineers study and interpret the logs to determine the presence and quality of oil or gas (fig. 2-1.80).

Another evaluation technique is a *drill stem test*. The logging crew makes up a drill stem test tool on the bottom of the drill stem and sends it down to the bottom of the hole. Formation fluids flow into the tool and pressure recorders chart pressure. When the pressure testing is done, valves in the tool close to trap a fluid sample, and the crew pulls the tool out of the hole. The recovered fluids and recorded pressure graph are analyzed for the presence and quantity of hydrocarbons.

In addition to well logging and drill stem testing, a geologist often takes *core samples* of the formation hole and examines them in a laboratory. Cores are cut with a special core bit with a hole in the middle. The core remains inside the *core barrel*, a sleeve lining the inside of the coring tool, and only a small ring of rock is actually drilled. When a core sample is taken, a cylinder of formation is extracted by the special bit, brought to the surface, and analyzed.

New tools have been developed for placement in the bottomhole assembly to allow samples of wellbore fluids to be taken in position to minimize contamination and improve the quality of the test.

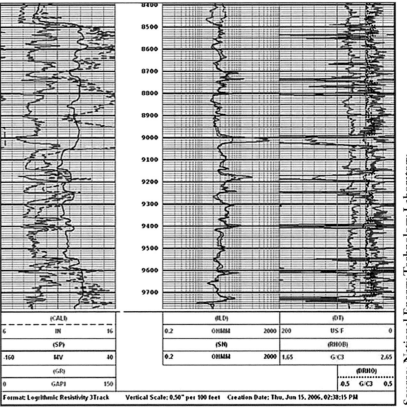

Source: National Energy Technology Laboratory

Figure 2-1.80. An electric log is one type of log that helps determine whether oil and gas are present in a drilled formation.

Measurement while drilling (MWD) is also used. This wireless, self-contained instrument transmits mud pulse signals up the hole through the drilling fluid in the drill stem to a readout device at the surface (fig. 2-1.81). This system gives the driller information from the bottom of the hole without stopping drilling. MWD has become the method of choice for most current directional drilling operations worldwide.

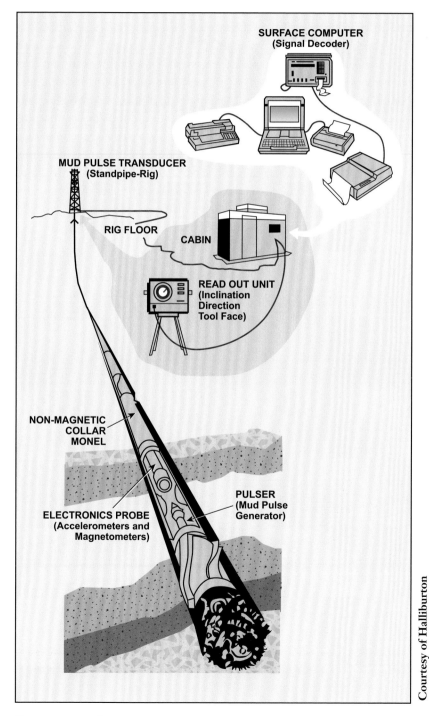

Courtesy of Halliburton

Figure 2-1.81. Measurement while drilling system

MWD and LWD MWD encompasses an array of downhole measurements that optimize or enhance the drilling process by measuring static and dynamic drill string position and motion. *Logging while drilling (LWD)* involves measurements on the drill string to determine the volume and type of hydrocarbons present within the formation. LWD measurements are designed to duplicate the various measurements available on wireline. Typically, both MWD and LWD measurements are acquired at the same time in the same *bottomhole assembly* to obtain both types of information while drilling. Considerable knowledge can be gained by using both types of measurements synergistically.

The ability to make these measurements downhole while drilling has been possible by advances in the printed circuit board and its components and microprocessors. The reduction in size and mass of circuit boards and microprocessors has allowed not only the development of more sophisticated measurements but also improved ruggedness. As a result, these measurements are widely used in any drilling conditions and throughout various geologic basins.

Typically, the flow path within the drill collar is modified so data sensors can be placed within the collar. The ability of the sensors in the bottomhole assembly to convey the measurements while drilling to the surface is a critical development. The drilling mud provides the medium for this communication. Newer developments involve electromagnetic transmission of signals through the Earth and, more recently, through electrical wires within the drill pipe.

Nearly all the borehole geophysical measurements available on wireline are available as LWD measurements. Some LWD measurements are improved over those taken by wireline because they use the rotating drill pipe to acquire *azimuthal data* around the circumference of the borehole. The operator decides whether to run either or both MWD/LWD and wireline. Generally, the determining factors are the importance of timely data and economics.

If timeliness is critical, the operator will opt to obtain LWD measurements when there is a need to perform *petrophysical evaluations* of the formation immediately after the bit penetrates the rock to limit the effects of the invading drilling mud on the measurements.

LWD is also chosen if the operator needs to know while drilling that the well is in the correct geological structure for vertical wells or in the correct geological layer for high-angle and horizontal wells. If the wellbore position is incorrect, a sidetrack can be made immediately instead of waiting until the well is drilled and then logged by wireline.

Regarding economics, MWD/LWD measurements are chosen when costs warrant, such as when comparing the high cost of an idle rig running wireline logs to the cost of obtaining the same information while drilling. Data risk also influences the decision. If there is a high risk that one conveyance type cannot deliver the required data, then the operator will choose another conveyance method. Many service companies offer measurements on both MWD/LWD and wireline.

Operators and service companies first developed the concept of measuring formation resistivity from a sensor on the bottomhole assembly as early as the 1920s. The need for directional measurements while drilling fueled the commercialization of MWD measurements in the 1960s. Initially, these directional measurements were made while the bottomhole assembly was stationary.

MWD grew, in large part, to the development of techniques to transmit the measurements to the surface while drilling. In the mud *siren technique* illustrated in figure 2-1.82, the electromechanical controlled rotor creates a *time varying pressure wave* in the mud column.

The Development of MWD/LWD

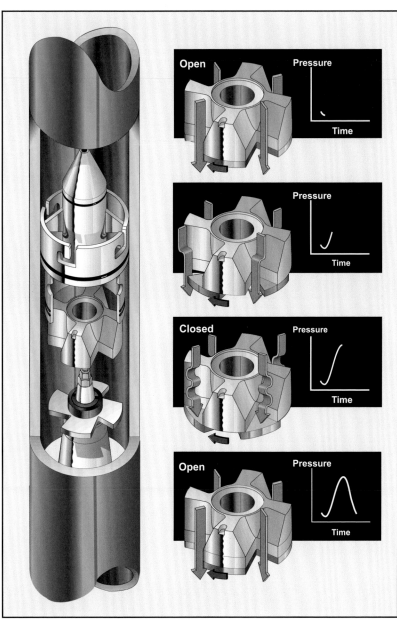

Figure. 2-1.82. Schematic of the mud siren technique of MWD/LWD data transmission

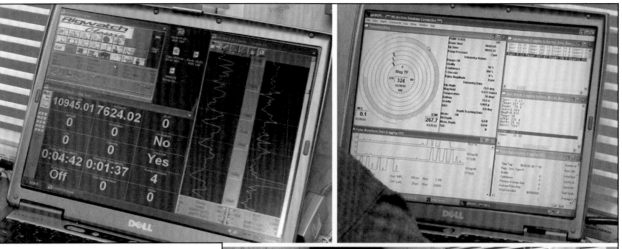

Figure 2-1.83. Data from downhole being decoded into digital form for display and recording at the surface in an Anadrill logging unit

By manipulating the rotation of the rotor and, in turn, the characteristics of the pressure wave, data can be encoded within the pressure wave and then decoded at the surface by pressure transducers (that convert input pressure energy to output electrical energy) using special software (fig. 2-2.83).

Next were advancements in measurements of bottomhole-assembly vibrations, weight on bit, torque on bit, pressure, and temperature. Service companies were successful in demonstrating the reliability and usefulness of these measurements while drilling and proceeded to add formation evaluation measurements to the bottomhole-assembly collars. Teleco, Sperry Sun, and Anadrill commercialized natural gamma-ray and resistivity LWD measurements in the 1980s.

LWD measurements were developed at a rapid pace, and today, most wireline measurements are duplicated in the suite of LWD measurements. Overall, MWD/LWD measurements have had a dramatic impact on drilling efficiency and formation evaluation (figs. 2-1.84, 2-1.85, and 2-1.86).

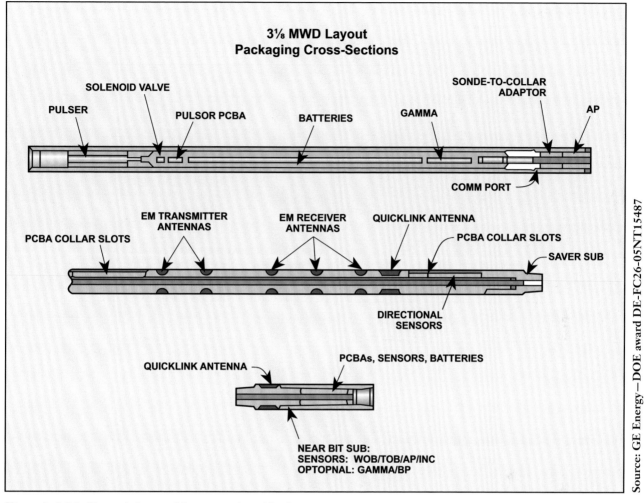

Figure 2-1.84. Bottomhole assembly cross-section, side view

Source: GE Energy – DOE award DE-FC26-05NT15487

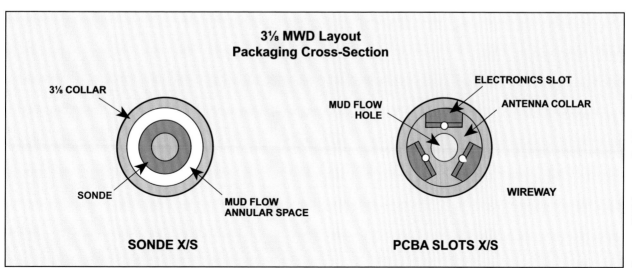

Figure 2-1.85. Bottomhole assembly cross-section, top view

Source: GE Energy – DOE award DE-FC26-05NT15487

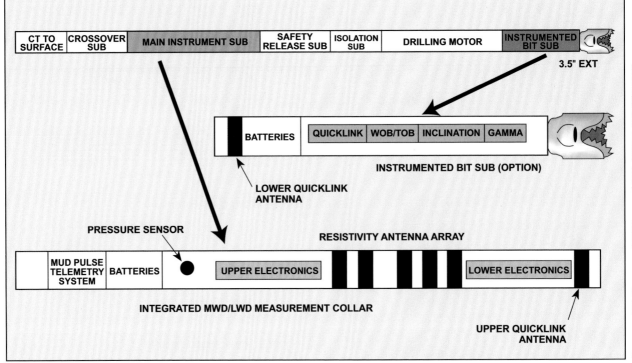

Figure 2-1.86. Integrated LWD/MWD measurement system in coiled tubing drilling bottomhole assembly

Source: GE Energy—DOE award DE-FC26-05NT15487

Measurements and Applications

MWD determines wellbore path in three directions:
- Depth
- North-south
- East-west

Directional Measurements

MWD directional measurements help operators correctly position the wellbore. Directional measurements allow the location of the wellbore path through the Earth to be computed in three directions: depth, north-south, and east-west departures from the surface location. To do this, the survey sensors measure both the inclination and azimuth of the well and combine them with the measured depth. Well inclination is measured by using multiple accelerometers to determine the angle of the wellbore from vertical. The survey package uses several magnetometers to sense the relationship of the well azimuth to the Earth's magnetic field (fig. 2-1.87). By knowing the orientation of the Earth's magnetic field, the orientation of the well can be computed.

The position of the wellbore is needed for several reasons. One primary reason is to legally verify that the location of the well is within the operator's lease. Knowing the wellbore position and having the geologic, seismic, and LWD measurements enables the operator to properly position the wellbore relative to the geologic structure, or position it in the correct geologic layer for high-angle and horizontal wells.

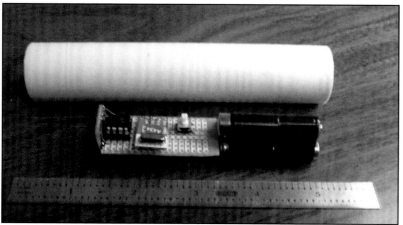

Courtesy of Wellog

Figure 2-1.87. This small magnetometer can sense the relationship of the well azimuth to the Earth's magnetic field.

Weight and Torque-on-Bit

The ability of the bit to efficiently crush and shear rock depends on the proper weight and torque being applied to it. Surface measurements of weight and torque-on-bit are inaccurate when the drill pipe encounters varying wall friction that inhibits the transfer of weight and rotation to the bit. When the drill pipe encounters significant wall friction while drilling, the downward motion of the drill pipe is opposed by this friction, causing the surface-derived weight and torque-on-bit surface measurements to be large when in fact the actual applied downhole values are much less. Weight and torque-on-bit measurements in the bottomhole assembly are not affected by friction on the drill pipe above, enabling more accurate weight and torque-on-bit measurements.

Annular Pressure

The pressure in the annulus is a function of the static mud density, the frictional pressure losses in the annulus caused by the motion of the fluid, and most importantly, the weight of the suspended cuttings in the annulus mud. By measuring the annulus pressure and comparing it to the static mud pressure, the driller can determine when excess cuttings are building up in the annulus and need to be eliminated. Excessive annulus pressures create the probability that the drilled formations will fail and the mud will be lost into them. This could potentially cause a lost-circulation event and an eventual blowout due to the loss of mud pressure in the annulus. Monitoring the annular pressure eliminates any abnormal buildup of pressures (see later section on *The Use of Mud Density*).

Bottomhole Assembly Vibrations

Measuring bottomhole assembly vibrations helps drillers manage vibrations and protect the drill string components. Often, the bottomhole assembly motion is violent from both axial and lateral motion, and the resulting accelerations from hitting the wellbore wall range in hundreds of g-force magnitude. If this occurs over sustained periods of time, the bottomhole assembly connections will fail, resulting in the bottomhole assembly being lost in the hole. MWD/LWD sensors are susceptible to these excessive accelerations, and risk of their failing increases with time under high accelerations. The driller routinely alters the drilling parameters to reduce these vibrations to ensure the reliability of the drill string components.

LWD Measurements and Applications

Natural Gamma Ray

The measurement of naturally occurring gamma rays in the formation is obtained with a *sodium-iodide scintillation counter*. Most of the detected gamma rays are from the single nonseries radioactive decay of the K^{40} potassium isotope to Ar^{40}. The series radioactive decay of $Uranium^{238}$ and $Thorium^{232}$ also contribute to the total gamma rays detected. The decay product Bismuth is the main contributor to the Uranium gamma ray spectrum while the decay product Thallium is the main contributor to the energy spectrum of the Thorium series.

Weathering of parent rock containing potassium feldspar and micas into clay minerals results in some K^{40} becoming attached to the clay minerals. This is because potassium has a relatively large ionic radius and remains ionically bound to the clay sheet particles with limited mobility. Most is dissolved and transported with the sediments to be taken up during deposition and during the montmorillonite-illite transformation. The relative abundance of the K^{40}-generated gamma rays is therefore proportional to the clay volume in the sediments.

Uranium is easily oxidized into the uranyl ion by bacterial action, which is very soluble and mobile. The uranyl ion forms ionic complexes with carbonates and with organic compounds under reducing conditions. It therefore has a strong correlation with organic carbon content and radioactive salts.

Thorium is released during the weathering of siliceous igneous rocks. It is insoluble, has limited mobility, and concentrates in residual minerals such as bauxite, heavy minerals, and clays. Thorium is never associated with chemical sediments. Thorium has a strong correlation with clay volume and heavy minerals.

A measurement of potassium- and thorium-generated gamma rays therefore gives a measure of the relative amount of clay minerals in the formation. This allows a petrophysicist to determine the ability of a formation to hold hydrocarbons and produce commercial quantities of hydrocarbons, because clay materials are detrimental to both.

LWD units of measurement:
- Natural gamma ray
- Resistivity
- Density
- Neutron porosity
- Velocity
- Magnetic resonance
- Spectroscopy

The signature of the gamma ray log can be correlated over large geo-graphical areas in clay-bearing rock, allowing the geologist to construct the individual formation layer positions over entire basins.

Resistivity

Another valuable measurement helps reveal the volumes of water and hydrocarbons in the formation. A series of coils mounted in a drill collar generate electromagnetic currents in the formation (fig. 2-1.88). The ability of the formation to transmit this current is inversely proportional to the resistivity of the formation. Both the rock mass and hydrocarbons in the pore volume resist the flow of these currents. Only the water volume in the formation contributes to the signal. This phenomenon allows the relative volumes of hydrocarbons and water in the pore spaces to be calculated once the total pore volume is determined from the other measurements.

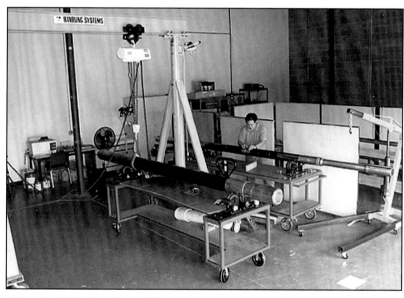

Source: GE Energy—DOE award DE-FC26-05NT15487

Figure 2-1.88. Final assembly area: 6.75-inch and 4.75-inch resistivity collars in process

Density

Density measurement helps determine the total volume of pores in a formation. This type of measurement is based on the concept that a measured number of gamma rays detected a distance from their source is logarithmically inversely proportional to the electron density of the material being bombarded. The electron density of most earth forma-tions of interest is also directly proportional to the bulk density. The formation's bulk density is used to compute the pore volume of the formation once grain density and fluid density in the pores are known. In conventional reservoirs, the pore volume contains the hydrocarbons. The grain and fluid densities are determined with the help of additional measurements, one of which is the neutron measurement.

Neutron Porosity

Porosity within the formation is another key measurement. Neutron measurements are based on the physical phenomena that the number of epithermal and/or thermal neutrons detected a distance from a neutron source is inversely proportional to the hydrogen content of the material they pass through. This is due to the neutron and hydrogen molecule having similar masses, with the hydrogen most efficient at slowing the neutron down to the type of energies the detector is measuring before it reaches the detector. The water molecule in the pore space of the formation contains most of the hydrogen in the formation. Once the hydrogen content of the rock mass and pore fluids are known, the porosity of the formation can be computed.

Velocity

Measuring the speed of a sound wave traveling through a formation helps petrophysicists and geophysicists better understand a formation's properties. The sound velocity is measured by placing a *piezoelectric transducer* on the drill collar to stimulate a pressure wave in the mud column, which transmits the disturbance to the formation. A series of receivers on the drill collar located a distance away from the transmitter detects the arrival of the sound-wave components. By measuring the arrival times of the wave at the various receivers, and knowing the distance between them, the wave's velocity can be computed. The compressional velocity is proportional to the stiffness of the formation, which is inversely proportional to the pore volume and proportional to the grain-to-grain stresses. Combining the compressional and shear velocities with the bulk density measurement, the *bulk and shear moduli* can be computed. These calculations are useful for studying formation compaction, predicting hydraulic fracture geometry, and determining rock type and pore fluids. The compressional velocity can be combined with the measured bulk density to compute the *acoustic impedance* to compare to surface seismic measurements.

Magnetic Resonance

Another type of pore volume measurement involves magnetic resonance. Measurements of magnetic resonance rely on the principal that certain atomic nuclei respond to an applied magnetic field in a predictable and measurable manner. Atoms with unpaired protons or neutrons such as hydrogen have a magnetic moment (a net magnetic charge), which causes them to behave like tiny bar magnets in an applied fixed magnetic field. They are then exposed to a second radiofrequency-induced periodic magnetic field orthogonal to the first. The alignment is imperfect and takes time because the spinning nuclei precess about their axis, much like a toy top or gyroscope. Interactions between the polarized nuclei, the external magnetic fields, and the pore surfaces can produce measurable signals in an antenna mounted on the drill collar. The time-varying amplitude of the signal from the hydrogen nuclei decays can be used in making important petrophysical measurements, primarily of pore volume and the relative surface-to-pore volume areas. One advantage of this measurement is that the rock matrix does not contribute to the signal, unlike other pore volume measurements described earlier.

Spectroscopy

Bombardment with neutrons from either chemical or electronic sources creates inelastic- and elastic-type nuclear reactions in the individual atomic nuclei in the formation. When the excited nucleus eventually relaxes to a lower and stable state, a gamma ray or photon is released. The relative energy of this photon is unique to the type of nucleus from which it was released. By measuring the energy of these gamma rays with a detector in the drill collar, the abundance and type of the various nuclei in the formation can be determined. This greatly aids in determining the type and amount of minerals making up the formation, allowing a more accurate pore volume to be computed from the density and neutron measurements.

Complete or Abandon

After the drilling contractor has drilled the hole to final depth and the operating company has evaluated the formations, the company decides whether to set the final string of casing or *plug and abandon* the well. This final string is called the *production casing* (see fig. 2-1.77 earlier in this chapter).

> A dry hole means the well cannot produce enough oil or gas in commercial quantities.

If the company believes a well cannot produce enough oil or gas to pay for its *completion*, then the well is judged to be a dry hole. This means the well is not capable of producing oil or gas in commercial quantities. If this occurs, the company plugs the well by putting in several cement plugs to seal it permanently and then abandons it. Plugging and abandoning a well is considerably less expensive than *completing* it. A dry hole might contain oil and gas but not in sufficient quantity at the current price of oil to justify the expense of completing the well. If evaluation shows that commercial amounts of hydrocarbons exist, the company could decide to set casing and complete the well.

To set the casing, the casing must be hauled to the location. The drilling crew pulls the drill stem from the hole and lays it down one joint at a time to transport it more easily to the rig's next drilling location. Then a crew runs and cements the production casing in the well.

After drilling the hole and setting and cementing the production casing, the drilling contractor's job is almost finished. The last task is *completion*. Sometimes, the same rig and crew remain on the location to *complete* the well. Completion involves:

- Running tubing, which is a string of small-diameter pipe inside the casing through which the hydrocarbons flow out of the well
- Setting the wellhead of steel fittings that support the tubing and contain a series of valves and pressure gauges to control oil flow

In other circumstances, the drilling contractor moves the rig and equipment to the next location after cementing the production casing. If so, the operator hires a special completion rig and crew to finish the job.

Other Land Operations

In pad drilling, multiple wells are drilled near one another.

Some land rigs today are built for *pad drilling*. For this type of operation, the drilling site is larger than normal to accommodate multiple wells drilled near one another. The rig's substructure and derrick can be skidded from one slot to the next with the engines, mud treatment, accommodation trailers, and so on left undisturbed. The wells start out vertically for several hundred feet and then are deviated to drill a spread pattern in the subsurface that reaches deep into the reservoir. Pad drilling reduces the costs of preparing the site and reduces time in moving between wells.

After Drilling

In all cases, after drilling is finished, the site must be cleaned and returned to its original condition. All waste is hauled away to special waste treatment facilities. Any empty reserve pits are filled with dirt, and trees and grass are usually replanted. In addition, other necessary remediation tasks are performed as required.

Equipment and techniques for drilling wells from offshore locations are similar in function but different in appearance to those used for drilling wells on land. The rigs used to drill offshore wells are equipped to handle specialized methods of operation to meet the unique challenges presented by offshore drilling operations.

Offshore petroleum operations began as extensions of land operations. The first offshore well in the United States was drilled in 1897 off the coast of southern California. A wooden pier extending about 300 feet (91 metres) into the Pacific Ocean was built from the shore. Near the end of the pier, a drilling rig was erected and a well drilled to tap oil and gas that lay in a reservoir below the water. Because oil companies had already drilled and produced several successful wells on the beach, it was natural for them to extend drilling seaward.

By the late 1930s, geologists had conducted seismic surveys in the coastal marshlands, bayous, and shallow bays next to the Gulf of Mexico. Many surveys showed underground formations that might contain hydrocarbons. Oil companies dredged a channel 4 to 8 feet (1.2 to 2.4 metres) deep in the marshes and bays and towed a barge into the channel to drill exploratory wells in these potential reservoirs. They submerged the barge, securing it with wooden pilings, and erected a rig on the barge's deck above the waterline.

Another method of drilling exploratory wells involved building a wooden platform on timber piles and erecting a rig on the platform. A barge brought supplies to the platform. To accommodate trucks, trestles were built from the shore to the platform creating a road.

OFFSHORE DRILLING

A Look Back

The first offshore well was drilled off the coast of California in 1897. In the late 1800s, drilling in deep waters was costly and time consuming because platforms were immobile.

The first specially designed steel platform was installed in 1947 in the Gulf of Mexico at a depth of about 20 feet (6 metres). Operators anchored surplus barges from World War II, called *tenders*, alongside the platform. Tenders carried supplies and provided living quarters and circulation equipment (fig. 2-1.89). These platforms worked in waters of 60 feet (18 metres) or less, and after drilling the well, the operator would move the rig to another location. In the decades following, more than 2,000 fixed platforms sprang up in the Gulf of Mexico in depths ranging up to 1,200 feet (366 metres).

As offshore exploration techniques revealed the presence of possible reservoirs in deeper waters from 50 to 300 feet (15 to 91 metres), it was found that the existing barges and platforms had limitations. For example, the operator could not submerge a barge in waters deeper than about 10 feet (3 metres) without its deck becoming covered by water. Mooring and anchoring problems in less-sheltered ocean areas caused damage to the platform. While operators could construct platforms in deeper waters, the platforms were not mobile. Once built, an operator could not move a platform without totally disassembling it. Mobility was important to drilling exploratory wells because usually, the oil company drilled several wells in one area before striking oil or gas. Because most exploratory wells turned out to be dry holes, building a new platform for each well was expensive and time consuming.

Courtesy of SeaDrill Asia Limited

Figure 2-1.89. Seadrill SSETR or semisubmersible self-erecting tender rig

Drilling in deeper waters required some type of mobile, or movable, offshore drilling rig. Engineers and naval architects researched the problem, and in 1948, they built the first mobile offshore rig (fig. 2-1.90). This rig consisted of a barge with several steel beams, or posts, attached to its deck. On top of the posts was an upper deck that held drilling equipment. The first rig of this type was floated out to a drill site near the mouth of the Mississippi River in the United States. There, water was allowed to enter the barge hull at a controlled rate to slowly submerge the unit until it came to rest on the seafloor. The posts extended the drilling deck well above the waterline and provided a stable platform for the drilling operation. After drilling the first well successfully in the Mississippi River in about 18 feet (5.48 metres) of water, the contractor pumped out the water in the barge hull and once again, the entire unit floated on the water surface. The rig was then towed to another location, submerged, and used to drill another well. This mobile design, called a *posted barge rig*, was so successful that manufacturers are still building a few similar units for drilling in relatively shallow waters of bays, inlets, lakes, and marshes.

> The first posted barge rig was invented in 1948 and provided a mobile platform.

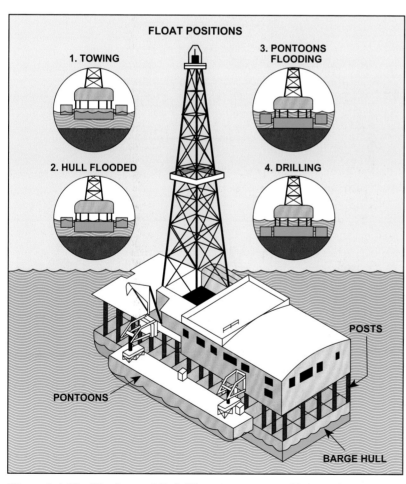

Figure 2-1.90. The first mobile drilling rig was a posted barge submersible designed to drill in shallow water.

Modern Offshore Operations

The type of rig used in offshore drilling depends on whether the company is drilling for exploration or for development. Other factors include water depth and weather constraints. *Development wells* are those drilled in a reservoir found as a result of exploratory drilling. Oil companies almost always use mobile rigs in exploratory drilling. For development drilling, they often use fixed platforms for their production and well maintenance facilities. Increasingly, companies are using production methods for development wells that do not require fixed platforms, such as subsea satellites.

Mobile Offshore Drilling Units

To drill an exploratory offshore well, the operating company often employs a drilling contractor who owns mobile offshore rigs called *mobile offshore drilling units (MODUs)*. Several types of MODUs are available and can be classified as either bottom-supported or floating units (fig. 2-1.91).

When a bottom-supported unit drills a well, part of the structure contacts the seafloor while the rest stays above the water surface. The unit floats on the surface only when being moved to another drill site. In contrast, floating units do not rest on the seafloor but float on or slightly below the water surface when drilling on site.

Bottom-supported units include:

- Submersibles
- Jackups

Floating units include:

- Inland barges
- Drill ships and ship-shaped barges
- Semisubmersibles

Figure 2-1.91. Types of MODUs

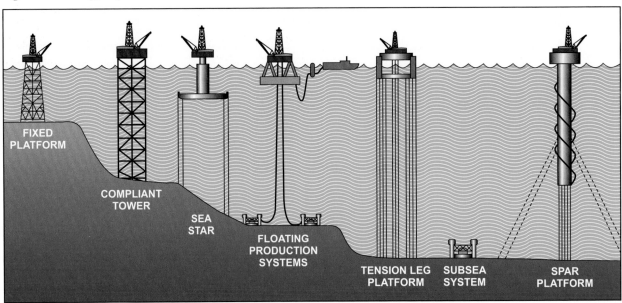

Submersibles are bottom-supported offshore drilling rigs. They can be further divided into posted barges, column submersibles, and Arctic submersibles.

- *Posted barges are* the earliest submersible design. Like the first posted barge built in 1948, one consists of a barge hull with several steel posts supporting an upper deck with the drilling equipment on deck (see fig. 2-1.90). Posted barges are used in relatively shallow waters of less than about 30 feet (9 metres).

- *Bottle-type submersibles* are an early design with several steel cylinders, or bottles, on top of which is a deck to hold drilling equipment (fig. 2-1.92). When the bottles are flooded with water at a controlled rate, the rig submerges until it rests on the ocean bottom. When the rig is moved to the next drilling location, water is pumped out of the bottles until the unit floats again. This *ballasting* and *deballasting* operation is similar to that used on submarines. Towboats are used to move the rig to the new site. Modern bottle-type submersibles usually drill in maximum water depths of about 100 feet (30 metres).

- Arctic submersibles are units uniquely designed for drilling in waters where moving pack ice could damage or destroy conventional submersibles. Pack ice occurs in Arctic areas where winter temperatures can be low enough to freeze seawater. When subjected to strong currents and winds, ice tends to break apart and move with currents. Moving ice can destroy a MODU unless it is constructed to withstand such collisions. Several types of Arctic submersibles share a common feature: a steel or concrete watertight chamber called a caisson that rests on the seafloor when the rig is drilling (fig. 2-1.93).

Submersibles

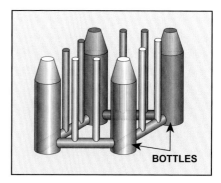

Figure 2-1.92. When flooded, the bottles cause a bottle-type submersible to rest on the seafloor.

Figure 2-1.93. A concrete island drilling system features a reinforced concrete caisson with a steel base.

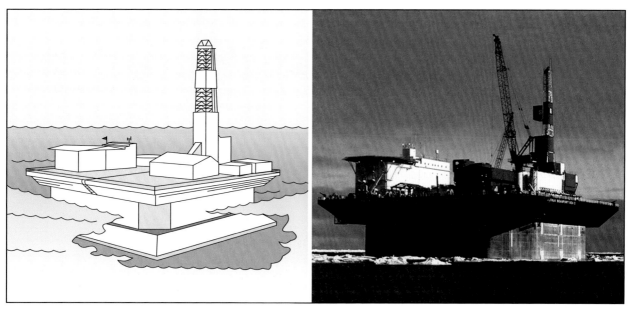

The caisson is rectangular or cone-shaped. The drilling equipment sits on a deck or on a platform above. The walls of the caisson protect the drilled wells from being damaged by moving ice. The platform is also reinforced to withstand any impact and destruction by ice. Arctic submersibles can drill in water depths of up to about 150 feet (46 metres).

Jackups

The first *jackup*, or *self-elevating rig* was built in 1954 and rapidly became the most popular offshore rig design. Jackups can drill in deeper water up to about 550 feet (168 metres), and they provide a highly stable drilling platform. They are fairly easy to move to alternate locations, and they generally cost less than other types of MODUs. A large jackup can drill 35,000 feet (10,668 metres) deep and withstand 130 mile per hour (209 kilowatt per hour) winds.

A jackup rig has three or four legs that pass through its hull and can be jacked up or down (fig. 2-1.94). The bottom of the leg is usually flush with the bottom of the rig. When the rig is at the drill site, the legs are jacked down until they rest on the seafloor. By continuing to jack the legs down, the hull is raised above the water surface high enough to allow the drilling crew to work undisturbed by tides and waves.

Jackups:
- Can drill in waters up to 550 feet (168 metres)
- Are highly stable
- Are easily moveable

Figure 2-1.94. The hull of a jackup is raised well above the water surface before drilling begins.

The legs of a jackup can be columns or trusses. Columnar legs are steel cylinders, and open-truss legs resemble high-voltage towers because they have several steel members, or trusses, that crisscross between structural corners, as shown in fig. 2-1.94. Columnar legs are less expensive to fabricate than truss legs but are more susceptible to twisting stresses. Because of this weakness, jackups with columnar legs are unable to operate in waters as deep as jackups with open-truss legs.

Both types of jackups have watertight barge hulls that can float on the water while the unit is being moved to drill sites. Usually a jackup is towed, but sometimes a jackup is self-propelled by two engine-driven propellers, or *screws*, that power the unit as it floats. A third and faster way to move a jackup rig is on the flat deck of a large ship. The rig is loaded onto the ship's deck to transport the rig to a new location. This transport method is used mainly for long-distance moves.

An *inland barge rig*, considered a floating unit, is shaped much like a traditional barge. It is flat-bottomed and flat-sided. The drilling rig sits on the deck of the barge, and the entire unit is towed to the drill site. At the site, the barge is anchored for drilling (fig. 2-1.95). However, in shallow water, the hull is sometimes flooded and the inland barge rig becomes a submersible unit. Also called *swamp barges*, inland barges are used in relatively shallow waters such as the swamps and bays of western Africa, or in large inland waters such as Lake Maracaibo in Venezuela.

Inland Barges

Swamp barges are generally used in shallow waters.

Figure 2-1.95. An inland barge rig at work

Drill Ships and Ship-Shaped Barges

Drillships station themselves at a worksite with:
- Anchors
- Dynamic positioning

Ship-shaped MODUs include *drillships* and *ship-shaped barges*. They have streamlined bows and squared-off sterns and can drill wells in water as deep as 10,000 feet (3,050 metres) where bottom-supported units are not practical. Drillships and ship-shaped barges float on the water surface and as such, are sometimes called *surface units* (fig. 2-1.96). The main difference between a drillship and a ship-shaped barge is a drillship is self-propelled and a barge is towed.

Both drillships and ship-shaped barges have a derrick near the middle of the ship. Most also have a *moon pool*, which is a walled opening below the derrick that is open to the water surface through which various drilling tools pass down to the seafloor. Drillships are highly mobile and require a ship captain and crew in addition to a drilling crew, making them more expensive to operate than ship-shaped barges. Because of their mobility, drillships are often useful for drilling wells in remote areas far from land. In addition, a drillship's load-carrying capacity makes them ideally suited for one-well programs. All the consumable materials needed to drill and complete a well can be loaded in port. After the well is finished, the drillship can return to port to load up for the next well.

Once a drillship or barge is on the drill site, or *on station*, it can be kept there in two ways:

- By several anchors from the vessel to the seafloor, much the same way any oceangoing vessel is anchored

- By *dynamic positioning* with a system of propellers, or *thrusters*, mounted on the vessel hull below the waterline (fig. 2-1.97). An onboard computer system controls the thrusters to maintain the unit precisely on station (fig. 2-1.98). Wind and current sensors provide information on the environmental forces acting on the rig. Seabed hydrophones and satellite navigation systems are used to provide the positioning information that keeps the rig precisely over the wellhead.

Figure 2-1.96. The Deepwater Pathfinder drillship travels to a remote drill site.

Courtesy of Transocean

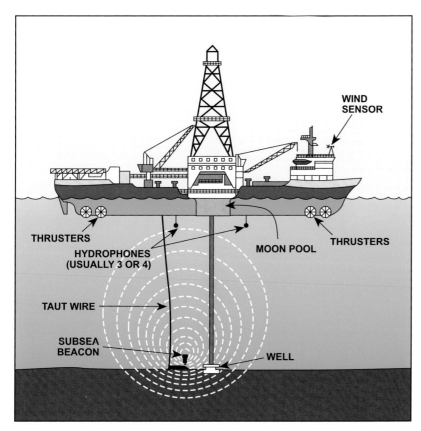

Figure 2-1.97. Dynamic positioning systems use global positioning systems (GPS) and hydrophones to measure the vessel's position and send computer-controlled commands to thrusters to hover over the wellhead.

Courtesy of Ebbe Holsting

Figure 2-1.98. Dynamic positioning systems have computerized controls on board the vessel.

Semisubmersibles

Semisubmersibles are sturdy enough to operate in rough waters.

Semisubmersibles are among the largest and most expensive of all MODUs. Operating companies worldwide use them in rough seas because they are more stable than ship-shaped vessels and can be used in deep water (fig. 2-1.99).

Courtesy of Transocean

Figure 2-1.99. A semisubmersible drilling unit floats on hulls that are flooded and submerged just below the water surface.

The design of modern semisubmersibles is based on a *column-stabilized* semisubmersible unit consisting of two or more pontoon-shaped hulls attached to several vertical cylinders (columns) (fig. 2-1.100). The main deck rests on top of the columns, and a derrick or mast and other drilling equipment sit on the deck. Only the hull is submerged when towing to reduce drag and increase towing speed.

Both the hulls and columns can be flooded with water or pumped dry. To move the unit, water is pumped out of the hulls and columns to float the unit on the surface with only the hulls under water. The unit is usually towed to the drill site. Sometimes, it is self-propelled or assisted by propulsion. At the drill site, the hulls and columns are flooded with enough water to submerge it to the required *drilling draft*, which is the depth below the surface. Anchors or dynamic positioning keep the unit on station.

Because much of a semisubmersible's mass is below the water surface, it does not roll or pitch as much as a ship. Instead, it moves up and down—or heaves. This motion is controlled by special *heave compensators* that ensure the drilling string is kept stable on bottom.

Column-Stabilized Semisubmersibles

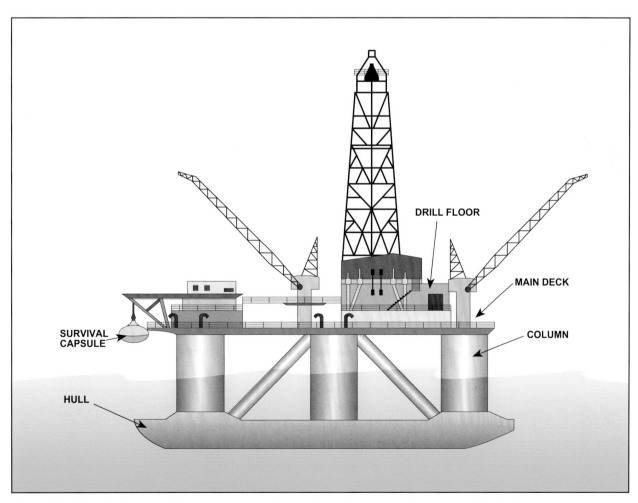

Figure 2-1.100. A column-stabilized semisubmersible rests below the waves and waterline while drilling.

Offshore Drilling Platforms

Types of rigid platforms:
- Steel-jacket
- Concrete-gravity
- Caisson-type

Operating companies generally use MODUs to drill exploratory wells. Once a company knows an offshore reservoir contains enough oil or gas to make development economically feasible, it will drill more wells. Sometimes companies use MODUs to drill the development wells, but when they begin full drilling operations, they often do so from fixed *drilling platforms*.

Similar to a mobile rig, modern drilling platforms are large enough to house all operations including the equipment, crew quarters, offices, galley, and recreation rooms. However, drilling platforms can also carry the large equipment required for production operations (fig. 2-1.101).

Platform rigs vary in design and appearance. They are often built of steel or concrete and can be rigid or pliant. More recent designs include spars and tension-leg platforms used in deepwater drilling.

Courtesy of BP p.l.c.

Figure 2-1.101. A self-contained platform such as the Thunderhorse in the Gulf of Mexico (pictured) houses drilling and production equipment and facilities for the crew.

Rigid Platforms

Rigid platforms are the oldest design among offshore platforms. They are frequently used in development drilling in water less than about 1,000 feet (305 metres) deep. Rigid steel platforms are common in the Gulf of Mexico, in the Pacific Ocean off the coast of California, in the North Sea, and in other areas of the world.

Types of rigid platforms include:
- Steel-jacket platform
- Concrete gravity platform
- Caisson-type platform

The most common type of platform, the *steel-jacket platform* consists of a *jacket*—a tall vertical section made of tubular steel members that form the foundation of the platform. This type of platform is supported by piles driven into the seafloor and extends upward so the top rises above the waterline. Additional sections on top of the jacket provide space for crew's quarters, a drilling rig, and the drilling equipment. Jackets stand in water at least 1,000 feet (305 metres) deep. Their height depends on the depth of the water. Additional sections on top of the jacket can extend the height of the structure. One tall platform in the Gulf of Mexico is 1,736 feet (529 metres) high. Platform jackets are so large they must be constructed on land, placed on a barge, towed to the site, and then launched in the water.

A jacket is usually built on its side (fig. 2-1.102). Several tubular members of the jacket are sealed airtight, so when launched in the water, the jacket floats on its side as it was constructed. At the site, large barge-mounted cranes stabilize the jacket while the tubular members are flooded. The jacket is lowered to a vertical position as the legs come to rest on the seafloor. Piles might be driven through several of the legs and deep into the ocean bottom so the jacket can be pinned firmly to the bottom. In other cases, the jacket is lowered over prepositioned pilings. Cranes then place the remaining elements of the platform on the jacket (fig. 2-1.103).

Steel-Jacket Platform

Figure 2-1.103. A large crane hoists a deck section onto the jacket.

Figure 2-1.102. Constructed on its side, and loaded onto a transportation and installation barge, this jacket will be towed offshore and launched at the installation site, and set using a derrick barge.

Courtesy of McDermott International Inc.

Concrete Gravity Platform

Another type of rigid platform built from steel-reinforced concrete is the *concrete gravity platform* (fig. 2.1-104). Concrete platforms are constructed in protected waters near shore, then they are floated and towed to the drill site in a vertical position. Tall caissons, or columns, resembling smokestacks made of steel-reinforced concrete are the dominant feature of concrete gravity platforms.

At the site, the commissioning crew floods the caissons until they rest on the seafloor. The caissons are extremely heavy so the force of gravity alone is sufficient to keep them in place, making pilings unnecessary. Crew quarters, drilling equipment, and other equipment sit on a deck on top of the caissons.

An advantage of concrete gravity platforms is the operator can arrange special concrete cylinders around the base of the caissons on the seafloor to store up to about one million barrels of oil. The capacity to store oil offshore is an advantage when no pipeline exists for transporting oil to shore for refining. Produced oil is temporarily kept in these special caissons before being transported to shore by shuttle tankers. Another advantage of concrete gravity platforms is they can withstand extremely rough seas due to their tremendous weight. They are therefore used extensively in the North Sea and Eastern Canada where offshore conditions are extremely harsh.

Figure 2-1.104. A concrete gravity platform is so heavy that gravity holds it in place.

The *steel-caisson platform* is a type of rigid platform designed specifically for use in the Cook Inlet of Alaska where fast-moving tidal currents carry pack ice capable of destroying conventional steel-jacket platforms (fig. 2-1.105). One design uses a rectangular platform with a caisson at each of the four corners with each one firmly affixed to the seafloor. The drilling and production decks rest on top of the caissons, which are made of two layers of thick steel to prevent ice damage. Development wells are drilled through the middle of each caisson, so the drilling rig is designed to be moved across the platform to each of the four caissons. The caissons also protect the top part of each well from moving ice.

Using rigid platforms in water over 1,000 feet (305 metres) deep is not practical because they are generally expensive to build and limited by their design.

Steel-Caisson Platform

Source: U.S. Coast Guard. Photo by PA1 Sara Francis

Figure 2-1.105. These steel-caisson platforms rest in the Cook Inlet of Alaska.

In deeper water, operating companies use *compliant platforms* because they contain fewer steel parts and are lighter than rigid steel-jacket platforms. Compliant means they yield with wind and water movement, much the way floating rigs do. Types of compliant platforms include:

- Guyed-tower platform
- Tension-leg platform
- Spar platform

Compliant Platforms

Guyed-Tower Platform

Compliant platforms include:
- Guyed-tower—less expensive to build than rigid platforms
- Tension-leg—affixed to seafloor with steel tendons
- Spar—moored to seafloor with counterweight

The guyed-tower platform is similar to a rigid steel-jacket platform with the bottom of the platform or jacket pinned to the seafloor. However, the guyed jacket is slimmer and does not contain as much steel as a rigid jacket. This makes it lighter and less expensive to build. Several *guy wires* are attached to the jacket relatively close to the waterline and spread out evenly around the jacket (fig. 2-1.106). The guy wires are anchored to the seafloor by means of *clump weights* that fit together, similar to a bicycle chain. The weights lie flat on the ocean floor, and as the platform moves, they lift off the floor. As the platform moves back, the clump weights once again lie on bottom. Clump weights allow the guy wires to move with the platform's movement while firmly anchoring the wires. With one end secured to the seabed with a pile or a drag anchor, the clump weights cannot move horizontally.

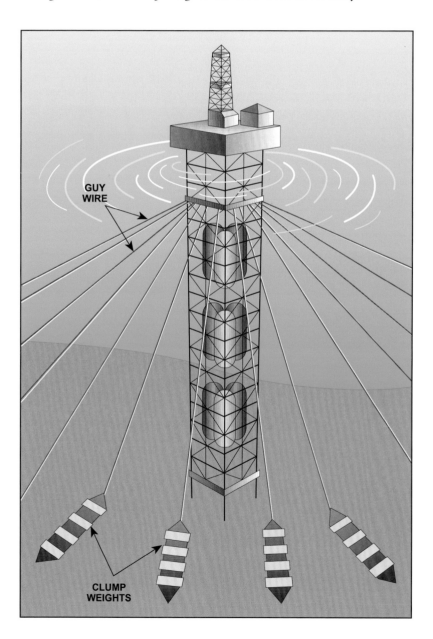

GUY WIRE

CLUMP WEIGHTS

Figure 2-1.106. This relatively light-weight jacket of a guyed-tower platform is supported by several guy wires and clump weights.

Like guyed towers, *tension-leg platforms* move with wind, waves, and currents. The top of the platform resembles a semisubmersible drilling unit with hulls that can be partially flooded. Unlike a semisubmersible, a tension-leg platform is attached to the seafloor by several steel tubes called *tendons* running vertically between the unit and the seabed. With the tendons firmly affixed to the platform and seafloor, the buoyancy of the platform pulls and stretches the tendons, placing them under tension (fig. 2-1.107).

Newer tension-leg platforms are designed to support drilling in water 4,000 feet (1,220 metres) deep and even deeper. Units are being constructed to operate in more than 10,000 feet (3,048 metres) of water depth. This platform can move as much as 100 yards (90 metres) in any direction under hurricane-force winds and waves with very little heave.

Tension-Leg Platform

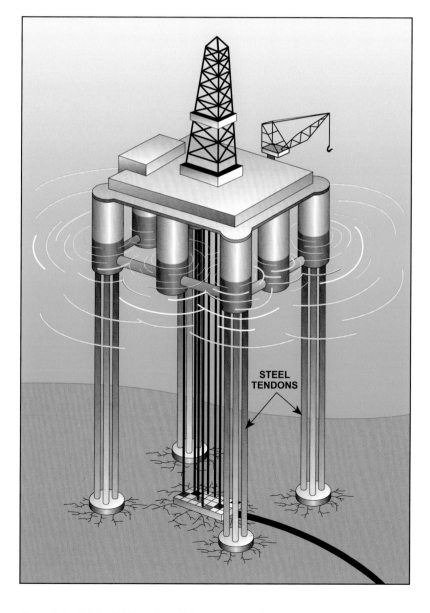

Figure 2-1.107. Steel tendons are kept in tension by the buoyancy of the platform on a tension-leg platform.

Spar Platform   *Spar platforms* are some of the largest platforms in use. Below the waterline is a large cylinder providing buoyancy to support the topside, which is the structure containing the drilling and production equipment (fig 2-1.108). At the bottom of the cylinder are features that engineers have designed to compensate for the forces of wind and waves and to assist in mooring the spar to the seabed. A spar might have submerged pontoons and columns that look like those of a semisubmersible. It might also have a steel truss like the legs of a jackup or a concrete hull like that of a gravity-based platform. Some spars are connected to the seabed using tendons like a tension-leg platform, or they might use a catenary mooring system like that of a ship. The mooring lines can be attached to pilings, anchors, or clump weights, which are large counterweights that lie on the seabed. A combination mooring system might exist that applies more than one of these designs. The main characteristic of spars is to provide a high payload in very deep waters. They are often used in water depths of 3,000 feet (914 metres) or more. Existing technology allows spars to be used in water depths of 7,500 feet (2,286 metres).

Courtesy of Chevron

Figure 2-1.108. The Genesis spar platform in the Gulf of Mexico

Offshore drilling continues to explore greater water depths and more hostile environments, which significantly increases drilling costs. The result is the need for larger *petroleum reserves* to justify the cost of drilling. Petroleum reserves are the estimated quantities of crude oil claimed to be recoverable under the existing economic and operating conditions.

In some cases, oil companies must consider a reserve estimated at 100 million barrels (16 million cubic metres) of oil to be marginal. If they estimate they can recover only 100 million barrels from a reservoir, then that reservoir will not be profitable due to the high costs of drilling, producing, and transporting the oil to shore. Commercial reserves begin at 300 million barrels (48 million cubic metres) of anticipated production for some oilfields. However, exploring for offshore oil and gas continues expanding as improvements in drilling and production techniques reduce cost and increase success.

Commercial Reserves

Although wellbores are frequently drilled vertically, there are situations that require drilling at an angle, especially in offshore operations. This variation from drilling a straight hole is known as *controlled directional drilling*. This advancing technology makes it possible to reach multiple underground locations, often far away, from one primary point to accomplish drilling tasks that cannot be completed using straight holes.

The discipline of directional drilling involves planning and drilling the well *trajectory*—or path—from the rig site to the target points underground. If these points are in a vertical line from the rig, the well is considered vertical; if not, it is considered a directional well.

A *directional driller* plans the well trajectory and ensures the path is achievable while considering the following:

- The formations to be drilled
- The mechanics associated with the bending of the drill string
- The limits of the drilling tools being used

While drilling both vertical and directional holes demands trajectory control, directional drilling requires highly advanced precision technologies to control and monitor the hole as it progresses toward locations far more challenging to reach than conventional straight holes.

The basic science of directional drilling is not new. Its beginnings date back to 1895 when curved wells were drilled to sidetrack equipment stuck in holes. In the 1960s, directional drilling became more scientifically controlled, and developments in the 1980s transformed it into a full-scale engineering discipline. Today, complex models accurately predict hole behavior and conditions, making it possible to carefully steer multiple wells from one location to several separate destinations at a significant cost savings to drillers.

CONTROLLED DIRECTIONAL DRILLING

Considerations in planning well trajectory:
- Formations to be drilled
- Mechanics of bending drill string
- Limits of drilling tools

Build rate is the rate at which a well angle and depth increases.

Directional wells are drilled straight to a predetermined depth and then gradually curved, or *deviated* (fig. 2-1.109). The curvature of each well is planned so the straight, rigid drill stem and casing can follow the curve of the well. Although the curve is gradual, directional wells can change course from vertical to a high degree of angle. Sometimes they run horizontally, in which case they are called *horizontal wells*.

The rate at which a directional well increases angle and depth is referred to as its *build rate*. Different inclination build rates require different approaches to planning and executing directional wells. The more common build rates for directional wells are:

- Between 2°/100 feet (30.48 metres) and 8°/100 feet for long-radius directional wells

- Between 6°/100 feet (30.48 metres) and 35°/100 feet for medium-radius directional wells

- Between 35°/100 feet (30.48 metres) and 65°/100 feet for intermediate-radius directional wells

- Between 65°/100 feet (30.48 metres) and 115°/100 feet for short-radius directional wells

- Above 115°/100 feet (30.48 metres) for ultra-short-radius directional wells

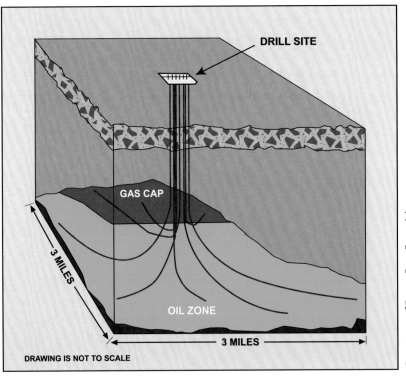

Courtesy of Lone Star Securities

Figure 2-1.109. Deviated wells can reach places conventional straight wells cannot. The technology has dramatically changed the business of drilling for oil and gas.

Over the years, vast improvements in directional drilling make it increasingly possible to recover oil from reservoirs that conventional straight-hole wells could not reach economically. Highly *deviated* (curved) or horizontal wells can increase reservoir exposure while reducing the risk for gas and/or water *coning*, which reduces well productivity, affecting the long-term economics of a development project. Coning is a reservoir engineering problem because the water flows easier than the oil in the reservoirs. If it finds a path to the wellbore, the oil production is reduced and replaced by the water from the reservoir. By placing a horizontal well away from oil/gas contact and oil/water contact and reducing the drawdown, horizontal wells can mitigate this problem.

Offshore Directional Wells

One of the most important uses of directional drilling is for drilling reservoirs offshore. Because of the huge expense of constructing offshore drilling and production platforms, operators cannot afford to tap offshore reservoirs unless they can drill several wells from a single structure (fig. 2-1.110). For example, a large platform in deep water might weigh 1.5 million tons (1.36 million tonnes), cover 4 acres (1.6 hectares), and cost more than $2 billion to build. Without the use of directional drilling, an operating company would have to build several such platforms to reach the available petroleum. With directional wells, operators can drill as many as 40 or more wells from one platform.

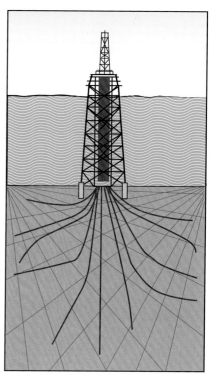

Figure 2-1.110. Several directionally drilled wells can tap multiple reservoirs.

Courtesy of Maersk Oil

Figure 2-1.111. Qatar's largest offshore oilfield: Al Shaheen

Directional wells can reach an incredible distance from the platform. In 2008, Maersk Oil Qatar AS set a world record for directional drilling by drilling a well 36,014 feet (10,977 metres) horizontally away from a platform offshore Qatar in the Al Shaheen field (fig. 2-1.111).

Onshore Directional Wells

Directional wells are also used to develop onshore oilfields. Although projects on land demand less costly techniques, directional and horizontal drilling methods are used to:

- Overcome environmental restrictions and reduce the environmental footprint by placing several wellheads in only one area
- Reduce costs associated with moving the drilling equipment from one location to another
- Take advantage of the increased reservoir exposure of highly deviated and horizontal wells
- Reach a pay zone offshore because it is cheaper to drill a well from land

When drilling a well onshore to reach an offshore target, there is no need to build an offshore platform, nor is there a need for tankers to transport the petroleum or service vessels to supply the offshore rig and crew.

- Offshore directional drilling—operators to drill up to forty wells from one platform.
- Onshore directional drilling—reduces risk of harm to the environment.

This type of directional well is safer for the environment because it reduces risk of oil spills, causes less air pollution, and does not harm local fishing industries. There are many examples of this type of directional drilling, the most famous being the Wytch Farm development project, which was the primary stimulus for developing drilling procedures for highly deviated wells. Wytch Farm, the largest onshore oilfield in western Europe, was discovered in 1973 and began producing in 1979. The project was started by British Petroleum in the early 1990s when the company wanted to drill beneath the English Channel, which is a congested waterway. This forced the adoption of the onshore-to-offshore directional technique. To make it viable to tap the offshore reservoir, *extended reach wells* were drilled to reach points as far away as 29,000 feet (8,800 metres) from the drilling rig.

Other Applications

In addition to offshore development drilling, directional drilling has several other uses (fig. 2-1.112). When it is not possible to erect a drilling rig over a desired location because of a river, hill, or other obstruction, the operator can place the rig at one side of the obstruction and *deviate* the hole to the *pay zone*.

Some other applications of directional wells include:

- In exploratory drilling, when the straight hole misses the reservoir (see Wells D and E in fig. 2-1.112). By drilling a new hole away from the original dry well, it is possible to intersect a pay zone without the expense of drilling a completely new well.

- In killing a *wild well*—one that has blown out, caught on fire, and cratered (caved in). A directional well called a *relief well* (Well F) is drilled so it bottoms out near the borehole of the blown-out well. The crew can then pump mud down the relief well to kill the wild well.

Figure 2-1.112. Some of the applications of directional wells

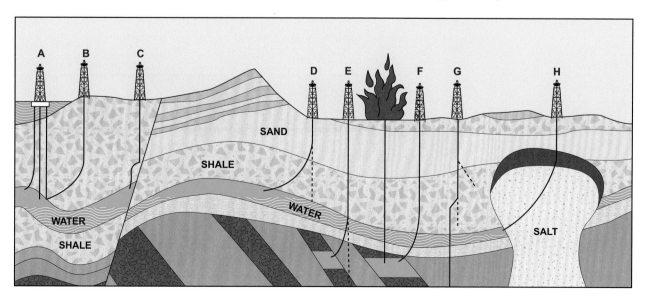

Horizontal wells can cross
parallel oil-containing fractures.

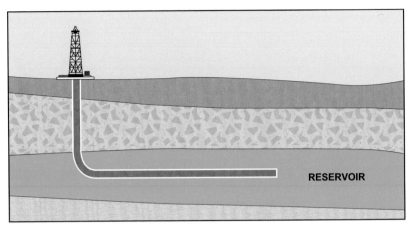

Figure 2-1.113. A long section of a horizontal well can pass through the oil in the reservoir.

- To straighten a crooked hole or to sidetrack around a *fish* (an object lodged in the borehole) that cannot be removed (Well G)

- When drilling into traps associated with salt domes (Well H). Typically the traps around salt domes lie on the edges of the dome and are difficult to accurately pinpoint. A directional well makes it possible to drill into the trap if the initial straight hole misses.

- To avoid a fault line that can cause problems in the hole

- To drill horizontally when the orientation of the well affects how efficiently it drains the reservoir (Well C). A well drilled horizontally instead of vertically through a horizontal oil layer produces more oil because the hole can contact hundreds or thousands of feet (or metres) of the oil-bearing formation instead of tens of feet (or metres) (fig. 2-1.113). A horizontal well can also cross oil-containing fractures that are parallel to each other (fig. 2-1.114). Operators have increased production as much as ten times in formations like this.

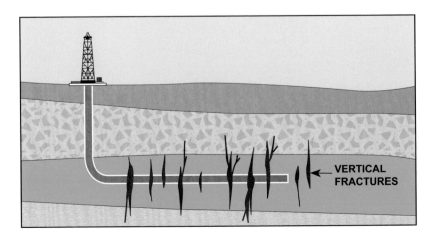

Figure 2-1.114. This horizontal well reaches several oil-containing vertical fractures.

Directional drilling requires special tools and techniques. Typical directional drilling tools include:

- Mud motors
- Nonmagnetic drill collars
- MWD sensors
- Rotary steerable systems

While drilling deviated holes, special attention must be given to the drilling mud because of increased friction between the drill string and the wellbore. There can also be hole cleaning problems associated with the inclined well and successive changes in the well trajectory.

New formulations of drilling mud are more slippery to reduce friction in the hole. These formulations must ensure specific flowing properties so cuttings can be easily carried to the surface and should be considered seriously while planning a more challenging well trajectory such as extended-reach or 3D wells and long horizontal sections.

Tools and Techniques

If drill collars were placed at the end of the drill string in a horizontal well, they would not add weight to the bit (fig. 2-1.115). That is why drill string designers place drill collars at the bottom of the vertical section of the string and above the lower section of drill pipe (fig. 2-1.116). Consider this situation: Think of a 10,000-foot (3,048-metre), 5-inch (127-millimetre) drill string as comparable to a $1/32$-inch (0.8-millimetre) hypodermic needle that is 60-feet (18-metres) long. It is apparent how strong the drill string must be to withstand the weight of the drill collars above it. Part of the solution in keeping drill pipe in the bottom string from buckling is to use stronger pipe. Manufacturers have engineered new types of drill pipe that are light and rigid for horizontal drilling.

Drill Pipe Design

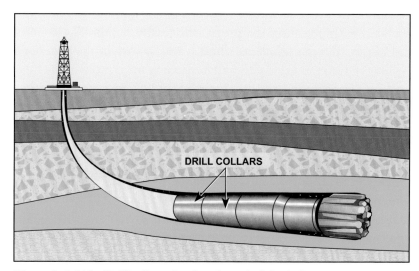

Figure 2-1.115. Drill collars placed at the end of the drill string in a horizontal well would not add weight to the bit.

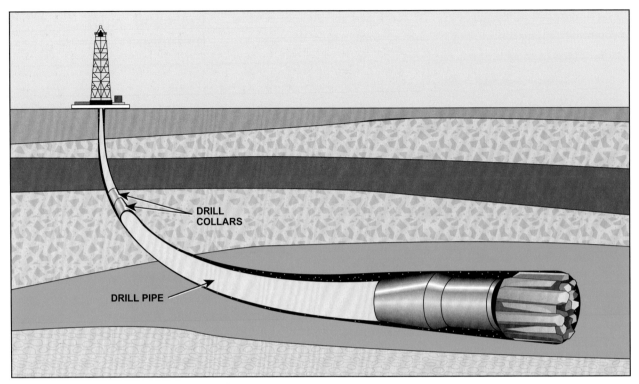

Figure 2-1.116. Here, the drill collars are below the vertical section of pipe and above the horizontal section.

Downhole Motor

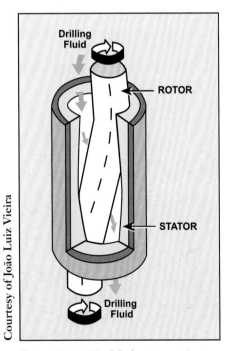

Courtesy of João Luiz Vieira

Figure 2-1.117. Mud motor section showing the flow path and the shaft (rotor) and housing (stator).

The basic principle of directional drilling is to force the bit to drill off-center and point in the desired direction. There are several ways to drill a directional hole, but the most common methods use a motor down the hole, called a *downhole motor*.

The downhole motor rotates only the drill bit connected to it, so the entire drill stem need not rotate to make hole. Downhole motors are hydraulic motors that function much the same as the mechanism described by R.J.L. Moineau, a French scientist in the 1930s who is credited with inventing the progressing cavity pump. The concept led to the Moineau principle, which is widely used in the petroleum drilling industry to drive drilling bits down at the bottom of the hole.

A downhole motor has a screw-shaped rotating shaft, or *rotor*, powered by the drilling fluid flowing through a housing called a *stator*, lined with a screw-shaped elastic substance with one lobe more than the rotor (fig. 2-1.117). The hydraulic power in the form of mud flow and mud pressure is converted by the mud motor into mechanical power to rotate the bit. While the mud flow passes through the motor, it forces the rotor to rotate clockwise, as shown in figure 2-1.117. Because the stator has one more lobe than the rotor, the pressure created by the mud pumps forces the fluid to move from one empty space between the rotor and the stator to the next. For this to happen, the helical-shaped rotor has to rotate.

To create the side force at the bit necessary to change the well trajectory, a bend in the lower section of the *bottomhole assembly* is needed. This bend can be created using a *bent sub* or by bending the mud motor housing.

A bent sub is a short piece of pipe with the lower pin tilted (fig. 2-1.118). Typically, the bend ranges from one-half to 3 degrees off vertical. The drilling crew places it in the drill stem between the bottommost drill collar and the downhole motor. The bent sub deflects the downhole motor and bit below it off vertical.

Some motors are built with a *bent housing*, which is a bend in the angle of the motor housing that deflects the drilling downhole. These motors are generally called *steerable motors*; they have a bend in the housing that can be adjusted or fixed. This innovation was a significant technological achievement for directional drilling operations because, unlike the bent-sub-plus-mud-motor solution, this type of motor can be rotated downhole. The normal operation of a bent sub was to slide the motor, changing the well trajectory as required, and then replace the bottomhole assembly for a conventional drilling assembly with stabilizers to resume drilling. If a correction to the trajectory was needed, this conventional assembly was pulled out of the hole and a new bent-sub-plus-mud-motor run was made until the required correction was completed and the bottomhole assembly was again replaced. But with steerable motors, operators can slide and rotate the bottomhole assembly without any problems, saving trip times (fig. 2-1.119). The bit rotates due to the mud motor, but the drill pipe does not rotate. The pipe just slides into the hole as the hole is drilled deeper.

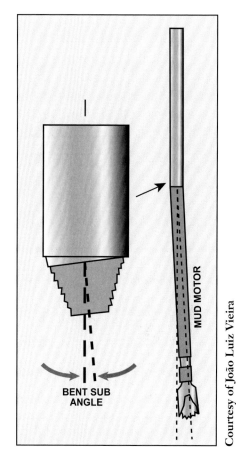

Figure 2-1.118. Bent sub

Courtesy of João Luiz Vieira

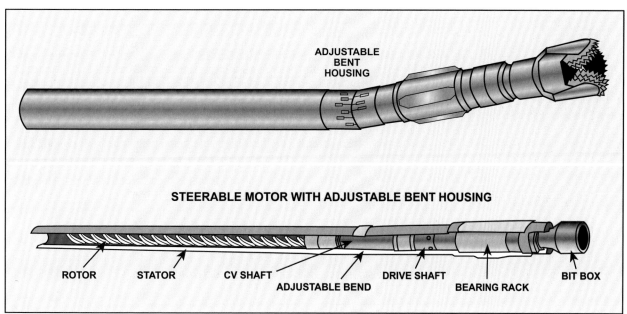

Figure 2-1.119. Steerable motor

Courtesy of João Luiz Vieira

Mud motors are available in many different configurations that give different output responses. The rotary speed, torque, working temperature, and maximum flow define the motor configuration for the specific application. Bit rotary speed and torque are inversely proportional in a mud motor, meaning the higher the speed, the lower the torque and vice versa. Due to the elastic properties in the stator, mud motors are sensitive to high temperatures and chemical characteristics of the mud. A directional driller is expected to choose the motor configuration and characteristics that best apply to the planned operation.

Orienting the Hole

Nonmagnetic drill collars are used to alleviate interference with steel tools.

A challenging decision involves how to orient the hole in the desired direction while drilling. One method uses a directional instrument containing a magnetic or *gyroscopic compass* and an *inclinometer*, which is an instrument that measures the angle of the hole. Drilling stops while the crew runs the instrument down to the bit and then retrieves it. This equipment is a type of survey tool. Survey tools allow operators to monitor the well inclination, direction, and orientation of the bit— also called the *tool face*. The trajectory of the hole is calculated using:

• Measured depth where the survey was taken

• Hole inclination and direction

This calculation is compared to the planned trajectory to define the intervention necessary to ensure the well reaches the target.

Another method to obtain the inclination, direction, and tool face is to use an instrument known as a *steering tool*. This type of tool continuously sends directional information up the hole through a conductive wireline to a monitor on the rig floor. Drilling need not stop for a survey to be taken using a steering tool. For most of the current directional drilling operations taking place worldwide, MWD has replaced other survey methods (see earlier section on MWD and LWD).

Because most directional sensors use the Earth's magnetic field to measure hole direction, extra care is needed to avoid magnetic interference from different steel tools in the drill string. The use of nonmagnetic tools where sensors are run and as spacers to eliminate or reduce interference from below and above the sensors is mandatory. Nonmagnetic drill collars, also known as *monels*, are used. Their length and position are calculated by taking into consideration the well inclination, the well direction, and the intensity of the Earth's magnetic field at the location.

Mud motors are the most commonly used tools in directional drilling operations. As the search for oil has led oil companies to produce from deeper reservoirs, in deeper waters, and in more challenging geological environments, the need for directional wells with more complex trajectories has increased. Sliding with mud motors is not easy when drilling extended-reach wells and 3D wells because of the increased torque and drag created by the friction between the drill string and the wellbore (fig. 2-1.120).

Rotary steerables are tools that can change the well trajectory while the string is rotating. In other words, there is no need to slide or stop the string rotation to perform a change in well trajectory. There are two ways the rotary steerable tools force the bit to drill in the desired direction:

- By pushing the bit: Tools that create a lateral force at the bit by using a pad or piston to cause action against the wellbore are called *push-the-bit rotary steerable systems* (fig. 2-1.121).

- By pointing the bit: Tools that create a lateral force by bending the shaft connected to the bit, pointing it in the desired direction, are called *point-the-bit rotary steerable systems* (fig. 2-1.122).

Rotary Steerable Tools

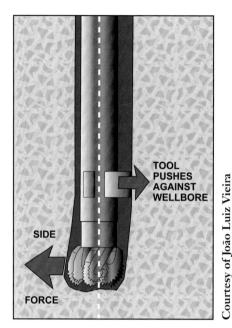

Figure. 2-1.121. Push-the-bit rotary steerable

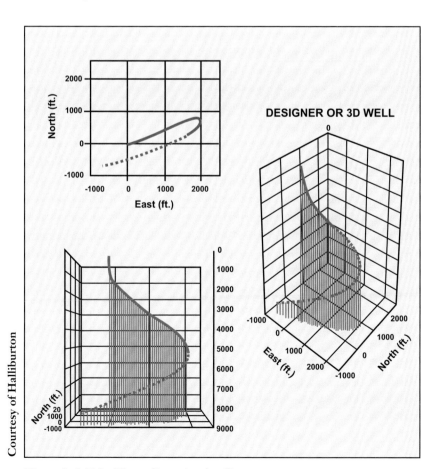

Figure 2-1.120. Three-dimensional well

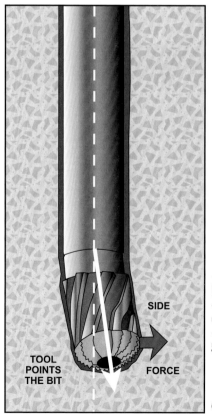

Figure 2-1.122. Point-the-bit rotary steerable

Vertical Drilling Tools

As mentioned earlier, drilling a vertical hole can be extremely challenging in certain environments. Regions with a history of tectonic activities normally show strong stresses in the formation layers. These stresses tend to deviate the bit from a vertical line while the well is being drilled. Areas close to salt domes and foothills are widely recognized for causing problems in vertical drilling.

In many cases, interventions in the well trajectory increase the cost of drilling. To minimize interventions and increase efficiencies, the industry has developed specialized tools for drilling vertically. The principles behind these tools are the same as those used for rotary steerables, and the same classifications can be applied. Because these tools are simpler than rotary steerables, their costs are generally lower, making them suitable for lower budget drilling projects.

Multilateral Wells

A *multilateral well* is a main wellbore with attached sidetrack wells, called *laterals* (fig. 2-1.123). The laterals can be completed as an *open-hole completion* or with *liners*. The openings in the casing from where the laterals are constructed are called *windows*. The competency of the formation at the window and the type of completion needed to drain the reservoir define what kind of junction is necessary.

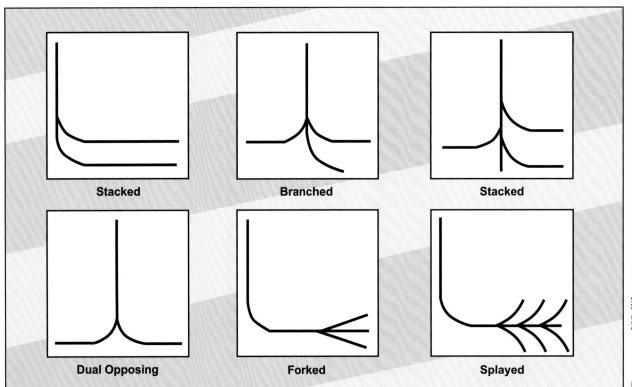

Courtesy of Halliburton

Figure 2-1.123. Types of multilateral well architectures

Copyright © The University of Texas at Austin—PETEX

A group formed by service company and operator representatives called *Technology Advancement of Multilaterals (TAML)* has created a classification system for the many different types of junctions available. These classifications include levels one through six, depending on complexity. Figure 2-1.124 further explains the classifications. Multilateral technology reduces overall well costs by using complex drainage architecture to increase the amount of reservoir exposure.

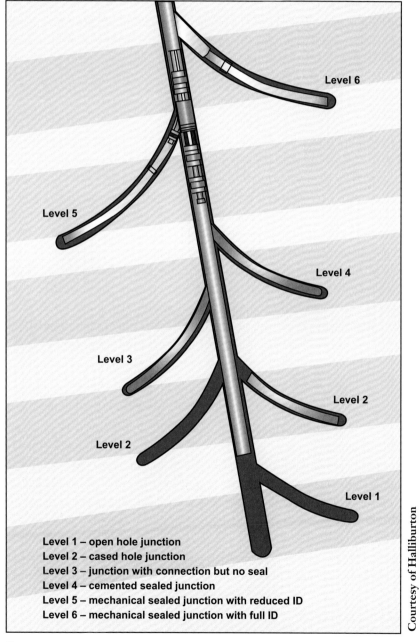

Level 6

Level 5

Level 4

Level 3

Level 2

Level 2

Level 1

Level 1 – open hole junction
Level 2 – cased hole junction
Level 3 – junction with connection but no seal
Level 4 – cemented sealed junction
Level 5 – mechanical sealed junction with reduced ID
Level 6 – mechanical sealed junction with full ID

Courtesy of Halliburton

Figure 2-1.124. Multilateral wells TAML classification

Advanced Engineering

Controlled directional drilling has become increasingly scientific. Advances in electronics that made computers more affordable in the middle 1980s completely changed directional drilling into an engineering discipline. Today, complex models accurately predict the behaviors of bottomhole assemblies, considering almost every detail in the drill string's mechanics and its interaction with the local geological profile, drilling fluids, and different types of drilling bits. New deflection tools, downhole sensors, and fast, reliable telemetry systems, along with complex computerized analysis of real-time-generated data, push the limits of well profiles. These limits are stretched to boundaries unimaginable a few short years ago. Advances in directional drilling continue at an accelerating pace as new technologies help provide cost and time savings in terms of production and rewards.

The Use of Mud Density

General zones of mud density:
- Overbalanced
- Managed pressure
- Underbalanced

Drilling fluid density, or mud weight, is the first line of defense against a well kick or blowout. Normally, the pressure in the wellbore is kept higher than the formation fluid pressure so there is no formation fluid influx into the wellbore. An influx entering the annulus of the well is referred to as a *well kick* and could possibly lead to a blowout if not controlled in a suitable manner. If the wellbore pressure is too high, the wellbore can rupture, creating large fractures. Drilling fluid enters the fracture and is lost; hence, the event is called *lost circulation*. If the wellbore pressure is high but below the fracture pressure, drilling rates will be very low. Drilling rates increase rapidly as the bottomhole pressure approaches the formation fluid pressure. These factors provide a great economic incentive for controlling the mud weight.

The bottomhole pressure has three contributing components:
- Mud weight
- Annular pressure to move the drilling fluid up the hole
- Drilled cuttings

When no fluid is being pumped down the drill pipe and up the annulus, bottomhole pressure is created by the mud weight and the quantity of cuttings in the annulus. This density is known as *Equivalent Static Density (ESD)*. When drilling fluid is flowing in the annulus, an additional pressure is applied at the bottom of the hole to move the fluid up the annulus (caused by the friction of the open hole and casing surfaces). These three components are usually expressed as *Equivalent Circulating Density (ECD)*.

There are three general zones of mud density:
- *Overbalanced density*, where the pressure created by the mud density is kept at, or more than, .5 pound per gallon (60 kilograms per cubic metre) higher than the pore pressure.

- *Managed pressure density*, where the mud density is about the same as the pore pressure. The well is drilled with a *rotating control device (RCD)* and a choke to hold some backpressure on the annulus.

- *Underbalanced density*, where the pressure created by the mud density is deliberately kept at less than the pore pressure. The well is normally drilled using an RCD to keep any wellbore fluid off of the drill rig floor.

When drilling a well, the density of the drilling mud is limited at the high end of the scale by *fracture pressure* and lost circulation; and at the bottom end of the allowable density by pore pressure (well kicks) or borehole stability (collapse pressure), as follows (fig. 2-1.125):

- In land drilling operations in some hard rock, the three limiting functions are not important because they fall outside the normal drilling fluid density range (normal density).

- In other areas, both land and marine, the upper and lower limit of mud density is set by statute. This might require the mud density to be at least equal to .5 pound per gallon greater than the equivalent pore pressure gradient. Another example is that the mud density must be high enough that a certain size well kick would not cause lost circulation at the shoe of the last casing (normal density).

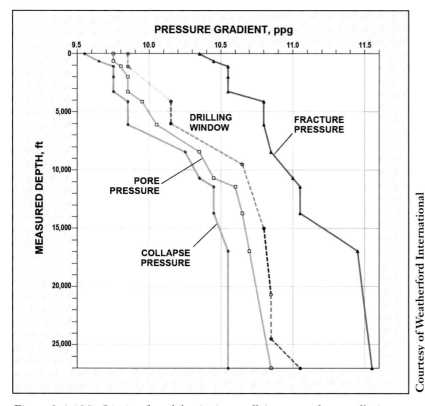

Figure 2-1.125. Limits of mud density in a well (ppg=pounds per gallon)

- In marine drilling in softer rock, the mud density that prevents a well kick or that properly supports the wellbore, and the mud density that causes lost circulation, approach each other, and there is a limited operational density range (managed pressure density) (fig. 2-1.126).

- In some areas of hard rock, the mud density is deliberately kept below the pore pressure because there is no danger of permeable formations that could cause a well kick (low pressure reservoirs), or the well is kept under control by an RCD and choke to allow only a limited amount of flow from the reservoir (underbalanced density).

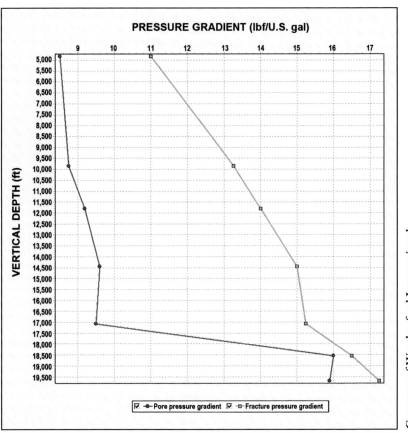

Figure 2-1.126. In some wells, the pore pressure approaches the fracture pressure.

Normal Mud Density

In the majority of wells, the mud density is programmed to be at about .5 pound per gallon (60 kilograms per cubic metre) higher than the pore pressure (.5 pound per gallon of mud density is normally enough to balance the bottomhole pressure when the pump is turned off and the drill pipe is pulled from the well). When the bottomhole pressure becomes high enough to cause lost circulation in the top of the hole, casing is set to protect the upper formations and the wellbore against lost circulation. Then the mud density is set to be higher than the new pore pressure, and drilling starts again.

For many years, it was simpler and perhaps cheaper to drill with a heavy mud weight and run casing when lost circulation or hole problems became too severe. Starting in 1966 with new concepts of reading formation pressure from drilling rate (*d exponent*) and well logs, the industry started to understand the cost in time and materials of lost circulation and well kicks.

As wells became deeper (and temperature and wellbore conditions became more critical), the drilling windows became narrower. This trend has cumulated in this decade with some new ideas and techniques that include *managed pressure drilling (MPD)*, wellbore strengthening, expandable casing, and casing or liner drilling. A relatively new technology, MPD helps a driller more precisely control annular pressures in the wellbore so that drilling-related problems can be prevented. MPD is a method of extending the wellbore deeper through the critical well kick or lost circulation zone without having to run an extra casing string.

Almost everyone familiar with drilling operations has seen the condition where the wellbore stays full or almost full of drilling fluid but will not circulate. That is because when the pumps are turned on, the flow of drilling fluid is subject to friction along the wellbore, the drill pipe, and within the fluid itself. The more viscous the drilling fluid, the greater is the friction. Friction is least with shallow air drilling and greatest with heavy drilling fluids in deep, slim holes. So eventually, in deep holes, every time the pumps are turned on, the friction will prevent flow, resulting in continual lost circulation (fig. 2-1.127). The simple solution is to reduce the mud density to compensate for the increased *ECD*. However, if the drilling fluid density (mud weight) is reduced to where it will circulate, the well could kick or the borehole could collapse.

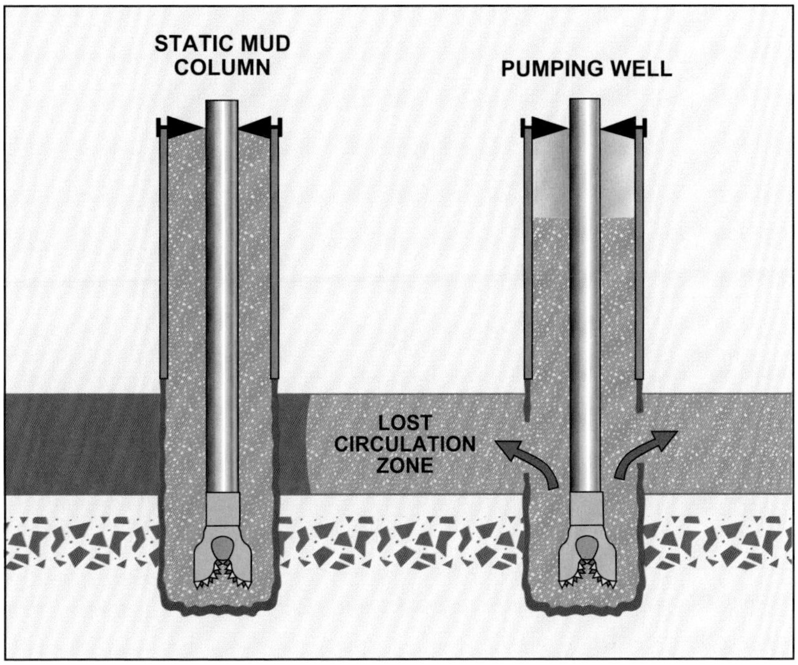

Managed Pressure Drilling and Density

Deeper wells brought new techniques to drilling:
- Managed pressure drilling
- Wellbore strengthening
- Expandable casing
- Liner drilling

Figure 2-1.127. Static mud column versus pumping mud column with lost circulation

Courtesy of Bill Rehm

Lost Circulation and Well Kicks

MPD is a solution to the problem of lost circulation and well kicks, allowing the driller to go deeper before running a new string of casing. The basic idea is simple:

- Reduce the drilling fluid density enough to compensate for the increased friction or ECD when the pumps are turned on so there is no lost circulation.

- Make up the loss in bottomhole pressure when the pump is turned off by holding the choke pressure at the surface annulus such that no well kick or borehole collapse will occur.

There is a complication to this simple solution. As the mud pumps are turned on, the friction pressure increases as the pump rate increases. The opposite occurs when the pump is turned off, causing a major problem for connections and trips. The solution is to vary the choke pressure depending on the pump rate to achieve constant bottomhole pressure (fig. 2-1.128). However, the friction pressure is not always linear, so the increase in choke pressure as the pump is slowed is not the same for every 10 or 20 strokes reduction in pump rate. Instead, it varies according to the flowrate and drilling fluid properties. While this change can be calculated, most systems depend on either a probe in the drill pipe that measures and transmits the bottomhole pressure or actual borehole observation and experience.

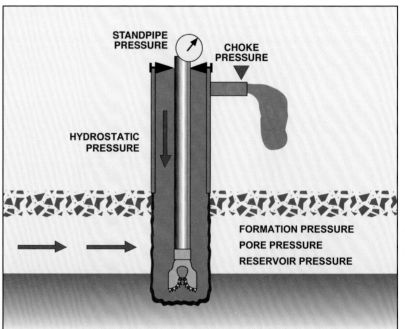

Figure 2-1.128. Controlling bottomhole pressure with surface choke and RCD

Most of the time, MPD is performed by a service company using a computer-controlled choke that is balanced against a measure of the pump rate or pump flow. This manages the annular surface pressure to control the change in bottomhole pressure. The system might also use precise flow meters to measure flow in and out, instead of depending on pump rate alone. This can also be done manually by creating a table or graph of surface annular pressure versus pump rate. Most service company systems also use a small triplex pump that pumps across the annulus before the choke to compensate for any sudden pump stop. Usually the systems take about 1 to 2 minutes to start and stop the rig pumps to allow time for the choke and mud system to react.

Pressure Control

Because a major problem is turning the pumps on and off, a further solution or enhancement would be constant circulation, where the pumps could run during connections and trips (fig. 2-1.129):

Constant Circulation

- A system is currently available that allows constant circulation and can be used in large-scale marine operations and on large drilling rigs.
- Another type of system uses "constant circulating subs" on each connection to maintain circulation (see fig. 2-1.129)
- The dual-casing string system is a simple method of providing a constant circulating system based on the depth of the last casing string (see fig. 2-1.129)

These systems are generally (although not always) used along with a commercial MPD system.

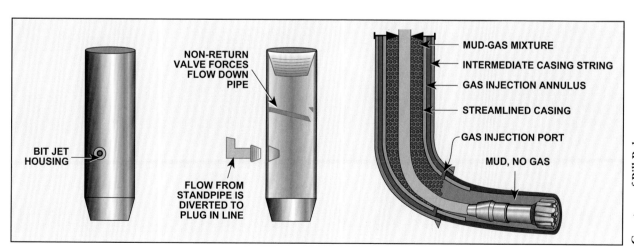

NON-RETURN VALVE FORCES FLOW DOWN PIPE

MUD-GAS MIXTURE

INTERMEDIATE CASING STRING

GAS INJECTION ANNULUS

STREAMLINED CASING

GAS INJECTION PORT

MUD, NO GAS

BIT JET HOUSING

FLOW FROM STANDPIPE IS DIVERTED TO PLUG IN LINE

Courtesy of Bill Rehm

Figure 2-1.129. Constant circulating sub

Underbalanced Drilling and Density

The opposite of both overbalanced mud density and managed pressure drilling philosophy is underbalanced drilling. The mud density is deliberately kept lower than the pore pressure to either protect a reservoir or increase the drilling rate as with gas and air drilling.

In hard rock areas, drilling with air or gas increases drilling rates above those achieved with liquid drilling fluids. Frequently, the drilling rates are more than ten times higher when using air or gas relative to normal drilling fluid practices. Gas and air drilling is only effective in dry rock. In hard rock like limestone, dolomite, hard sandstones, and basalt or granite, the effect on shale varies, with some shale dry enough to air drill.

Underbalanced drilling uses some of the same equipment as MPD operations. While drilling, reservoir fluids are brought to the surface. Provisions must be made to handle and store water or oil and flare gas (fig. 2-1.130). The minimum equipment required for underbalanced drilling includes:

- Rotating control device
- Choke and manifold

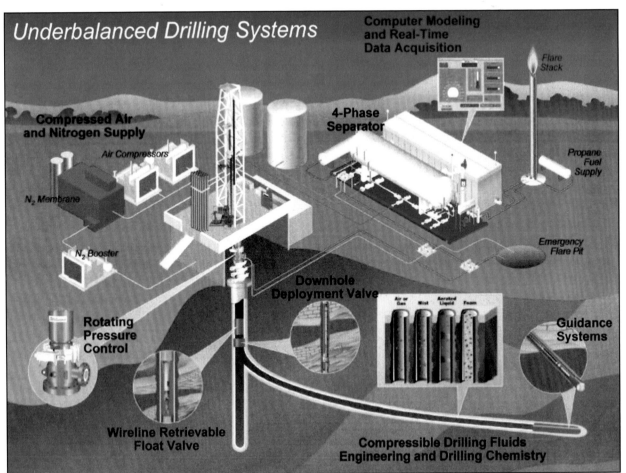

Figure 2-1.130. Underbalanced setup showing compressors, oil storage, and flare line

- Separator–gas/oil/drilling fluid
- Storage for oil or water
- Flare line and flare
- Compressors or gas source

Depleted and subnormally pressured formations form the majority of underbalanced drilling projects. The underbalanced condition protects the reservoir from an influx of drilling fluids and cuttings that can cause skin damage and reduce the output of the well.

Underbalanced can be accomplished with normal drilling fluids in formations that were high pressured but are now lower pressured because of depletion. Some of the Arab zone limestone in Saudi Arabia and the Trucial States of the Persian Gulf region are being drilled underbalanced with non-damaging drilling fluids. The drilling fluid might be an oil or water or water-based fluid depending on the reservoir content. The density of the fluid could be as low as 7.5 pounds per gallon (diesel, mineral, or synthetic oil) or as high as 18 pounds per gallon but is generally in the range of 8 to 10 pounds per gallon. In all cases, the pressure exerted by the column of fluid is less than the reservoir pressure.

Underbalanced with Light Drilling Fluid

Flow from the reservoir is controlled by mud density and sometimes, by exerting choke pressure to throttle the reservoir flow. For example, oil flow from the Bakken Formation in North Dakota (United States) dilutes and changes the properties of the *invert oil mud* used to drill the reservoir, so the flow from the Bakken is controlled by closely controlling the density of the oil mud. Choke pressure is used often, but not always.

Other methods of underbalanced drilling use a liquid plus gas or air—a *multi-phase fluid*—to lighten the drilling fluid column. The bottomhole pressure is reduced by adding gas to the drilling fluid column and displacing some of the liquid drilling fluid from the hole, reducing the pressure from the mud column. (General information on Air or Gas Drilling can be found later in this chapter.)

Multiphase Drilling Fluids

Gaseated Mud

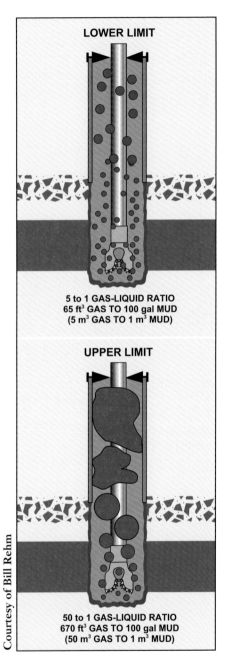

LOWER LIMIT

5 to 1 GAS-LIQUID RATIO
65 ft³ GAS TO 100 gal MUD
(5 m³ GAS TO 1 m³ MUD)

UPPER LIMIT

50 to 1 GAS-LIQUID RATIO
670 ft³ GAS TO 100 gal MUD
(50 m³ GAS TO 1 m³ MUD)

Courtesy of Bill Rehm

Figure 2-1.131. Different gas volumes in a gaseated hole

Figure 2-1.132. Gaseous systems: methods of adding gas (A) parasite string, (B) bull heading, (C) jet sub, and (D) dual-casing string

Gaseated mud, also called a gas/liquid mixture, is made by adding a gas (air, nitrogen, or natural gas) to the drilling fluid. The drilling fluid is normally a low-solids water or oil system. The oil is invariably a diesel or synthetic oil or dead crude oil. The gas displaces some of the fluid from the wellbore and lightens the fluid column. On the other hand, the increased velocity of the fluid being displaced from the hole increases friction, which adds to the bottomhole pressure. Calculation of actual bottomhole pressure with various volumes of gas and liquid is complex, because the gas occupies a different volume in the wellbore as pressure in the hole decreases toward the top (fig. 2-1.131). These calculations are made by one of the many underbalanced drilling models currently available.

The advantage of a gaseated system is that a liquid compatible with the reservoir can be used. Almost any drilling fluid can be gaseated. The problem with gaseated systems is the gas and fluid tend to separate unless kept mixed and under pressure. Mixing is generally the result of rotation of the drill pipe and the natural turbulent flow of the drilling fluid. The surface annulus is kept under pressure, normally at 100 to 300 pounds per square inch to keep the gas bubbles small, which helps keep them mixed.

There are several ways to add the gas to the drill fluid (fig. 2-1.132):

- The most common is by simply *bullheading, or injecting*, the gas into the standpipe along with the drilling fluid.

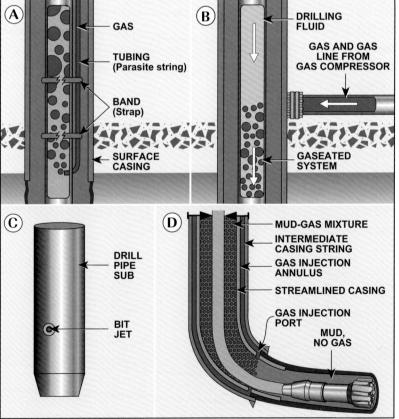

Courtesy of Bill Rehm

- With gas injected at the standpipe, a *jet sub* can be added to the drill string near the bottom of the surface casing to allow about 20% of the gaseated fluid to escape to the annulus. This is considered a *poor boy* type of gas lift.
- The gas can be added through a *parasite string* of tubing run alongside the surface casing. This makes it possible to keep the gas flowing while making a connection.
- The gas can be added by means of a dual-casing string, as described in the earlier section on MPD. The dual-casing annulus allows the gas to be added deep in the well and maintains constant circulation.

Foam is a very different drilling fluid. It has a high lifting capacity, even with a low annular velocity, so small volumes of water can be used. This allows the foam column to be extremely light because it is made up of mostly air (or gas) (fig. 2-1.133). For comparison, the closest common analog to drilling foam is shaving foam in the way it is compressed in a can and expands when released. With drilling foam, the foam bubbles are very small at the bottom of the hole, and the water is the continuous phase. When drilling foam is released to the pit, it is about 95% gas. The gas is the continuous phase, and the water is either free or tied up in the bubbles. When the bubbles burst in the pit, the rest of the water is liberated.

Foam for drilling a 6-inch (15-centimetre) hole might use as little as 20 gallons per minute of water while using about 1,500 standard cubic feet per minute of gas or air. The emulsion of gas in the fluid forms a flexible sort of plug that lifts cuttings out of the hole. In some workover operations where foam was used to clean frac sand out of the hole, the foam at the flow line held about 50% by volume of sand.

Foam Drilling

Foam drilling:
- Is beneficial when water supply is limited
- Has a high lifting capacity

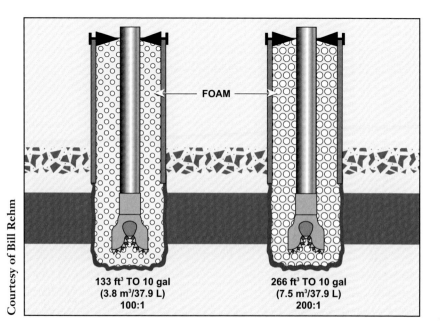

Courtesy of Bill Rehm

133 ft³ TO 10 gal
(3.8 m³/37.9 L)
100:1

266 ft³ TO 10 gal
(7.5 m³/37.9 L)
200:1

Figure 2-1.133. Different foam volumes

At present, most foam is used in workover operations to clean out a hole that has low bottomhole pressure. It is also a good fluid to use with milling operations because it easily carries shavings out of the hole.

Foam is not used as commonly as gaseated systems in drilling operations. However, it has been used successfully in Canada to drill gas fields and in North Africa to drill fractured oil reservoirs. It has been used extensively to drill in the depleted Hugoton Gas Field in western Kansas (United States), and as a surface hole drilling fluid in the Arctic and locations with fractured surface formations.

Use of foam drilling could increase as more reservoirs are depleted and require a very light fluid with a high lifting capacity.

The Key to Successful Drilling

Drilling fluid density is an important part of properly drilling a hole and protecting the reservoir. Proper use of density and the surface choke system along with an understanding of ECD (that is, increased bottomhole pressure due to friction when mud is flowing) is the key to successful and efficient drilling operations.

UNCONVENTIONAL DRILLING

Shale gas, produced from shale rock, is an increasingly important source of natural gas. In the past decade, interest has spread from the United States to Canada, Europe, Asia, and Australia. Shale is a fine-grained sedimentary rock composed of clay and tiny fragments of other minerals such as quartz and calcite. Shales generally have insufficient permeability to allow fluid flow, so most shales are not commercial sources of natural gas.

Shale gas areas are known as source plays because the shale is the source rock where the gas originates. In conventional plays, the gas migrates from the source rock to a permeable formation which is considered the reservoir.

Production of shale gas in commercial quantities requires extensive fractures to provide enough permeability. Modern technology in hydraulic fracturing has provided the means to create the artificial fractures necessary to access the gas via horizontal drilling methods. Because of the expense of hydraulic fracturing and horizontal drilling, shale gas tends to cost more to produce than gas from conventional wells. However, the size of the shale gas fields are vast, offering economy of scale. The gas might be located close to existing gas lines, making the overall investment worthwhile. For example, the Marcellus field in the northeastern United States is estimated to contain 200 trillion cubic feet of gas.

North America led the wave of development and production of shale gas with the economic success of the Barnett Shale play in Texas, spurring the search for other sources of shale gas in other regions. Shale gas remains one of several types of unconventional sources of energy along with coalbed methane, tight sandstones, and methane hydrates.

Steam-assisted gravity drainage (SAGD) has been used for a number of years, but its use has increased as directional drilling techniques and new completion techniques for horizontal wells have improved (fig. 2-1.134). Although largely a production process, SAGD uses drilling technology to inject steam into a well to heat the oil and lower the viscosity, which allows the oil to drain into the producing well and be pumped to the surface. This process is being used in the Athabasca Oil Sands in Alberta, Canada, and for the heavy crude in the Orinoco Basin of Venezuela where viscosity is so high the oil will not flow unless heated.

SAGD is used in areas such as the Athabasca sands where existing wells produce from *cold production* techniques or other types of enhanced steam-assisted production techniques (*see* Part 3. Production). The new wells must be designed to avoid collision with existing wells. Designs can vary, from one drilled above another, to multilaterals or a series of four or more wells. The wells are drilled in one direction with another group drilling perpendicular and below those wells. The preferred drilling technique is rotary steering using electromagnetic surveying techniques to drill to about 3,300 feet (1,000 metres) in length.

Steam-Assisted Gravity Drainage

Figure 2-1.134. Since SAGD drilling techniques were introduced, production efficiencies have increased in heavy oil reserves.

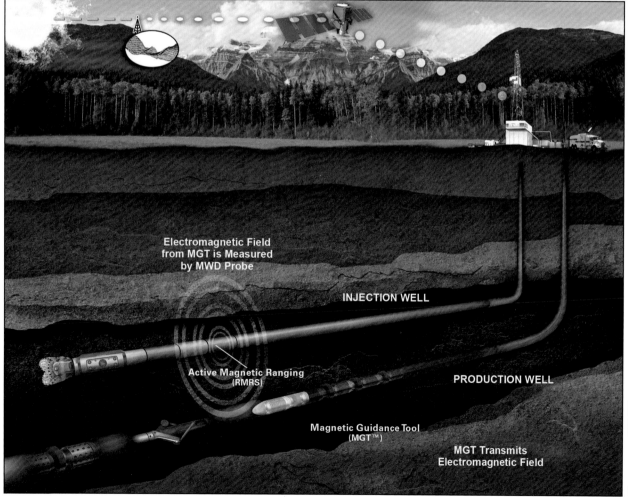

Electromagnetic Field
from MGT is Measured
by MWD Probe

INJECTION WELL

Active Magnetic Ranging
(RMRS)

PRODUCTION WELL

Magnetic Guidance Tool
(MGT™)

MGT Transmits
Electromagnetic Field

Courtesy of Halliburton

Longer extended-reach wells can be drilled, but distributing the steam in the wellbores becomes more difficult. The most economical and ecologically friendly plan is from 25 to 30 wells from one pad. These wells can be a combination of vertical, deviated, and horizontal wells.

Creating the steam needed to heat the reservoirs requires large amounts of gas, coal, or part of the produced oil. A large quantity of fresh water is also required to create the steam. Even though some of the water is recovered with the oil, water consumption remains high and can be a limiting factor to applying SAGD cost-effectively.

AIR OR GAS DRILLING

A highly successful alternate method of drilling with limited application is air or gas drilling. This method is useful when drilling through a depleted zone where the pressure drops off considerably.

Air or gas drilling can bring these results:

- Higher penetration rates

- Greater footage per bit

- Lower bit cost

Penetration is faster because air or gas cleans the bottom of the hole more effectively than mud. Mud is denser than air or gas and tends to hold the cuttings on the bottom of the hole. As a result, the bit cannot make hole as efficiently because the bit redrills some of the old cuttings instead of being constantly exposed to fresh, undrilled formation.

Air or *gas drilling* has more disadvantages than advantages:

- The hazard of fire or explosion is always present. Because air or gas does not create significant bottomhole pressure, drilling into a high-pressure formation is dangerous.

- Air and gas cannot prevent formation fluids from entering the well, and most deep wells eventually come across water-bearing formations, making the threat of water a problem. If there is much water in the wellbore, the air or gas might not be able to lift the water and cuttings to the surface.

- If the wall of the hole tends to slough or cave into the hole, the drill stem might stick, making air or gas circulation impossible.

- Corrosion of the drill stem can occur, although chemicals have been developed to reduce this problem.

To drill with air or gas, the contractor moves large compressors and related equipment to the site. Usually, only part of the hole is drilled with air or gas. Then casing is run and the rig is changed over to use drilling mud.

Air or gas is not circulated in the sense that it is used over and over again. Rather, it makes one trip from the compressors, down the drill stem, out the bit, and up the annulus back to the surface where it is blown out a *blooey line*, or vent pipe (fig. 2-1.135).

Air or gas drilling can result in:
- **High penetration rates**
- **Greater footage per bit**
- **Lower bit cost**

When air or gas is intentionally added to drilling mud, it is called *aerated mud*. This type mud has been successfully used to prevent lost circulation, which occurs when drilling mud leaks out of the borehole into a formation. The mud does not return to the surface but instead is lost downhole. When air or gas is added to the mud, it reduces the amount of pressure the mud exerts on the downhole formation and, therefore, helps prevent lost circulation.

Recently, newer additives such as glass beads and other agents to lighten the mud weight have been introduced and can be used in tandem or independently of air drilling.

Figure 2-1.135. Skid-mounted compressors furnish the high-pressure air used on this rotary rig for drilling (top). The air is blowing a cloud of dust out the blooey line (bottom).

FISHING

Fishing is the drilling term for retrieving an object, called a *fish*, from a wellbore. A fish can be part or all of the drill stem stuck or lost in the hole. A fish can also be smaller pieces of equipment, called *junk*, such as bit cones, hand tools, pieces of steel, or other items in the hole that cannot be drilled around or drilled out.

Freeing Stuck Pipe

To spot oil means to circulate oil down the drill stem onto the stuck pipe.

Drill pipe or drill collars get stuck in the hole for several reasons:

- The hole or swelling shale might collapse around the pipe.
- The pipe might become stuck in a *dogleg* or *keyseat*.
- Pressure can hold the drill collars so securely to the wall of the hole that no amount of pulling can free the pipe.

The most common reason for a stuck pipe is swelling or sloughing of the surrounding formation rock. When drilling through certain types of formation, in particular shale, water in the drilling mud tends to transfer to the *interstices*, or pores, of the rock. The water in drilling mud is called *interstitial water*. This can cause the formation rock to expand or slough off in thin layers that can fill the hole with debris. Either process can trap the pipe in the hole.

Pipe can also become stuck in a *keyseat*, which is caused by a *dogleg* (angle) or a very crooked section of hole (fig. 2-1.136). The drill pipe tends to lean against the side of the dogleg, and as it rotates, the pipe digs out a new, smaller hole about the diameter of the pipe in the side of the main borehole. Then, when the drill stem is pulled from the hole, a tool joint of the drill pipe or the wider drill collars can jam into the keyseat. When this happens, the equipment cannot be freed simply by pulling on it.

Using a top drive helps with keyseat problems because the pipe can be rotated while it is pulled. The rotation usually allows the tool joints, drill collars, and bottomhole assembly components to bounce off the keyseat while the driller is hoisting the string out of the hole. For severe keyseating, there is a special tool called a keyseat wiper designed to ream the groove of the keyseat. This increases its diameter and avoids change to the wellbore diameter that causes the pipe to hang up.

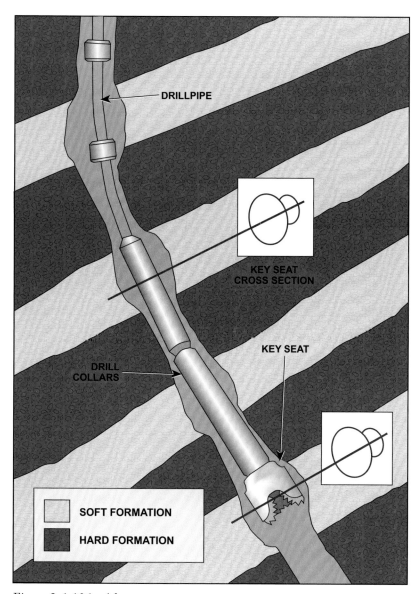

Figure 2-1.136. A keyseat

To free *wall-stuck* pipe, the crew can *spot oil* around the stuck portion and *jar on the drill stem*. To *spot oil* means to circulate oil (diesel oil or the base oil of oil-based muds) or some other lubricant down the drill stem and into the annulus onto the stuck pipe. To jar on the drill stem means to install a special device—a *drilling jar*—on top of the drill stem so the driller can strike heavy blows upward or downward on the stuck pipe. Spotting oil and jarring usually free wall-stuck pipe.

A free-point indicator determines the point where the pipe is stuck.

If pipe remains stuck in spite of spotting oil and jarring, the next step is to use a *free-point indicator* to determine the point at which the pipe is stuck (fig. 2-1.137). The indicator is lowered inside the drill stem, then the driller stretches the drill stem to pick it up. The indicator induces a magnetic field in the pipe and sends a signal to a meter on the surface. If the indicator is opposite a point where the pipe is free, the pipe stretches significantly and the meter registers strong signals by moving the needle rapidly. However, when the indicator is opposite the point where the pipe is stuck, the pipe stretches very little, the signals are weak, and the needle moves only slightly. By noting the depth at which the needle movement is slight, the crew can determine the stuck point.

Once the location of the stuck pipe is determined the drill crew can *back off*, or unscrew the pipe above the stuck point. They use a small explosive charge inside the drillstring much like someone hitting the lid of a hard-to-open fruit jar to get it unscrewed:

- The crew positions a *string shot* opposite a tool joint several joints above the stuck point. A string shot is a long, string-like explosive charge usually run below the free-point indicator.

- Before the string shot is set off, the driller turns the rotary to the left to back off the pipe.

- When detonated, the string shot loosens the threads of the pipe, allowing it to rotate and unscrew completely.

- Then, the crew trips the free pipe above the stuck pipe out of the hole. They usually back off the free pipe several joints above the stuck point to later run in additional tools. The extra joints of clear pipe guide the tools to the proper place.

- Sometimes, the crew can install a jar, run in and connect the fish, and try to free it.

- Sometimes, the crew may choose to cement the fish in place and drill around it. If they need to remove the stuck pipe left dangling in the hole, a special kind of pipe called *washover pipe*, or *washpipe*, is lowered into the hole over the stuck drill stem (the fish) and recovery operations begins with circulating and rotating.

- A special cutting device, the *rotary shoe*, on the bottom of the washpipe drills the shale or wall cake that is causing the pipe to stick.

- However, when all the material holding the fish is removed, the fish might fall to the bottom. To prevent this, the crew latches a *backoff connector* inside the washpipe (fig. 2-1.138). The connector is made up on the top of the fish before washover begins.

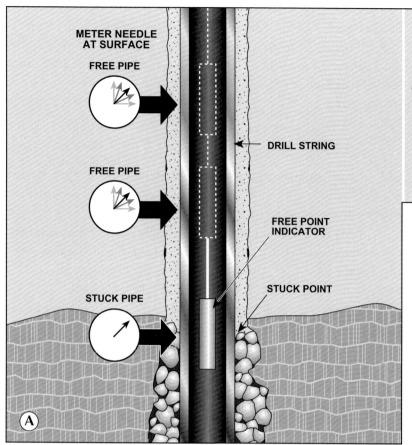

Figure 2-1.137. A. A free-point indicator locates stuck pipe. B. Diagram showing forces at work during differential sticking.

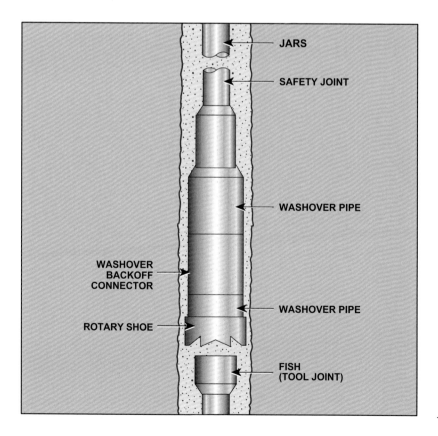

Figure 2-1.138. A backoff connector is used on stuck pipe inside the washover pipe to keep the drill pipe from falling when freed.

- As washover proceeds, the connector is designed to remain stationary on top of the fish. When the fish is washed free and starts to fall, the crew activates the connector. The connector grips the inside of the washpipe and prevents the fish from falling.
- After all the shale or wall cake is drilled out, the crew pulls both the washpipe and the drill stem secured by the backoff connector inside the washpipe out of the hole.

The fishing process is slightly different if the drill stem is stuck in a keyseat:

- The process begins by sending the free-point indicator and string shot down inside the pipe. When the crew locates the stuck point, they remove all but the last five or six joints above the stuck drill pipe or drill collar so the top of the fish is in the main borehole and not in the keyseat.
- Then, they lower a bumper jar down the hole, attach it to the fish, and jar the fish loose from the keyseat.
- Finally, a reaming device called a *keyseat wiper* made up on top of the jar reams the keyseat out to normal size.

Once the keyseat is reamed out, tool joints and drill collars should pass through without difficulty. If the rig has a top drive, the crew can rotate and pull at the same time to avoid sticking in a keyseat.

Another fishing situation occurs when pipe breaks in two. Such breaks, called *twistoffs*, are usually the result of metal fatigue or damage. Fishing for twisted-off pipe is often a simple operation, but in other cases can be difficult or even impossible.

Two commonly used tools for retrieving twistoffs are the *overshot* and the *spear*, used as follows (fig. 2-1.139):

- The crew runs an overshot or spear into the hole or the drill pipe until it contacts the top of the fish.

- An overshot goes over the outside of the fish and grips it firmly.

- A spear goes inside the fish and grips the inside of the pipe. A spear is used only when the diameter of the fish is close to the size of the hole, such as when a drill collar is involved.

Retrieving Twisted-Off Pipe

To repair a twistoff, an overshot and spear are used.

Figure 2-1.139. An overshot and spear are two commonly used tools for retrieving fish.

Courtesy of Logan Oil Tools Incorporated

- When the spear or overshot grips the fish, the crew pulls both the tool and the fish out of the hole together. Sometimes they use a special mill to smooth the top of the fish before running the overshot or spear. Milling the top of the fish makes attaching the fishing tool easier.

Fishing for Junk

Junk in the hole can bring drilling to a standstill because of the risk of damage to the bit. A variety of fishing tools can be brought in to retrieve junk. These devices include powerful magnets and special baskets through which mud can be circulated to capture junk and remove it from the hole.

SUMMARY

In the late 1800s, whale oil was used primarily for lamp lighting. As demand for lighting grew, crude oil became a necessity. The first oil-well was drilled in the Baku region of Azerbaijan in 1846. Demand for lighting began to grow within the United States and the quest began for a source other than whale oil.

Colonel Edwin Drake drilled the first well in the United States, which started the petroleum era in America. Countries such as Romania, Burma, India, and Venezuela also began drilling around this time. Cable-tool drilling and rotary drilling were the first forms of drilling. Cable-tool drilling used a wireline fastened to a mechanism to provide an up and down motion to dig a hole; whereas rotary drilling used the teeth of the bit to cut into the rock during rotation. This technology allowed for continuous drilling instead of having to stop drilling and remove cuttings. Advancements in technology have been made today, but rotary drilling is still the system of choice.

Rotary rigs now have mobility and can be moved from job site to job site, alleviating the cost of building a new platform at each workplace. Modern rotary systems include the rotating system and the circulating system. Drilling today begins with a contract between a company and an operator, ensuring that drilling is accomplished according to plan. Each operation involves a team of people including an operator, a contractor, a toolpusher, a driller, a derrickhand, rotary helpers, roughnecks, and lease hands. The drilling location and access are constructed to ensure that all operations can take place on site. The site and equipment are first prepared before drilling can begin.

Once drilling begins, several steps are taken to drill to final depth. When final depth is reached, further tests are performed to determine if the well will produce or should be abandoned. After drilling is finished, the site is cleaned and returned to its original condition.

Offshore drilling uses a variety of mobile units such as submersibles, jackups, inland barges, and drillships. Offshore drilling can also be conducted by constructing and moving a platform at the drilling site. These platforms stabilize themselves by legs sunk into the seafloor. These operations are more stable than mobile units and allow an operator to drill at deeper level formations in greater depths of water.

New drilling techniques improve safety and efficiency. Controlled directional drilling allows multiple wells to be drilled from one pad or platform, providing more flexibility regarding well location and design. This method even allows drilling beneath the ocean from a land drill site to improve economics and achieve less environmental impact. Air or gas drilling is used in certain formations to drill up to ten times faster than drilling with mud. Managed pressure drilling, including underbalanced drilling and other procedures, allows operators to drill wells that might otherwise be considered undrillable. Unconventional drilling methods, such as are those used with shale plays and coalbed methane, along with SAGD, are providing access to new reserves that will supply energy resources for years to come.

In this chapter:

- Definition of well control

- Crewmember roles in controlling a well

- Significance of wellbore pressure

- Process of shutting in a well

- Early detection signs and warnings

2.2
Well Control

Well control has been a critical component of operational aware-ness in oilfields for as long as wells have been drilled. A common example of a well that is out of control is Colonel Drake's historic well in Titusville, Pennsylvania, drilled in 1859. The explosion of oil at the surface of this well is classified as an *unscheduled event*. Today, such events are relatively rare and can be prevented due to proper planning, training, and communication.

A well is out of control when reservoir gas or fluids are flowing in a way that cannot be regulated or stopped. A well in an *underbalanced* condition can cause an unrecognized influx of either gas or fluids—or both—that has reached critical limits, beyond what normal operations can handle or contain (see section on The Use of Mud Density in *Part 2, Chapter 2.1: Drilling Operations*). This type of situation can cause a dramatic release to the surface, called a *blowout*, and present serious dangers to workers and resources (fig. 2-2.1).

AN OUT-OF-CONTROL WELL

Figure 2-2.1. A blowout and resulting fire at Greenhill Well in Timbalier Bay, Louisiana

Source: National Oceanic and Atmospheric Administration (NOAA)

The most spectacular and hazardous blowout is a *surface blowout*, which is just as the term implies: when reservoir fluids escape from a well at the surface. Surface blowouts can:

Two types of blowouts:
• Surface
• Downhole

- Lead to massive environmental damage and pollution
- Cause injury or fatality to people nearby
- Waste valuable resources by the unmanaged release of oil and gas
- Harm the long-term ability of the reservoir to produce
- Destroy a drilling rig and other expensive equipment at the well site

Uncontrolled flows that occur within a well underground can also create a *downhole blowout*. This occurs when a high-pressure reservoir is allowed to flow fluids into a lower pressure reservoir at a different well depth. A downhole blowout does not cause fluids to escape at the surface but rather wastes hydrocarbons by flowing them into other reservoirs where they can become unrecoverable. This situation might also damage the ability of the flowing reservoir to sustain long-term flow. It also can, and most probably will, charge the lower pressure zone with high pressure and create a future drilling hazard in the area.

First Line of Defense

Crewmembers are the first line of defense against blowouts. Each person is charged with monitoring changes in the well, because even the smallest change can lead to a serious problem. If not responded to properly in time, a recognized influx—called a *kick*—can become a disastrous blowout (fig. 2-1.2). Kicks and blowouts can be contained by controlling wellbore conditions; namely, pressure at the first sign of danger. It is important to understand that all blowouts occur through some form of human error, such as:

- Underestimated reservoir pressures
- Improperly controlled drilling mud weight
- Missed or misinterpreted signs of a kick
- Improper operation of the blowout preventers
- Poor maintenance or incorrect design or installation of prevention equipment

Courtesy of Great White Pressure Control

Kicks and blowouts are contained by controlling wellbore conditions such as balanced pressure.

Figure 2-2.2. Blowouts are dangerous, destructive, and avoidable if warning signs are recognized by watchful workers.

Wellbore Pressure

Pressure in the wellbore must be balanced in one of three ways:
- Subnormally pressured
- Normally pressured
- Abnormally pressured

All well control problems are related to an imbalance of wellbore pressures. The drilling and production fluids act as a primary barrier during operations and hydrostatically balance the well (fig. 2-2.3). As the Earth's formation fluids enter the wellbore, it pushes out the drilling mud. Drillers have to increase or decrease mud weight (density) to counteract such pressure. As little as 50 pounds per square inch of pressure can cause significant imbalance and subsequent problems. When this positive fluid pressure is not properly controlled downhole, a kick will likely occur. If the kick is not brought under control quickly, a blowout can occur.

Wellbore pressure can be subnormally pressured, normally pressured, or abnormally pressured. No matter the circumstances, the right balance is required. The drilling engineer and the mud engineer are responsible for predicting the necessary mud weight, or density. The derrickhand is responsible for mixing the mud at the correct weight. To keep the pressure inside the wellbore higher than the pressures in the reservoirs being drilled, the derrickhand sometimes increases weight by adding *barium sulfate (barite)* to the mud.

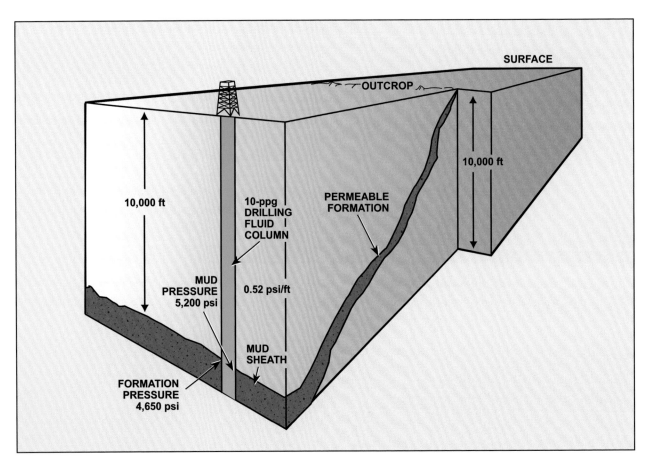

Figure 2-2.3. Hydrostatic pressure in a wellbore holds back formation pressure.

An obvious sign of an influx is an increasing level of mud in the active mud pits as reservoir fluids enter the borehole and push the mud out of the well. If the pumps are turned off during a kick, the well will flow on its own. Once the crew detects an influx, the well is *shut in* to slow the kick's migration to the surface. With the wellbore shut in, the pressure can be stabilized and the influx stopped. Then a determination of how to properly rebalance the well takes place by adjusting the mud weight and using pumps and choke manifolds to remove the influx from the well.

To shut in a well, crewmembers use *blowout preventers (BOPs)*. A BOP is a series of valves installed on the wellhead to prevent the escape of fluids from the casing and drill pipe (figs. 2-2.4). Several BOPs might be stacked on top of one another for maximum control. There are different types of BOPs. They generally consist of a special type of preventer on top and sealing *rams* positioned below. A BOP is typically set up as follows.

Shutting In a Well

Blowout preventers are a series of valves installed on the wellhead to prevent fluids from escaping.

Figure 2-2.4. Typical land BOP stack

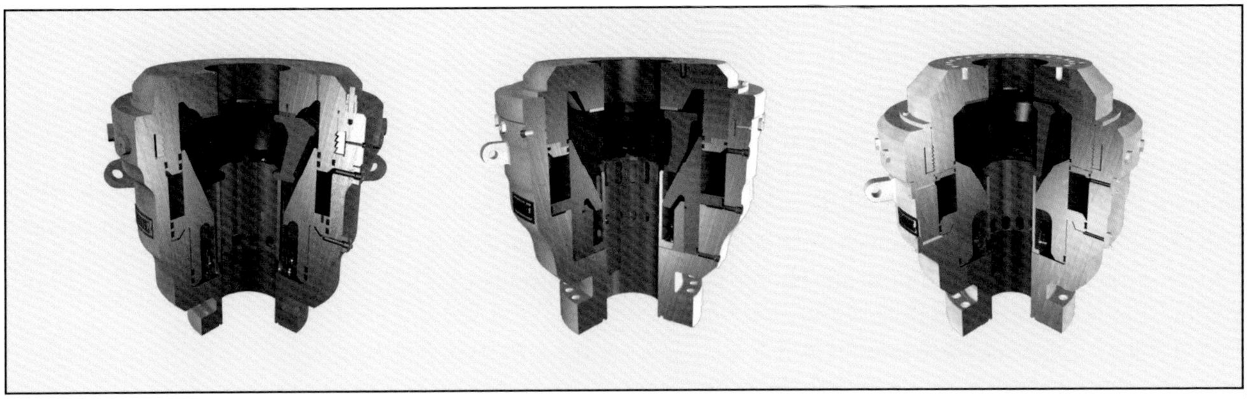

Figure 2-2.5. Types of annular blowout preventers: Hydril GL (left), Hydril GK small (center), Hydril GX (right)

The top BOP is always an *annular preventer* that can close and seal around any shape of pipe protruding through the preventer (fig. 2-2.5). This preventer can also close over an open hole when necessary. The annular preventer acts like a bag that inflates around the drill pipe or tubing. It is made of solid rubber with steel-reinforcing elements inside that are compressed to squeeze around the pipe in the hole. The pipe rams quickly close the external side of the pipe with fitted block seals specific to the type and size of pipe (fig. 2-2.6). Full-opening safety valves can be used to seal the interior of the pipe in these situations, cutting off pressure on the hole.

The ram-type preventers below the annular are a combination of pipe rams and blind rams:

- *Pipe rams* can close and seal only around a piece of pipe that matches the size of the hole machined into the ram. Some pipe rams have an adjustable feature allowing them to seal around more than one size pipe, but only within a limited range. These are called *variable bore rams*.

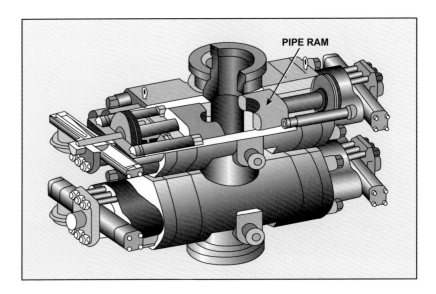

PIPE RAM

Figure 2-2.6. Cutaway diagram of a pipe ram

- *Blind rams* can close and seal over an open hole but will not close around a piece of pipe.
- *Shear rams* are a special type of blind ram that can cut any pipe in the ram and seal over the hole created after severing the pipe.

BOPs used onshore or on bottom-supported offshore rigs are installed beneath the floor of the rig. They can be operated manually or hydraulically. On floating offshore rigs, the BOPs are installed on the top of the wellhead on the ocean floor (fig. 2-2.7). They are operated either hydraulically or electrically. Subsea BOPs are connected back to the floating rig by a marine riser. Some countries allow the installation of a surface BOP on floating units like tension-leg platforms and spars, but not on MODUs.

> Ram-type preventers are a combination of:
> - Pipe rams
> - Blind rams
> - Shear rams

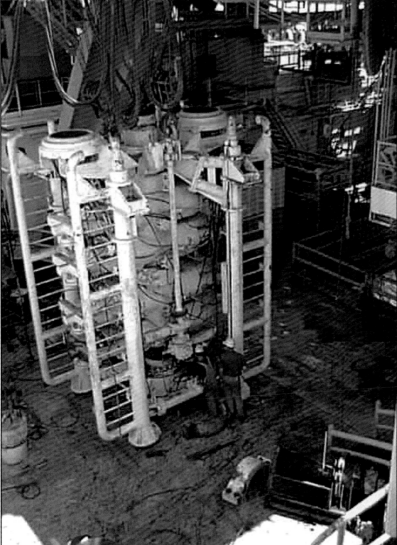

Courtesy of Cudd Well Control

Figure 2-2.7. A subsea BOP

To restore balanced well pressure conditions, crews use the:
- Driller's method
- Wait-and-weight method
- Tube-and-bleed method

When the drilling crew recognizes signs of a kick, the driller does the following:

1. Turns off the pumps.
2. Stops rotating the drill string.
3. Pulls the drill string off bottom, exposing the first tool joint above the slips. (For offshore operations with BOPs on the seabed, the driller pulls high enough to ensure the tool joint nearest the BOP is properly spaced out by raising it a safe distance about the BOP.)
4. Closes one or more of the BOPs so flow to the surface is stopped.

Once the BOPs are closed, the crew monitors the shut-in pressure of the well while preparing to circulate the influx of fluids out of the well. If the shut-in pressure is allowed to continuing growing, a lower and weaker pressure reservoir in the well could fracture. This allows the high-pressure reservoir to flow into the lower pressure zone and start a downhole blowout.

The drilling crew then circulates the reservoir fluids out of the well. The crew also circulates the old mud out of the well and replaces it with new mud with a higher weight. The weight must be high enough to create a wellbore pressure that is more than the pressure in the kicking reservoir. Circulation is accomplished using rig pumps and a *choke manifold* to control the escape of reservoir fluids and mud from the well (figs. 2-2.8, 2-2.9, and 2-2.10).

To reestablish balanced conditions, one of two methods is generally applied:

- *Driller's Method*—primarily employs the use of the existing pump system and applies back pressure at the choke to gain control of the well. Although this method is the fastest to employ, it might not be the most effective.
- *Wait and Weight Method*—requires an ability to analyze downhole conditions and build a fluid management system to create a hydrostatically stable well.

Other techniques include the *reverse, bullhead, volumetric,* and *lube-and-bleed methods.* Often, two or more methods might be used to achieve success.

After all the reservoir fluids and old mud are replaced by circulating new, heavier mud into the wellbore, the pressure in the well is once again higher than the reservoir pressure, and the reservoir fluid will no longer flow into the well. At this point, the well is said to be *dead,* or *static.* The BOPs can be opened, the mud conditioned, and drilling can safely resume.

Figure 2-2.8. Choke manifold

Figure 2-2.10. Remote choke panel with hydraulic module

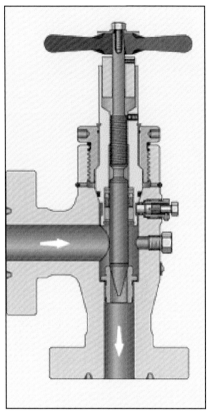

Figure 2-2.9. A positive adjustable choke with tungsten carbide wear surfaces

A choke manifold connected to rig pumps restores circulation by controlling the escape of fluids from the well.

In the event conditions become hazardous and the complete loss of control arises, all nonessential crew are evacuated from the rig. If a blowout and subsequent fire occurs, then specialized firefighters are called in to handle this type of critical situation in unique ways for which they are highly trained. If gases and oil are ignited, some of the gases released can be poisonous as with *hydrogen sulfide (H$_2$S)*. When H$_2$S is emitted, it presents extreme hazards to anyone within breathing distance. Inhalation can be fatal.

It is important to note that blowouts are reasonably rare. There are thousands of wells drilled without incident worldwide with relatively few well control problems. The well conditions, proximity to resources, isolation of the well location, language barriers, geographical restrictions, weather, and condition of equipment all play critical roles in the ability to manage difficult and often dangerous situations.

Early Warnings

> Workers must be mindful of three critical aspects:
> - Changes in daily routine
> - Reaction to changes with the proper response
> - Respect for nature's ability to impose change

Eighty percent of all blowouts involve warning signs that form a chain of signals indicating an influx. Awareness and effective communication are the best defense against this "domino effect." Workers are trained to recognize both subtle and obvious signals that require specific corrective actions.

The industry spends millions of dollars every year on safety training, crew awareness about well control, offshore safety operations, and best drilling practices. Awareness training and proper mitigation techniques are the cornerstones of well control. The industry offers many forms of specific training to ensure drilling and production teams know exactly how to detect, react, and mitigate unscheduled events safely and cost effectively.

Clear communication and understanding is essential. As the drilling industry expands the limits of its engineering and geologic expertise, new and challenging complications will arise in the area of well control. Extreme weather conditions, increasingly deep water depths, and more complicated extended-reach wells add to the complexities of managing a balanced wellbore. Proper training at all levels is the best preparation and enables proactive planning of wells and successful implementation of well control programs. All oil and gas industry personnel should be mindful of three critical aspects of awareness:

- Recognize changes in daily routine.
- React to changes with the proper response.
- Develop a healthy respect for nature's ability to impose change.

The industry requires all well-site staff to have certificates of competence appropriate to their respective job functions. Training assessment courses are managed through industry-accredited classes. Qualifications must be validated every few years, depending on the rules enacted by the various governments monitoring the drilling operations within their borders.

Well-site staff must comply with all necessary training, certification, and repeated validation.

Figure 2-2.11. Quality well control training is not only essential for rig workers but also important for all personnel involved in various aspects of drilling and production operations. Classroom instructors at the PETEX Training Center in Houston (above) teach the fundamentals of well control to a wide variety of employees and supporting personnel of the oil and gas industry.

SUMMARY   Awareness while working in oilfields is critical to well control. A well is no longer in control when gas or fluids flow in a way that cannot be regulated or stopped. To maintain a recognized influx of gas or fluids, a well must remain balanced. This can be done with pressure that is subnormal, normal, or abnormal.

The first line of defense in well control is the crew that monitors changes in the well. Pressure inside the wellbore must be greater than the pressures in the reservoirs being drilled. When imbalanced pressure occurs, there is in increase level of mud in the reservoir fluids. This excess mud is pushed out of the well. Once a crew detects this influx, the well is shut in using a blowout preventer (BOP). The BOP is usually an annular type and applies pressure through hydraulically operated ram sets. When a drilling crew detects a kick, the pumps are turned off, drilling is halted, and the BOPs are closed to stop flow to the surface.

Most blowouts can be prevented with awareness of all warning signs. Three critical aspects of this process include recognition of change, reaction with proper response, and respect for nature's ability to impose change. The industry requires well-site staff to maintain certification and to comply with regulations.

- Common drilling hazards
- Preparing the site for drilling
- Risks associated with drilling operations
- Safety as the highest priority

2.3
Drilling
Safety

Drilling rigs contain many hazards (fig. 2-3.1). The very nature of rotating machinery—engines, pumps, drawworks—and electrical equipment, confined spaces, chemicals, elevated work surfaces, and extreme noise creates serious hazards for workers. Of particular concern is the high pressure associated with circulating drilling mud. Workers must always be on guard for changing situations, particularly those that might lead to a blowout (discussed in *Chapter 2.2. Well Control*). Offshore rigs present additional hazards due to the harsh and remote aspects of deepwater marine environments.

Figure 2-3.1. Drilling rigs present potential hazards for all workers on site. Every worker must be thoroughly trained in the specific skills and requirements of their job to ensure safe operations.

COMMON HAZARDS

Records submitted to the *Occupational Safety and Health Administration (OSHA)* and the *International Association of Drilling Contractors (IADC)* reveal that the most common types of injuries on drilling rigs are categorized as follows:

- **Struck by:** Workers are frequently struck by moving equipment such as pipe, tongs, or the kelly. If the rotary hose breaks, it can whip around and strike a worker. There is always potential for tools, fittings, and other equipment to fall off the derrick and onto the rig floor, possibly harming someone nearby.

- **Caught in or between:** There have been many cases when workers have been injured by getting caught in the drawworks, rotary table, or other pieces of rotating equipment. Loose clothing can be easily caught in rotating equipment that is unguarded.

- **Fire, explosion, or high-pressure release:** Although quite rare, blowouts can occur when gas or liquids in the Earth overcome the forces of the drilling mud and flow to the surface. Fires are common due to escaping gas or oil, which is highly flammable (fig. 2-3.2). Other common sources of fires are welding, heaters in the *doghouse* (room used for eating, changing clothes), or poorly designed electrical equipment in areas where flammable natural gas exist.

Figure 2-3.2. Blowouts such as this can release hazardous gas that can quickly harm workers.

- **Rig collapse:** A structural failure of the rig is perhaps more common during rig-up or rig-down operations. Rigs that are not anchored can easily collapse when a load is placed on them. Overloading a rig or poor maintenance can also lead to collapse.
- **Falls:** Many parts of the rig are elevated above ground level, such as the rig floor and the monkeyboard. Workers must use handrails and follow safety procedures. When working at heights, harnesses might be required (figs. 2-3.3, 2-3.4, and 2-3.5).
- **Hydrogen sulfide exposure:** Hydrogen sulfide (H_2S), a poisonous gas often found dissolved within oil and gas, can accumulate in mud tanks while drilling. Other operations where H_2S might be present are swabbing, perforating, or well testing when downhole fluids are produced to open pits or tanks.

Figure 2-3.3. Handrails are essential safety devices on all drilling rigs.

Common rig injuries:
- Struck by
- Caught in or between
- Fire, explosion, or high-pressure release
- Rig collapse
- Falls
- H_2S exposure

Figure 2-3.4. **Don't:** *Some rig workers perform risky tasks high above the rig floor, but safety harnesses should be worn and not left on deck.*

Figure 2-3.5. **Do:** *Safety harnesses are required when performing any elevation work.*

The first step in drilling a new well on land is to build the drilling site, or *pad*, where the rig will sit. This usually involves grading an area of ground to make it flat for the rig, digging a reserve pit, and perhaps building a road to allow access to the location. Drivers of earth-moving equipment must observe caution to avoid tipping over or running into other vehicles in error.

Buried pipelines, communication cables, and power lines can be dangerous if encountered, so the lines need be located before any earth-moving or digging activities take place. All states have a *one-call system* where operators of underground lines will come out and mark the location of their lines so such activities do not damage them.

After the pad is leveled, workers install the conductor pipe, rathole, and mousehole (fig. 2-3.6). This usually involves large auger-type equipment on a boom. Dangers include drilling into underground lines, being struck by a large piece of equipment, and falling into holes not marked or protected.

PREPARING THE DRILL SITE

> The drilling site is first prepared with a one-call system where operators mark the lines in the ground to prevent damage.

Figure 2-3.6. A rathole rig drills the first part of the hole. However, these workers are not wearing protective gear and risk injury while performing this hazardous operation.

Installing the Rig

Drilling rigs are designed to be disassembled and transported across highways. Moving involves hoisting and lifting large pieces of equipment, requiring safe practices to ensure personnel are not struck or crushed when trucks are being loaded. Also, many of these loads are oversized for most highways and might require special warning banners and accompanying pilot cars.

Once the rig is unloaded at the location, it is hooked up (fig. 2-3.7). Several hazards are presented when assembling the rig. Workers must be careful to avoid being struck by a crane, truck, or forklift; pinching fingers when connecting equipment; being burned during welding, or falling from heights (fig. 2-3.8).

Courtesy of Bret Boteler, EnerMax, Inc.

Figure 2-3.7. Workers are assembling a land rig in the U.S. Permian Basin of Texas.

Once hooked up, the rig power systems present workers with a potential hazard of being shocked or electrocuted if electrical lines are improperly connected.

After rigs are set up for each new well, they are inspected. The driller or rig superintendent will walk around the rig and check for missing or loose pins, bolts, guards, or handrails and make sure the electrical system is hooked up properly.

Rigs can be hazardous to workers. Caution must be used to avoid bodily harm.

Figure 2-3.8. The construction of rigs involve tasks that must be performed high above the ground, making safety a primary concern.

Drilling Ahead

Drilling ahead involves moving drill pipe, collars, bits, and downhole tools in and out of the well. The following describes specific risk areas and certain precautions:

- The derrickhand must wear protection against falling while working up on the monkeyboard. Most rigs include a safety escape system or a *Geronimo line* that can be used in case of a fire or blowout.

- While handling pipe, floorhands must be careful of injury by the drawworks, rotary table, kelly, top drive unit, and tongs (fig. 2-3.9).

Figure 2-3.9. Crewmembers lower the bit into a surface hole.

Courtesy of Bret Boteler, EnerMax, Inc.

- The mud system pumps up the mud pressure to circulate it through the well. Drilling crews should make sure the rotary hose is properly connected and in good physical shape so it will not come loose and whip around.
- The drilling mud contains many different types of chemicals. Crews use a *Material Safety Data Sheet (MSDS)* to make sure they are using the proper *personal protective equipment (PPE)* and handling chemicals properly to avoid injury.

Although the causes and prevention of blowouts are discussed in the previous chapter, the general guidelines regarding proper safety are outlined here to reinforce their importance. From a safety perspective, managing blowouts includes:

- Carefully monitoring the drilling mud system for any warning signs such as an increase in the mud pit level or more gas breaking out at the shale shakers.
- If gas or oil does make it to the surface, a BOP is used to shut in the well while crews work to weight up the mud and start pumping it into the well while slowly releasing pressure at the surface using a choke.
- If gas or oil escapes from the rig uncontrollably, then the rig is evacuated. Special blowout crews are brought in to try to cap the well or use other techniques like drilling a relief well to stop the blowout.

Blowouts

Increased mud in the pit level or gas emitting from the shale shakers is a sign of warning that a blowout might occur.

Completing the Well

Once the well is drilled, the casing is often perforated to allow the oil and gas to enter the well from the formation. Perforating involves explosive charges, making it necessary to observe the following:

- Precautions must be taken to handle explosives properly.
- Stray electrical charges might set off the explosive charges. During lightning storms, radio transmissions are stopped and perforating should not be performed.
- Some wells might be fracture-stimulated to increase production. Fluids and proppants such as sand, bauxite, or ceramic beads are pumped into the well at high pressures. Operators often install special equipment designed for these abrasive fluids. The equipment can cut quickly through steel in the well.

SUMMARY

Fluids and proppants are used to fracture a well. Examples are:
- Sand
- Bauxite
- Ceramic beads

Modern drilling rigs are specially designed for safe operations (fig. 2-3.10). Everything from blowout preventers to guards on the drawworks are designed to prevent people from getting hurt. However, safety also requires that personnel be knowledgeable and follow all safety procedures properly while on the drill site. The bottom line is that people are the ones who create safe operations. It is extremely important that everyone involved in drilling develop the attitude that every job can be done safely and that all injuries are preventable.

Courtesy of Ensco International

Figure 2-3.10. Safety is top priority; proper training and communication are key components of safe operations.

PART 3
Production

The Authors

PRODUCTION PRACTICES

Paul Bommer

*Senior Lecturer, Petroleum and Geosystems Engineering
The University of Texas at Austin*

Paul Bommer, university instructor and co-owner of Bommer Engineering Company, has spent over 25 years in industry as an oil and gas operator and consultant in Texas and other parts of the United States. A third-generation oil man, Bommer joined the faculty of The University of Texas at Austin in 2004 and teaches courses in drilling, production, artificial lift, and facilities. His many years in private practice involved specializing in drilling and production operations and oil and gas appraisals. Bommer has published articles on solution mining, beam pump design, and well log analysis. He is the author of the best-selling book, Primer of Oilwell Drilling, 7th edition, published by PETEX. He has served as an instructor in petroleum-related courses at The University of Texas at Austin, the University of Houston at Victoria, and at Bee County Community College. Bommer is a Registered Professional Engineer in the State of Texas, a member of the Society of Petroleum Engineers and the American Petroleum Institute, and a member of the PETEX Advisory Board. He received his B.S., M.S., and Ph.D. degrees in Petroleum Engineering, all from The University of Texas at Austin.

PRODUCTION SAFETY

Jim Johnstone

*President and Co-founder
Contek Solutions LLC*

Jim Johnstone, a 30-year veteran of the oil and gas business, has worked with various companies to implement management systems and set up exemplary safety programs. He has led process hazard reviews, implemented behavioral-based training programs, conducted safety training, led safety compliance initiatives and investigated incidents. Johnstone began his career with ARCO (now BP) and later became responsible for all its process safety and support of environmental health and safety regulatory compliance for worldwide operations. He has participated in numerous technical committees and authored technical content, including safety publications for the American Petroleum Institute. He holds a B.S. in Mechanical Engineering from Washington State University and a Certified Safety Professional certificate from the Board of Certified Safety Professionals. Johnstone is a member of the Society of Petroleum Engineers, American Society of Safety Engineers, and American Society of Mechanical Engineers.

In this chapter:

- Completing the well for production to begin
- Wellhead equipment that controls fluid flow
- Fluid pressure and initiating flow
- Artificial methods of lifting fluids
- Mechanisms that drive fluids from the reservoir
- Methods of handling well fluids on the surface
- Well servicing and workover operations

3.1
Production Practices

In the petroleum industry, *production* is the phase of operation that deals with bringing well fluids to the surface and preparing them for transport to the refinery or processing plant. Production begins after drilling is finished and the *borehole* is carefully evaluated and determined to be economically productive. On the other hand, a borehole judged to be economically unproductive is plugged and abandoned.

Production is a combination of these operations:

- Preparing the borehole for production
- Bringing fluids to the surface
- Separating into oil, gas, and water streams that are measured for quantity and quality

For boreholes drilled to economically productive reservoirs, the first step is to *complete* the well—that is, to perform operations necessary to start the well fluids flowing to the surface. Routine maintenance operations are expected. *Servicing* such as replacing worn or malfunctioning equipment is standard during the well's producing life. Later, more extensive repairs, known as *workovers*, might be necessary to maintain the flow of oil and gas.

Well fluids, usually a mixture of oil, gas, and water, must be separated when they reach the surface. Water must be disposed of and equipment installed to treat, measure, and test the oil and gas before transporting them from the well site.

Detailed discussions on these concepts follow in this order: completion, fluid flow, reservoir drive mechanisms, improved recovery, surface handling, well servicing, and remote production environments.

THE EARLY DAYS

The earliest methods of well completion are attributed to the Chinese. Historians believe that they completed gas, water, and saltwater wells as early as 1000 B.C. The gas was transported through bamboo pipelines to light the Imperial Palace. Chinese technology passed down through the centuries with few changes. New technologies began to emerge in the 1800s to satisfy the growing demand for high-quality lamp oil, called kerosene, distilled from crude oil.

Completion

An early example of *completion* technology is attributed to two West Virginia saltwater well drillers, David and Joseph Ruffner in 1808. The Ruffner brothers used an open-hole completion to extract brine for use in making salt, valued for preserving food. Shallow sands held less concentrated salt water than the sands at the bottom of the well. Salt water from all of these layers mixed and produced diluted salt water that was less desirable. The brothers decided to seal the shallow sands behind a tube of some sort. Lacking steel pipe, the Ruffners constructed wooden tubes that were secured together with rope (fig. 3-1.1). Bags filled with sand were placed around the bottom to create a reasonably effective seal at the bottom of the wooden tube. This early example of well casing stabilized the wellbore and segregated fluids, in this case, brine, found at different depths in the well.

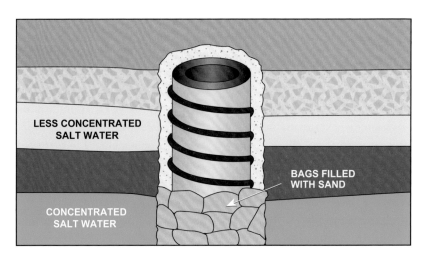

Figure 3-1.1. Running a pipe to line the sides of a well and sealing off the outside of the pipe near the bottom prevented fluids from the formations near the surface from entering the well.

Another important innovation borrowed from the water-well industry is the use of the reciprocating *walking beam* to operate a pump. In the decade after Drake's well in 1859, a cable-tool drilling rig with a walking beam remained on a well. The walking beam the driller used to raise and drop the bit could also reciprocate the plunger in a pump placed at the bottom of the well. One steam engine was used to power one pump. The cable-tool derrick and hoist remained at the well site to raise and lower the pump from the well whenever repairs were needed.

The oil industry developed its first major innovation in production equipment—central pumping power—around 1880. Central pumping consisted of using a single steam engine to pump several wells through a series of rods connecting a large wheel, called the *bull wheel*, to each well. When the bull wheel was turned by the steam engine, the connecting rods moved back and forth along the ground and activated the walking beam of the pumping unit at each well.

More developments followed at the turn of the century. Rotary drilling rigs and well service rigs evolved into units that could be transported from well to well. *Internal-combustion engines* began to replace steam engines and became inexpensive enough so that individual engines were placed on pumping units, replacing the central power units and surface connecting rods.

All these inventions laid the groundwork for continuing improvements in equipment and procedures. The *electric submersible pump* was developed in 1930 to pump large volumes of liquid, followed by the development of marketable *gas-lift devices* a few years later.

Pumping

Central pumping power was the oil industry's first major innovation in production equipment.

Early operators dug earthen pits for temporary storage of oil. For many years, redwood tanks were the standard for storing oil and produced water, followed later by steel tanks. Wooden barrels were used to ship petroleum (fig. 3-1.2). The *barrel* became the standard for measuring petroleum, and remains so today. A barrel of crude equals 42 gallons, or 0.15899 cubic metres (1 cubic metre is 6.2897 barrels).

After 1920, great advances were made in operating lease facilities. Over time, petroleum engineers have improved methods for separating oil, gas, and water; treating emulsions; and handling water. The emphases now are on making lease operations as efficient as possible to improve profitability, while maximizing recovery and reducing the environmental impact.

Storage and Handling

Figure 3-1.2. Wooden barrels were the first containers for produced oil.

WELL COMPLETION

After a well has been drilled and the reservoir is determined to be economical to produce, the well is prepared for production, or *completed*.

Modern completion equipment and methods are quite varied. Operators decide what to use in a well based on the type of oil or gas accumulations, the requirements expected during the life of the well, and the current economic circumstances.

Production Casing and Liners

Many oil and gas wells require four concentric strings of large pipe, each one reaching to the surface (fig. 3-1.3). The four strings include:

- *Conductor pipe*
- *Surface casing*
- *Intermediate casing*
- *Production casing*

Production casing is often called the *oil string* or the *long string* and is the final casing for most wells. The other casing strings are installed during the drilling phase to stabilize and protect shallower portions of the well. Usually, the production casing extends through and completely seals off the producing formation. However, in some reservoirs, the production casing stops near or just on top of the reservoir (often called the *pay zone*). In either case, the production casing serves to stabilize the borehole above the reservoir and isolate the reservoir beneath or behind the production casing.

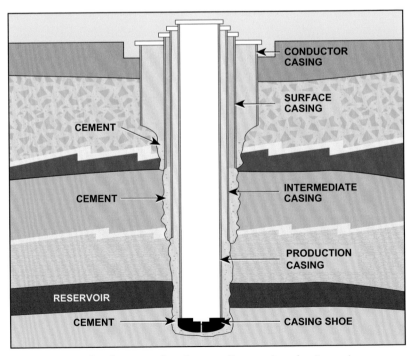

Figure 3-1.3. Conductor, surface, intermediate, and production casing are cemented in the well. Note the production casing is set through the producing zone and seals it off.

Another type of production casing often used in deeper wells (over 10,000 feet or 3,048 metres) is called a *liner*. Liners are just like casings. They serve the same purpose and are made of the same material, but they do not extend all the way to the surface (fig. 3-1.4). Instead, a liner hangs from the end of larger casing above it by means of a *liner hanger*. A liner can function as production casing, in which case it is called a *production liner*. If necessary, the liner can be extended or *tied back* to the surface by installing casing from the top of the casing hanger back to the surface. Because the liner initially does not extend back to the surface, it can be installed in a shorter time period and does not require as much pipe, making it less expensive than a full string of production casing. Regardless of length, production casing is held in place by cement pumped through the inside of the pipe into the space between the borehole and the outside of the casing, called the *annulus*. If the production casing extends to the surface, it is secured in a wellhead.

> A liner uses less pipe and requires shorter installation time, therefore it is less expensive than production casing.

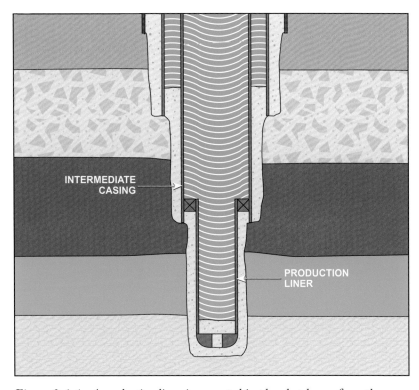

Figure 3-1.4. A production liner is cemented in place but hangs from the bottom of the intermediate casing rather than extending to the surface.

Completion Types

Completion requires a rig to install the necessary pipe and equipment. Onshore, it is common to use a *completion rig* that is smaller and less expensive than the large drilling rig used to drill the hole and install the casing. Offshore, it is common to use the drilling rig to install the completion to avoid the cost of bringing in different rigs. In some parts of the world, depending on the availability of rigs, onshore wells are also completed with the drilling rig.

Today's wells can be drilled vertical or at an angle deviated from vertical. Deviated wells are often used to drill wells from isolated surface locations, such as offshore platforms, or to reach otherwise inaccessible locations, such as under lakes or towns. The deviation of a well can be horizontal (90 degrees from vertical) or at an inclining angle greater than 90 degrees. Wells that are horizontal in the reservoir can expose long sections of the reservoir to a flow path to the surface.

No matter the type of well path or well location, the following completion styles can be applied.

Open-Hole Completion

An open-hole completion has no production casing or liner set through the producing formation (fig. 3-1.5). With no casing in the way, reservoir fluids flow unrestricted into the open wellbore. This type of completion is limited to consolidated reservoirs in which the reservoir rock will not collapse or come apart and fill up the hole when fluid flows.

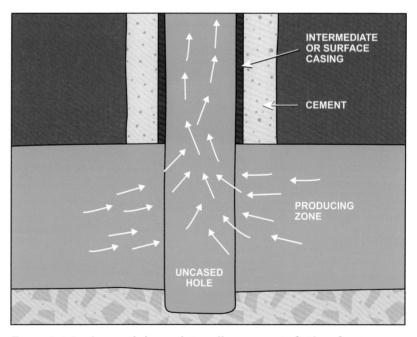

Figure 3-1.5. An open-hole completion allows reservoir fluids to flow into an uncased hole.

One style of open-hole completion has casing set just above the pay zone, and drilling proceeds into the *producing zone* as far as necessary to complete the well. A second variation has the open hole drilled first through the reservoir and casing set at the top with a special cementing shoe that prevents cement from falling into the open hole. Open-hole completions have the advantage of exposing the maximum reservoir surface area to flow. This is true of both vertical and horizontal wells. Horizontal wells have the extra advantage of requiring less pressure drop in the reservoir on a volume-produced basis compared to vertical wells. Open-hole completions do not separate portions of the reservoir from one another. Therefore, care must be taken to expose only the portions of the reservoir that contain the reservoir fluid the well operator wants to produce. For example, if a water-bearing portion is exposed, water will flow into the well, and it might prove difficult to stop. Because the open-hole completion does not isolate portions of the exposed reservoir, it is more difficult to selectively stimulate the reservoir, if that becomes necessary.

One variation of an open-hole completion uses a slotted liner to hold the hole open in the event the reservoir collapses after flow begins. The liner consists of casing with slots. The slots can be carefully sized and cut to exact size, or the slots can be cut with a torch if exact size is not critical. The entire liner length or only portions can be slotted. The liner is either suspended in the open hole with a liner hanger in the casing set above the reservoir, or it is simply placed in the open hole and stood up on bottom. The slotted liner is not cemented in place.

A cased and perforated completion requires the production casing to be run completely past the reservoir and cemented in place. The casing and external cement create a complete seal between the reservoir and the inside of the casing. It is critical that the best materials and practices be used for the cement job to achieve an external seal. The cement isolates the productive reservoir from other portions of the wellbore that contain water or other undesirable fluids. The connection between the inside of the casing and the producing reservoir is made by *perforating holes* through the casing and the cement.

> The production casing and external cement create a complete seal between the reservoir and the inside of the casing.

Cased and Perforated Completion

Perforating is the process of piercing the casing wall and the cement behind it to provide openings through which formation fluids can enter the wellbore. A *perforating gun*, or *perforator*, makes these openings. The completion crew lowers the long cylindrical gun down the production casing or liner until it is adjacent to the reservoir zone. The perforator carries several bullets or special explosive charges called *shaped charges* aimed at the walls of the casing or liner (fig. 3-1.6). The shaped charges or bullets shoot holes in the casing or liner and penetrate the rock as well. The explosion of a shaped charge is actually a jet of high-energy gases and particles, so it is called *jet perforating*.

A cased and perforated completion has the advantage of opening only carefully selected portions of the reservoir. This limits the migration of undesirable fluids into the well and makes it possible to stimulate selected parts of the reservoir. The perforations are also much easier to seal later, if needed, than portions of an open-hole segment. The flow characteristics of an open hole can be approximated using carefully designed perforations. Cased and perforated completions can be used in both vertical and horizontal wells, although conveying the perforating gun into the horizontal portion of the well requires special techniques that do not rely on gravity.

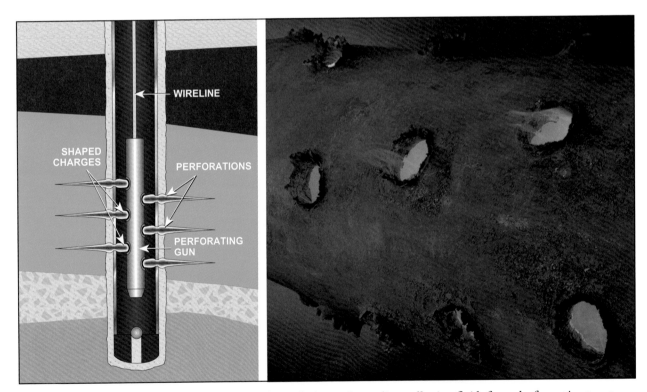

Figure 3-1.6. A perforating gun creates holes in the producing casing or liner, allowing fluids from the formation to enter the well.

Once the casing is installed and the open hole is drilled or perforations in the casing are made, the well is ready to begin to flow. If the well is allowed to produce by flowing to the surface through the production casing, it is called a *tubingless completion*. *Tubing* is a smaller pipe run inside the production casing. Many wells begin life as tubingless completions and are later converted to use tubing. The advantage of a tubingless completion is primarily cost, because no tubing is required and the well can be completed faster. It is sometimes possible to install smaller casing if tubing will never be used, further reducing the high cost of the casing.

Tubingless completions have several disadvantages including:

- Fluids flowing through the casing can cause corrosion problems. To prevent this, the fluids must not be corrosive. Because the casing is permanently installed in the well, repairing holes caused by corrosive fluids is difficult, expensive, and not always successful.

- The casing used must be designed to withstand reservoir pressures along the entire length of the casing, which may increase the cost of the casing.

- Reservoir fluids do not always flow efficiently up large casing, in which case tubing would need to be installed.

Tubingless Completions

A tubingless completion is one where the well produces by flowing to the surface through production casing.

Tubing and Packers

After cementing the production casing and creating an open hole or perforations, the completion crew runs a final string of pipe, called *tubing* (fig. 3-1.7). Well fluids flow from the reservoir to the surface through this tubing. Unlike casing, tubing is not cemented but hangs from the wellhead at the surface. Tubing is smaller in diameter than casing. The outside diameter typically ranges from about 1 to 4.5 inches (about 25 to 114 millimetres).

Tubing can be easily removed if it becomes damaged or corroded. In cases of extremely corrosive fluids, tubing strings made from *corrosion resistant alloys (CRAs)* can be used. Sometimes reservoir fluids flow more efficiently through smaller diameter tubing. Tubing is also used to convey any pumps and artificial lift devices into the well to keep fluids flowing to the surface.

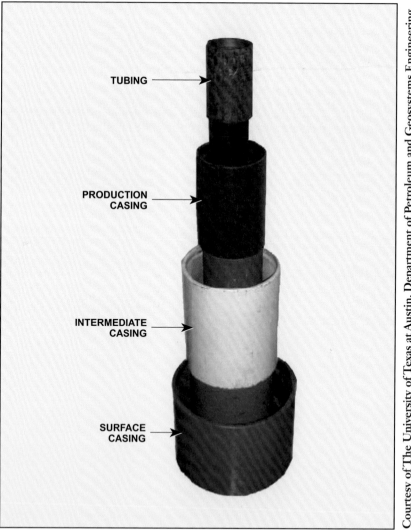

TUBING

PRODUCTION CASING

INTERMEDIATE CASING

SURFACE CASING

Courtesy of The University of Texas at Austin, Department of Petroleum and Geosystems Engineering

Figure 3-1.7. Tubing is smaller in diameter than casing. The casing is shown in colors to differentiate between the strings; they are actually unpainted steel.

In addition, tubing can be sealed at the bottom using a *packer*. While not always necessary, a packer can protect the production casing from high pressures, simulation treatment, and exposure to reservoir fluids.

A packer consists of metal housing with external slips, rubber elements, and an internal flow tube. It provides a secure seal between everything above and below where it is set (fig. 3-1.8). It keeps well fluids and pressure away from the casing above it. Because the packer seals off the space between the tubing and the casing, formation fluids must flow up the tubing to reach the surface.

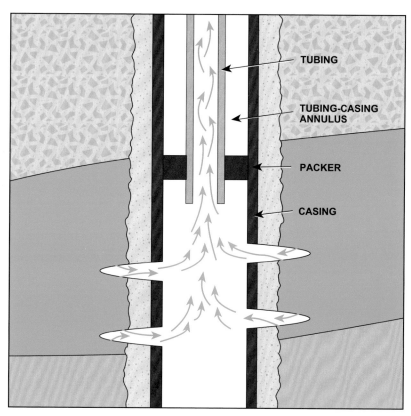

Figure 3-1.8. A packer between the casing and tubing keeps well fluids out of the tubing-casing annulus.

Figure 3-1.9. The slips grip the walls of the casing to hold the packer in place.

The external slips on a packer (fig. 3-1.9) are engaged against the casing to hold the packer in place. Once the slips have been engaged, the dense synthetic rubber sealing element is expanded against the side of the casing. A packer can have one sealing element or several separated by metal rings (fig. 3-1.10).

Packers come in two broad categories:

- Permanent: conveyed into the well on an electric wireline and set in place by a hydraulic setting tool driven by an explosive device. Once set, this style of packer cannot be removed without physically drilling and destroying the outer slips of the packer.

- Retrievable: can be unset and recovered intact from the well.

As a general rule, permanent packers have higher temperature and pressure ratings and fewer moving parts than retrievable packers.

Figure 3-1.10. A packer can have one sealing element or several separated by metal rings.

The operator uses a *multiple completion* when one wellbore passes through two or more zones containing oil and gas that are to be produced simultaneously (fig. 3-1.11). Usually, a separate tubing string with packers is run in for each producing zone. For example, a triple completion can have three tubing strings and three packers, with each zone producing independently.

Multiple completions have the significant advantage of allowing production and monitoring of separate reservoirs in one wellbore. They are much more expensive and complicated to install than a single-zone completion but are generally less expensive than drilling individual wells to produce each reservoir. It is more difficult to employ pumps in multiple completions than in single-zone completions. Repairs to one completion might take longer to perform, especially if other completions in the well are still producing.

Multiple Completions

Multiple completions:
- Allow production of separate reservoirs in one wellbore
- More expensive and complicated to install
- Often less expensive to drill than multiple wells
- More difficult to employ pumps
- Repairs can take longer

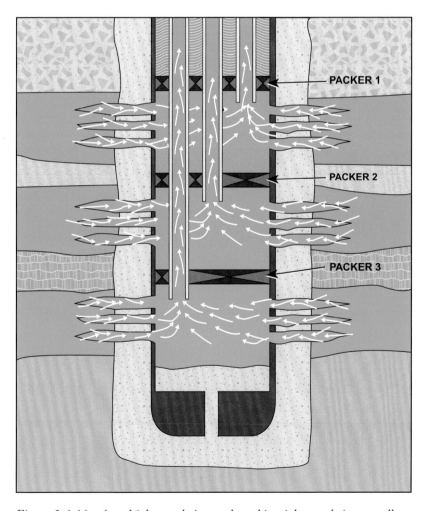

Figure 3-1.11. A multiple completion, such as this triple completion, usually has a separate tubing string and packer for each producing zone. Also, the casing is perforated opposite each producing zone.

Subsurface Safety Valve

Every tubing string used in offshore wells must have a subsurface safety valve.

A *subsurface safety valve (SSSV)* is required in every tubing string on all offshore wells (fig. 3-1.12). The most common type of SSSV operates as follows:

- The SSSV uses a piston and flapper powered by hydraulic pressure from the surface.
- The hydraulic pressure is conveyed to the valve through external hydraulic control lines strapped on the outside of the tubing.
- The valve remains open as long as hydraulic pressure is supplied to keep the piston pushed down in the valve that holds the flapper open.
- If hydraulic pressure is removed by the operator or due to a malfunction on the surface, the piston allows the flapper to close, stopping the flow of fluid up the tubing.

The valve must be set several hundred feet (or metres) below the ocean floor (mud line) to prevent pollution in case of a catastrophe, such as loss of the wellhead in a storm. Because the SSSV is a part of the tubing, there are no tubingless completions done offshore. The SSSV can be used onshore but not as a requirement. Because of its importance as a well- and pollution-control device, the SSSV is tested according to a schedule. If the SSSV fails to function, a workover is required to repair the valve.

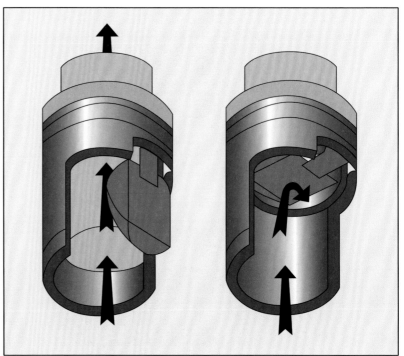

Courtesy of Schlumberger

Figure 3-1.12. Subsurface safety valve

Some reservoirs produce not only oil and gas but also sand. A formation produces sand when the individual grains making up the reservoir rock are unconsolidated. In other words, the rock grains do not adhere to each other. Sand can flow into the well along with fluids and can clog the well, which can reduce or stop production. Sand also damages equipment in the hole.

To prevent sand production from an *unconsolidated reservoir*, several varieties of control methods are used. The most common method of controlling sand is called a *gravel pack*. In a gravel pack, well-sorted sand (called gravel to differentiate it from reservoir sand) is pumped through the perforations (fig. 3-1.13). Some of the gravel is left inside the wellbore and held in place by a wire-wrapped screen (fig. 3-1.14). The gravel permits passage of only the smallest sand particles from the formation, and the screen prevents passage of gravel into the wellbore.

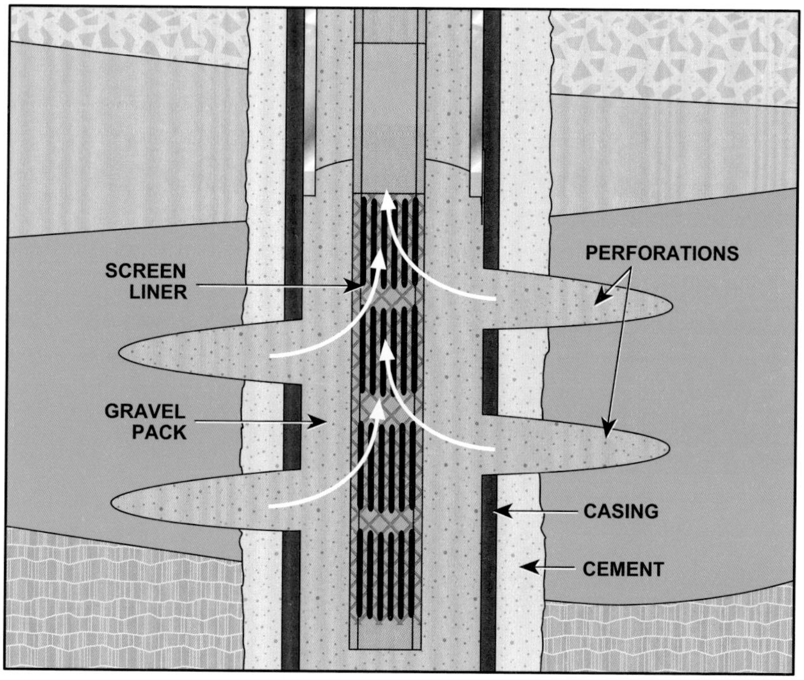

Gravel Pack Completions

Figure 3-1.13. A wire-wrapped screen, or screen liner, is often combined with a gravel pack inside perforated casing.

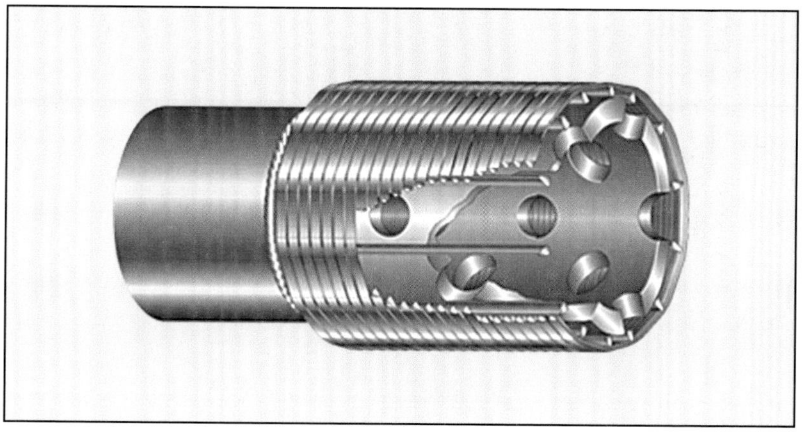

Figure 3-1.14. A gravel pack screen

One variation of this method is the *frac-pack*. In a frac-pack, a small fracture is created in the reservoir outside the wellbore. The fracture is packed with gravel. Gravel is also left in the perforations and inside the well where it is held in place with a screen. A frac-pack often requires less reservoir pressure drop for a given produced volume than a gravel pack because of the beneficial influence of the small fracture.

A less popular method of sand control is to try to consolidate the reservoir material near the wellbore. This is done by injecting chemicals that "glue" sand grains together without plugging the connected pore spaces between the grains.

The Wellhead

The *wellhead* includes all equipment on the surface that supports various pipe strings, seals off the well, and controls the paths and flow rates of reservoir fluids. The operator determines the type of wellhead according to the conditions in the well. For instance, a simple wellhead might have a valve placed on top of a casing string that is cemented from the bottom of the well to the surface. The cement supports and seals the casing, and the valve on top controls flow from the casing. This basic configuration does not apply to most wells where more than one string of casing is required and tighter flow control is necessary.

A typical wellhead for an onshore well or offshore platform is shown in figures 3-1.15 and 3-1.16.

Courtesy of Stream-Flo Industries Ltd.

Figure 3-1.15. Valves on the Christmas tree control the flow of fluids from the well.

A wellhead has valves that control fluid paths and flow rates during both onshore and offshore production operations.

Courtesy of The University of Texas at Austin, Department of Petroleum and Geosystems Engineering

Figure 3-1.16. This cutaway of a wellhead shows its inner workings. A wellhead usually has one or more casingheads, a tubinghead, and a Christmas tree.

Casinghead

A Christmas tree has:
- One or more master valves
- A flow tree
- A wing valve
- A choke

Each string of casing usually hangs from a *casinghead*, which is a heavy steel fitting at the surface. Metal and rubber seals in the casinghead prevent fluids from moving within the wellhead or escaping to the atmosphere. Each casinghead also has at least one outlet from where fluids can flow and pressure can be monitored.

The first casinghead (shown as the lowest casinghead in fig. 3-1.15) is welded or, in some cases, screwed on the top joint of the surface casing. The first casinghead is often called the *bradenhead* or the "A" Section. The surface casing is cemented in the well from the bottom to the surface. The surface casing and the bradenhead become the anchor point for all other casing and tubing strings placed in the well. If intermediate casing is run in the well, it is made to land in the bradenhead and then sealed.

The second casinghead (shown above the bradenhead and below the tubing head in fig. 3-1.15) is placed over the intermediate casing. The second casinghead is called the *intermediate spool* or the "B" Section. If no intermediate casing is required, the intermediate spool is not needed. *Production casing* is landed either in the bradenhead or in the intermediate spool and sealed. The *tubing head* ("C" Section if placed on top of the intermediate spool or "B" Section if placed on top of the bradenhead) is placed on top of the production casing.

Tubing Head

Similar in design and use to the casinghead is the tubing head, which supports the tubing string and seals off pressure between the casing and the inside of tubing. Like the casinghead, the tubing head has outlets to allow access to the annulus for gauging pressure or connecting valves and fittings to control fluid flow. Placed on top of the tubing head is a series of valves called the upper tree assembly, also called a *Christmas tree*.

Christmas Tree

The valves on the Christmas tree control flow from the tubing. The main valve, the *master valve*, is just above the tubing head. When the master valve is opened, it lets fluids flow to the rest of the tree. Closing it shuts off flow entirely. Some high-pressure wells call for more than one master valve in case one valve fails. A *flow tee* above the master valve or valves diverts flow from the tubing through a side valve, called a *wing valve*.

The flow rate from the well is controlled by a slight restriction in the flow line, called a *choke*. The choke can be created by a small-diameter tube (called a *positive choke*) or by a small adjustable annulus (called an *adjustable choke*). A larger opening in the choke causes a greater flow rate from the tubing.

For offshore wells in deepwater where a platform is not possible, the wellhead must be placed on the seafloor or mud line. Subsea wellheads are called *wet trees* because they are under water. Wellheads placed on an offshore platform above sea level are called *dry trees*. A subsea wellhead serves the same purpose as any wellhead. The main architectural difference between subsea trees and those used above sea level is the way in which the various casing and tubing strings are suspended and sealed.

In a subsea tree, the first component is the top portion of the conductor casing, called a *guide plate*. The guide plate rests on the seafloor. The surface casing is run inside the hole drilled through the guide plate.

The top component of the surface casing is a special tool called the *high-pressure connector* that fits into a recess in the guide plate (fig. 3-1.17). The surface casing is secured in the drilled hole by pumping cement from the bottom of the casing back to the seafloor. While the well is drilled deeper, all other casing and tubing strings run into the well will be suspended and sealed in the part of the high-pressure connector fitted to each size of pipe. During drilling, the blowout preventers are secured to the outside of the high-pressure connector and connected to the floating drilling rig by a pipe called a *marine riser*.

Subsea Wellheads

Courtesy of The University of Texas at Austin, Department of Petroleum and Geosystems Engineering

Figure 3-1.17. High-pressure connector cutaway view

After the well is finished, the blowout preventers are removed and the subsea tree is secured to the outside of the high-pressure connector (fig. 3-1.18). Flow from the tubing in the well is controlled by chokes placed on the wet tree. The fluids are produced through a long subsea flow line to either the closest available platform or to some form of floating production vessel.

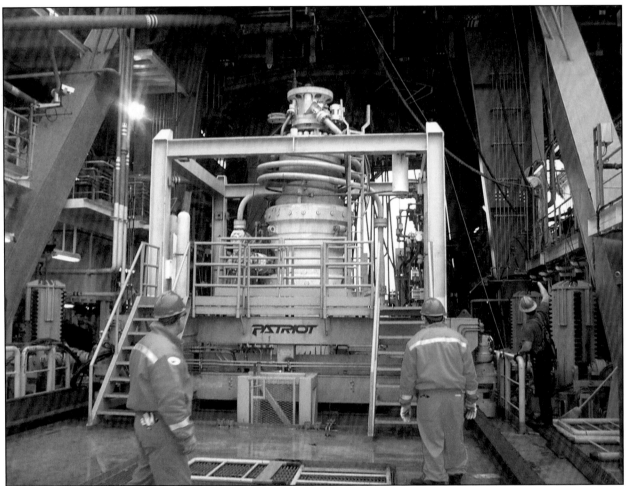

Figure 3-1.18. Subsea production tree

Courtesy of TSC Offshore

As a well is drilled, pressure in the production zone is offset by drilling fluid pressure in the hole. The drilling fluid is replaced by some form of completion fluid during completion. The completion fluid might have the same heavy density as the original drilling mud, or it might have lesser density. Either way, the completion fluid is normally clear and free of solids, which would run the risk of plugging the producing reservoir or settling on top or inside the equipment placed in the well. Once completion with correct fluids is achieved and equipment is installed in the well, flow of reservoir fluids begins.

If the completion fluid in the well exerts a higher pressure than the reservoir, no reservoir fluids can enter the well. Some of the heavy completion fluid must be removed from the well or replaced with a less dense fluid so the reservoir pressure can allow fluids to flow into the well.

One method of removing some of the heavy completion fluid is *swabbing*, which is accomplished by lowering a series of flexible rubber cups into the tubing suspended on a wire rope. When the wire rope is reeled out of the well, the *cups* trap the completion fluid in the tubing above the cups and force the fluid out of the well. Removing the completion fluid reduces the pressure at the bottom of the well. When enough completion fluid is removed, the reservoir pressure causes fluids to flow into the bottom of the well. This flow pushes the remaining completion fluid out of the well with the reservoir fluids flowing to the surface. The process of removing the completion fluid from the well is called *unloading* the well.

An alternative to swabbing is *jetting*, often done using a special device called a *coiled tubing unit*. Coiled tubing is a continuous reel of steel pipe small enough to fit inside the tubing through the top of the Christmas tree. The coiled tubing unit has a connector that seals around the coiled tubing and a device that pushes or injects the tubing into the well. Once in the well, less dense fluids or inert nitrogen gas can be pumped through the coiled tubing and used to circulate the heavy completion fluid from the well. Once the heavy fluid is replaced by the less dense fluid, the reservoir pressure causes the reservoir fluids to flow into the well. The coiled tubing is reeled back out of the well.

There are many methods to cause reservoir fluids to flow into the well. One option is to replace the heavy fluids with less dense completion fluid before perforating the well. When the well equipment is installed and the well is made ready to flow, the perforations are made with the knowledge that the reservoir pressure will now be greater than the pressure exerted by the completion fluid. The pressure will be high enough to flow reservoir fluids into the well and unload the completion fluid from the well.

INITIATING FLOW

To remove heavy completion fluid in a well, the following methods are used:
- Swabbing
- Jetting
- Replacing fluids with less dense fluids

When reservoir fluids flow out of the well, they go through a pipe called the *flow line* to a production facility where the oil and gas are made ready for sale and any produced water is disposed of.

Some wells will not generate enough reservoir pressure to flow fluids all the way to the surface. These wells require extra equipment to artificially lift the fluids to the surface.

Stimulation

Three main ways to stimulate permeability:
- Explosive fracturing
- Acidizing
- Hydraulic fracturing

Some reservoir rocks have few or small pathways to the well. The measure of the size of the pathways that exist in a rock is called permeability. Permeability is measured in *darcy units*, named after the French engineer who conducted early experiments of liquid flow through sand. The larger the value of permeability, the larger the pathways through the rock, and the easier it will be to flow reservoir fluids through the rock into the well. For reservoirs with small values of permeability, it is often possible to improve permeability by applying one or more *stimulation* techniques. Stimulation can often restore permeability of rock damaged or partially plugged over the course of time.

There are three main ways to stimulate permeability:

- The first and oldest method is *explosive fracturing*.
- The second method, available in the 1930s, is *acid stimulation*, or *acidizing*.
- The third method, introduced in 1948, is *hydraulic fracturing*.

Explosives

As early as the 1860s, crews exploded nitroglycerin inside wells to improve productivity. Workers carefully lowered a nitro charge into the open hole on a conductor line and protected the upper part of the well by placing some sand on top of the charge. The explosion pulverized rock around the well, and rock fragments frequently had to be bailed out of the well. The result was a cave or rubble-filled area around the detonation point that made the wellbore larger, vastly improving permeability for flow. *Nitro shooting* became fairly routine until the advent of acidizing and hydraulic fracturing. For a while in the 1960s, certain oil and gas companies, in conjunction with the Atomic Energy Commission, experimented with nuclear explosives in a limited number of gas wells. The result was a large rubble zone or cave that had enhanced flow, but the edges of the rubble or cave were turned to glass, cutting off any further fluid migration into the fractured area. The cost of this technique was extremely high.

One explosive technique still used in limited applications is a charge of solid propellant detonated inside a well. The resulting high-pressure gases are expelled into the reservoir where they form some localized fractures.

Hydraulic fracturing stimulations are successful in all types of reservoirs. Such stimulations create fractures that penetrate deeply into a reservoir. The fractures are created by high-pressure injection of fluids at rates that cannot be absorbed by the reservoir rock (figs. 3-1.19a and b). The hydraulic pressure exerted by the fluid actually splits, or fractures, the rock. The continued injection of fluid at this pressure causes the fracture to extend into the reservoir. The casing in the well is not harmed in this process because the injection pressure is lower than the burst rating of the casing.

Hydraulic fracturing improves the productivity of rock with low permeability because the fracture acts as an extension of the wellbore, exposing a large surface of the reservoir to a pathway into the well. Fracturing is also used to bypass reservoir areas that have become severely damaged over time.

Hydraulic Fracturing

Courtesy of Bret Boteler, EnerMax, Inc.

Figure 3-1.19a. Powerful truck-mounted pumps perform fracturing at the well site.

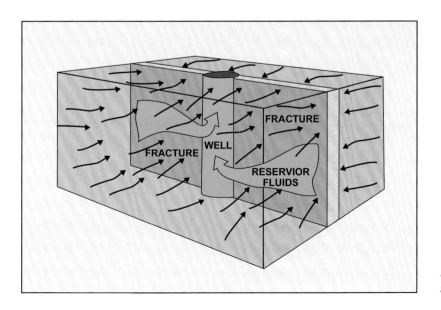

Figure 3-1.19b. Reservoir fluids flow into the fracture and the well.

Proppants   Hydraulically formed fractures tend to heal or close after parting pressure is released, unless the fracture is propped open in some manner. *Proppants*, or *propping agents*, hold the fractures open. Sand is used as a proppant (fig. 3-1.20). Higher strength proppants such as manmade ceramic beads or *bauxite* are used in reservoirs where the closing stress imposed by the reservoir would crush a lower strength material such as sand.

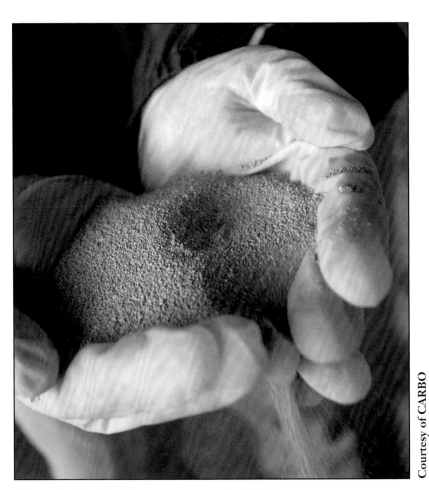

Courtesy of CARBO

Figure 3-1.20. Sand is one proppant used to hold fractures open.

Fracturing Fluid   Fracturing fluid can be created using either oil or water. In fact, the first fracturing fluid was *napalm* (gelled gasoline). Water is a popular base fluid because it is safe, available, and inexpensive. Some fracturing fluids are gels, which create a wider fracture and suspend the proppants better than water. Additives reduce friction between the fluid and the walls of the tubing and reduce fluid leak off into the reservoir.

In acid stimulation, or acidizing, an acid reacts chemically with the rock to dissolve it (fig. 3-1.21). The existing pathways or permeability in the rock will be enlarged and some new pathways created. Acidizing can be divided into categories by rock type as follows.

Carbonate rocks are *limestone* (calcium carbonate) and *dolomite* (a mixture of calcium and magnesium carbonates). One acid that reacts well with carbonates is called *hydrochloric acid (HCl)*. HCl reacts with carbonates almost as fast as the acid touches the rock surface. Acid can be pumped into a carbonate reservoir slowly and at a pressure below fracturing pressure to contact the rock near the well as uniformly as possible. This process is limited in treating areas near the well because the acid reacts so quickly with the rock. It is often called a *matrix acid job* because the entire rock surface area near the well is exposed to acid and reacts to some extent. Because it impacts only the rock volume near the well, a matrix acid job is useful for improving nearby permeability or removing damage formed near the well.

Another method requires injection of larger volumes of HCl at rates and pressure great enough to fracture the rock. The acid etches the sides of the fracture and some of the rock near the fracture face, so when pressure is reduced and the fracture closes, the etched pathways to the well remain. This process is called *acid fracturing* and is used solely in carbonate reservoirs. The challenge in acid fracturing is having live acid reach the end of the fracture before it is spent from the rapid rate of reaction between the HCl and carbonate rock. This technique can create an etched fracture that extends deep into a reservoir. The fracture is essentially an extension of the wellbore and provides a pathway into the well.

Minerals found in sandstone reservoirs, such as clay, silica, and feldspar, can be dissolved using *hydrofluoric acid (HF)*. The reaction of HF and the sandstone minerals is extremely slow, especially when compared to the reaction of HCl and carbonate rock. The HF reaction is also prone to form secondary products that could plug permeability of the sandstone. These facts limit use of *sandstone acidizing* to near-wellbore matrix treatments designed to remove damage caused primarily by clay from water-based drilling mud. HF acid is never used in a fracturing treatment because of its slow reaction rate and possibility of damaging byproducts.

Acidizing

Carbonate Acidizing

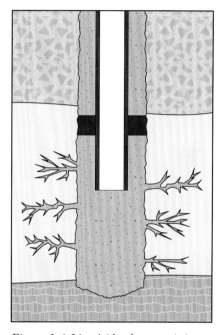

Figure 3-1.21. Acid enlarges existing channels or makes new ones.

Sandstone Acidizing

Additives

Additives are used with oilfield acids for many reasons. One of the most important reasons is to prevent or delay corrosion—that is, to inhibit acid from attacking the steel tubing or casing in the well. A *surfactant*, or surface active agent, is a type of additive. It is mixed in small amounts with an acid to prevent spent acid and oil from forming emulsions. An *emulsion* is a thick mixture with a consistency similar to common mayonnaise. It is difficult to remove emulsion from rock once it forms.

Common types of acid additives:
- Surfactants
- Sequestering agents
- Antisludge agents
- Corrosion inhibitors

Other common additives are *sequestering agents*, which prevent precipitation of ferric iron during acidizing, and *antisludge agents*, which prevent acid from reacting with certain types of crude and forming an insoluble sludge that blocks channels or reduces permeability.

Perforating Acid

Acid can be used to ensure perforations are free of any cement debris. HCl can be used for this purpose, but care must be taken so acid does not attack the steel casing. A milder acid, *acetic acid*, is available for perforation cleaning. It does not have the corrosive reaction with steel that HCl does. Acid jobs can be pumped with *ball sealers* that temporarily seal a perforation, forcing the remaining acid to flow through a different perforation. Using these mechanical diverters ensures some acid will flow through every perforation.

When the pressure in the reservoir falls to the point where reservoir fluids can no longer flow to the surface, an artificial method of lifting the hydrocarbons is necessary. The most common ways of providing artificial lift are discussed next.

ARTIFICIAL LIFT

The most common method of pumping oil from the formation to the surface in land-based wells is *beam pumping*. The beam pumping method involves surface and subsurface equipment. The pumping unit itself sits on the surface (fig. 3-1.22). The unit converts the rotary motion of the prime mover to reciprocating, or up-and-down, motion at the *horsehead*, which is the component on the unit that resembles the basic shape of a horse's head (fig. 3-1.23).

Here is how a beam pumping unit operates:

- A wire rope *bridle*, *carrier bar*, and clamp are used to suspend a string of *sucker rods* made of steel or fiberglass and steel inside the tubing in the well.

- The rod at the surface, the *polished rod*, moves up and down through a rubber packing element called a *stuffing box*. This *arrangement* prevents fluids from escaping at the surface.

- The sucker rods are attached to a *positive displacement pump* at the bottom of the well.

- When the pumping unit reciprocates, the motion is passed through the motion of the rods to the pump.

Beam Pumping

Figure 3-1.22. Beam pumping units like this one are a common sight in certain areas where oil is present.

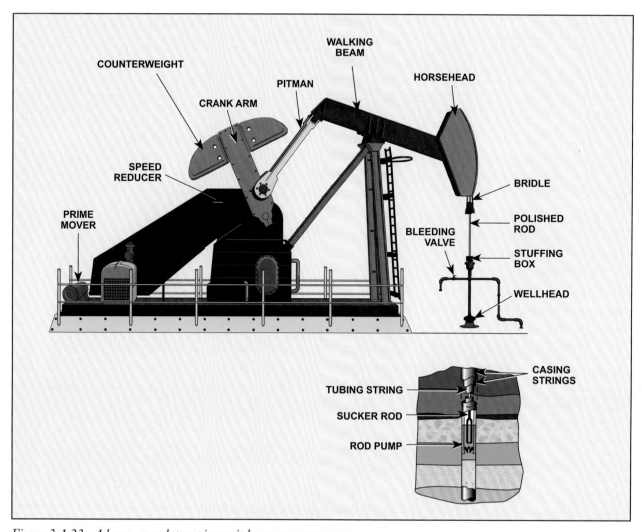

Figure 3-1.23. A beam, or rod, pumping unit has many components.

- A plunger in the pump is moved up and down with the motion of the pumping unit.
- On the upstroke, fluids are trapped above a *traveling valve* in the plunger and moved one stroke at a time toward the surface.
- During the upstroke, reservoir fluids enter the barrel of the pump that is being emptied by the upward motion of the plunger.
- On the downstroke, a *standing valve* at the bottom of the pump closes, trapping the fluid inside the barrel, then the traveling valve opens, allowing the plunger to fall back into the now-full barrel.
- This process repeats while pumping liquid to the surface.

Beam pumping, known as *beam lift*, is extremely versatile and can lift fluid from both shallow and deep depths in volumes of a few barrels to several hundred barrels per day. Beam lift can economically lift fluids from reservoirs with extremely low reservoir pressure. The reservoir pressure needs to be enough to cause fluid to fall into the bottom of the well. After that, beam lift can take over.

Electric submersible pumps (ESPs) are centrifugal pumps linked to a motor. The pump and motor are placed in the well at the end of the tubing. The motor is powered by electricity sent down an armored cable from the surface (fig. 3-1.24). The cable is strapped to the outside of the tubing. A protector is placed between the pump and motor and seals the well fluids away from the motor. The pressure required to move fluids from the bottom of the well to the surface is developed by stacking a large number of centrifugal impellers on top of one another in the pump section. Each impeller takes fluid at the discharge pressure of the impeller just below. The fluid velocity is increased by the rotation of the impeller. Then part of that velocity energy is converted to pressure as the fluid exits the impeller and enters the impeller above.

As many as 100 impellers, called *stages*, can be used in ESPs. The great advantage of ESPs is their capability to pump extremely large volumes of fluid. Volumes from several hundred to several thousand barrels per day can be pumped by an ESP. The disadvantages of ESPs are that they are sensitive to sand and gas entering and damaging the impellers, and they must never be allowed to pump dry or the motor will overheat. ESPs are expensive to buy, and their electric power cost can be very high. ESPs are used in high-volume wells where volumes pumped are larger than can be handled by other artificial-lift devices.

Electric Submersible Pumps

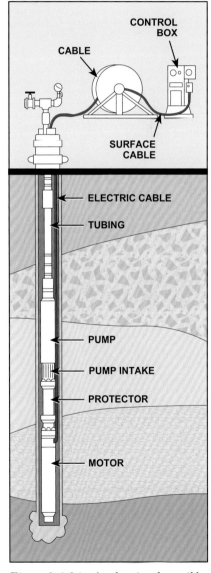

Figure 3-1.24. An electric submersible pump

Subsurface Hydraulic Pumps

Subsurface hydraulic pumps are placed at the bottom of the well in the tubing and function by pumping power fluid down to the pump (fig. 3-1.25). The power fluid can be oil or water. A pump at the surface pumps the power fluid back down the well through tubing to the pump. At the bottom of the tubing, the power fluid causes the subsurface pump to function. The power fluid mixes with the produced fluid and is pumped back to the surface through a parallel string of tubing or up the tubing-casing annulus. Next, the power fluid is separated from the produced fluid in the surface facility and reused. Subsurface hydraulic pumps are applied where there are more volumes of fluid to be pumped than a beam pump can handle but less fluid volume than an ESP can pump. Subsurface pumps are expensive and subject to erosion by produced fluid, especially fluids that contain gas or solids.

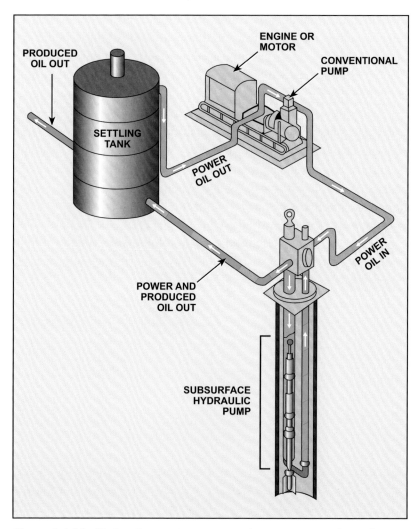

Figure 3-1.25. Hydraulic pumping system with components on the surface and in the well

Progressing cavity pumps (PCPs) are positive displacement pumps run on the bottom of the tubing. The pump is made up of a helical stainless steel rotor that fits inside a helical rubber-lined stator, or pump body, that has a slightly different pitch than the rotor. The differences in shape of the helix between the rotor and the stator form cavities as the rotor turns inside the stator. The cavities fill with fluid and the motion of the rotor sweeps out the fluid into the next cavity above. The rotor turns by steel sucker rods connected to a motor and gear box at the surface or to a downhole motor and gear box connected either to the rotor at the bottom of the well, similar to the motor and pump of an ESP. PCPs can handle fluid in volumes between what a beam lift and an ESP can handle. They are limited to roughly 5,000 to 6,000 feet (1,524 to 1,828.8 metres) in depth in which they can be run due to their limited discharge pressure capacity. In addition, PCPs can handle viscous and dirty fluids, and even some gas, but with decreased pump efficiency, as is the case with all pumps mentioned.

Progressing Cavity Pumps

Wells that no longer have sufficient reservoir pressure to flow to the surface can be induced to flow again if the density, or weight, of the well fluid can be lessened. *Gas lift* does this by mixing natural gas from another source with the reservoir fluids in the well. The added gas reduces the mixture density to a point where the remaining reservoir pressure causes the fluids to flow to the surface. The extra gas needed to reduce fluid density is injected down the tubing-casing annulus from the surface. The gas enters the tubing either at the bottom, if the tubing is not sealed, or through a gas-lift valve, if the tubing is sealed in a packer.

Gas lift does not require a pump or any moving parts other than a few gas-lift valves. In fact, gas lift can work with only an entry way for gas to enter the tubing from the tubing-casing annulus. No special wellhead equipment is required, and no special surface equipment, other than perhaps a gas compressor and a gas-liquid separator, are required. This works for wells where pulling the tubing to repair the downhole pumping equipment would be very expensive, or where surface space is limited as with offshore wells. Gas lift is well suited for lifting hundreds to thousands of barrels per day. Its lifting capacity is between that of beam lift and ESPs. Gas lift does not have a depth limitation but requires an outside gas source. Enough reservoir pressure must remain to cause the lower density fluid mixture to flow to the surface. If the reservoir pressure is lower than this limit, gas lift will not work and some other method, such as beam lift, will be necessary.

Gas Lift

Gas lift can bring up thousands of barrels a day from any depth with proper reservoir pressure.

Plunger Lift

Commonly used methods of artificial lift:
- Beam pumping
- Electric submersible pumps
- Surface hydraulic pumps
- Progressive cavity pumps
- Gas lift
- Plunger lift

Plunger lift is a method of lifting small volumes of liquid from a gas well or an oilwell with a high gas-oil ratio. The liquid volume is usually a few barrels up to a few tens of barrels per day. The gradual accumulation of liquid in the well develops a *liquid segment* that is too heavy or dense for the reservoir pressure to flow it to the surface. A plunger is placed in the tubing and allowed to fall to a bumper at the bottom of the tubing. The plunger acts as a restriction in the tubing but has ports that allow liquid to accumulate on top of the plunger. The well is temporarily shut in at the surface, allowing the reservoir pressure to build up beneath the plunger. When the surface control reaches a set point of pressure, it opens the surface valve and the trapped pressure beneath the plunger causes the plunger with fluid on top to rise to the surface. The plunger is held at the surface while the well fluid flows down the flow line. When the surface pressure falls to a set point, the plunger is released and the well is shut in so the cycle can repeat. This type of well might also unload liquid using a beam pump or, in some cases, using gas lift.

When the well is completed, gas and oil flows from the reservoir into the bottom of the well. If sufficient reservoir pressure remains at the bottom of the well, the fluid flows to the surface. Otherwise, the fluid will be artificially lifted to the surface.

The flow of fluid always occurs from an area of high pressure to an area of low pressure. The bottom of the well is a lower pressure area compared to the pressure in the reservoir. Thus, fluid flows from the reservoir into the well. The pressure in the reservoir is generally reduced over time as fluid is removed from the reservoir. The longer reservoir pressure is maintained at a higher value, the longer flow continues into the well and the larger will be the final recovery of oil and gas from the reservoir. The first period in the producing life of a reservoir is called *primary recovery*, or *primary production*. During this stage, natural energies in the reservoir cause fluids to flow into the bottom of the well. These natural energies are known as *reservoir drive mechanisms*.

Reservoir drive mechanisms include:

- Depletion drive
- Water drive
- Gravity drainage
- Combinations of these

RESERVOIR DRIVE MECHANISMS

Depletion drive is the expansion of the reservoir as fluid is produced. The reservoir fluids, and even the reservoir rock, are compressible to a certain extent, depending on the type of fluids and rock. Gas is a highly compressible fluid. Oil and water are only slightly compressible, and consolidated rock is almost incompressible. The reservoir is under original pressure created by the depth at which the reservoir exists and the geologic processes that created the reservoir. The pressure exerted on the reservoir acts to compress the rock and fluids. As fluids flow out of the reservoir and no fluids are put back in, the reservoir pressure begins to decline. When the pressure decreases, the compressed fluids and the reservoir itself begin to expand. This expansion keeps reservoir pressure from declining rapidly. There is a limit to how much each part of the reservoir can expand:

- Rock expands only slightly.
- Oil and water in the reservoir can expand slightly more than the rock.
- Gas that is dissolved in the oil will bubble out of the oil and expand even more, compared to rock, water, or oil.
- If there is a free-gas section on top of the oil, called a gas cap, this gas will expand even more because of the concentrated amount in one place.

Depletion Drive

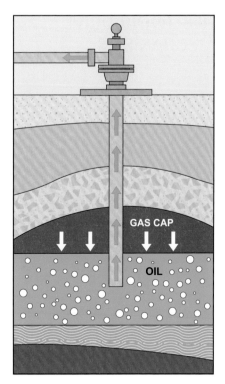

Figure 3-1.26. In a gas-cap drive reservoir, the free gas in the cap and the gas dissolved in the oil expand to move oil up to the surface.

The amount of pressure support that gas can provide is proportional to the volume of gas present. So, a large free gas cap on top of the oil will expand for a longer time, as opposed to small volumes of gas that might be dissolved in the oil. The expansion of a gas cap is called *gas-cap drive* (fig. 3-1.26). The expansion of gas originally dissolved in oil is called a *solution-gas drive* (fig. 3-1.27). For oil reservoirs, the primary recovery from a solution-gas drive will be only about 10% to 15% of the original oil in place. A gas-cap drive might recover as much as 20% to 25% of the original oil in place.

Gas reservoirs also produce by depletion drive. Gas is a highly compressible fluid and it has a very low viscosity compared to liquid. Gas flows efficiently due to gas expansion alone. As long as the reservoir pressure is slightly larger than the pressure in the well, gas will continue to flow. The recovery of gas by depletion drive is normally very high, as much as 80% or more of the original gas in place.

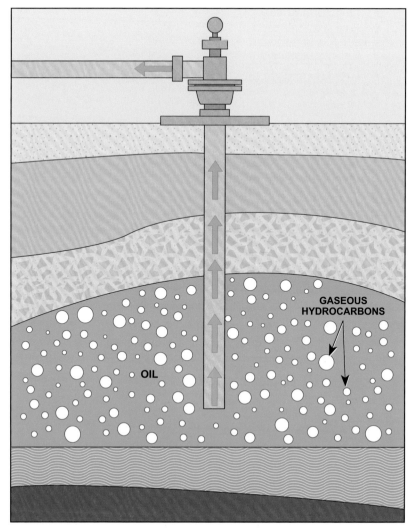

Figure 3-1.27. In a solution-gas drive reservoir, gas comes out of the oil, expands and lifts it to the surface.

Water drive is also normally caused by fluid expansion. In this case, the oil or gas reservoir exists on top of a large water section (figs. 3-1.28 and 3-1.29). The water-bearing part of the reservoir is called the *aquifer*, and it can be many times the size of the oil- or gas-bearing portion of the reservoir. While it is true that water is only slightly compressible, due to the size of the aquifer relative to the oil or gas portion, the water can provide enough expansion to keep the reservoir pressure high. If the aquifer is not large compared to the oil or gas portion, the support from the water pressure will not last long before the water expands to its full extent. After full expansion occurs, the drive reverts to a depletion or gravity drainage mechanism, or both. However, if the aquifer is extremely large, water expansion will last a long time, perhaps long enough to flow all the oil or gas displaced by the invading water out of the reservoir. If this occurs, the water expansion will eventually cause water to flow into the bottom of the wells (fig. 3-1.30). In very rare instances, the aquifer might actually emerge, or outcrop, supported by water recharge. For example, this has occurred with oil reservoirs located below the Andes Mountains.

Water Drive

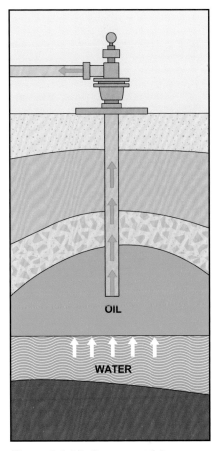

Figure 3-1.28. In a water-drive reservoir, saltwater under the oil pushes the oil to the surface.

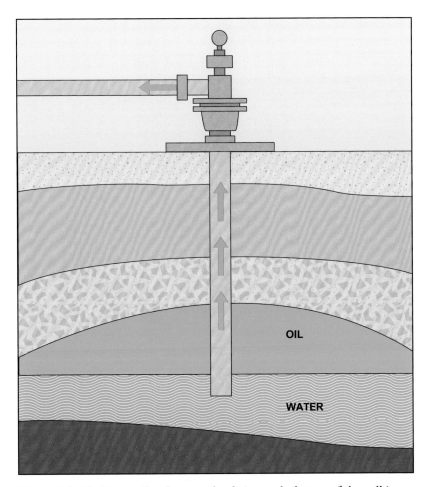

Figure 3-1.30. Eventually, the water level rises to the bottom of the well in a water-drive reservoir.

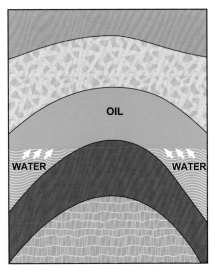

Figure 3-1.29. Water at the edges of the reservoir helps drive the oil into the wellbore.

For oil reservoirs, the recovery of oil pushed by expanding water is relatively efficient, especially compared to depletion-drive recoveries. With a strong water drive, oil recovery can reach 50% to 60% of the original oil in place. Limited water drives have recovery fractions that are better than depletion drive, but not as good as strong water drives.

Gas reservoirs can also experience a water drive. A water drive in a gas reservoir is not desirable because the gas expansion alone is a highly efficient gas recovery mechanism. A strong water drive might actually cause water to flow around and trap pockets of gas in the reservoir that would otherwise have been recovered.

Gravity Drainage

Gravity drainage occurs in steeply dipping reservoirs where a well has been drilled *downdip* or in the downhill part of the reservoir (fig. 3-1.31). The force of gravity causes oil to flow downhill into the well. The force exists even after most of the original reservoir pressure has been exhausted.

The force of gravity alone does not provide very much pressure to keep the fluids flowing, so the production rate is low when only gravity is at work. Many old wells are still producing today because of gravity drainage. Oil recovery with the assistance of gravity drainage can be as high as 50% of the original oil in place, but recovery time can be long and oil production rates low.

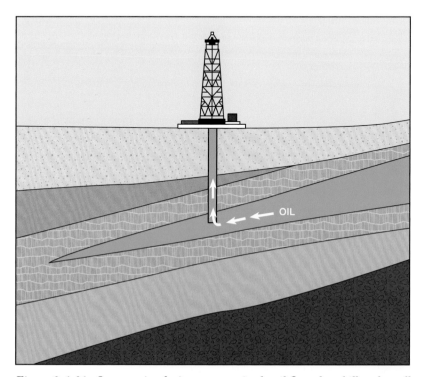

Figure 3-1.31. In a gravity-drainage reservoir, the oil flows downhill to the well.

Gas reservoirs can also exist in steeply dipping reservoirs. Gravity drainage is not as helpful in gas reservoirs because gas is much less dense than oil, so the effect of gravity is much less and the recovery of gas by gas expansion is already extremely efficient.

Combination Drives

Combination drives are a combination of the drive types discussed. The recovery of oil and gas from a reservoir with a combination drive will reflect the types of drives at work. As mentioned in the water drive section, it is possible to have a limited water drive that is exhausted first and followed by depletion drive. The oil recovery from such a combination would be better than just the depletion drive alone, but not as good as a strong water drive, perhaps between 25% and 40% of the original oil in place, depending on the strength of the water drive.

WELL TESTING

Well testing is done for many reasons and in many different ways. Tests can be used as follows:

- To monitor the production capability of a well
- To determine changes in production capability over time
- To determine the reservoir drive mechanism
- To estimate how much oil or gas might be recovered over time

There are many types of well tests. Two broad types are discussed next.

Potential or Production Tests

A well is produced at varying flow rates for a given time period. Production rates and flowing pressures are carefully measured over the period of flow. Flow pressures are always recorded at the surface. They can also be pressures recorded down in the well.

Lease operators collect produced fluid samples to analyze. They perform *potential tests* when first producing the well and again many times over the life of the well to monitor changes in the well's production capability. Government regulatory agencies usually require potential test information to establish well capability. Producing companies use the information for the same purpose. They also use the information to detect changing conditions in the well and reservoir and to estimate oil and gas recovery.

Bottomhole Pressure Test

A *bottomhole pressure test* uses a gauge to measure pressure at or near the bottom of the well. The recording instrument can be a retrievable gauge placed in the well temporarily for the test using wireline. Pressure gauges can also be permanently installed on the tubing. Data can be transmitted to the surface through an electric wire or a fiber-optic cable strapped to the outside of the tubing.

The pressure at the bottom of the well is a direct measurement of reservoir pressure near the wellbore. This data is more easily interpreted than pressures recorded at the surface, because the pressure interference caused by flow to the surface is absent. Pressure data recorded over time is a good indicator and can be used to detect reservoir damage that might occur near the well.

IMPROVED RECOVERY TECHNIQUES

Reservoir drive mechanisms cannot draw all the oil from a well, so special methods can be applied to boost recovery of more oil.

Depending on the reservoir drive mechanism, a substantial amount of oil will be left in the reservoir at the end of primary production. For example, depletion drives generally leave between 75% and 90% of the original oil in place. Techniques have been developed to improve recovery. They can be used in certain reservoirs with certain types of oil, if there is enough oil left behind to recover economically.

The major methods of improved oil recovery are:

- Water flooding
- Gas injection
- Chemical flooding
- Thermal recovery

Table 3-1.1 summarizes each process and its primary use.

Table 3-1.1.

Improved Recovery Methods

Method of Recovery		Process	Use
Waterflooding	Water	Water is pumped into the reservoir through injection wells to force oil toward production wells.	Method most widely used in secondary recovery
Immiscible Gas Injection	Natural gas, flue gas, nitrogen	Gas is injected to maintain formation pressure, to slow the rate of decline of natural reservoir drives, and sometimes to enhance gravity drainage.	Secondary recovery
Miscible Gas Injection	Carbon dioxide	Under pressure, carbon dioxide becomes miscible with oil, lowers the oil viscosity, and enables the oil to flow more freely. Often followed by injection of water.	Secondary or tertiary recovery
	Hydrocarbons (propane, high-pressure methane, enriched methane)	Either naturally or under pressure, hydrocarbons are miscible with oil. Might be followed by injection of gas or water.	Secondary or tertiary recovery; not common because of the market demand for the hydrocarbons
Chemical Flooding	Polymer	Water thickened with polymers is used to aid water flooding by improving fluid-flow patterns.	Used during secondary and tertiary recovery
	Surfactant	A solution of surfactant (soap) lowers the interfacial tension of oil and allows it to flow to a well. The same effect as washing oil off hands with soap. Polymers can also be used to improve the flow pattern.	Secondary or tertiary recovery
	Alkaline (caustic)	Less expensive alkaline chemicals are injected and react with certain types of crude oil to form a soap.	May be used with polymer; has been used for tertiary recovery after secondary recovery by water-flooding or polymer flooding
Thermal Recovery	Steam drive	Steam is injected continuously into heavy-oil reservoirs to lower the oil viscosity and allow flow to wells.	Primary recovery; secondary recovery when oil is too viscous for waterflooding; tertiary recovery after secondary recovery by water flooding or steam soak
	Steam soak	Steam is injected into the production well and allowed to spread during a shut-in soak period. The steam heats heavy oil in the surrounding formation to lower the viscosity. The well is then produced to recover the oil.	Used during primary or secondary production
	In situ combustion	Part of the oil in the reservoir is set on fire, and compressed air is injected to keep it burning. Gases and heat advance through the formation, thinning the oil and pushing it to a well.	Used with heavy-oil reservoirs during primary recovery when oil is too viscous to flow under normal reservoir conditions; this process is rarely used

Waterflooding

Waterflooding is used in depletion-drive oil reservoirs or in water-drive reservoirs with limited natural water drive. Carefully selected wells undergo an injection of water to refill the reservoir and restore reservoir pressure (fig. 3-1.32). Once reservoir pressure is restored, continued water injection begins sweeping oil toward the producing wells. When correctly used, waterflooding will recover the same fraction of oil as a strong natural water drive, which is normally between 50% and 60%. Waterflooding requires large volumes of acceptable water; that is, water that is clean and completely compatible with the reservoir rock and fluids. This prevents scale or emulsion from plugging the reservoir.

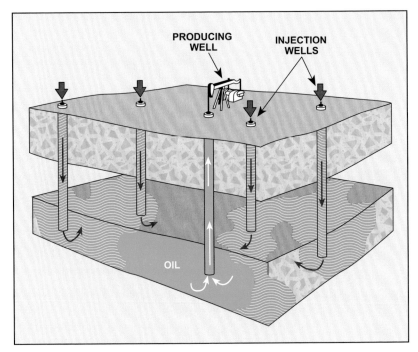

Figure 3-1.32. In waterflooding, water is injected into wells around the producing well. This is a five-spot pattern—four injection wells and one producer—but many other patterns can be used.

An *immiscible gas* is one that will not mix with oil. Such a gas can be injected into wells in alternating steps with water to improve recovery. The water injection step improves flow of the gas into the reservoir by preventing or slowing down the spread of the low-viscosity gas through the higher viscosity oil. Immiscible gases include natural gas at reservoir pressures below the miscibility pressure with oil, nitrogen, or flue gas. This process is called *immiscible gas injection*, and when it is alternated with water injection, it is called *water-alternating gas (WAG)* injection.

Immiscible gas injected into the well behaves in a manner similar to that in a gas-cap drive. The gas expands to provide additional reservoir pressure to keep the oil flowing to a well. Gas injection requires the use of compressors to raise the pressure of the gas so when it enters the reservoir, it can expand to support the reservoir pressure.

Immiscible Gas Injection

A second type of gas injection, *miscible gas injection*, uses gas that is miscible (mixable) with oil. When the gas mixes with oil, the oil's viscosity is reduced, allowing the oil to flow more freely to the well (fig. 3-1.33). The injection pressure with added gas causes support of the reservoir pressure, which provides pressure drive for fluid flow in the reservoir.

The petroleum industry first began using miscible gas injection in the 1950s. Injection gases include *liquefied petroleum gases (LPGs)* such as propane, methane under high pressure, methane enriched with light hydrocarbons, and carbon dioxide used alone or followed by water. LPGs are appropriate for use in many reservoirs because they are miscible with crude oil. However, LPGs are in high demand as a marketable commodity, which has limited their use in improved recovery.

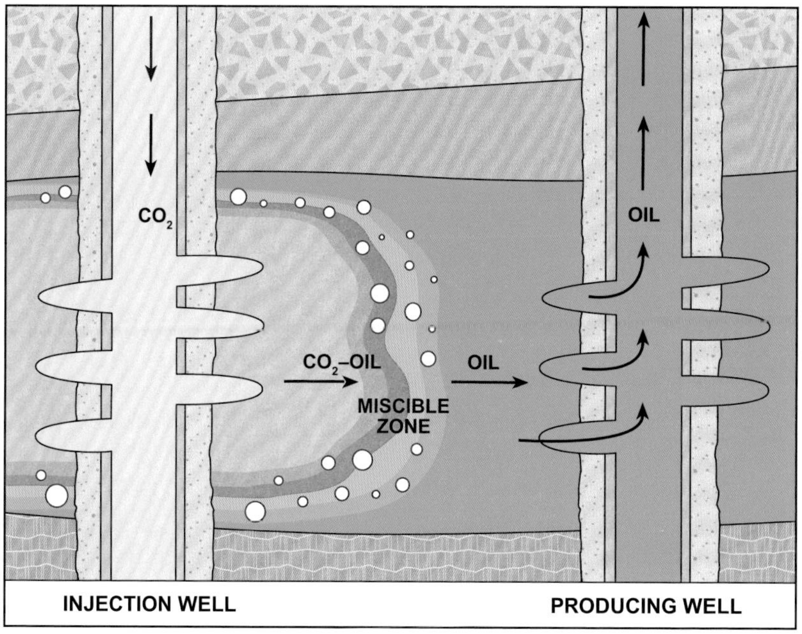

Miscible Gas Injection

Figure 3-1.33. Miscible gas injection

In the 1970s, carbon dioxide began to be used frequently as an injection gas. Carbon dioxide is miscible with oil under correct conditions. Methane is also miscible under correct conditions, but its use is limited because of its high market value. In areas with a ready supply of carbon dioxide, it is an attractive choice because it costs less than LPGs and methane. Carbon dioxide is a greenhouse gas, so when it is used this way, the process becomes a method of storing the gas to reduce carbon dioxide emissions.

Chemical Flooding

Chemical flooding is a general term for injection processes that use special chemicals in water to push oil out of the formation (fig. 3-1.34). The principle is to add a *surfactant* such as soap to the injection water. For example, ordinary dishwashing detergent contains surfactants. A surfactant molecule is attracted to both oil and water, so it reduces surface tension that otherwise holds portions of the oil in the pores of the rock. By reducing the *interfacial tension*, more of the oil is freed to flow to a well.

In one type of chemical flooding, *surfactant-polymer flooding*, a batch, or *slug*, of water containing surfactant is injected into the reservoir, followed by a volume of water thickened with *polymer*. Polymers increase water viscosity, decrease effective rock permeability, and can change viscosity with flow rate. This evens out the flow pattern of water through a reservoir and makes it less likely to bypass oil in low-permeability rock.

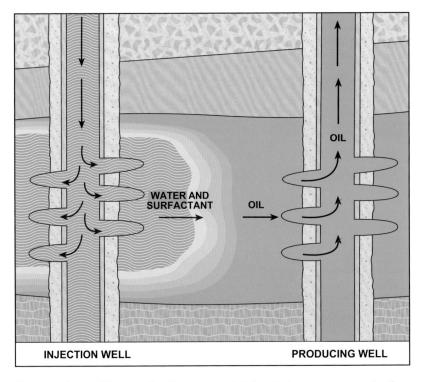

Figure 3-1.34. Chemical flooding uses special chemicals in water to push oil out of the formation.

In *alkaline flooding*, or *caustic flooding*, the chemicals react with natural acids present in certain crude oils to form surfactants within the reservoir. The surfactant formed in the reservoir works the same way as an injected surfactant to release additional amounts of oil to flow to the well.

Thermal Recovery

Oil in some reservoirs is so viscous, or thick, that it cannot flow through the reservoir and into a well. Just as tar or other solid materials can be forced to flow with heat, so can some viscous oils. Recovery techniques that use heat are called *thermal processes* or *thermal recovery*.

Steam Drive

Steam injection, also known as *steam drive* or *continuous steam injection*, involves generating steam on the surface and forcing it down injection wells into the reservoir (fig. 3-1.35). When the steam enters the reservoir, it heats up the oil and reduces its viscosity. The steam flows through the reservoir, cools a little, and condenses (forms hot water).

The heat from the steam and hot water vaporizes lighter hydrocarbons, or turns them into gases. These gases move ahead of the steam, cool, and condense back into liquids that dissolve in the oil. In this way, the gases and steam provide additional gas drive. The hot water acts like a waterflood and moves the thinned oil to production wells where oil and water are produced.

In some shallow, heavy-oil reservoirs, horizontal wells are drilled one on top of another. Steam is injected into the top well, heating the oil and allowing gravity to assist flow into the lower well. This process is called *steam-assisted gravity drainage (SAGD)*.

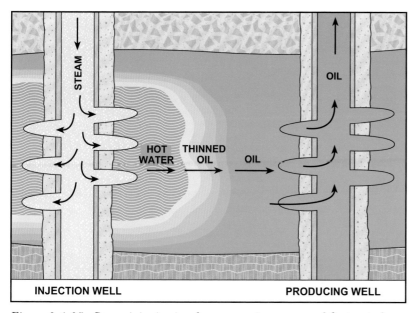

Figure 3-1.35. Steam injection involves generating steam and forcing it down injection wells into the reservoir.

Cyclic Steam Injection

Another injection method is *cyclic steam injection*, or *huff and puff*. Each huff-and-puff operation involves only one well, although many wells can be treated at one time.

As in steam drive, the cyclic steam injection method injects steam down the well and into the reservoir to heat the oil. Then steam injection stops, and the operator closes in the well to let the reservoir soak for several days. In the reservoir, the steam condenses, and a zone of hot water and less-viscous oil forms. Finally, the crew reopens the well, and the hot water and thinned oil flow out.

This process of steam injection, soaking, and production can be repeated until economic oil recovery stops.

Fireflooding

Still another way to use heat in a reservoir is *fireflooding*, or *in-situ combustion* (fig. 3.-1.36). In-situ means "in place." In fireflooding, a fire is ignited in place in the reservoir.

To do this, compressed air is injected down an injection well and into the reservoir because combustion cannot take place without air. A special heater in the well ignites the oil in the reservoir and starts a fire. As the fire burns, it begins moving through the reservoir toward the production wells. Continued compressed air injection behind the fire provides oxygen to continue combustion. Heat from the fire thins the oil around it, causes gas to vaporize from it, and changes water in the reservoir to steam. Steam, hot water, and gas act to drive oil in front of the fire toward the production wells.

This technique has been successful but is rare compared to the other thermal methods.

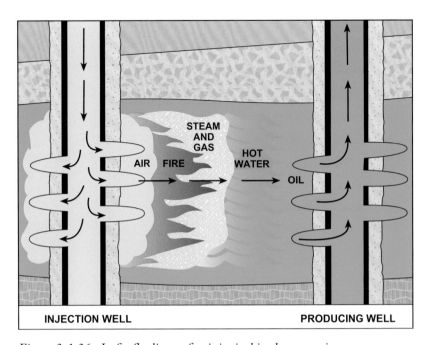

Figure 3-1.36. In fireflooding, a fire is ignited in the reservoir.

Oil and gas are not usually salable directly from the wellhead. Fluids typically exit a well as a mixture of oil, gas, and water, and several steps are necessary to prepare the oil and/or gas for sale (fig. 3-1.37).

The general process is as follows:

- The well stream is passed through a series of separating and treating devices to separate the oil, gas, and water.
- The oil is temporarily stored and tested for quality. It is then sold and transported to a refinery through a pipeline or by truck, tank car, barge, or tanker.
- The gas is tested for hydrocarbon content and impurities. It is sometimes compressed to a pressure high enough to enter the pipeline. The gas is then sold through a pipeline.
- The water is reused or sent to a disposal well.

SURFACE HANDLING OF WELL FLUIDS

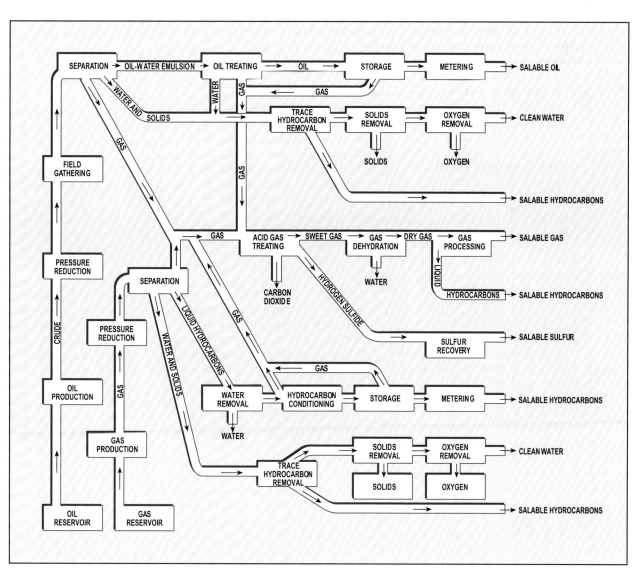

Figure 3-1.37. Steps are necessary to ready oil or gas for sale.

Separating Liquids from Gases

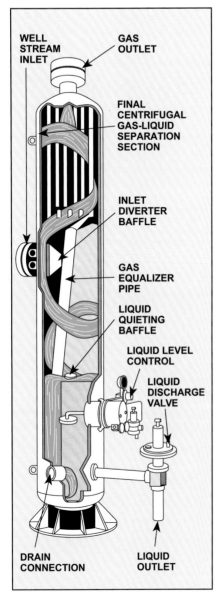

Figure 3-1.38. Gravity is used to separate well fluids in a vertical separator.

When field processing fluids from a well, the first step is to separate most of the gas from the liquids with a *two-phase separator*. This type of separator can be a vertical or a horizontal vessel (figs. 3-1.38 and 3-1.39).

The gas separates from the liquid inside the vessel using the force of gravity. The less-dense gas quickly rises to the top of the vessel, while the denser liquid collects in the bottom. A pressure sensor or a float monitors the liquid level inside the separator and opens a valve to automatically let some liquid flow out of the vessel when the correct level is reached. A device on the gas outlet, called a *back-pressure regulator*, holds a certain amount of pressure on the vessel. This regulator keeps constant pressure inside the vessel. Gas pressure from this vessel can sometimes be kept high enough for the gas to exit directly into a pipeline, if the pipeline quality requirements have been met. If not, the gas can be boosted to the correct pressure by a gas compressor so it can enter the pipeline. Removing the majority of the gas, not only allows the gas to exit the separator at the highest possible pressure, but also removes a large volume of the gas from the produced stream so smaller separators can be used next.

Courtesy of KW International

Figure 3-1.39. A horizontal separator

The liquids dumped from the high-pressure, two-phase separator are oil, water, and possibly an emulsion (water-in-oil or oil-in-water). The water not emulsified with oil is known as *free water*. Because water is heavier than oil, gravity alone will supply sufficient force to separate this free water from the oil and the emulsion when given the opportunity.

A *free-water knockout (FWKO)* is a vertical or horizontal vessel that provides a space for free water to settle out of the well stream (fig. 3-1.40). This vessel operates at a lower pressure than a two-phase separator, so some gas still dissolved in the oil will bubble out in this separator. The gas that evolves from the oil in this separator is removed and can be compressed and added to the gas from the two-phase separator, or used as fuel. There are three phases separated in this vessel: free water, emulsion or oil, and gas that comes out of the oil. Therefore, this type of separator is called a *three-phase separator*.

The advantage of removing the free water at this point is to reduce the volume of liquid that must be treated in the final separator. This allows use of a smaller final emulsion separator. If no emulsion is in this vessel, it could be the final device used to separate the water from clean oil. A back-pressure regulator holds a set amount of gas pressure in the separator, and dump valves regulate the level of oil or emulsion and free water inside the vessel. Then the water is dumped to a water treatment or disposal facility. If the oil is in the form of an emulsion, it is passed to a final separator. If the oil is clean, it is dumped to a holding tank.

Removing Free Water

Vessels used in separating gas from liquids:
- Two-phase (gas-liquid) separator
- Free-water knockout
- Three-phase (gas-water-oil) separator

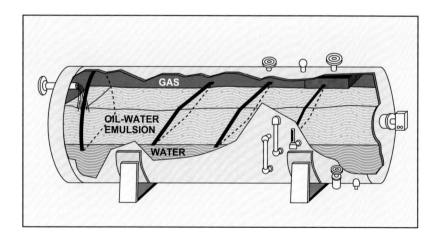

Figure 3-1.40. A horizontal, three-phase free-water knockout provides space for the free water to settle out and the gas to rise.

Treating Oilfield Emulsions

Emulsifiers that help form petroleum emulsions:
- Asphalt
- Resinous substances
- Oil-soluble organic acids

If an emulsion is present, the final separation occurs in an emulsion treater, three-phase separator that not only allows the emulsion time to separate by gravity but also provides extra mechanisms that help the emulsion come apart or break.

The two liquids that form an emulsion—oil and water, in this case—are *immiscible* liquids, meaning they do not mix together under normal conditions (fig. 3-1.41). Instead, they form an emulsion only when agitated to disperse one liquid as droplets in the other and when the mixture contains an emulsifying agent, or *emulsifier*. Emulsifiers commonly found in petroleum emulsions include asphalt, resinous substances, and oil-soluble organic acids.

To break down a stable emulsion into its components, some form of treating is necessary. An emulsion is described as tight (difficult to break) or loose (easy to break). Whether an emulsion is tight or loose depends on the properties of the oil and water, the percentage of each found in the emulsion, and the type and amount of emulsifier present.

Treating facilities might use a single process or a combination of processes to break down an emulsion, depending on the emulsion being treated. To break down a common water-in-oil emulsion, the properties of the emulsifying agent must be neutralized or destroyed so the droplets of water can come together. Such treatments use chemicals, heat, or electricity, along with gravity.

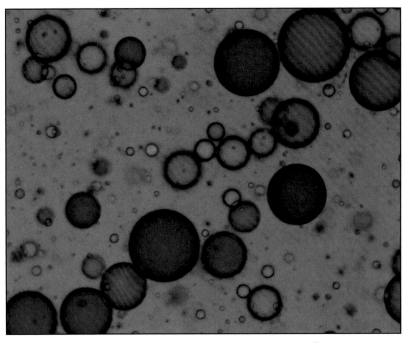

Courtesy of N. Bremond/LCMD-ESCPI

Figure 3-1.41. An emulsion is made up of two liquids that will not mix together under normal conditions.

Chemicals called *demulsifiers* are added to the emulsion to make the droplets of water merge, or *coalesce*. When droplets coalesce, they get bigger, and big water droplets settle out faster than small ones. A *bottle test* helps determine which chemical is the most efficient demulsifier for a particular emulsion (fig. 3-1.42). Results from a bottle test also indicate the smallest amount of treating chemical necessary to break the quantity of emulsion being produced. A demulsifier can be injected into the separator to help the emulsion break.

Chemical Treatment

Courtesy of BJ Services

Figure 3-1.42. A bottle test helps determine which chemical is the most efficient demulsifier for a particular emulsion.

Heat is used to break emulsions. When an emulsion is heated, it becomes less viscous, and the water and oil molecules move about rapidly, causing the water droplets to strike each other. When the force and frequency of the collision are great enough, the film of emulsifier that surrounds each droplet breaks, and the water droplets merge and separate from the oil.

Heat Treatment

Electricity is also used to help break emulsions, usually in conjunction with heat and chemicals. The film around the water droplets formed by the emulsifier is composed of molecules that have a positive and a negative end, much like a bar magnet. When an electric current disturbs this film of polar molecules, the molecules rearrange themselves. Then the film is no longer stable and adjacent water droplets coalesce freely until large drops form and settle out by gravity.

Treatment with Electricity

Types of Emulsion Treaters

Heater-Treater

A *heater-treater* is a three-phase separator with an internal fire tube (figs. 3-1.43 and 3-1.44). The emulsion enters the area around the fire tube where heat is added to the emulsion, normally by burning natural gas in the fire tube. Emulsions are heated to around 100° Fahrenheit (38° Celsius) in the heater-treater. The heater-treater is a three-phase separator where the oil that separates from the emulsion floats to the top of the emulsion, the water that separates sinks to the bottom, and any gas evolving from the oil exits the top.

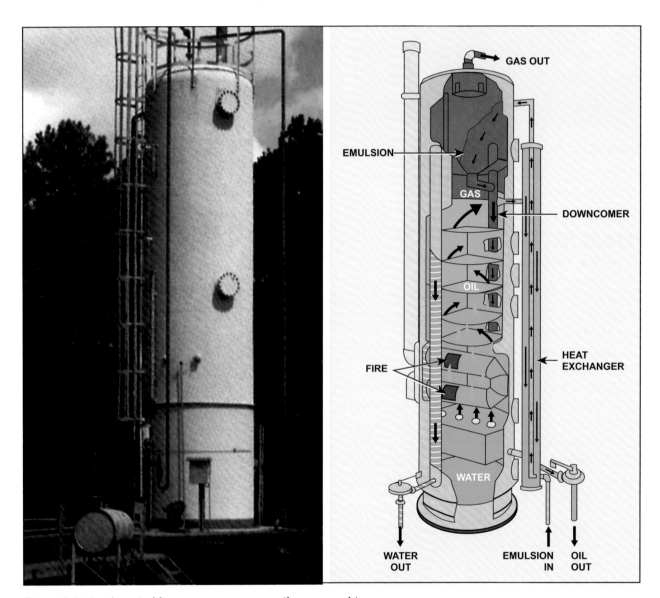

Figure 3-1.43. A vertical heater-treater separates oil-water emulsions.

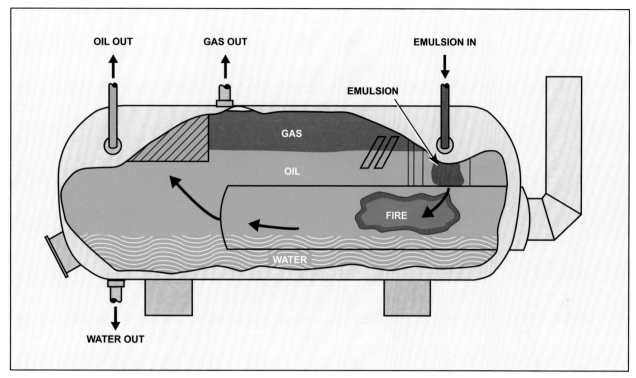

Figure 3-1.44. Horizontal heater-treater

Electrostatic Treater

Similar in design and operation to a horizontal heater-treater is an *electrostatic treater*. This treater features a high-voltage electric grid instead of a fire tube. The emulsion rises to the grid and receives a charge that causes the water to coalesce and settle out. The advantage of an electrostatic treater is that no fire is present. The disadvantages are that electricity must be available and the electric grid inside the vessel is more prone to break down than the gas-fired treater.

Controlling Paraffin

Paraffin is a white, hydrocarbon wax sometimes found in petroleum. When it invades surface equipment used to treat well fluids, it causes problems. Paraffin can severely reduce the efficiency of oil and gas separators and make the equipment inoperable by building up in the vessel or blocking fluid passages. Paraffin problems can also occur in the well (see Well Servicing and Repair later in this chapter). Paraffin forms from oil with a high paraffin content that cools below the *cloud-point temperature*. Below this temperature, paraffin precipitates from the oil and forms solid wax. Steaming and using solvents are effective controls, but the most common method of preventing paraffin buildup is to keep the oil at a temperature warmer than the cloud point.

Handling Natural Gas

Once the gas has been separated from the liquids, it generally requires further processing. Whether this processing happens in the field in a gas processing plant, or not at all, depends on the following factors:

- Type of well
- Content of the well fluids
- Climate conditions
- Sales contract

Whether or not the gas is processed in the field, its pressure must be regulated before sale. The operator installs a regulator to reduce pressure or a compressor to raise pressure as needed.

Preventing Hydrate Formation

Most natural gas contains substantial amounts of water vapor. If the water vapor cools below a certain temperature, *hydrates* can form. A hydrate is a solid crystalline compound formed by hydrocarbons and water at a particular temperature and pressure. It often resembles dirty snow.

For natural gas, at the pressures at which it is normally produced, the hydrate formation temperature is well above the normal freezing point for water. When gas comes from the wellhead, it is usually at a high enough temperature that hydrates will not form. Once the gas exits the well, the flow of the gas is controlled using a choke (a small-diameter tube or restriction). As the gas expands through the narrow choke, a large cooling effect occurs. The gas is often cooled below the hydrate-formation temperature and ice crystals begin to form. Hydrates can pack solidly in gathering lines and equipment and block the flow of gas (fig. 3-1.45).

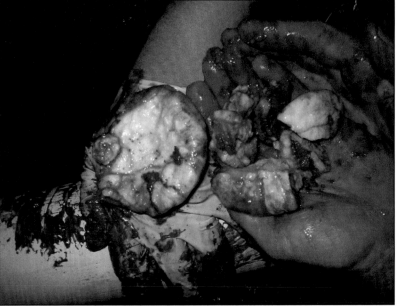

Figure 3-1.45. A gas-hydrate plug taken from an offshore production line

Courtesy of Bill Winters, U.S. Geological Survey

There are two common methods of preventing natural gas hydrates from forming:

- Heat the gas so it does not fall below the hydrate-formation temperature.
- Inject an antifreeze to lower the hydrate-formation temperature. The most common antifreezes are methanol or glycol (fig. 3-1.46).

An *indirect heater* is the most common equipment for heating gas because it is simple, economical, and relatively trouble-free. It consists of a heater shell, a removable fire tube and burner assembly, and a removable coil assembly (fig. 3-1.47). The heater shell is usually filled with water that completely covers the fire tube and the coil assembly. The fire tube heats the water bath, the water bath heats the coil assembly, and the gas is heated as it passes through the coil assembly. The choke is often placed at the entrance to the heater so the gas can be rapidly heated above the hydrate temperature after being cooled by expansion across the choke.

Figure 3-1.46. Methanol or glycol is injected into the gas stream to prevent hydrate formation.

Prevent natural gas hydrates from forming by:
- Heating the gas to the right temperature
- Injecting antifreeze

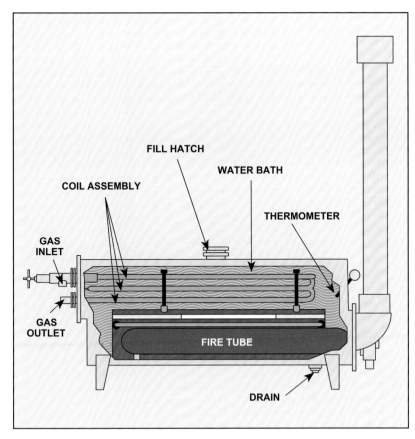

Figure 3-1.47. An indirect heater warms the water bath, which in turn warms the gas flowing through the coil assembly.

Dehydrating

Two dehydration methods are used:
- Absorption—gas is bubbled through a liquid desiccant.
- Adsorption—water vapor-laden gas is passed through a solid desiccant.

Besides forming hydrates, water accelerates corrosion of pipeline and equipment. Water vapor reduces the heating content of the gas. Gas purchasers are buying the heating content or BTUs (British thermal units) of the gas. This means that any reduction in the heating value of gas will reduce the sale price. Many pipeline companies will not buy gas containing more than 7 pounds (3.1752 kg) of water per million cubic feet of gas. To prevent operating problems and also meet contract specifications, the water in the gas must be removed by a process called de*hydration*.

Two dehydration methods are used: *absorption* and *adsorption*. In absorption, the gas is bubbled through a contact tower filled with a liquid *desiccant* called glycol that absorbs the water vapor (fig. 3-1.48). A desiccant is a substance with a special attraction for water vapor. The dehydrated gas exits the top of the contact tower. The liquid glycol becomes saturated with water from the gas, but the saturated glycol can be regenerated in a boiler. Water boils at a lower temperature than glycol, so the water is boiled out of the glycol and collected as steam (fig. 3-1.49).

Courtesy of DPS-Delta

Figure 3-1.48. The glycol liquid-desiccant dehydrator unit is skid-mounted.

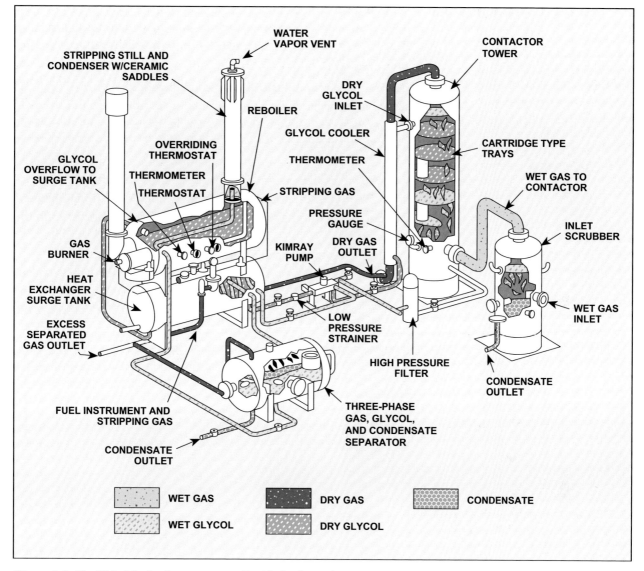

Figure 3-1.49. This dehydration system uses liquid glycol as a desiccant.

The regenerated glycol is sent back to the contact tower to be reused. The steam is condensed and the waste water is then disposed of. Contact time between the gas flowing up and glycol flowing down is improved by either *bubbling the gas* through *bubblers* on trays inside the tower or, even more efficiently, by flowing the gas through corrugated metal packing.

In adsorption, the water vapor-laden gas is passed over a solid desiccant in an *adsorption tower*. The water adheres to the solid desiccant and the dehydrated gas flows out of the adsorption tower. The desiccant bed can be reused after it is dried by heating and vaporizing the water.

Each process has its own unique advantages and disadvantages. Dry-bed adsorption is more likely to be used in a gas processing plant than in the field, due to difficulties in handling dry desiccant.

Removing Contaminants

Natural gas often contains carbon dioxide and hydrogen sulfide. These gases are called *acid gases* because they form acids or acidic solutions in the presence of water. Gases with high concentrations of sulfur are also called *sour gases*. If present in significant quantities, acid gases must be removed from natural gas. Both carbon dioxide and hydrogen sulfide are corrosive when water is present, and hydrogen sulfide is extremely poisonous in relatively small concentrations. Removing these contaminants from natural gas is often called *sweetening* the gas.

The processes for sweetening natural gas are similar to ones used for removing water vapor. Absorption and adsorption processes are used. Two types of absorption processes are applied using chemical and physical means to selectively remove certain acid gases from the natural gas.

In *chemical absorption*, the liquid absorbent reacts chemically with the acid gases but not with the natural gas. The purified gas flows out and heat or low pressure is used to separate the acid gases from the absorbent so the absorbent can be used again. Amine processes are the most widely used sweetening processes in the industry (fig. 3-1.50). They use a continuous operation that applies a solution of water and a chemical called amine to remove carbon dioxide and several sulfur compounds.

Figure 3-1.50. This sweetening unit uses an amine to remove carbon dioxide and sulfur compounds.

In *physical absorption*, the acid gases physically dissolve in the liquid absorbent and the natural gas does not. Again, heat and low pressure are used to separate the acid gases from the absorbent so the absorbent can be reused. Commercial processes of this type include the Selexol™, sulfinol, Rectisol®, and Fluor Solvent™ processes.

In *adsorption*, or *dry-bed processes*, the acid gas stream flows over a solid adsorbent, as in dehydrating. Rather than removing water, this adsorbent removes sulfur compounds and carbon dioxide. Heat or lowered pressure vaporizes the acid gas and removes it from the adsorbent bed. The residue of these processes is carbon dioxide and concentrated hydrogen sulfide. Both of these byproducts require careful handling to prevent escape to the atmosphere. Carbon dioxide once was allowed to vent to the atmosphere, but this is no longer permissible. In the near future, it is likely that carbon dioxide will be injected into a disposal zone to prevent emissions. If there is enough concentrated hydrogen sulfide, it is often economically feasible to convert it to elemental sulfur. If this process is not practical, the concentrated hydrogen sulfide can be injected into an underground disposal zone.

Natural gas is a mixture of methane, ethane, propane, and some heavier hydrocarbons such as *butane* and natural gasoline, ranging from *pentanes* through *nonanes* or *decanes*. In field separators, some of the heavier hydrocarbons liquefy and are removed and sold. For economic reasons, the lease operator often wants to liquefy some or all of the remaining ethane and heavier hydrocarbons and remove them from the methane gas. The liquefied hydrocarbons, known as *natural gas liquids (NGLs)*, are more valuable as liquid fuel or refinery feedstocks than as components of natural gas. Also, if butanes and heavier hydrocarbons are allowed to remain in the natural gas stream, they might condense in the transmission lines during cold weather.

When gas is produced from high-pressure gas wells, the NGLs are usually separated in field facilities. Generally, it is more economical to process gas from an oilwell in a gas processing plant due to the relatively small volumes of gas associated with oilwells.

Natural gas is a mixture of:
- Methane
- Ethane
- Propane
- Butane
- Pentanes
- Nonanes
- Decanes

Removing Natural Gas Liquids

The usual equipment for processing gas from a gas well is a *low-temperature separation unit* (fig. 3-1.51). This equipment partially dehydrates the gas stream and removes NGLs. It takes advantage of the fact that the gas stream coming from the wellhead is under high pressure. After passing through a free-water knockout, the compressed gas is expanded across a choke into a separator vessel. This expansion cools the gas and condenses the heavier hydrocarbons and some of the water vapor into liquids. The NGL and water are collected and separated at the bottom of the vessel, and the gas passes out the top. Then the gas is dehydrated, if necessary, and allowed to enter the gas gathering system. The NGL is stored in a low-pressure tank and the water is disposed of.

Figure 3-1.51. A low-temperature separation unit separates NGLs produced from a gas well.

Oil, natural gas liquids, and water that have been separated are temporarily stored in a group of *stock tanks* or a *tank battery* (fig. 3-1.52). The number and size of tanks in a battery varies, depending on daily production of the wells and frequency of pipeline runs. Onshore, the total storage capacity of a tank battery is usually three to seven days of production. As long as a battery has two or more tanks, one tank can be filling while oil is being run from another. Offshore, it is possible to store large volumes of liquids in a tanker or other structure, although after treating, the oil and gas are generally sent to shore in a pipeline.

Before a tank battery is put into operation, each tank is *strapped*, or calibrated. A strapping contractor measures the dimensions of the tank and computes the amount of oil it contains for each height increment of the tank. The contractor prepares a *tank capacity table* showing the capacity in barrels according to the height of liquid in the tank. This table commonly shows capacity in increments of 0.25 inch (6 millimetres) from the bottom to the top.

Storing Crude Oil

- Onshore, tanks usually store 3-7 days of oil production.
- Offshore, tanks temporarily store oil until transported to shore.

Courtesy of Unit Liner Company

Figure 3-1.52. A battery of stock tanks that temporarily store oil, natural gas liquids, and water after separation.

To measure the oil in a tank:
- A gauger lowers a steel tape.
- The tape indicates level or height of oil.
- The gauger records the level and calculates volume using tank tables.

To measure the amount of oil in a tank, a technician called a *gauger* lowers a steel tape, that has been carefully grounded with a weight on the end, into the tank until it just touches the bottom. The highest point at which oil wets the tape shows the level or height of oil in the tank. The gauger records the oil level. The volume in the tank is determined by reading the tank capacity tables at the measured tank level. A gauger might work for either the lease operator or the pipeline company that intends to buy the oil.

An *automatic tank gauge* consists of a steel gauge line contained in housing. A float on the end of the line rests on the surface of the oil in the tank. The other end of the line is coiled and counterbalanced on the outside of the tank. This end runs through a reading box that shows the height of oil in the tank. Automatic tank readings are possible and data can be transmitted to an office offsite.

Another form of automatic tank gauge uses radar.

Tank Construction

Most tanks are constructed of either bolted or welded steel. They have a bottom drain outlet for draining off *sediment and water (S&W)*, also referred to as *BS&W* (basic sediment and water). Sometimes a worker must enter an empty tank to clean out paraffin and sediment that cannot be removed through the drain outlet. Entering a tank should always be done with caution as the tank might contain lethal gas fumes. Breathing apparatus might be required, and proper safety procedures must be followed.

Oil enters the tank at the top at an *inlet opening*. The pipeline outlet is usually approximately 1 foot (30 centimetres) above the bottom of the tank. The space below this outlet provides room for the collection of S&W. A metal seal closes the pipeline outlet valve when the tank is being filled and is similarly locked in the open position when the tank is being emptied. The seals guarantee the buyer receives the quantity and quality of oil mutually agreed upon by the buyer and the lease operator (often called the *producer*).

Water is frequently stored in fiberglass tanks. Fiberglass is used because it is less expensive than steel and does not corrode when filled with water. It is not safe to use fiberglass or plastic tanks for oil or natural gas liquids because these materials are more easily punctured than steel. They are also insulators and can establish a static charge on the liquid that could lead to an explosion and fire.

The lease operator owns the oil or gas as it comes from the well. The operator then sells it, and the pipeline company transports it to the buyer. The operator, pipeline company, and buyer measure and test the oil and gas at different times.

The pipeline company is often referred to simply as the *pipeline*. The pipeline might test the oil it receives at any time. Therefore, to assure the pipeline company will accept the oil, the operator should sample and test the oil in the same manner as the pipeline. Because the procedures for taking samples and testing water and sediment vary among fields and companies, both the operator and pipeline must agree on how they are done.

Many methods exist for sampling oil. Generally, sampling can be done either automatically or manually. A gauger frequently samples the oil in lease stock tanks manually using *thief sampling*, sometimes called *core sampling*. In thief sampling, a round tube about 15 inches (38 centimetres) long called a *thief* is lowered into the tank to any level within 0.5 inch (13 millimetres) from the bottom of the tank (fig. 3-1.53). A thief has a spring-operated sliding valve that can be tripped to trap the sample. *Petcocks* can be added to the thief to allow for easy removal of the sample from the thief. The thief also has a stinger rod that assists in proper sampling at the pipeline outlet and in obtaining the clearance sample.

    A better but more difficult method of manual sampling is *bottle sampling*. Because of the difficult nature of this method, it is rarely used for lease tanks. One approach uses a 1-quart (approximately 1-litre) bottle or beaker with a stopper and cord (fig. 3-1.54). The sealed bottle sampler is lowered to the desired depth, the stopper removed, and the bottle or beaker is pulled to the top at uniform speed. If pulled at the proper speed, the bottle should be about three-fourths full of liquid; if not, the process must be tried again.

Oil Sampling

Sampling Methods

Figure 3-1.53. The sampler lowers a thief to obtain an oil sample from a storage tank.

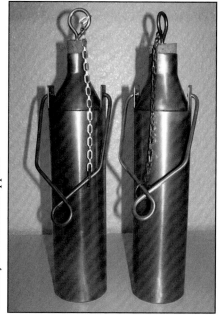

Courtesy of Channel Supplies

Figure 3-1.54. A 1-quart (1-litre) beaker is used in bottle sampling.

Types of Samples

The number of samples required is a function of the capacity of the tank and the height of the tank. Typically, for small lease tanks of less than 1,000 barrels, an upper and an outlet sample spot sample are taken for the S&W determination. A middle sample is taken for the determination of the gravity of the product. A sample can come from different parts of the tank, and all parties concerned should agree on where it is to be taken. There are three main types of samples:

- *Average sample* consists of proportionate parts from all sections of the tank.
- *Running sample* is a bottle sample taken while the sample bottle is moving.
- *Spot sample* is obtained at a specific location in the tank using a thief or bottle. This is the most common method for lease tanks.

Measuring and Testing Oil and Gas

Crude oil is bought, sold, and regulated by volume, S&W content, sulfur content, and oil gravity or density. The operator usually measures the volumes of oil, gas, and saltwater produced by each lease at least once every 24 hours.

When measuring crude oil, the volume must be corrected for any S&W present. The volume varies according to temperature, so the volume must also be corrected to a standard base temperature of 60°F (15.5°C). These requirements call for a series of tests for temperature, density, and S&W content. Gaugers run these tests and measurements, sometimes in the presence of witnesses. The information they get is written on the pipeline *run ticket*.

Temperature Measurement

Generally, the temperature of oil in lease stock tanks is close to that of the air surrounding the tanks, unless the oil has just recently been produced and still has a higher temperature, or if the oil has been heated in a fired heater-treater to separate it from S&W or saltwater. Temperature is usually measured with a cupcase or an electronic thermometer lowered into the oil on a line and then withdrawn to observe the reading. The length of time the thermometer needs to be in the oil before it is removed and the temperature read is a function of the gravity of the fluid. As the API gravity decreases the length of time required increases. For gravities between API 20 and 29 degrees, the cupcase thermometer should be in the oil column for 45 minutes, if kept stationary. (API specifies the time requirements in Chapter 7 of the *Manual of Petroleum Measurement Standards*.)

The S&W content and the API gravity (specific gravity, or density, measurement) of oil in stock tanks are measured from samples taken from the tanks. Samples are taken by using a thief or similar device. Various buyers require different levels of cleanliness, but the maximum S&W content in most states is 1%. Most pipeline companies accept all oil from 4 inches (10 centimetres) below the bottom of the pipeline connection on up. A *centrifuge test*, also called a *shake-out test*, determines the S&W content of the samples (fig. 3-1.55). The test uses a glass centrifuge tube that is graduated so the percentage of S&W can be read directly.

An instrument called a *hydrometer* measures the API gravity of the oil. The gauger obtains the crude oil sample into a thief and lowers the hydrometer into it (fig. 3-1.56). The hydrometer floats at a certain level in the crude: the higher it floats, the lighter the oil.

Gravity, S&W, and Sulfur Content Measurement

Figure 3-1.55. A centrifuge test uses a graduated glass centrifuge tube that is placed in a high-speed centrifuge by which precise percentages of S&W can be read.

Figure 3-1.56. A hydrometer test

The markings on the thermohydrometer show the observed gravity. Because the gravity, or density, of oil varies with its temperature, the gauger must correct gravity readings of oil at temperatures other than 60°F (15.5°C) using tables created for this purpose.

Sulfur content affects the value of the oil because sulfur makes the oil more expensive to refine. High-sulfur oil is called sour crude and is generally less valuable and more costly to refine than low-sulfur oil, called sweet crude. The sulfur content of oil must be determined in the laboratory using an oil sample.

LACT Units

The development of *lease automatic custody transfer (LACT) units* has improved efficiency and reduced the time necessary to measure, sample, test, and transfer oil (fig. 3-1.57).

Figure 3-1.57. A skid-mounted LACT unit is an efficient system for measuring and testing oil.

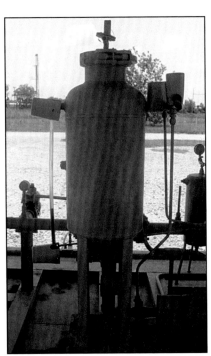

Figure 3-1.58. A sample container on a LACT unit holds oil samples automatically taken from the oil stream flowing through the unit.

Automatic equipment can perform the following tasks:

- Measure and record the volume of the oil.
- Detect the presence of water in the oil stream and divert the flow to a *slop oil* tank if excessive, or back to the separator.
- Determine and record the temperature of the oil.
- Allow for the verification of the accuracy of flow meters.
- Take samples from the stream in proportion to the rate of flow and hold these for conventional test procedures to determine the S&W content and API gravity of the oil sold (fig. 3-1.58).
- In case of a malfunction, shut in the wells and relay an alarm signal to a remote point.

LACT units are necessary in installations that process a large volume of oil every day. Large central production facilities both onshore and offshore have LACT units to monitor and sell oil.

Like oil, gas must be sampled before it can be sold. Sampling is the way the operator determines the composition (including impurities), heating value, specific gravity, and natural gas liquid potential of the gas being produced from a specific well. Although a gas sample can be taken at any point in the production process, the most common places are at a separator and at the sales point, with the sample taken near the sales point being used for custody transfer purposes.

The sample must be representative of the gas flowing past the sample point. If a probe is installed in a pipeline, for example, it should extend into the center one-third of the pipe.

Several manual methods are used to sample gas. They all require that sampling or testing equipment is free of leaks and that sample containers are purged of all gases or vapors other than the natural gas. Samples are shipped to a laboratory for analysis.

Although manual sampling methods are more common, automatic sampling devices connected to the pipeline are also used. These devices allow gas to flow into the sample container over a certain period of time. In most cases, field samples are sent to a laboratory for testing. However, in some cases, automatic samplers are connected to analyzing equipment and field samples are analyzed automatically. These devices take a predetermined "bite"-sized sample based on the flow rate. The cylinder is kept pressurized to retain the sample properly.

Gas Sampling

Gas Testing

Gas testing determines the composition of the gas. The results of the tests determine the Btu (British thermal unit) content and gravity of the gas. Although there are several methods to test gas, the most common is fractional analysis.

Fractional Analysis

Fractional analysis is a laboratory test that determines the exact composition of the gas. This method usually reveals not only the percentage composition of each hydrocarbon present, but also the amount of each component that can be condensed in gallons per thousand cubic feet (litres per cubic metre). It also demonstrates the heating value of the gas.

Heating value is the amount of heat in Btu/scf (British thermal unit per standard cubic foot) that the gas will produce when burned. The gas composition and the temperature and pressure of the sample can be used to compute how much of the gas can be converted to natural gas liquids. The analysis also determines the quantity of impurities in the gas, such as oxygen, nitrogen, carbon dioxide, and hydrogen sulfide. Because hydrogen sulfide reacts with metal and is reduced by contact with the sample container, this impurity must be analyzed at the well site. Compositional analysis of the gas is also the basis for computing emissions from the production facility.

Gas Metering

Gas metering is the process of measuring the volume of natural gas flowing past a particular point. Gas is compressible, so the volume flowing past any point will change if the temperature, pressure, or gas composition changes. The gas volume at any flowing pressure and temperature is converted to a standard or base temperature and pressure, normally 60°F (15.5°C) and 14.73 pounds per square inch (1 atm). The gas volume at standard conditions places all gas metered over a wide range of flow conditions at the same reference point. In the United States, some states have other standards; for example, Texas and Oklahoma are 14.65 and Louisiana is 15.025.

Every gas purchase or sales contract made between suppliers and consumers is concerned with metering methods, calibration, and equipment to determine the volume and the value of the gas. Therefore, gas must be metered whenever there is a change of custody or ownership. Gas metering also allows the producer to determine how much gas is produced from a well every day. This fundamental measurement allows the producer to monitor the performance of each well. The heating content of the gas is measured in Btu/scf. Today, gas is sold in *therms*, or *dekatherm*, which is a type of Btu measurement.

A number of different types of meters can measure gas, but the most common method at the production site is the *orifice meter* (fig. 3-1.59).

Metering the Gas

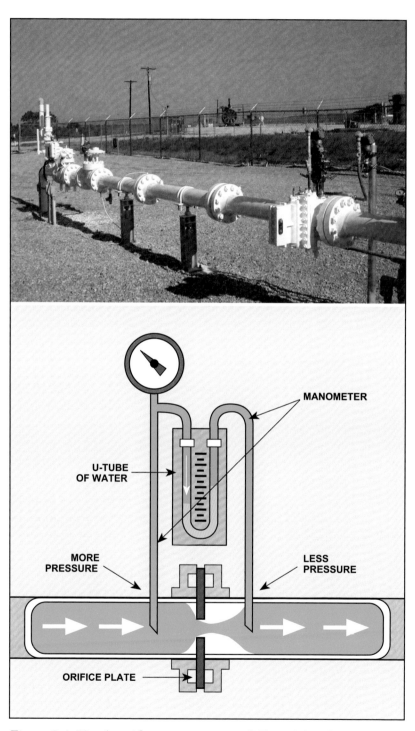

Figure 3-1.59. An orifice meter measures differential and static pressures of a stream of flowing gas.

Operators calculate gas flow rate using:
- Differential pressure
- Static pressure
- Flowing temperature
- Gas density
- Size of meter run
- Size of orifice

An orifice meter has a finely machined plate with an orifice, or hole, in its center mounted vertically in a gas line. Because the orifice is smaller than the gas line (called the meter run), the orifice acts as a small restriction to flow. This causes a small pressure loss as gas flows through the orifice. This pressure loss or drop, called *differential pressure*, is measured and recorded on a chart or electronically. Also measured and recorded is the *static pressure*, which is the pressure in the line upstream from the orifice plate. By using these two measurements along with flowing temperature, gas density, and the size of the meter run and orifice, operators can calculate the gas flow rate passing through the orifice.

Recording the Data

Paper charts can be used to record the orifice meter data. Electronic flow computers can also gather this data from the meters, accurately calculate the flow rate in the field, and transmit the information to the office, making this technology very popular. The recording devices are installed in a location so the presence of liquids does not interfere with measuring. Other potential problems in gas measurement are gas pressure and flow pulsations. *Pulsations* are cyclical pressure surges caused by gas compressors or valves that open and close on the pipeline. Meter installations are installed as far away from pulsation sources as possible to ensure accurate readings. Some gas lines require *pulsation dampeners*, which are devices that minimize pressure surges.

It is not unusual for an existing well to require either repairs or enhancements during the life of the well. These jobs can be separated into two broad categories:

- *Well service*—maintenance work usually involving repairs to equipment installed during the completion of the well.
- *Well workover*—procedures viewed as more complicated and expensive conducted on a well to restore or increase production. These jobs typically include repairs to the equipment or to the well.

Many workover jobs involve treating the reservoir rock or abandoning a depleted zone in favor of a new zone in the well. A workover is also used to install new equipment in the well, such as when artificial lift is applied in a previously flowing well.

WELL SERVICE AND WORKOVER

In the early days, drilling crews set up a permanent derrick at each well to drill and maintain the well throughout its life. Today, an onshore drilling rig is moved to a new site when drilling is finished, and the well is left with only a wellhead. Therefore, service and workover companies must bring a special mobile rig and any auxiliary equipment to the well site to perform remedial work.

Most of the discussion that follows describes onshore work. Offshore work can be done in a similar fashion, depending on the facilities available at the site. Some offshore platforms and structures have a special rig and equipment on site. Others might require a mobile service rig be brought to the well. Additionally, some offshore wells can be serviced from a boat or barge.

Service and Workover Equipment

Rigs

Service and workover rigs, like drilling rigs, are machines that hoist pipe and tools into and out of a well (fig. 3-1.60). They have a mast, drawworks, and power source. Unlike drilling rigs, they do not always have circulation or rotating systems.

A single-size rig might function as a drilling rig, servicing rig, or workover rig for wells of different depths, depending on the amount of weight it must hoist.

Figure 3-1.60. Typical well servicing and workover rig

Service and workover rigs come in a variety of sizes depending on the weight that must be hoisted from the well. The rig type depends in part on the weight and size of the equipment it must carry. Manufacturers build service and workover rigs in three common variations for transportation on land:

- *Truck-mounted rigs*—small rigs that usually rest on custom-built trucks
- *Trailer-mounted rigs*—large rigs that sit on trailers pulled by tractors
- *Carrier rigs*—rigs that have a built-in cab for an operator so the rig can be driven from location to location.

Compared to large drilling rigs, the portable rigs are relatively easy to move and quick to assemble in the field. Any necessary auxiliary equipment can be shipped on a truck to the site.

Wireline Units

Wireline operations are procedures performed with tools suspended on wireline. *Wireline*, in essence, is a strong, thin length of wire mounted on a powered reel at the surface of a well. Wireline comes in three common varieties:

- The simplest and weakest type is a single stainless steel wire called a *slick line*. Slick lines can hoist lightweight tools into a well.
- A stronger wireline is a *braided steel line*. It is used to hoist heavier tools in a well. Similar to the braided steel line is a *braided electric line* used with tools that transmit electric signals to and from a *surface control panel* or computer.

Among the more common jobs performed with wireline are:
- Measuring depth, temperature, and pressure
- Logging
- Perforating
- Controlling sand and paraffin
- Fishing and retrieving junk
- Manipulating subsurface well pressure and flow controls

Wireline, along with the equipment required to perform various wireline operations, are usually housed in a truck or a small portable house or on a skid and are called *wireline units*. On land, these units are usually truck-mounted (fig. 3-1.61). Marine wireline units are mounted on skids and transferred to the well site on boats or barges. Regardless of the type, a wireline unit contains a reel of wireline; a power system to let out and retrieve the line; instruments to indicate weight, line speed, and depth of the tool string; and a string of tools attached to the end of the line to perform the particular job. Electric wireline units also must have the controls and data acquisition units for the electronic equipment. *Lubricators* are carried with the unit and allow the wireline tools to be run into and retrieved from the well under pressure.

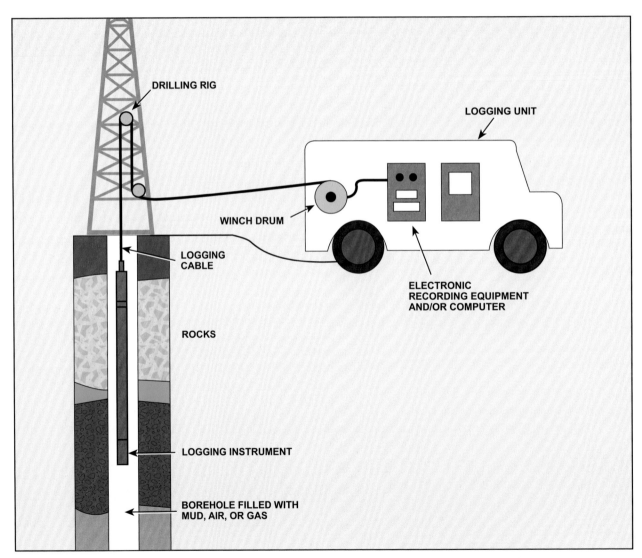

Figure 3-1.61. Reels of wireline mounted on the back of a truck used for completion and workover jobs

A *coiled tubing unit* is a reel of flexible continuous steel tubing coiled onto a drum (fig. 3-1.62). The coiled tubing is transported to a well on a truck, barge, or service boat. The unit has an injector head that pushes or pulls the tubing into or out of the well. A set of blowout preventers also come with the unit to control well pressure. An operator controls the rate at which the tubing is unspooled or spooled. Coiled tubing usually has a small diameter, 1 to 2 inches (25.4 to 50.8 millimetres), but large sizes up to 4.5 inches (114.3 millimetres) are available. Due to weight limitations, the smaller the diameter of the tubing, the longer the length of tubing that can be placed on a reel. Up to 25,000 feet (7,620 metres) of diameters up to 1.25 inches (31.75 millimetres) can be carried on one reel. Depending on the size and type, coiled tubing can be used with pressures up to 15,000 psi (1,019 atm) and in some highly corrosive fluids, such as hydrogen sulfide.

Coiled Tubing Units

Courtesy of Stewart and Stevenson

Figure 3-1.62. Coiled tubing unit

Coiled tubing is used in place of jointed tubing to convey treatment fluids to the bottom of a well, to jet fluids from a well using a gas such as nitrogen, to wash out sand, or to drill using a downhole motor and a bit (fig. 3-1.63). On many jobs, using a coiled tubing unit instead of a workover rig and jointed pipe is faster and less expensive. Rig-up time is less when using the coiled tubing unit. Coiled tubing can generally be run and pulled faster than jointed tubing. It also allows the crew to work on a well under pressure.

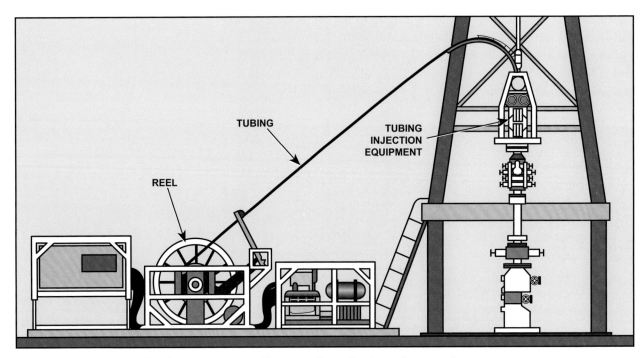

Figure 3-1.63. A coiled-tubing unit runs tubing into the well using a large reel.

Snubbing Units

Snubbing units are rigs that allow jointed pipe to be run into or pulled out of a well while the well is under pressure (fig. 3-1.64). They generally perform the same tasks as a coiled tubing unit but with jointed pipe rather than continuous coil. Operations using jointed pipe are preferable to coiled tubing if the well pressure is higher than the pressure rating of the coiled tubing, or if the job is extremely hazardous where the extra coiled tubing on the reel could be exposed to fluids or pressures that might cause it to rupture. The snubbing unit has a top and a bottom set of blowout preventers. The top and bottom set are opened and closed in sequence to allow the joints of pipe to pass into the well and for new pipe to be added at the surface. In this way, all of the pipe, except the top joint being added, is down in the well.

Two general types of snubbing units:
- Hydraulic unit—uses hydraulic system
- Rig-assisted unit—uses drawworks

Figure 3-1.64. This snubbing unit operates with a self-contained hydraulic system.

Categorized according to power source, the two general types of snubbing units are:

- *Hydraulic unit*—operates with a self-contained hydraulic system and uses single or multiple hydraulic cylinders to move the pipe in or out of the well
- *Rig-assisted unit*—uses the rig drawworks in a block-and-pulley arrangement to move the pipe

Auxiliary Equipment

Auxiliary equipment that might be required by a well servicing and workover rig includes:

- Crew quarters
- Electric generators and lights
- Fuel tanks
- Blowout preventers
- Makeup and breakout tongs
- Racks for storing pipe
- Top drive or a rotary to rotate pipe
- Pumps
- Mud mixing equipment
- Mud or completion fluid storage tanks

Fluids

The circulating fluid used in servicing and workover is called *workover fluid*. This type of fluid can be the same drilling mud as that used to drill the well, although this is relatively rare because the drilling mud might be harmful to the well equipment or the formations over the long term. More often, the workover fluids are *brine*. The brine can be field saltwater produced by other wells in the field, or it can be seawater or brine made from potassium or calcium chloride. Extremely dense workover fluids can be made from calcium or zinc bromide, or potassium or cesium formate.

Well Servicing and Repair

Well equipment frequently becomes worn from corrosion, abrasion or erosion, or metal fatigue. Produced fluids can cause corrosion and resulting pitting in the well tubing. Any equipment in the well that has moving parts will suffer metal fatigue and sometimes abrasion, corrosion, and erosion. All equipment that breaks must be repaired or replaced.

Beam Pumping Equipment

Modern beam pumping units can perform a long time with proper care if they are not overloaded. Proper care includes correct lubrication and counterbalance adjustment.

Sucker rods, couplings, and downhole pumps can fail for many reasons:

- Corrosion due to oxygen (rust), hydrogen sulfide (sour corrosion), or carbon dioxide (sweet corrosion) in the well can cause metal sucker rods to become pitted and eventually break (fig. 3-1.65).

- Metal also can be removed from the rods and pump by fluid erosion or because of wear from friction. The most common source of friction is when the rods are allowed to contact and rub against the tubing (fig. 3-1.66).

- When the sucker rods were installed in the well, they were screwed together. If the correct makeup torque was not achieved, the couplings can come apart.

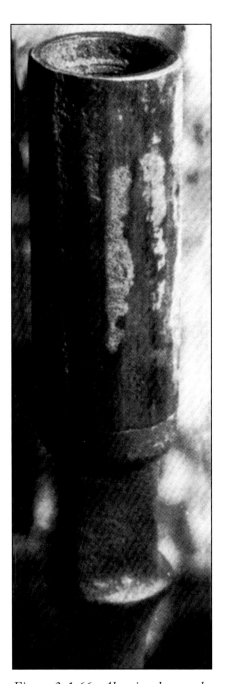

Figure 3-1.66. Abrasion damaged these sucker rods and their coupling.

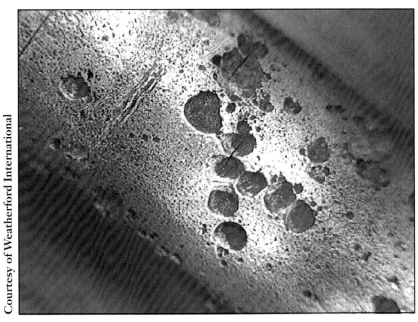

Figure 3-1.65. Corroded sucker rods must be replaced to keep the pumping well in good condition.

- If the crew was not careful in handling the sucker rods, they could have damaged the metal by denting it. These dents reduce the area of the steel and become *stress risers* that eventually cause the rod to break.

- Even if the rods and pump are operated properly, they have a service life. This means that moving parts will eventually break due to metal fatigue.

When the rods break (part) or the pump ceases to function, the service crew will pull the broken rods and pump from the well and repair or replace them. When such problems occur, the well ceases to produce.

Tubing and Packers

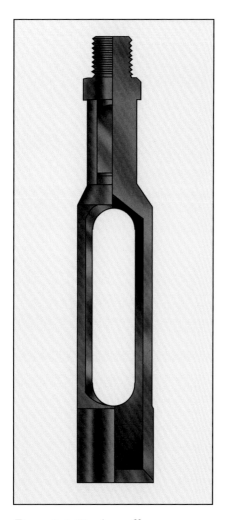

Figure 3-1.67. A paraffin scraper

Over time, tubing can become worn by abrasion with sucker rods (known as *rod cut*) or pitted due to corrosive attack. The abraded or pitted areas have a thinner wall thickness and will eventually rupture. The tubing must be pulled from the well, inspected, defective sections replaced, and the tubing string run back in the well. It is not always easy to see worn tubing. An inspection can locate worn tubing before it fails in the well.

Tubing inspections come in several variations. *Hydrostatic testing* is a simple method that tests tubing with water pressure to a predetermined value. The accuracy of this test is limited by the test's short duration. The worn tubing can actually pass a brief test but fail again shortly after being exposed to continuous well pressure. A more comprehensive and expensive method is an *electronic test*. This test inspects tubing with an electronic device that measures the wall thickness of the tube. Any abraded areas or pits show up as areas of reduced wall thickness.

Production packers come in two broad types: permanent and retrievable. A retrievable packer has a mechanism that allows the packer to be unset and retrieved when tubing is pulled. Permanent packers must be milled over and recovered in a special packer-catching device or on a spear.

Paraffin deposits along the walls can reduce the diameter of the tubing and slow production or prevent tools from fitting through the tubing. The crew can clean out tubing with a *scraper* run in on wireline or by pumping hot oil or hot water down the casing to melt the paraffin inside the tubing (fig. 3-1.67).

Scale can form inside tubing under certain conditions of pressure and water chemistry. As mentioned earlier, some scales can be dissolved from inside the tubing using an acid.

A well will not flow if brine with heavy density is pumped to offset the bottomhole pressure in the well. To lower the pressure inside the well so the formation pressure can cause fluids to flow to the surface, some brine must be removed. Swabbing brine out of the tubing is one way to remove liquid from the well. Swabbing is accomplished by lowering a flexible rubber swab cup into the tubing on wireline. The cup is lowered normally 1,000 to 1,500 feet (305 to 457 metres) into fluid in the tubing. The wireline is then spooled back out of the well. The flexible cup expands against the wall of the tubing, and the trapped fluid above the cup is removed or swabbed from the tubing. Many workover rigs have a braided swab line on a second drum (called the sand line) in addition to the heavier drawworks containing wire rope for hoisting operations. Smaller rigs that do nothing but swab are also available at a less expensive rate.

Swabbing

Workover Operations

Workover jobs are intended to improve production from the well, although repairs are sometimes included as part of the process. Workovers include cleaning sand out of the well, adding a means of preventing sand from entering the well, plugging an old zone in the well and recompleting in a new zone, repairing casing, and drilling deeper.

Sand Cleanout

Some reservoirs consist of sand that is not well consolidated. If the fluid velocity is high enough in the reservoir, the produced fluid might carry with it some reservoir sand. The sand enters the wellbore and often begins to settle in the well. This leads to plugging the bottom of the well with produced sand.

The sand can sometimes be cleaned out of the well with a wireline bailer lowered to the bottom of the well. The bailer is filled with sand, retrieved, and emptied. This process is repeated until the well is free of sand.

If there is more sand in the well than can be economically removed with a bailer, it is sometimes possible to wash or circulate the sand out of the well using fluid.

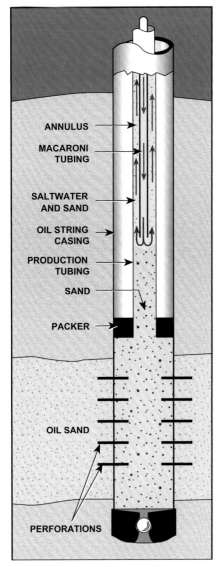

Figure 3-1.68. Macaroni tubing fits inside the production tubing to wash sand out.

A small tubing string called a *macaroni string* (fig. 3-1.68) or coiled tubing (fig. 3-1.69) can be lowered inside the tubing and a pump can circulate fluid to carefully wash the sand from the well. If the sand is packed hard in the well, a small bit with a downhole motor can be used on coiled tubing to drill sand out.

Tubing can also be used in the well to wash sand out, although this might require the packer to be unset or removed so the tubing can be lowered to reach the sand.

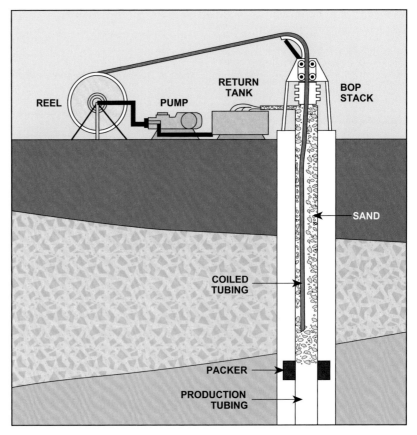

Figure 3-1.69. Coiled tubing also washes sand up the annulus between the production tubing and coiled tubing.

For wells that continue to produce sand, it is possible to add mechanisms to prevent flow of sand into the wellbore. The procedure is called gravel packing, and it is often done when the well is completed. Gravel packs can be added later if the well begins to produce sand, as shown in figures 3-1.13 and 3-1.14 early in this chapter.

Another method is to glue the sand grains together in the reservoir with a plastic or resin. This process is known as *chemical consolidation*. A third method is to create a small fracture at the well and pack it full of high-quality, resin-coated sand. This technique is called *frac packing*, and with a gravel pack it can be a very effective barrier to sand production.

Plug-back cementing is a process that places a cement plug at one or more points in a well to shut off flow. The most common reason for plug-back cementing is to isolate a lower zone from the upper part of the well, usually because the lower zone is depleted or not productive of oil and gas. The cement plug shuts off and isolates the lower part of the well (fig. 3-1.70). The plug keeps produced fluids from migrating into the lower zone. It also prevents saltwater in the lower zone from migrating to the higher zone.

Other reasons for setting cement plugs are to seal off a dry or depleted well before abandoning the entire well, and to plug the hole when preparing to sidetrack. *Sidetracking* is the process of drilling a new hole that is deviated to change the location of the bottom of the well. The workover crew places the plug at the depth where they are to start the sidetrack, and the hole is drilled directionally to a new location.

Sand Control

Plug-Back Cementing

A cement plug can isolate a zone in a well. The plug can shut off part of the well to protect fluid from migrating upward.

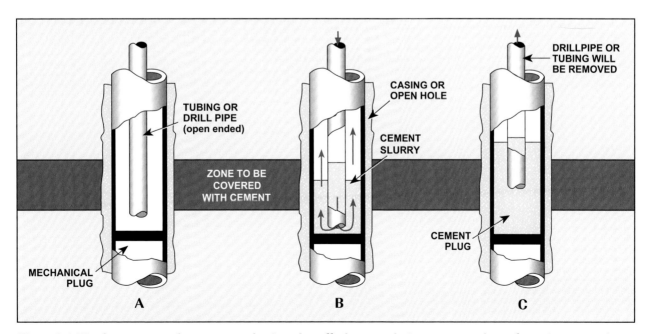

Figure 3-1.70. One reason to place a cement plug is to shut off a lower producing zone to produce a formation nearer the surface.

361

Casing and Production Liner Repair

Casing and liners sometimes develop holes caused by corrosion or abrasion. Holes in casing are a serious problem because unwanted fluids and pieces of formation can enter the well. Unlike tubing, casing is often impossible to recover from the well to replace damaged sections. Even if casing can be recovered, replacement is often a difficult and expensive process. Therefore, casing repairs are attempted while the casing is left in place in the ground.

Squeeze cementing is one way of repairing holes in casing. Other methods are patching it with a liner patch, replacing part of the string if it can be recovered from the well, or running a liner and cementing it in place to cover the damaged place in the casing string. *Expandable tubulars* are also used as a patch or liner to help preserve the largest diameter of casing available.

Squeeze Cementing

Unlike tubing, casing is often impossible to recover from the well to replace damaged sections, so repairs are done in place in the ground.

Squeeze cementing is used to seal openings in a well. These openings can be holes or splits in casing or perforations intentionally shot through the casing. Unlike plug-back cementing, the cement is forced to go outside the casing and into the formation beyond the casing. In this way, the cement forms both an external and internal seal. To perform squeeze cementing, cement is pumped down the drill pipe or tubing to an opening in the well casing, then pressure is applied. A tool on the end of the drill pipe or tubing, called a *cement retainer* or a *squeeze tool*, prevents the cement from flowing up the annulus. Pumping pressure forces the cement into the opening in the casing and into the formation behind it (fig. 3-1.71). Workover crews can also squeeze cement into a part of the hole with no casing (as in an open-hole completion). Squeeze cementing is also used to try and place cement outside the casing where no cement exists or to fill channels in the cement that were allowed to form.

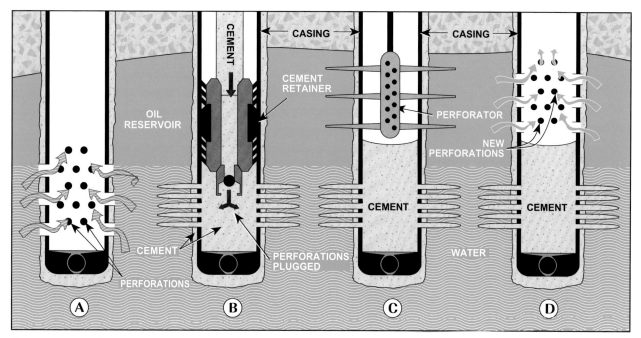

Figure 3-1.71. Squeezing cement through the lower perforations seals them (A, B). Then, the upper part of the zone is perforated (C, D).

Production is the operating phase that brings well fluids to the surface and prepares them for transport to a refinery or processing plant. After a well is drilled and the reservoir is determined to be economical to produce, the well is completed. Many wells require four strings of casing: conductor, surface, intermediate, and production. Production casing is often the final casing.

The wellhead includes all essential equipment to support pipe strings, seal off the well, and control the flow of reservoir fluids. As a well is drilled, pressure in the production zone is offset by drilling fluid pressure in the hole, so the drilling fluid must be replaced by completion fluid. Once completion with correct fluids is achieved and equipment is installed in the well, flow of fluids from the reservoir begins.

Some reservoir rocks have low permeability and require application of one or more stimulation techniques to enable the flow of hydrocarbons. When the pressure in the reservoir falls to where fluids can no longer flow to the surface, an artificial method of lifting the hydrocarbons is necessary. Natural energies in the reservoir will cause fluids to flow into the bottom of the well, leaving a substantial amount of oil in the reservoir at the end of primary production. To produce more fluids, special techniques have been developed to improve recovery.

SUMMARY

Fluids typically exit a well as a mixture of oil, gas, and water, and several steps are necessary to prepare the oil and/or gas for sale. The products that have been separated are temporarily stored in a tank battery, but first, each one of the stock tanks must be strapped. The lease operator owns the oil or gas coming from the well and sells it; the pipeline company transports it to the buyer. The operator, pipeline company, and buyer will all measure and test the oil and gas at different times.

Existing wells require repairs or enhancements during and after use, requiring well servicing and workover operations. Workover jobs can involve treating the reservoir rock or abandoning one zone in the well for another. They can also involve special remedial procedures to remove or replace tubing or install new equipment when artificial lift is applied.

When production operations end, modes of transportation are engaged to take the separated fluids to the appropriate facilities for refining and processing, where they will be transformed further into marketable products.

In this chapter:

- Producing wells offshore
- Completing wells in deep waters
- Special fluid-handling requirements
- Submerged production systems
- Permafrost considerations

3.2
Remote Production

Hydrocarbons produced from offshore and Arctic wells require the same general types of completions and surface separation and handling as land wells. The main differences are due to the remoteness of the locations and the special challenges of the environments.

OFFSHORE PRODUCTION PLATFORMS

If the ocean water depth is shallow enough to allow construction of a drilling platform, and if one or more development wells are drilled and production takes over as the main activity then the drilling platform will also become a production platform (fig. 3-2.1). The operator sometimes removes the drilling rig or allows it to remain on the platform to service the producing wells. Some platforms are designed so that a mobile offshore jackup drilling rig can set up over the platform to drill and complete a well through the platform or through a single well caisson (fig. 3-2.2)

Courtesy of Hibernia Management and Development Company Ltd.

Figure. 3-2.1. This self-contained platform, the Hibernia, houses all the drilling and production equipment and facilities for the crew. The Hibernia is located off the coast of Newfoundland and is the world's largest oil platform in terms of weight.

Figure 3-2.2. The hull of a jackup can be raised well above the water's surface.

Figure 3-2.3. Helicopters and cranes are common sights around an offshore operation.

The modern platform houses the wellheads and all the usual production equipment. A platform generally has a helipad, one or more cranes, antipollution devices, and a myriad of safety devices such as firefighting equipment and escape capsules. Helicopters and crew boats are used to transport people and supplies to and from the platform (figs. 3-2.3 and 3-2.4).

Communications to and from the platform include remote monitoring of production equipment, closed-circuit television, radio transmissions, and recording devices of all kinds. The use of interactive computer terminals in every phase of operation keeps the offshore drilling and production platforms in touch with the rest of the world. The platforms are normally shut in and the crew evacuated in the event a severe storm such as when a hurricane threatens the area.

A modern production platform contains:

- Wellheads
- Helipad
- Cranes
- Antipollution devices
- Safety features
- Firefighting equipment
- Escape capsules
- Monitoring systems
- Water-treating facilities

Courtesy of Reflex Marine Limited

Figure 3-2.4. Work boats transport crew and cargo between shore and platform. A crew transfer in the Gulf of Mexico is pictured above.

Platforms are carefully designed to prevent any oil from flowing off the platform. They also incorporate high-capacity water-treating facilities to ensure the produced water is clean enough to either inject safely underground or discharge into the ocean.

Offshore Completions

- Wellheads above the ocean level are called dry trees.
- Wellheads placed on the seafloor are called wet trees.
- SSSVs are required for all offshore wells.

A well completion offshore is much like one on land. For wells drilled and completed from a platform, the wellhead is above the ocean on one of the platform decks (fig. 3-2.5). The wellhead equipment is the same as that used onshore and is called a *dry tree*.

When the water is too deep to construct a platform in place, the wells are drilled from a floating drilling vessel. When the well is completed, the wellhead is placed on the ocean floor and is called a *wet tree* (fig. 3-2.6).

Figure 3-2.5. Example of a small, shallow water production platform

Courtesy of Cameron

Figure 3-2.6. In a wet subsea completion, valves and equipment to control the flow of hydrocarbons are placed on the seafloor. Pictured is an all-electric subsea tree in the North Sea being lowered for installation.

One important piece of equipment added to the well tubing is a subsurface safety valve (SSSV), installed at a depth of several hundred feet (or metres) below the ocean floor. The SSSV is a flapper held open by a piston (see section on Subsurface Safety Valve in Chapter 3.1; also see fig. 3-1.12). Hydraulic pressure forces the piston down to open the flapper against a spring. As long as there is sufficient hydraulic pressure to force the piston down, the flapper remains open and fluids can flow up the tubing. In the event hydraulic pressure is lost, the spring forces the piston up and closes the flapper to seal the well. This is an important fail-safe antipollution device that prevents flow from the well into the ocean if the wellhead becomes lost or damaged by an accident or severe weather.

Offshore Fluid Handling

An elaborate subsea system of widely scattered satellite wells flow fluids to a centralized production operation or an FPSO.

The offshore operator generally removes water and other impurities from well fluids before putting the oil and gas into tankers or pipelines for transportation to shore. The production facility must contain separating and treating equipment, compressors, pumps, dehydrators, water treating and disposal equipment, LACT units to measure the produced oil, and gas measurement devices. A platform has all of this equipment along with the wellheads.

For subsea completions, oil, gas, and water exit the subsea wellheads into flow lines that run from wells to a *production riser*, or pipe. Production flows up the riser to a floating production platform or shallow water (shelf) stationary platform that has the same kind of production equipment as a platform. The floating production facility is either a vessel built for that purpose or a converted tanker. The floating facility is often referred to as a *floating production, storage, and offloading (FPSO)* system.

Submerged Production System

A more elaborate subsea system consists of a group of satellite wells that flow to a centralized floating production system or to the nearest fixed platform (fig. 3-2.7). Flow lines attach these satellite wells, often widely scattered on the ocean floor, to a central platform for treating. This *submerged production system (SPS)* brings several subsea completions to a common production facility so that an entire field can be developed without holding individual wellheads on the platform.

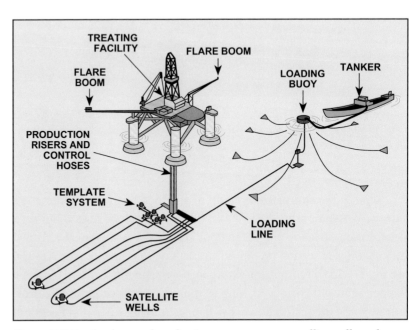

Figure 3-2.7. A submerged production system connects satellite wells to the production platform for treating and then to a mooring buoy where tankers receive the oil.

The first successful SPS was tested in the Gulf of Mexico between 1974 and 1979. The major components include using a *seabed template*. This template is a steel pattern that lies on the seafloor with built-in accessories, connectors, and guides for the subsea flow lines. The seabed template ties together several satellite wells. Pipelines and risers connect the template to a conventional platform or to a floating production facility. A *robot maintenance system (RMS)* services the underwater equipment. Subsea pumps can be installed to boost the flow from the wells down the pipeline. This might be necessary if the wells are connected to the closest fixed platform by a long subsea pipeline.

Arctic Production

The main difficulties associated with Arctic production are related to temperature. If produced fluids are allowed to cool once they reach the surface, paraffin or asphaltene plugs can form in pipelines and production facilities. If the soil in the Arctic is warmed by drilling and producing operations, the permanently frozen layer of soil known as *permafrost* will melt, making the location unstable (fig. 3-2.8). Therefore, drilling and completion operations must be designed to insulate permafrost from any heat, and fluids must be insulated from the Arctic cold.

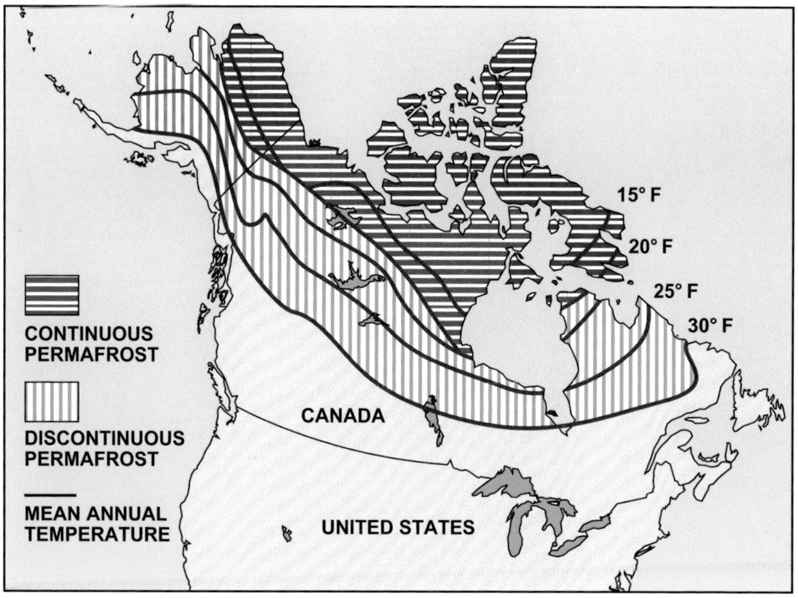

Figure 3-2.8. Arctic production must take into account areas of permafrost shown here in North America.

This extreme cold also requires workers to take special safety precautions. More time is normally required to perform tasks in extreme cold than in more temperate regions. The remoteness and cold of the Arctic can also create significant transportation problems. Travel by water is only possible a few months of the year. During summer, travel over land can be difficult or impossible because boggy areas make road building complicated and expensive. Traveling by road is easier in winter when ice roads to remote sites can be properly maintained. Permafrost also makes it difficult to bury pipelines. Pipelines are often mounted above ground and carefully insulated against the cold as demonstrated by the Trans Alaska Pipeline System. This engineering masterpiece extends from the North Slope to Valdez Harbor across Alaska in the United States (fig. 3-2.9).

Courtesy of the Aleyska Pipeline Company

Figure 3-2.9. The Alaska pipeline from the North Slope to Valdez harbor is an Arctic engineering masterpiece.

Hydrocarbons produced from offshore and Arctic wells require the same general types of completions and surface separation and handling as land wells with the main differences related to the remoteness of the locations and the special challenges of the environments.

An offshore drilling platform might also become a production platform. The operator might remove the drilling rig or allow it to remain on the platform to service the producing wells. The modern platform houses the wellheads and all the usual production equipment.

Platforms are carefully designed to prevent any oil from flowing off the platform. They also incorporate high-capacity water-treating facilities to ensure the produced water is clean enough to either inject safely underground or discharge into the ocean.

For wells drilled and completed from an offshore platform, the wellhead is called a dry tree and is located above the ocean on one of the platform decks. In deep waters, the wellhead is placed on the ocean floor and is called a *wet tree*. The well tubing contains an important device called a subsurface safety valve with a flapper that can seal the well if the wellhead becomes damaged by an accident or severe weather.

An offshore production facility contains separating and treating equipment, compressors, pumps, dehydrators, water treating and disposal equipment, LACT units to measure the produced oil, and gas measurement devices. For subsea completions, oil, gas, and water flow to a floating production facility, which is either a vessel built for that purpose or a converted tanker. A more elaborate subsea system consists of a group of satellite wells that flow to a centralized floating production system or the nearest fixed platform. This way, an entire field can be developed without holding individual wellheads on the platform.

Arctic production presents unique problems related to temperature. Drilling and completion operations must be designed to insulate permafrost from any heat, and fluids must be insulated from the Arctic cold.

SUMMARY

3.3
Production Safety

In this chapter:

- Safety in all aspects of the production process
- Hazards that commonly occur in production
- Factors in monitoring process conditions
- Common production hazards

Production safety encompasses a wide variety of jobs and functions spanning from when the well is first brought into production to when the well is abandoned and the facilities are removed. Production workers need to understand how to work safely when conducting various jobs on a production site (fig. 3-3.1). During the course of each day, production workers are frequently called upon to drive to a well site or production facility, diagnose equipment or well problems, make repairs to wells and equipment, adjust process settings, and ensure that safety equipment is working properly. Each task has its own inherent safety hazards and particular safety requirements.

Figure 3-3.1. Production worker controlling flow of fluids with valve

On production sites, all workers must understand all aspects of equipment and procedures.

To keep production workers safe, companies must enact overarching safety policies and procedures to assure that all possible jobs are being conducted safely. It is critical that each worker is trained and experienced in the company's safety policies and practices (fig. 3-3.2). The implementation of strict safety standards and effective training programs helps ensure that every job is performed safely.

Figure 3-3.2. Production personnel must fully understand all aspects of equipment and procedures to ensure safe operations. These workers are participating in hands-on training at the PETEX West Texas Training Center in Odessa, Texas.

MOST COMMON HAZARDS

Diverse job requirements mean that production personnel are exposed to a multitude of hazards in the course of their daily work. The most common hazards at production sites include:

- **Driving:** Vehicle accidents are the leading cause of serious injuries in the oilfield. Production workers commonly have to drive long distances to well sites and facilities that are spread out over large geographic areas. Drivers must transport well servicing and maintenance equipment from one site to another (fig. 3-3.3). Many roads leading to leases have gravel or dirt surfaces that make travel difficult in inclement weather.

- **Struck by an object:** A loose pipe or a piece of equipment that breaks away from tie down or a pipe wrench falling off an elevated walkway are examples of situations where objects could strike workers and cause injury.

- **Falls:** Workers are often required to climb on equipment or use scaffolds or aerial lifts to access equipment, presenting a danger of falling. Falls are more likely to happen when surfaces become slippery or when workers are not secured properly when elevated.

Figure 3-3.3. *Driving vehicles and working around hazardous chemicals present dangers for workers.*

Fires and explosions can occur if valve maintenance, equipment failure, or leaks are not handled safely.

- **Fire and explosions:** Fire and explosions are an ever-present danger when working around flammable liquids or gasses. Leaks, maintenance operations, and equipment failure can easily lead to a fire (fig. 3-3.4).

Figure 3-3.4. *High-pressure gas or liquid escaping from a valve can injure personnel.*

Conditions to monitor during production:
- Pressure
- Temperature
- Noise
- Chemicals

- **Mechanized equipment:** Engines, motors, pumps, compressors, and other types of mechanized equipment commonly found at production sites present potentially hazardous conditions. For example, unguarded equipment could entangle a worker or a serious hand injury could occur if the hand is placed improperly around pinch points.
- **Electrical:** Electricity is commonly used for powering motors, communications, and control equipment. Being shocked or electrocuted is possible if proper controls are not in place.
- **Process conditions:**
  - *Pressure:* High-pressure gas or liquid escaping from a valve or fitting can injure personnel. Such pressures might be encountered anywhere from the wellhead to the sales line.
  - *Temperature:* Fired heaters, heater-treaters, steam generators, reboilers, and other equipment can be extremely hot and cause burns to unprotected skin. Cold temperatures are often found in gas plants when separating heavier gases. Workers often perform jobs outside where ambient cold or hot temperatures can cause injury or discomfort.
  - *Noise:* Hearing damage can occur if workers do not use ear protection around noisy equipment. Compressors, pumps, flow-through valves, and other treating equipment can be extremely noisy.
  - *Chemical:* Corrosion inhibitors, glycol, amines, emulsion breakers, acids, biocides, and other chemicals are commonly used in production operations. Workers can be exposed to these chemicals when filling containers, testing, or conducting maintenance (fig. 3-3.5).

Failure to wear protective gear during production threatens the safety of workers.

Figure 3-3.5. Workers must wear protective gear when exposed to chemicals.

With so many different production activities, companies mitigate risks by implementing a comprehensive safety program that addresses common workplace hazards (figs. 3-3.6, 3-3.7, and 3-3.8). In this way, workers learn how to remain safe no matter what type of job they are performing. In addition, a company will typically have more specialized safety rules and requirements to deal with specific high-risk jobs such as cleaning a particular tank or repairing a line containing hydrogen sulfide gas.

CONTROLLING HAZARDS

Figure 3-3.6. Many production lease activities are accompanied by inherent dangers while working with fluids.

Figure 3-3.8. Safety programs include group training to ensure all workers are aware of hazards.

Figure 3-3.7. Caustic chemicals are commonplace on many worksites.

Structured programs are put in place to protect workers from hazards.

Common hazard areas:
- Fire/hot work
- Welding
- Heights
- Confined spaces
- Driving
- Excavation

Programs to cover the more common production hazards encountered generally include:

- **Personal Protective Equipment:** Most workers are required to have basic *Personal Protective Equipment (PPE)*. This collection of equipment consists of a hardhat, steel-toed shoes, ear plugs, and safety glasses. Workplace evaluations will determine any other PPE safety requirements. Examples of when other types of PPE are needed include handling chemicals, welding, and working at heights.

- **Fire and Safe/Hot Work permits:** Leaks for gas or other flammable materials must be located and safety measures taken before any welding, sparks, or open flames can be permitted. A *Fire and Safe/Hot Work* permit is issued after the area has been thoroughly checked to ensure it is safe to proceed with any fire or *hot work*.

- **In-service welding and hot tapping:** Often, it is necessary to weld pipes in service while well fluids are flowing through them. Procedures have been developed to allow this type of work under special circumstances.

- **Working at heights:** Working unprotected at heights over 4 feet (1 metre) for general industry and 6 feet (2 metres) during construction requires workers to use or wear some type of fall-protection device. Fall-protection harnesses connected using a lanyard to an anchor point are commonly used.

- **Tagging and flagging:** Tags and flags signal workers whether valves and other devices are in temporary positions, require maintenance, are unsafe to use, or do not function properly.

- **Lockout/tagout:** *Lockout/tagout (LOTO)* programs are used to protect workers from unexpected releases of stored energy. Examples include trapped pressure and electrical, thermal, chemical, or mechanical energies. Each worker is required to put a lock out on the device when necessary to ensure it does not activate during maintenance. Tags are also required to signal others as to why the device is locked out.

- **Blinding:** Blinds are used on pipes and vessels to positively isolate work from process fluids. The right blinds and techniques must be used to ensure the safety of personnel working near pipes or equipment that contain process fluids.

- **Confined space entry:** Often, it is necessary to enter a tank or process vessel to clean it out. Safety procedures have been developed to make sure the tank or vessel has been taken out of service effectively, that safe breathing air is available, and that rescue personnel are standing by in the event of an emergency.

- **Excavations and trenching:** If not designed properly, trenches used for pipelines can cave in and trap workers. Procedures for excavations and trenches depend on the type of soil and depth of the excavation or trench. The local *dig alert* agency is called first to determine if there are any buried pipelines, power lines, or cables in the area where work is to be done.

- **Management of change:** All affected parties must know about all operational changes being made, such as installation of new equipment, new operating procedures, or changes in job responsibilities. The purpose of managing change is to make sure everyone affected by a change has input and knowledge about the occurrence.

- **Driving safety:** Driving represents a major hazard to operations. Safe driving programs include defensive driving programs and instruction on driving rules and reaction in emergencies.

- **Hazard communication:** All employees and contractors must be made aware of any hazards they might encounter in their work. Hazard communication programs include training on using a *Material Safety Data Sheet (MSDS)* for chemicals, conducting a *job safety analysis* prior to starting a job, and remaining alert to changing conditions.

> **Risk is reduced through:**
> - Properly designed equipment
> - Safety procedures
> - Proper training

SUMMARY

Companies have developed safety procedures to cover almost every situation. To reduce risks, equipment is carefully designed to prevent injuries. In addition, workers must be trained in how to operate and maintain the equipment and in the safety procedures that apply. The last component of safety is that each person must cultivate a positive attitude towards safety to assist in the prevention of all injuries.

PART 4
Transportation and Refining

The Authors

TRANSPORTATION/ PIPELINES

Larry Bennington
Owner and Pipeline Consultant
Milepost Consulting

Larry Bennington has over 35 years of experience dealing with all aspects of pipelining. He currently provides consulting services to the pipeline and related industries in areas of operations, maintenance, engineering, construction, planning, regulatory compliance and litigation support. His expertise includes pipeline operations, maintenance, planning, project engineering, technical services, and engineering services including construction management, right-of-way, and records management. He has held key positions at Amoco Pipeline Company and American Oil Company and is a Registered Professional Engineer. Bennington holds a B.S.C.E. in Civil Engineering and an M.B.A. from Kansas State University. He is a current pipeline instructor at the PETEX Houston Training Center and for special PETEX programs at client locations.

LIQUEFIED NATURAL GAS

Stanley Huang
LNG Process Engineer
Chevron Corporation

Stanley Huang specializes in cryogenic applications, particularly in liquefied natural gas and gas processing. For nearly 15 years, he has worked on numerous projects devoted to LNG baseload plants and receiving terminals and has contributed to process and technology improvements through more than 20 publications and corporate reports. Before joining Chevron, Huang worked for IPSI (an affiliate of Bechtel) and KBR. He began his career with Exxon Research and Engineering Company and later joined D.B. Robinson and Associates in Canada. An expert in thermodynamics, Huang has given seminars on thermodynamic applications and, in recent years, has presented on gas processing and the LNG industry at meetings of the Association of Chinese American Professionals and at the Universities of Houston and Wyoming. He also instructs classes on LNG processes at the PETEX Houston Training Center. Huang received a B.S. from National Taiwan University and an M.S. and a Ph.D. in Chemical Engineering and an M.S. in Physics from Purdue University.

REFINING AND GAS PROCESSING

Stephen Long
Technology Advisor
Valero Energy Corporation

Stephen Long has 35 years of experience in the refining and petrochemical industry working in operating, engineering, and consulting companies and as an independent contractor. He is currently Technology Advisor in Strategic Sourcing for Valero Energy Corporation in San Antonio, Texas.

Prior to Valero, Long served the refining and petrochemical industry as an independent consultant associated with several company expansion projects. He spent 18 years devoted to the operating side of the industry as a refinery process engineer, plant process engineer, technical manager, operations manager, and refinery manager. His operations experience included virtually all types of refinery units.

Long's background includes several years with Stone and Webster focused on technology and process activities. In 2001, Long became President and Director of Energy Management Corporation in Houston, Texas, providing operations and maintenance services for a small niche refinery overseas. He served as General Director and an owner of Azov Oil Company from 2002 to 2004.

In this chapter:

- Transportation in the early days
- Ground modes of transport
- Marine transportation for oil and natural gas
- Pipeline infrastructure and operations
- Liquefied natural gas shipping and offloading

4.1
Transformation

Transporting and distributing petroleum products and natural gas from oilfields to refining and processing plants requires a complex transportation system (fig. 4-1.1). Tank trucks, rail cars, marine transportation, and crude oil, products, and gas transmission pipelines each have an important role in the oil and gas transportation industry.

Crude oil was first transported in wooden barrels carried by horse-drawn wagons to nearby streams. As consumer demand for petroleum grew, so did the methods of transportation. Today, millions of barrels of crude oil, gasoline, fuel oils, and other petroleum products, along with billions of cubic feet of natural gas, are moved daily from the wellhead to refineries. They are also moved from refineries to product terminals, from one refinery to another, from offshore to onshore, and from continent to continent to reach consumers.

Figure 4-1.1. The transportation industry is responsible for moving millions of barrels of crude oil daily across land and water to reach processing facilities and consumers.

Photo by Mark Toigo. Courtesy of www.seefloridago.com

EARLY METHODS OF TRANSPORTATION

The Drake well began an oil transportation boom in the United States. Demand for crude oil increased and companies competed to transport it.

New methods of moving oil from a well site to a processing location became necessary when the Drake well began producing quantities of 25 barrels (4 cubic metres) of crude oil per day. This began an oil transportation boom in the United States near Oil Creek, a tributary of the Allegheny River in Pennsylvania, where the oil could be moved up and down stream (fig. 4-1.2).

The first *refinery* (where the oil was processed and made into products for sale) was constructed in a location in Pennsylvania known as Oil City. Later, a refining complex was developed about 75 miles (121 kilometres) downstream on the Allegheny River at Pittsburgh, causing the U.S. city to become a major refining and oil transportation center. Demand for crude oil increased and many companies competed for the opportunity to transport the oil to the nearest waterway, railhead, pipeline dump tank location, or refinery.

Figure 4-1.2. The Oil Creek tributary of the Allegheny River in Pennsylvania (U.S.)

Because rivers and streams were near the productive Drake well, a massive system of boats, barges, and wagons operated by *teamsters* became a convenient solution to the transportation challenge. Horse-drawn wagons carried wooden barrels of oil to the streams where they were manually loaded on barges and boats of all types and sizes. Local sawmill operators agreed to release the water normally kept for floating logs downstream, and the oil boats (and sometimes the barrels themselves) were floated down the Allegheny River to Pittsburgh.

Until the invention of the steamboat, barges filled with oil were pulled by horses walking along the river banks, or they were floated downstream and were dependent on the river current for power (fig. 4-1.3). At the height of these operations, approximately 1,000 boats were used, including 20 to 30 steamers, passenger boats, and towboats, for pulling and pushing barges.

Wagons and Water

Figure 4-1.3. Horse-drawn wagons and barges were initially used to move oil to rail and water shipping points.

Rails and Tank Cars

Wooden barrels were replaced by tank cars that transported oil by new railways.

In the early days, water transportation was hazardous, resulting in many lost barrels of oil due to accidents. The oil industry turned to railroads as an alternate way to move petroleum and petroleum products. To meet this demand for railroad transportation, construction of area railroads grew rapidly. In the mid-1800s, tracks were quickly laid in the United States to move crude oil to and from Titusville, Pennsylvania. By 1864, the U.S. rail network was able to provide crude oil to Cleveland, Ohio, and New York State.

Because the *railheads* were distant from the wells, teamsters still transported crude oil barrels in their horse-drawn wagons. Each wagon could carry between five and seven 360-pound (163-kilogram) oil barrels. About 2,000 teams per day moved on mud roads into Titusville transporting oil to the railway for $1 to $5 per barrel. The wooden oil barrels were then transferred to railroad boxcars for shipment to refineries. However, the wooden barrels were expensive and required loading and unloading. They also tended to leak, were easily damaged, and were frequently stolen.

The problems with wooden barrels resulted in the development of the wooden tub-type tank car by Charles P. Hatch in 1865. In 1866, Amos and James Densmore of Meadville, Pennsylvania, improved on the design and patented the first tank car used to ship oil from Pennsylvania to New York City in the United States. Their tank car consisted of two 1,700-gallon (6,435-litre) wooden tubs glued, banded with iron hoops, and mounted on a flatcar (fig. 4-1.4).

In 1869, a horizontal tank rail car with an expansion dome was developed and has remained the industry's basic design. The *expansion dome* at the top of the tank car provides a collection space for any gas that separates out of the oil. It prevents damage from the pressure buildup in the tank car.

Figure 4-1.4. The Densmore brothers patented this early railway tank car design.

Pipelines are a major network of small and large arteries that give oil producers transportation to the crude oil market. The original reason for building pipelines was the high cost of moving oil from the oilfield to shipping points. In 1865, Samuel Van Syckel succeeded in building a pipeline and started the first oil pipeline business. Syckel's Oil Transportation Association laid a 2-inch (5-centimetre) wrought-iron line in Pennsylvania from Pithole Creek, 8 miles (13 kilometres) from Oil City to the Miller Farm railroad station, 5 miles (8 kilometres) away.

After Syckel built a second pipeline, he was able to move 2,000 barrels of oil per day at the low cost of $1 per barrel, much lower than the (approximately) $2.50 per barrel the teamsters charged for the same distance. Faced with the possibility of losing their monopoly, the teamsters reacted by tearing up portions of the pipeline. Ultimately, they were unsuccessful in stopping the construction of pipelines as more companies developed crude oil *gathering systems* and *trunklines*.

Railroad companies were the first to construct and buy their own pipelines and form exclusive arrangements with pipeline transportation companies. To maintain a monopoly over the oil transportation business, the U.S. railroads tried to prevent other pipeline companies from crossing their rail lines (fig. 4-1.5). With public opinion rising against monopolies, the Pennsylvania and Ohio state legislatures passed laws in 1872 that granted common carrier pipelines the privilege of *eminent domain* in obtaining their *right-of-way* law. Eminent domain is the right of the government or a common carrier to buy private property for public use.

The First Oil Pipelines

Crude Oil Trunklines

Figure 4-1.5. When denied the right to cross a railroad, one pipeline company used tank wagons to transfer the oil from the pipeline to holding tanks on the other side and then back into the pipeline.

This law helped ease land procurement in the development of cross-country oil trunkline systems. These systems made it possible to connect oil production centers directly to refineries and provide more economical transportation.

Until 1900, crude oil production was concentrated in Pennsylvania, West Virginia, Ohio, and other eastern states. Refineries were also centered on the eastern U.S. population centers. Between 1901 and 1905, oil was discovered away from the eastern states in Texas, Kansas, Oklahoma, Louisiana, and California. This forced the eastern refineries to seek additional crude oil supplies from western production centers.

During this period, the invention of the internal combustion engine increased the demand for crude oil and refined products. A greater volume of oil was needed, causing companies to invest in progressively larger scale trunklines. For example, by 1914, the U.S. midcontinent oilfields supplied 60% of the crude oil to the eastern refineries. As demand grew by 1940, they were supplying over 85% of the crude oil through cross-country pipelines. Several pump stations were installed along the pipelines to assist in moving the crude oil through the larger diameter mainlines (fig. 4-1.6).

Figure 4-1.6. An early pipeline pump station used steam power to build sufficient pressure to move the oil.

Depending on where the refining center was located, some crude oil supplies were transported by ships or barges. The combined system of waterway transportation and pipelines worked well until World War II when enemy submarines began sinking many of the oil tankers destined for wartime industries and U.S. consumers on the east coast. The U.S. federal government partnered with the petroleum industry to construct the first large-diameter cross-country crude oil pipeline, called *Big Inch* (fig. 4-1.7), and a refined products line, called *Little Big Inch*. Big Inch was 24 inches (61 centimetres) in diameter, while Little Big Inch had a 20-inch (51-centimetre) diameter. Both pipelines were constructed between 1942 and 1943. Prior to their construction, the largest pipelines were 12 inches (31 centimetres) in diameter.

> The U.S. federal government partnered with the petroleum industry to construct the first large cross-country pipelines for crude oil and refined products.

Source: Library of Congress LC-USW4-029616

Figure 4-1.7. Construction of the cross-country Big Inch pipeline

Gathering Systems The earliest pipelines were usually not connected directly to the oil-wells but received their oil from large *dump tanks* located at strategic shipping points. A dump tank is a calibrated metering tank that could release a measured amount of liquid. Pioneer Henry Harley was the first to build a pipeline to carry oil from wells to his dump tanks, a job generally handled by teamsters. Soon after Harley built two lines from the Benninghoff Run lease to tanks at the Oil Creek railroad loading depot, a serious dispute developed between the teamsters and pipeliners. A bitter fight resulted in significant destruction to the pipeline facilities, but the pipeliners persisted.

In 1866, A. W. Smiley and G. E. Coutant formed the Accommodation Pipeline Company and constructed the first *gathering lines*, a network of 2-inch (5-centimetre) pipe some 4 miles (6.4 kilometres) across to connect tanks at the wells with the dump tanks owned by the pipeliners. As production grew, gathering lines were connected directly from the well leases to the trunklines.

Products Pipelines The demand for refined petroleum products grew with the widespread use of automobiles. Product pipelines could efficiently transport all oil products to help meet consumers' growing needs. Extensive construction of products pipelines did not begin until 1930 when the growth of large population centers in the Midwest created new markets for refined products. Before pipelines, products were transported by horse-drawn carts and later, by early model trucks to consumer outlets. These methods worked well in areas where consumer demand was relatively close to retail centers.

During the economic depression of the 1930s, established oil companies competed for a share of the refined products market. Competition required an inexpensive transportation method such as pipelines that could transport many grades of refined products from the refinery to the market. To meet this need, 3,000 miles (4,830 kilometres) of products pipelines were placed in operation during 1930 and 1931. In some instances, older crude pipelines were cleaned and the direction of flow reversed to move products in the United States from the east coast to the Midwest.

The writings of Confucious dating back to 600 B.C. indicate that along the Tibetan border were wells 100 feet (30.48 metres) deep containing water and natural gas. The Chinese used natural gas and piped it through hollow bamboo poles (fig. 4-1.8). As early as 400 B.C., a pipeline system made of bamboo transported natural gas, enabling the Chinese to light the capital city of Peking. However, the widespread use of natural gas did not develop until it became available at competitive prices.

A gunsmith named Aaron Hart drilled the first American natural gas well in 1821. He drilled only 17 feet (5 metres) when a hissing sound signaled he had encountered something other than water, which turned out to be gas. Hart experimented with the gas in hopes of finding possible uses for it. His experiments led him to string together a few hollowed logs to make a gas pipeline. With this primitive system, Hart managed to transmit the gas to provide lighting for some nearby buildings. It took decades to solve the problem of finding a practical and economical method of transmitting gas from the fields where it was produced to the cities and factories where it could be used, but it was the start of further developments.

Gas Transmission Pipelines

Figure 4-1.8. Using bamboo poles, the Chinese were among the first to pipe natural gas.

After World War II, private industry bought Big Inch and Little Big Inch and converted them to natural gas transmission lines to supply gas at competitive rates.

By the beginning of the twentieth century, natural gas was used as fuel in homes and industries. However, costs were high because its delivery system was inefficient and demand was slowing. Until heavy equipment was invented in the 1920s, construction of the pipelines was done largely by hand labor assisted by horses and mules, including clearing right-of-way, digging ditches, screwing ends of pipe together, lowering pipe, and *backfilling* (figs. 4-1.9 and 4-1.10).

The first large-scale natural gas pipelines were a direct result of World War II initiatives. After the war, private industry bought Big Inch and Little Big Inch and converted them to natural gas transmission lines, thereby solving the problem of supplying gas to markets at competitive rates.

Figure 4-1.9. True horsepower was used in early-day construction of gas pipelines and compressor stations.

Figure 4-1.10. Hand tongs were used by early pipeline construction workers.

The transportation of petroleum in barrels or in bulk can be hazardous due to the risk of fire and explosion. Transporting oil in large bulk tanks did not immediately replace barrels, because the tanks presented the problem of oil shifting in the tank. Oil moving in a tank could throw a ship off balance or *ballast*. Also, the loading and unloading of such large tanks was a problem.

As a result of European industrialists promoting their refining capabilities, oceangoing ships were designed to carry bulk crude oil from the producing countries (United States and Russia) to Europe. During the 1860s, a few sailing ships fitted with iron tanks began hauling crude oil across the Atlantic Ocean. In 1886, a ship named Gluckauf made its maiden voyage from New York City in the United States to Bremen, Germany, hauling refined oil. Designed by Wilhelm Riedemann, a German importer, the Gluckauf was the first successful *oceangoing tanker* that used the ship's hull as part of the storage compartments (fig. 4-1.11).

New designs stored oil in separate steel compartments with pipes for loading, unloading, and venting gas accumulations. The change from sail to steam power revolutionized the tanker as a means of transporting petroleum and its products. By 1900, U.S. companies were shipping products from their Gulf Coast plants to the east coast and abroad. In 1901 at the time of the Spindletop boom, Sun Oil bought a cargo vessel, the S. S. Paraguay, and converted it into a tanker to ship oil from Gulf Coast ports. Other companies followed suit and bought or leased tankers to ship their oil.

After World War I, steam-powered tank ships were developed with cargo capacities of 9,000 deadweight tons (9,145 tonnes) and with double bottoms. *Deadweight tonnage* is a ship's empty weight subtracted from its loaded displacement, expressed in metric tons (2,204 pounds in a metric tonne).

Diesel engines replaced steam engines as an improved power source for ships. In World War II, fleets of U.S. tankers called T-2s carried 14,000 deadweight tons (14,225 metric tonnes) and supplied petroleum for wartime industries on the East Coast. T-2s also shipped products from the Western Hemisphere to the war zones. These tankers were prime targets for enemy submarines, forcing the United States to expand its pipeline network, which was seen as a less vulnerable mode of transportation.

Ships at Sea

Figure 4-1.11. The Gluckhauf was the first successful oceangoing tanker that carried oil in storage tanks built into its hull.

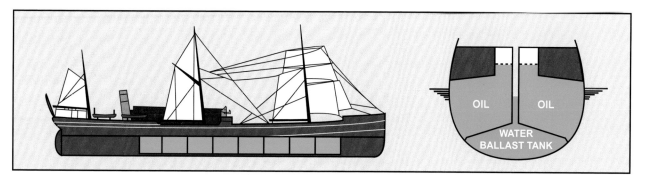

Tank Trucks   At the end of the nineteenth century, tank trucks were the next generation of horse-drawn, tank carrying wagons used to transport crude oil from the wellhead to the pipeline and other shipping outlets (fig. 4-1.12). During World War I, better-designed trucks overcame the inadequate power, small size, and lack of safety features of the earlier models. Welding replaced riveting as a means of fabricating the tanks. During and after World War II, *liquefied petroleum gas (LPG)* became a major commodity for tank truck transportation. Tank trucks, specially designed to contain the pressures of LPG, transported the gas not only to dealers throughout the country but from the dealers to their many rural customers. Subsequently, aluminum, stainless steel, and plastic tanks replaced many of the steel tanks. The transport of chemicals and corrosive commodities and the development of new welding methods were largely responsible for improvements in tank construction.

As gathering pipelines increasingly took over the transportation of crude oil, tank trucks were used less frequently in large oilfields. Tank trucks continued to be useful in locations where a relatively small volume of oil was brought from widely scattered sources. Today, tank trucks are mainly used in distributing refined products from product terminals to service stations and other outlets.

Figure 4-1.12. An early tank truck hauls crude oil from the well's wooden storage tank.

The railway system is a vital link in the petroleum transportation net-work, although the total percentage of petroleum and its derivatives shipped by rail is relatively small. Railway systems transport:

- Crude oil and other *feedstocks* to refineries

- Refined products to demand centers

- Petrochemicals between plants and to consumers

Rail is used where combined volume concentrations and distance between supply and demand points exceed motor carrier capabilities but are not large enough to justify other transportation modes such as pipelines or waterway carriers.

As an example, today's rail industry in the United States is made up of seven railroads. Each railroad influences rail business practices, and no one company controls the market. These separate railroads are interdependent and share certain assets such as railway tracks by agreement. Railroads own and maintain their infrastructure, having spent billions of dollars for improvements and maintenance. According to the *Association of American Railroads (AAR)*, that infrastructure includes approximately 140,000 miles (225,308 kilometres) of tracks and accounts for 43% of intercity freight volume.

The chemical industry relies heavily on rail tank cars to transport millions of gallons (thousands of cubic metres) of petroleum-based chemicals, or *petrochemicals*, used in various manufacturing processes. Many chemicals are shipped from refineries and chemical plants to manufacturing centers for conversion into plastics, synthetic fibers, paints, and other products. Although previously transported by rail, most LPG now moves through pipelines.

Tank cars are also used to ship crude oil and refined products to and from refineries (fig. 4-1.13). Most refineries have rail lines running through their plants with loading and unloading *racks* (fig. 4-1.14).

RAILWAY SYSTEMS

Petroleum Products Transported by Rail

Courtesy of John McKey, 4rail.net

Figure 4-1.13. Tank cars are also used to ship crude oil and refined products to and from refineries.

Courtesy of Carbis, Inc. of Florence, South Carolina

Figure 4-1.14. Railcar loading racks for loading and unloading products from tank cars

Railway systems move:
- Crude oil and feedstocks to refineries
- Refined products to demand centers
- Petrochemicals to plants and consumers

With the increased use of ethanol as a blended component of gasoline, rail traffic and its importance to the fuels market has increased. In the United States, corn-based ethanol must be moved from the Midwest where the corn is grown to gasoline refining and blending facilities located mainly on the Gulf Coast and other parts of the Midwest.

Ethanol must be moved by rail because it can cause *stress corrosion cracking* in pipe, which damages the sealing materials used in pipelines. The volume concentrations and market demand for ethanol have not reached levels high enough to justify new pipelines to transport this product alone.

Because most petroleum derivatives are considered hazardous materials, the *Federal Railroad Administration (FRA)* of the *U.S. Department of Transportation (DOT)* controls their transport within the United States. Rail tank car design is regulated by the DOT. The FRA was formed as a result of the Department of Transportation Act of 1966. Among its stated goals and purposes is to "promulgate and enforce rail safety regulations."

U.S. Government Regulation

While tank car exteriors might appear identical, they are customized to carry specific products (fig. 4-1.15). Special tank linings and insulation along with metals unaffected by corrosive liquids are required for the specific product transported.

These cylinder railcars can range in length from 24 to 64 feet (7.3 to 19.5 metres) and are up to 15.5 feet (4.7 metres) high and 10.5 feet (3.2 metres) wide. A general-purpose car carries 20,000 to 33,000 gallons (76 to 125 cubic metres) or more of liquid, compared with an LPG tank car that carries about 33,500 gallons (127 cubic metres). Railcar size, length, width, and height are limited by the rail system infrastructure such as track layout, bridges, and tunnels. Tank cars that move liquids rarely exceed 40,000 gallons (151,416 litres), or 1,000 barrels, capacity.

All tank cars are built to industry standards and must meet government agency regulations for the specific tank car design before construction begins. In addition to meeting specifications, each tank car design must be reviewed and certified in writing by the AAR before it can be built and placed in service.

Other than the tank, the components of tank cars are common to all other railroad cars. Tank car components such as wheels, axles, brake systems, bearings, and couplers are built by specialty suppliers to satisfy industry standards and government regulations.

Tank Car Design and Manufacture

Courtesy of Global Trans

Figure. 4-1.15. General-purpose rail tank car

Safety

Tank cars are regularly inspected and monitored by the rail company. Safety inspections and regularly scheduled tests of pressure ratings and checks for valve leaks are required. Since the *Railroad Tank Car Safety Research and Test Project* in 1970, tank car manufacturers have greatly improved the safety of tank cars. Tank car engineers and manufacturers continue to research and develop metal alloy, optimum tank capacity for each material, improved safety features, and the best valves and fittings.

Tank Car Strings and Unit Trains

In the 1970s, the *General American Transportation Corporation (GATX)* developed the *TankTrain*™, a system of interconnected tank cars for transporting bulk liquids. A TankTrain consists of interconnected cars that can be loaded or unloaded through a single connection. The company claims a TankTrain can be loaded or unloaded at a rate of 3,000 gallons (11,356 litres) per minute, with a five-car string loading in just 90 minutes and a 90-car train in less than five hours. Previous tank cars were loaded and unloaded individually.

A large flexible hose connects each tank car to the one in front of it, and petroleum is loaded into all the cars through a single connection on the first car. During loading, displaced vapors are collected in the last car and processed through a flare or scrubbing unit or a vapor recovery system. The entire car string is unloaded by injecting compressed inert gas to push the liquid out. Often, a pump is used to increase the flow rate.

Loading and unloading systems—closed and simplified—handle petroleum products with a wide range of viscosities and volatilities (fig. 4-1.16). A *closed system* is used when products have flammable or

Figure 4-1.16. Conventional tank cars are loaded and unloaded individually (right) while interconnected tank cars can be handled from one loading rack (left).

toxic vapors. A *simplified system* handles products with low volatility and no vapor hazard.

Before the TankTrain, transporting crude oil from a production field to a refinery long distance by rail was costly and time consuming. One U.S. company's system proved successful in moving crude regularly from its California oilfield to the refining complex 250 miles (400 kilometres) away. This system consisted of 72 insulated tank cars, each holding almost 550 barrels (87.5 cubic metres) of warm crude oil, making a single shipment of almost 40,000 barrels (6,360 cubic metres). Five 3,600-horsepower (2,520-kilowatt) diesel-electric locomotives led the train with six more locomotives interspersed throughout, providing 43,200 horsepower (30,240 kilowatts) to push and pull the fully loaded 12,000-ton (10,900-tonne) train. To handle high-volume shipments, the company required some changes from the railroad. Loading and unloading facilities were modified, heavy-duty roadbeds were laid, and new sections of track were installed to facilitate unloading six strings of twelve cars each simultaneously. At the train's refinery storage end, a two-person crew and a rail equipment operator unloaded the entire train in about five hours (fig. 4-1.17). Similar equipment is used for loading and unloading a *unit train*.

Although the TankTrain is efficient for transporting petroleum, the unit train is preferred by railroads because there is much less effort involved in separating, spotting, and positioning different cars. A unit train consists of a number of the same type of rail cars made into a train of over 100 cars carrying the same commodity. Positioning cars for loading and unloading has been simplified with small power units in the rack siding locations. Coal unit trains are the most common, but unit trains are also used for moving petroleum.

- A TankTrain™ consists of interconnected tank cars transporting bulk liquids.
- A unit train consists of multiple cars carrying the same commodity.

Figure 4-1.17. Interconnected hoses and valves allow the entire train to be loaded and unloaded in short time.

Courtesy of BTB Refining

MOTOR TRANSPORTATION

Trucking companies own, lease, operate, maintain, and staff the motor carrier industry. In the United States, this industry is made up of about 500,000 carriers. Most companies are single-unit businesses, although there are a few multibillion-dollar corporations with thousands of vehicles.

While motor transportation carries only about 3% of the total ton-miles of petroleum moved, it still plays a key role in the transportation of petroleum and its derivatives. Motor carriers provide flexibility because they can respond to short lead times and can reach numerous locations not practical using other modes of transportation. However, the cost per unit of volume is high because of operating expenses, and the volume handled per load is relatively small. For example, a typical motor carrier can haul about 9,000 gallons (34,069 litres) of gasoline and 7,500 gallons (28,391 litres) of diesel fuel due to *gross vehicle weight (gvw)* restrictions of typically 80,000 pounds (36,288 kilograms).

Motor carriers are used when volumes are relatively small and receipt and delivery locations are widely scattered. They are primarily used to move refined products from distribution terminals to service stations for consumers to access.

Types of Vehicles

Many types of motor vehicles transport petroleum, refined products, and gas:

- A *tank truck* is a self-propelled vehicle that carries a tank on its own chassis.
- A *truck tractor* is usually diesel powered and is designed to pull a *trailer*.
- The combination of rigs is commonly called a *tractor-trailer*, a *semi*, or an *eighteen-wheeler*.
  - The *semi-trailer* has part of its weight resting on the tractor and part on its trailer wheels.
  - A *full-trailer* is like a semi-trailer, except its full weight is on the trailer wheels and it is designed to be pulled by a truck or behind a tractor-trailer.

To carry petroleum products, all vehicles other than the truck tractor have cylindrical, horizontal tanks, depending on the products carried. Many tank trailers, especially those hauling refined products to service stations, have separate compartments within the tank that allow several products to be hauled in one truck.

Crude Oil Trucks

Crude oil is transported by trucks from many locations in oil-producing regions. They are especially useful in new oilfields of uncertain long-term production levels where pipelines cannot be initially justified. The crude oil is loaded at the production lease where tank batteries accumulate the oil. Most of these locations are automated. This allows authorized carriers using key cards or other security devices to enter the facility and unlock valves, pumps, and meters to start the flow of oil into the truck tanks.

Crude oil is usually carried in a general-purpose tank pulled by large diesel-powered trucks (fig. 4-1.18). Most tanks do not require compartments, special insulations, or multiple outlets because only one type of liquid—crude oil—is being moved. The crude oil is usually hauled to a nearby pipeline gathering station or directly to a refinery or other receiving location. There it is unloaded for movement to its final destination.

Figure 4-1.18. A general-purpose fuel tank truck

Refined Products Transport

Most refined products can be transported in a general-purpose tank divided into compartments and shaped to ensure complete drainage. Each compartment has its own outlet, enabling it to carry more than one product such as gasoline, kerosene, and diesel at the same time. These trucks are designed to allow more liquid volume while safely hauling the products.

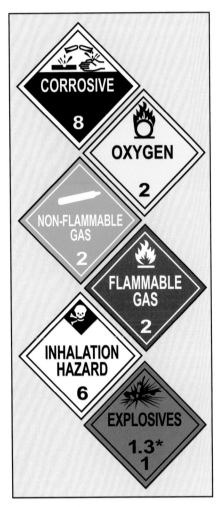

Figure 4-1.19. Diamond-shaped placards are used to signal hazardous contents.

Today, general-purpose aluminum tanks are designed to operate at atmospheric pressure. If they contain hazardous materials, federal regulations require that numbered diamond-shaped placards be posted on the tanks to indicate the nature of the hazardous contents (fig. 4-1.19).

Special-purpose tanks are designed for corrosive products or products requiring special equipment. For example, an *asphalt tank* that contains heating equipment is insulated, because it might carry products that have temperatures of up to 400° F, or 204° C. Corrosive liquids such as caustics and acids require tanks made of noncorrosive materials and with special linings and seals. Products carried in special tanks include heavy oils or sulfur that must be heated for loading and unloading.

Some refineries and product terminals pipe gasoline, kerosene, and diesel to remote terminals equipped with *truck racks* and meters for self-service loading by large tanker trucks (fig. 4-1.20). Authorized truck drivers can pull into the terminals and take in fuel at the computer-controlled truck loading rack any time of the day or night. Billing and recordkeeping are also automated. This allows truck drivers to load their tanks any time without oil company personnel present.

Most truck racks handling fuel are equipped to load trucks from the bottom of the tank and vent the top to equipment designed to recover the vapor. These features are used to minimize fumes and reduce air pollution.

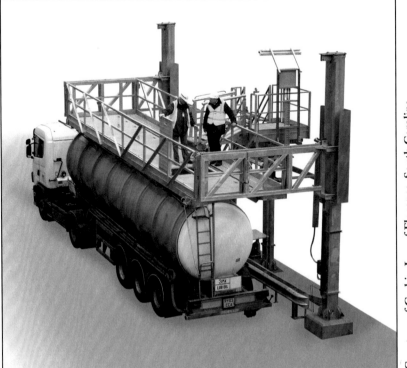

Figure 4-1.20. Tank truck loading rack

Courtesy of Carbis, Inc. of Florence, South Carolina

Some products require refrigerated pressure tanks. LPG such as butane and propane, as well as ethylene and similar products, must be transported in tanks designed for pressures between 100 and 500 pounds per square inch (0.7 to 3.4 megapascals). Pressure and very low temperatures are used to liquefy the gases before being loaded into the tanks. The products are kept liquefied with insulation or cooling equipment. Air compressors or pump units are used to unload gas products from the tanks. These pressure tanks are usually made of high-tensile steel and are not compartmentalized (fig. 4-1.21).

LPG can also be dispensed to trucks from remote storage locations supplied by pipeline. For example, one company's propane flows through an 8-inch (20-centimetre) pipeline from storage tanks 100 miles (161 kilometres) away directly into the propane trucks via a propane loading facility. This system eliminates area storage problems and makes loading easy for truck drivers. Computers and special meters measure monitor product flow and volume, print bills of lading, and provide a security system to ensure safe operations.

Liquefied Petroleum Gas Transport

LPG must be:
- Liquefied at low temperatures
- Transported in special tanks
- Kept liquefied with cooking equipment
- Unloaded using air compressors or pump units

Courtesy of Richard Mohr

Figure 4-1.21. An LPG transport truck is used to carry propane to various LPG storage units.

Government Regulation

In addition to tanks meeting specifications, drivers and safety equipment must meet state and federal regulations. In the United States, regulations vary by state concerning the operation of motor vehicles carrying petroleum and petroleum products. Driver training qualifications, driving rules, licensing equipment and accessories, accident reporting, maintenance requirements, and vehicle weights and sizes are governed. The *Surface Transportation Board*, an autonomous entity within the U.S. DOT, oversees regulations at the federal level.

MARINE TRANSPORTATION
Inland Waterways

Petroleum and petroleum products are transported by barge wherever there is a waterway and a need for the products. Barges carrying gasoline, asphalt, crude oil, chemicals, and industrial fuel shuttle back and forth on a network of lakes, rivers, channels, and intracoastal canals. The basic equipment use for this mode of transportation is the barge and towboat. This combination is called a *tow*.

Barges

A *barge* is a vessel that usually has a flat deck and flat bottom. It is a series of floating tanks or compartments made of welded steel plates assembled with hatches and piping for loading and unloading. Most barges today are double-hulled for added safety.

An empty barge rides high in the water, showing its *draft marks*, or *waterline marks*, by the line between different colored, painted areas on the barge's side (fig. 4-1.22). As it is filled, the barge rides deeper and deeper in the water. Tonnage is estimated by reading the marks on the hull. The exact volume of the loaded and unloaded barge is typically supplied with calibrated measuring systems. Barges usually have no power to move on their own. They depend on tugboats, towboats, and water currents to move.

In the United States, oil barges first traveled more than 1,000 miles (1,610 kilometres) from the *Gulf Intracoastal Waterway* to Carrabelle, Florida. This waterway made the U.S. Gulf Coast the nation's leading oil refining region. Barges on this waterway provide a safe method of moving petroleum because the barrier islands, peninsulas, and inland routes protect barge tows from the rough waters and storms in ocean waters.

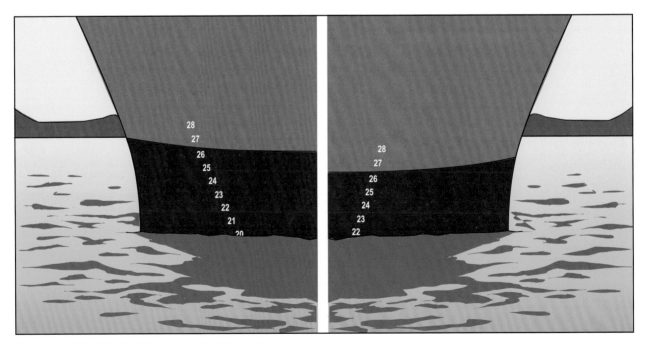

Figure 4-1.22. The draft marks on the side of a barge or ocean vessel indicate how full or empty the vessel is.

Tugboats are powered vessels designed to push or pull other vessels in harbors, on inland waterways, and in coastal waters. Although comparatively small, a tugboat has a large engine capable of towing a vessel many times its size. Tugboats help maneuver barges into line to make a barge tow or hold a barge in place at the dock for loading and unloading (fig. 4-1.23).

Tugboats

Figure 4-1.23. A tugboat pulls a loaded barge out of the harbor.

Unlike the tugboat, the *towboat* is a relatively flat-bottomed boat with a square front, or *bow* (fig. 4-1.24). Affixed to the bow are large upright *knees* used for attaching and pushing barges. Towboats also have a large engine (or engines) and are extremely maneuverable. *Bow thrusters*, which are powerful propellers in the front, assist in maneuverability when combined with the aft-powered propeller drive. Diesel towboats can push a string of barges carrying thousands of barrels of petroleum products over great distances at low cost.

   A towboat can range from 600 to 2,400 horsepower (420 to 1,680 kilowatts). Some towboats can be as tall as a four-story building.

Towboats

Courtesy of Capt. John C. Farmer, NavCal Marine Services LLC.

Figure 4-1.24. A towboat has large upright knees on its bow to facilitate pushing.

A large towboat can push about forty barges carrying over 18,000 tons (16,300 tonnes) of cargo in a tow. This string, or *tow travel*, can move at approximately 6 miles per hour (10 kilometres per hour), depending on waterway conditions such as current, crosscurrents, sandbars, wind, ice, and other traffic. On the river, the tow going with the current has right-of-way. Barges going against the river current must stop and wait for oncoming traffic to clear the waterway before they can proceed.

The towboat crew typically consists of a captain, a ship's mate, a chief engineer, an assistant engineer, a tankerman, a pilot, a cook, and deckhands. The crew builds the tow by hooking a number of barges together. Oil barge tows can be strung out for more than 1,000 feet (305 metres) and are made up of barges 54 feet (16.5 metres) wide and almost 300 feet (91.5 metres) long. The barges are lashed together so they can be steered as a single unit. A barge tow might be loaded with as much as 60,000 barrels (9,540 cubic metres) of oil. A river tow might be two side-by-side strings, each stretching around 800 feet (244 metres).

All personnel, from the captain to the deckhands and attendants on the docks, who work on U.S. waterway vessels must be trained and certified under the U.S. Coast Guard rules and regulations.

A towboat crew could be moving up the Mississippi River for nearly a month. A trip from Tulsa, Oklahoma, down through the rivers and canal to plants in Nederland, Texas, might take 16 to 18 days. After picking up a string of barges, a towboat seldom stops. Fuel and supplies are furnished by service boats that come alongside the tow in midstream.

Oceangoing Tankers

Crude oil shipped short distance in simple floating tanks powered by steam engines is a mode of transport that dates back to the 1870s. The tanks were small, around 200 feet (60.96 metres) long, and traveled from production areas to manufacturing centers. In the early 1900s, the discovery of oil in the Middle East and an increasing demand for oil by industrialized nations led to increased shipping further across the open seas.

During World War I, oceangoing transport of crude oil and refined products grew to support the war effort in Europe. During World War II, oceangoing ships grew larger in size to where a typical oil tanker was 16,500 deadweight tons (16,765 metric tonnes) and about 500 feet (152.4 metres) long.

After World War II, oceangoing tankers became the major mode of transporting oil. Crude oil tankers vary in size from smaller tankers of 20,000 deadweight tons (20,321 metric tonnes) or less to huge carriers with capacities exceeding 500,000 deadweight tons (508,023 metric tonnes). There are only a few of the larger vessels compared to vessels of the medium or small size. Besides crude oil, oceangoing vessels also transport refined products, *natural gas liquid (NGL)*, and *liquefied natural gas (LNG)*. Modern tankers transport nearly two-thirds of the petroleum produced in the world.

As larger refineries were built, larger vessels were needed to move petroleum products more economically. In 1979, *Seawise Giant*, the largest oceangoing vessel at the time, weighing 564,000 deadweight tons (573,050 metric tonnes), was built (fig. 4-1.25). It was so large that it could not pass through the English Channel.

To meet the transportation demand, companies operated *very large crude carriers (VLCC)* and *ultra-large crude carriers (ULCC)*. Besides the cost, a major drawback was that many ports, harbors, and waterways could not handle these enormous vessels. A VLCC has a deadweight range of about 160,000 to 400,000 deadweight tons (162,568 to 406,419 metric tonnes) while ULCCs range from 320,000 to over 550,000 deadweight tons (325,135 to 558,826 metric tonnes). *Supertanker* is the term used to describe these large tankers. Today, the term is applied to VLCCs and ULCCs with capacity of over 250,000 deadweight tons (254,012 metric tonnes).

Supertankers can be up to 1,500 feet (457.2 metres) long and move at about 18 miles per hour (28.98 kilometres per hour). These ships can transport about 2 million barrels (317,974,591 litres) of oil. A single supertanker carrying 2 million barrels (317,974,591 litres) can transport enough petroleum to heat the homes and power the cars of a city of 85,000 people for one year. Navigational aids, electronic control systems, automated power plants, satellite communications, and radar equipment allow for maximum security and a minimum crew.

There are only a few supertankers in use today. During their prime, supertankers filled a specific need: to transport huge amounts of crude from new oilfields to the new refineries being built to supply an increasingly energy-hungry population. Today, smaller tankers have largely replaced the global fleet of supertankers once deployed worldwide.

Supertankers

Modern tankers transport nearly two-thirds of the petroleum produced in the world.

Figure 4-1.25. The Seawise Giant, an oceangoing supertanker

Courtesy of Auke Visser, Holland

Average-Size Tankers

An average-sized tanker ranges in size from 30,000 to 80,000 deadweight tons (30,480 to 81,280 tonnes) (fig. 4-1.26). The use of smaller tankers has grown due to the following:

- Construction of new pipelines
- Flexibility and lower investment cost of such tankers
- Increased transport of refined products worldwide
- Deepening and widening of canals and waterways able to accommodate average-sized tankers
- Discovery of new oilfields that eliminated the necessity of many long hauls
- Global conservation programs

Tankers are designed to ensure safety and reliability. Using a sophisticated network of telecommunication and satellite systems, a company can locate any of its tankers at any time. On board the ships, crews receive rigorous safety training and follow strict measures to ensure personal safety and minimize oil loss. Automatic collision-avoidance systems track approaching ships, alerting a tanker to any obstruction on its course. The percentage of crude oil lost to spills and environmental damage each year is small compared to the total amount of oil now transported by tankers.

Figure 4-1.26. Tanker for transporting crude oil

In the Arctic Ocean, Baltic Sea, and other ice-laden seas, tankers need *hulls* strong enough to prevent damage and spills while considering the high cost and weight of the thick steel hull plating. Some tankers have double hulls, which manufacturers believe are safer.

There is considerable growth among global icebreaker fleets. Because they are necessary to transport on frozen seas, these tankers can charge higher rates than normal tankers. Newer vessels are double-acting, icebreaking tankers with a hybrid bow that reaches the edge of an ice cover, turns around, reverses the rotation of its propellers, and starts to break the ice using its *stern* (fig. 4-1.27). The vessel can cut through a 27-inch (70-centimetre) thick layer of ice and ice ridges 42.6 feet (13 metres) thick.

Recent advances in ship propulsion have produced new experimental icebreakers. Some have propellers driven electrically and mounted to steerable pods under the ship. These *azimuth thrusters* improve fuel efficiency and steering and docking of the ship so rudders are not needed (fig. 4-1.28). The thrusters allow the ships to travel backwards with ease.

Icebreaking Tankers

Courtesy of Aker Arctic Technology, Inc.

Figure 4-1.27. A double-ended tanker can plow through ice in reverse because of its hardened stern, and travel in open waters with its conventional bow.

Courtesy of BOURBON

Figure 4-1.28. Azimuth thrusters allow ships to travel backwards with ease and enable steering and docking without the use of rudders.

Natural Gas Tankers

• Natural gas is liquefied before being transported.
• The LNG is regasified when it reaches its destination.

Tankers equipped with pressurized, refrigerated, and insulated tanks (*cryogenic* tankers) NGL and LNG. NGLs are hydrocarbon liquids that are gaseous in the reservoir but liquid in field facilities or gas processing plants. Gas liquids that are not highly *volatile* (easily vaporized) are treated and shipped as natural gasoline or added to the crude oil. If separated before shipment, butane, propane, and ethane (referred to as LPGs) must be transported in tankers designed to handle the high pressures and low temperatures needed to keep these hydrocarbons in a liquid state. NGL is usually transported as a mixture and separated into LPG, natural gasoline, and ethane after it reaches the refinery.

Natural gas is liquefied at the source before it is transported by special LNG tankers. LNG is then regasified and fed into the natural gas transmission system when it reaches its destination. For example, one company that furnishes natural gas to Tokyo liquefies the gas near its source by lowering its temperature to -259° F (-162° C). As the gas liquefies, it shrinks to 1/600th of its original volume. The LNG cargo is kept in its liquefied state during a 3,000-mile (4,830-kilometre) journey and then is converted back to its gaseous state as it enters natural gas pipelines in Japan. (More information on LNG transportation is found later in this chapter. For additional information on this growing industry, refer to *LNG: Basics of Liquefied Natural Gas*, published by The University of Texas at Austin-PETEX.)

Figure 4-1.29 pictures an LNG containment ship known as a Kvaener-Moss design. Due to the space between spheres and ship hulls, the use of the hull space is somewhat compromised. The unused space makes it relatively easy to perform periodic inspections for structural integrity.

Courtesy of HÖEGH LNG

Figure 4-1.29. The Arctic Princess, an LNG containment system of Kvaener-Moss design

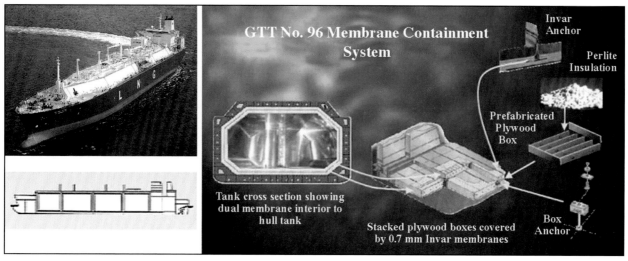

Figure 4-1.30. An LNG ship: a Gaz Transport No. 96 membrane containment system

Two types of membrane tank designs were independently developed and marketed by different companies. These systems are known as the Gaz Transport (GT) No. 96 system and Technigaz Mark III system (figs. 4-1.30 and 4-1.31). After the merger of the two companies in the mid-1990s, the resulting company called GTT now offers a third type of membrane tank design called the Composite System (CS1).

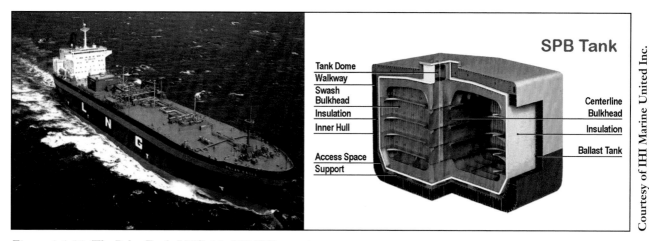

Figure 4-1.31. The Polar Eagle LNG ship IHI SPB containment system

Loading and Offloading Facilities

Because few ports are large enough to accommodate supertankers, oil *ports of entry* use methods of loading and offloading at sea. Most world ports capable of handling supertankers have offshore *mooring facilities* and underwater pipelines that transfer oil from shore to ship, ship to ship, or ship to barge. They can also offload their cargos at refinery loading and unloading docks or from ship to shore.

In the United States, shuttle tankers and barges take the oil or products to shore or inland through some of the major waterways maintained by the U.S. Army Corps of Engineers. Many of these waterways are deep-draft canals and channels, deep enough and wide enough to handle small tankers (fig. 4-1.32).

The largest mainland U.S. deepwater port equipped to handle supertankers is the *Louisiana Offshore Oil Port (LOOP)*. According to the Louisiana Department of Transportation and Development:

> "Tankers offload at LOOP by pumping crude oil through hoses connected to a Single Point Mooring (SPM) base. Three SPMs are located 8,000 feet [2.4 kilometres] from the Marine Terminal. The SPMs are designed to handle ships up to 700,000 deadweight tons [635,000 metric tonnes]. The crude oil then moves to the Marine Terminal via a 56-inch [1.4-metre] diameter submarine pipeline. The Marine Terminal consists of a control platform and a pumping platform."

Oil is then transported via pipeline to refineries along the Gulf Coast, the Mississippi River, and as far as the Midwest. Tankers of various sizes transport North Slope crude oil from the *Trans-Alaska Pipeline System (TAPS)* at the Valdez Marine Terminal in southern Alaska and deliver it to ports in the lower 48 states (fig. 4-1.33).

Figure 4-1.32. A tanker shuttles down a U.S. coastal waterway.

Figure 4-1.33. Tankers of various sizes transport North Slope crude oil from the Trans-Alaska Pipeline System at the Valdez Marine Terminal in southern Alaska and deliver it to ports in the lower 48 United States.

Oil companies often use converted tankers as offshore floating production, storage, and offloading units to transfer crude oil from onshore production units or offshore platforms to tankers. Well production is often transferred by subsea pipeline to a moored tanker outfitted with storage and treating equipment. The treated crude, which is sold by *custody transfer metering*, is picked up by tankers that dock at the floating production, storage, and offloading unit for loading.

Crude Oil Pipelines

The construction of U.S. oil pipelines increased during and after World War II. From prewar deliveries of less than 50,000 barrels (7,950 cubic metres) per day, daily pipeline shipments eastward grew to 754,000 barrels (120,000 cubic metres). The companies east of the Rockies increased their total daily movements about 60% between 1941 and 1945. Companies found that large-diameter crude oil trunklines could be operated as flexibly as smaller lines, thereby significantly reducing transportation costs per barrel (cubic metre). Pipelines devoted to the transportation of petroleum liquids have increased from 124,000 miles (200,000 kilometres) postwar to more than 200,000 miles (322,000 kilometres) today. Crude oil gathering and trunkline mileage account for about 95,000 miles (152,950 kilometres).

Pipelines transporting petroleum liquids have increased:
- From 124,000 miles postwar
- To more than 200,000 miles today

Actual crude oil pipeline mileage has declined somewhat, but total quantities shipped have steadily risen because of larger diameter lines and the *looping of long lines*—that is, laying additional lines alongside existing pipelines. A major contributor to the increased quantities of oil transported is TAPS with its 48-inch (122-centimetre) diameter pipeline that runs from Prudhoe Bay to Port Valdez, spanning a distance of some 801 miles (1,290 kilometers). At its peak, it delivered 2 million barrels (318,000 cubic metres) per day of oil to the Valdez Marine Terminal. Sophisticated handling facilities, including four tanker *berths*, allow tankers to load oil at rates up to 110,000 barrels (17,500 cubic metres) of oil per hour. These tankers subsequently move the Alaskan crude oil to reception points in the mainland United States.

As U.S. domestic crude oil continues to decline, more foreign oil is being used to supply refineries in the Gulf Coast and inland as well. The increased demand for offshore crude oil has led to the construction of a number of large-scale trunklines. Increased imports of Canadian crude oil have likewise made it necessary to construct more pipelines and expand and redirect existing trunklines. As Canadian supplies rise and begin to replace volumes from foreign offshore oil, further reversals and new lines will continue being developed around the world.

An oilfield might have several hundred wells with flow lines that carry crude oil from the wells to the lease tanks. Various tanks and treating vessels are often a part of the field gathering system. Pipelines move crude oil from wells without having tanks or other aboveground equipment. The oil is gathered from the field, monitored for quality, measured precisely, and tested before entering the pipeline. The custody of the oil is assigned to the pipeline for movement to its final destination. Figure 4-1.34 shows an overflow of crude oil from the oilfield to its final destination.

Gathering system operations are typically unmanned or lightly manned. Personnel monitor, adjust, and prove the precision measurement devices and pumping equipment in the gathering system. Maintenance, both routine and unplanned, involving mechanical and electrical equipment is usually done by maintenance technicians.

Field Gathering Systems

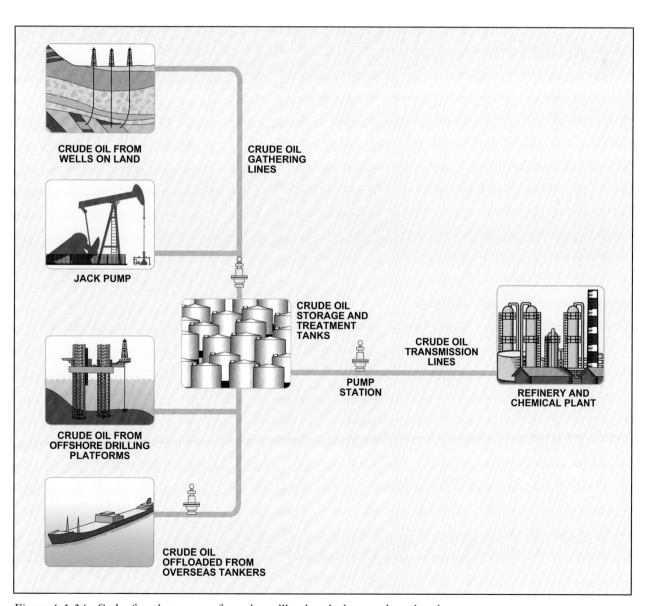

Figure 4-1.34. Cycle of crude transport from the wellhead to the lease tanks and to the consumer

Pump Station Operation

Pumps at *pump stations* located along the pipeline move oil into and through the pipeline (figs. 4-1.35 and 4-1.36). Pump stations can be gathering stations, trunkline stations, or a combination of both.

A *gathering station* is in or near the oilfield and receives oil through a pipeline gathering system, usually from the producers' tanks. From the gathering station, oil is moved to a *trunkline station* located on the mainline or trunkline. With its greater capacity, the trunkline station relays the oil to refineries or shipping terminals. Because the pressure gradually drops as the oil moves through the pipeline due to friction losses, booster pump stations are spaced along the trunkline to add pressure as needed so the oil will continue to move along in the pipeline. *Tank farms* along the line serve as receiving, separating, and holding locations. A special array of lines and valves called a *manifold* maintains separation and regulates the oil that enters and leaves the tank farms and pump stations.

Components of a pipeline gathering system:
- A pump station moves oil into the pipeline.
- A gathering station receives oil from the system.
- A trunkline station relays oil to refineries and terminals.

Figure 4-1.35. Pipeline pumps and motors

Figure 4-1.36. Alaskan pipeline pump station

The gathering station might include one or more pumps that move up to thousands of barrels of oil from various producers' tanks and gathering station tanks each day. Pumping units are usually relatively small, electrically driven reciprocating or centrifugal pumps. Internal-combustion engines used earlier have been almost totally replaced by electric motors as *prime movers*.

Operations at a gathering station depend on the station's size and function. At gathering stations, the oil changes *custody* from the producer to the pipeline company. The pumps are activated either by a *gauger* or a measurement technician, or with remote controls (fig. 4-1.37). On leases using a *Lease Automatic Custody Transfer (LACT)* unit, pumps start automatically or by remote control. These operations are typically overseen by field personnel. After the oil is received at the gathering station, it is pumped to another gathering station closer to the trunkline or directly to a trunkline station.

Gathering Station

Figure 4-1.37. A gauger measures the volume and draws samples to test before pumping begins.

Trunkline Station

A trunkline, or *mainline*, station is located on a main petroleum-carrying artery. It might serve as a gathering station if it is near the oil source, but usually, a trunkline station either originates the oil flow or boosts it to the next pump station down the pipeline. Today, pumps used in trunkline stations are typically high-speed centrifugal units driven by large electric motors. Internal combustion engines and gas-turbine drivers are no longer widely used.

A large station usually has a series of pumps to increase the pumping power capability. Sufficient pumps in the desired configuration are used to achieve the required pressure, and oil is moved down the pipeline to the next station. *Suction boosters* aid in maintaining pressure at the main units (fig. 4-1.38).

Booster stations along the trunkline are located to ensure the hydraulic requirements are achieved and balanced. The *hydraulic factors* are determined by throughput requirements, the density and viscosity of the fluid, and the friction created as the fluid moves along the pipe.

Figure 4-1.38. Booster pumps pull oil from storage tanks and move it to the suction of the trunkline pumps.

A tank farm is a place where oil in transit can be temporarily sidetracked for separation, measurement, and rerouting, or held for such things as repairs on a pipeline or pump station. A tank farm can also be a receiving station where oil comes in from the producing fields or from other carriers to be incorporated into the pipeline transportation system (fig. 4-1.39). Trunklines may bring crude oil belonging to many different shippers to the tank farm. (A *shipper* is any company that transports oil or gas.) By segregating shipments into tanks, the pipeline company can make controlled deliveries to various shippers at refineries or terminals at desired pumping rates, while maintaining the shipper's expected commodity quality.

Station Tank Farm

Courtesy of Larry Bennington

Figure 4-1.39. A tank farm is an integral component of a pipeline system.

Pump Station and Tank Farm Station Manifold

A manifold is an auxiliary system of piping that:
- Separates flow into paths
- Combines several flows
- Reroutes flow to destinations

Manifolds are typically located at origination stations, delivery terminals, and tank farms (4-1.40). A *manifold* is an auxiliary system of piping that separates the flow into several paths, combines several flow paths into one, or reroutes the flow to any one of several possible destinations. It can be complex in a main station or simple at intermediate locations. A manifold might connect a mainline, a field gathering line, a number of tanks, and one or more pumps. This network of lines and valves operated by personnel at a tank farm station or control center can do the following:

- Pump oil through the trunkline while the tanks are offline
- Receive production from the oilfield into tanks
- Receive oil from a trunkline into various tanks
- Transfer oil from one tank to another
- Pump oil from any tank into the trunkline
- Isolate all pumps and tanks while an upstream trunkline station bypasses the location
- Inject oil from any tank into the stream being pumped through the trunkline

Figure 4-1.40. The manifold at a pump station and tank farm permits routing of the oil stream to its destination.

The coordination of shipments for liquid petroleum pipelines, whether for crude oil or refined products, is a critical function due to the large volumes and high market value of petroleum. The process begins several weeks before the start of the next month's operations. Shippers inform the pipeline's oil-movements group of the *nominations* of their *tenders* for the next month. The nominations are submitted on specific calendar dates as outlined in the pipeline's governing rules and regulations. These nominations include the type of crude oil shipped during the next month, the origin and destination of shipments, and the volume needed during the pipeline's shipment cycle. Usually, nominations are transmitted to the pipeline through secure internet connections.

After receiving the shipper's tender information, a scheduler uses computerized scheduling tools to lay out the next month's pumping sequences and compiles a schedule to meet each shipper's needs. The schedule for crude oil pipelines shows shipments on a monthly cycle. This schedule (or pumping order) is given to controllers at the pipeline's control center to implement in the upcoming month. This information is also sent to any connecting carriers, manned receipt and delivery terminals, and shippers.

This coordination ensures that shippers have enough tank space to receive each scheduled delivery at its destination. It also ensures that the equipment and piping configuration at the receipt location can receive the oil at the carrier's pumping rate. To contain shipping costs, crude oil pipelines must handle large volumes, high throughput, and operate efficiently. A single shipment, or batch, must meet both a minimum volume of several thousand barrels and quality specifications. A single pipeline might handle several types of oil for each of several shippers.

A pipeline shipment might need to accumulate over several days before it is moved into the pipeline. Each day, part of the shipment is delivered from oilfield leases to the pipeline company tanks where it is held until the required volume is ready for movement on account. The pipeline company takes custody at the lease where the oil is produced and holds it for the shipper until delivery.

To illustrate how this process works, suppose that transit time takes ten days to move a shipment from its origin to its final destination and that ten different shippers might regularly use this particular pipeline. At any given time, each of these shippers might have several shipments in a pipeline and its tanks, which can amount to thousands of barrels of various shippers' oil. As oil is pumped in *upstream*, an equal volume is pumped out *downstream*. Each shipper continually puts oil in the line and receives deliveries based on the pipeline schedule. Thus, each active shipper always has a balance of oil, called line fill, in the system and the pipeline company maintains accurate records to account for all shippers' oil in its system.

Control of Oil Movements

While their oil is in transit, shippers might trade it to another shipper. The pipeline can change routing and deliver the oil to the new owner at a different destination. This buying, selling, trading, and rerouting of shipments is common in pipeline operations.

Like a rail oil shipment that can be transported on more than one railroad line, a crude oil shipment can travel via more than one pipeline system between its origin and destination. Requests for shipping space in one part of a pipeline can be greater than those in other sections of the same line due to transfers to or from another pipeline system downstream from the originating station. Volumes of oil might be brought into a pipeline at an intermediate point by an interconnecting pipeline or by injections. Pumping rates are adjusted to accommodate volume change. These adjustments consider the changes in hydraulics, and controllers change the pumping equipment configurations to assure smooth, continuous operation of the pipeline.

Today, pipeline controllers handle a pipeline's operation by remote control using a supervisory control and data acquisition (SCADA) system from a central control center linked to remote locations via satellite or other types of communication links (fig. 4-1.41). The controllers continuously monitor hydraulic, electrical, mechanical, and other control parameters and control movements by issuing commands to operate valves of manifolds, start-stop pumps, and other equipment. A backup control center that can take over operations in an emergency or major disruption is often located away from the main control center. In many cases, pipeline companies manage and operate both crude oil and refined products lines from the same control center.

Figure 4-1.41. Pipeline control room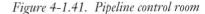

Courtesy of Kinder Morgan

Liquid petroleum pipelines have support services to assure accurate measurement and tight quality control. This is accomplished by following strict procedures and adhering to comprehensive industry standards. These support services train personnel and monitor methods and equipment used by field personnel to measure, sample, and analyze oil moving through the pipeline. They also advise on the management of the pipeline and the performance of *oil loss control* and the *quality assurance processes*. The entire process provides accountability for billions of dollars of petroleum commodities, beginning with crude oil and ending with refined products.

The basic accounting document used for buying, selling, and taking custody of crude oil is the *run ticket*. Each time custody of oil changes hands, a run ticket is generated showing the precise measurements of the quantity and quality of the commodity. The ticket is usually signed and witnessed by the entity receiving the oil and the one delivering the oil. Run tickets are also the basis for transportation charges (*tariffs*) billed to the shipper by the carrier. A similar process is used throughout the oil industry for all petroleum and its derivatives worldwide.

Precise measurement, strict quality control, and accurate accounting at each point of custody transfer or ownership change ensures commodity control. This way, each party receives the correct value for its commodity.

MEASUREMENT AND QUALITY ASSURANCE

Oil Accounting

> Precise measurement, strict quality control, and accurate accounting ensure commodity control.

PRODUCTS PIPELINES

A *products pipeline* transports *refined products* derived from crude oil, such as gasoline, diesel fuel, kerosene, jet fuel, heating oil, and other liquid hydrocarbons. Products pipelines usually start at or near refineries and end at terminals in areas of high market demand for the products (fig. 4-1.42). Most of the nation's large-scale products pipeline systems originate in and around the Gulf Coast area, because many refining companies and petrochemical plants are located there.

Shipments in products pipelines are of higher value compared to crude oil, and product quality specifications are stringent, therefore, products pipeline operations are set up to recognize and handle these factors. In the United States, there are approximately 95,000 miles (152,950 kilometres) of products pipelines.

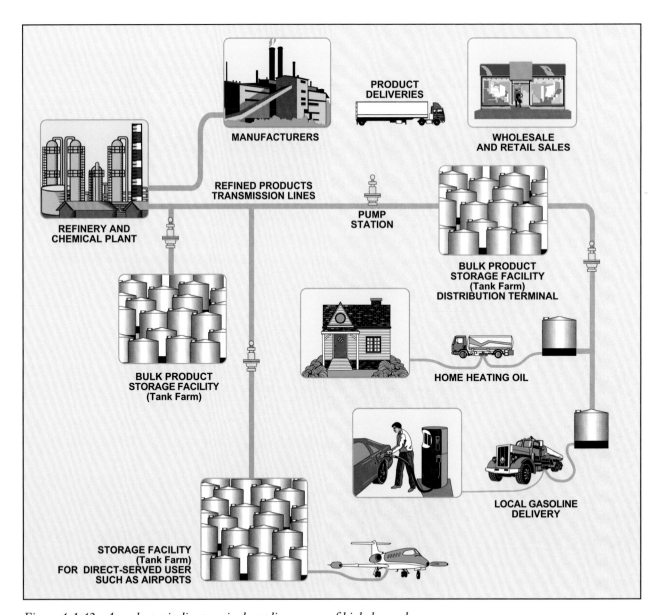

Figure 4-1.42. A products pipeline terminal supplies an area of high demand.

Products pipelines operate in a similar manner to crude oil pipelines. The process begins with shippers' tender nominations for the upcoming month, usually done around the middle of the preceding month. The process identifies volumes of each type of product, their origins, their destinations, and other information such as the volume needed for each movement cycle. Pipelines typically have many shippers and numerous types of products requiring a weekly *movement sequence* or cycle. A schedule is developed that lists the volumes and movement sequences, or batches, over the upcoming month by cycle.

Like crude oil pipelines, the schedule is sent to controllers at pipeline control centers for implementation. The information is also sent to the shippers, refineries, manned terminals, and interconnecting pipelines. Using the SCADA system, controllers operate pump stations, receipt and delivery terminals, and other interconnected facilities. With monitoring devices at remote locations and the SCADA system, the controllers watch suction and discharge pump pressures, flow rates, and product identification information to determine each shipment's location and ascertain its arrival time (fig. 4-1.43).

Breakout tanks, located at the origin, intermediate, and destination locations, are tanks that hold petroleum liquids until they can be delivered or relayed to local shipper's tanks or product terminals further up the pipeline. Breakout tanks and manifolds ensure product quality standards are met and that pipeline operations are smooth and continuous.

Control of Products Movement

Courtesy of Kinder Morgan

Figure 4-1.43. A dispatcher controls product movement and monitors other operations from the main computer console.

Batching

Liquid petroleum pipeline operations, both crude and refined, rely on the capability to move different liquids continuously through the pipeline. This capability is called *batching*, and it directly affects the efficiency of pipeline transportation and the cost of pipeline transportation.

Batching is the pumping of different crude oil or refined products in a sequence in the same line. Crude oil and refined products are rarely moved in the same pipeline system. The batch is usually one kind of petroleum liquid pumped next to a different type (fig. 4-1.44). As long as the pipeline flow and pressure remain high and the line is "packed," the mixing, or interfaces, between batches is relatively small compared to the very large batches on either side of it. This slight mixing, called *transmix*, is put into a tank when the batches are delivered for later disposition.

The pipeline company sets up a schedule with its cycle. Each shipper can repeat the sequence of shipments of any crude oil or product type depending on the volume and type of commodity shipped. The shipper's exact place in the cycle is determined by the type and volume of liquid petroleum being shipped and that of other shippers. The cycle also helps minimize the amount of transmix.

A pipeline company might handle as many as thirty different types of products, depending on the pipeline. The development of multiple gasoline grades and *reformulated gasoline (RFG)* mandates for meeting air quality attainment goals has increased the complexity of separation during the transportation of gasoline.

Batches are continuously monitored with sophisticated instrumentation to identify physical properties, specific gravity, color, and other parameters. This monitoring allows tracking of each batch and its precise location along the line (called batch tracking). Monitoring verifies the separation and transmix of one shipment from another. The SCADA system provides this monitoring information to the controller. Each batch is named using a coding convention so the pipeline controller can track the movement of batches and predict the time of arrival at the destination. Batch tracking is displayed on the pipeline controller's control console.

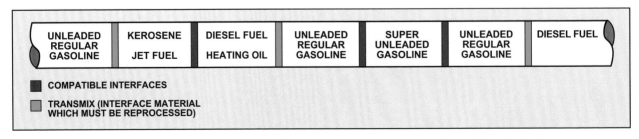

Figure 4-1.44. A products pipeline runs batches of different products in sequence, similar to this typical cycle.

Although most petroleum transportation involves crude oil and refined products, other materials are moved by pipeline. These products include NGLs, LPGs, CO_2, petrochemicals, and *slurries*. The pipeline operations usually follow the same process and procedures as their larger counterparts. The objectives remain the same—to safely and reliably transport material in the correct quantity and of the expected quality to the right place at the right time.

Other Types of Liquid Pipelines

Keeping accurate records of crude oil shipments can mean the difference between profit and loss. Precise records can also show the difference between legal and illegal operations. Many states in the United States require pipeline companies to keep track of large oil company shippers and independent shippers to ensure each is complying with the established monthly schedules. Companies must file monthly forms with the appropriate state agency to show the quantity of oil taken from each lease.

State and Federal Regulations

The pipeline industry is a highly regulated business. In the United States, regulations are typically promulgated at the federal level but are also extensive at state, county, and local levels. They encompass such areas as financial, safety, environmental, and pipeline placement issues.

To ensure fair treatment of shippers and competition among pipelines and to limit exclusive control of any one group, U.S. regulations were established to limit the rate of return for pipeline companies. This regulation was first handled by the *Interstate Commerce Commission (ICC)* and later taken over by the *Federal Energy Regulatory Commission (FERC)* within the *U.S. Department of Energy (DOE)*. To uniformly determine rates of return for pipelines with a wide range of facilities regarding their age of service and levels of investment, a complex accounting system must be used by the industry. Gas pipelines are regulated in a similar rate-based manner, first by the *Federal Power Commission (FPC)* and now also by the FERC.

Safety and environmental protection regulations that cover design, construction, operations, and maintenance are administered under the U.S. DOT through its *Pipeline and Hazardous Materials Safety Administration (PHMSA)* office. Liquid pipelines are covered by the Pipeline Safety Act as amended under 49CFR195, while natural gas lines fall under 49CFR192. Before these regulations were promulgated, major pipeline companies, both liquid and gas, followed industry standards, practices, and codes to ensure safe, reliable operations and to protect their high-cost assets.

Regulatory Environment

The pipeline industry must adhere to strict regulations regarding these aspects of business:
- Financial
- Safety
- Environmental
- Placement

Other regulatory agencies involved with pipelines include the *U.S. Environmental Protection Agency (EPA)* for clean air and water issues, the *Occupational Health and Safety Administration (OSHA)* for personnel safety, the Minerals Management Service for offshore facilities, and the U.S. Army Corps of Engineers for inland waterway crossings.

State and local governments present further restrictions and challenges for pipelines through additional regulatory requirements and project permit provisions.

NATURAL GAS PIPELINES

Historically, gas pipelines and oil pipelines have been managed and operated by different companies because their operations are specific to the commodity transported. A *gas pipeline* uses pressure from compressors as its driving force. An oil pipeline uses pump pressure. Gas pipelines move their volumes in a gaseous state—methane—as opposed to a liquid state in the oil pipelines. Because of these factors, different agencies govern their operations. The sale and transportation of gas are controlled by the FERC of the U.S. DOE.

Modern Transmission Systems

Since 1950, the natural gas industry has grown tremendously as technological advances have cut the cost of installing pipe and moving gas. From 1950 to 1975, the number of gas pipelines tripled. Of the more than 1.8 million miles (2.9 million kilometres) of U.S. gas pipelines in use today, about 278,000 miles (447,398 kilometres) are natural gas transmission trunklines both onshore and offshore, with the remaining pipelines consisting of gathering and distribution lines (fig. 4-1.45).

About 20,000 miles (32,200 kilometres) of natural gas gathering lines move natural gas to numerous transmission pipelines that cross the United States moving the gas to population centers. The natural gas ultimately makes its way to consumers via distribution lines. The large distribution lines that transport gas to and around population centers are called *mains*. These mains and the local lines that bring gas to homes, businesses, and other consumers operate underground beneath streets and other rights of way to bring natural gas directly to consumers. Due to the vast network within most cities and towns, these distribution lines account for the majority of the 1.8 million pipeline miles (2.9 million kilometres) in the United States alone.

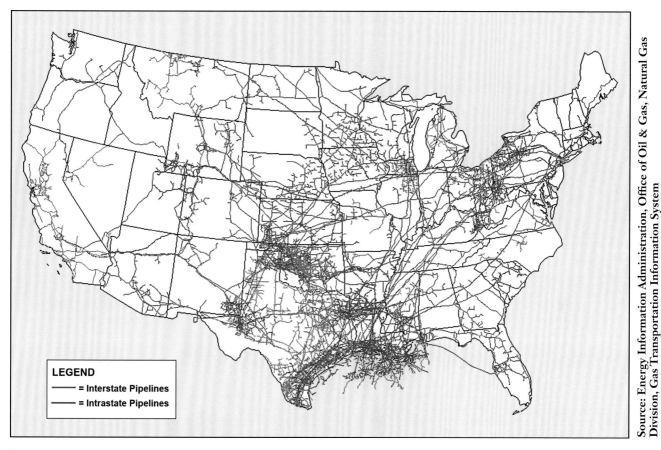

Source: Energy Information Administration, Office of Oil & Gas, Natural Gas Division, Gas Transportation Information System

Figure 4-1.45. Major U.S. natural gas pipelines connect supply areas and demand centers.

The method used for collecting, conditioning, and transmitting gas to its primary destination depends on the individual situation. Gas gathering systems have specialized equipment for:

- Conditioning the gas so it will flow safely and steadily
- Controlling, measuring, and recording its flow through the pipeline
- Ensuring gas quality specifications are met

Conditioning and Compressors

Conditioning equipment includes processing equipment such as separators, heaters, and dehydrators located at the wellhead or at other locations in the field. This equipment removes water, NGLs, LPGs, and undesirable components such as nitrogen and oxygen, leaving a relatively clean commodity—methane. In addition, large compressors compress the gas to the required discharge pressure. *Compressor stations* usually use large *reciprocating compressors* driven by gas engines, but they might also use *centrifugal units* driven by gas turbines or electric motors (fig. 4-1.46 and fig. 4-1.47). Some large compressor stations along the pipeline are often fueled by natural gas from the pipeline. At the point of delivery, regulators lower the high pressure of the transmission pipelines to that required by the distribution systems receiving the gas.

Courtesy of Siemens

Figure 4-1.46. A gas pipeline compressor stations

Figure 4-1.47. A gas turbine used in gas compressor stations

As with liquid pipelines, gas pipelines are automated with a SCADA computer system that monitors, controls, and coordinates operation of the pipelines, valves, prime movers, and conditioning equipment. A computer receives transmitted input from each part of the system. If there is an operational electrical malfunction or a mechanical problem at any point in the process, the control system and its controllers will seek solutions and implement corrective actions. Appropriate alarms will be actuated depending on the malfunction or anomaly, and the system will generate and archive investigative logs for recordkeeping or regulatory purposes (fig. 4-1.48).

Automation

Figure 4-1.48. A control center using numerous automated features monitors and controls the pipeline and keeps tabs on deliveries throughout a gas pipeline system.

Odorants Natural gas is typically odorless as it comes from processing facilities. If the gas is to be used for fuel in homes or occupied facilities, a chemical *odorant* called a *mercaptan* is added to the gas to give it a distinctive, pungent odor so people can smell it in the event of a leak. Generally, odorants are not introduced into feedstock gas sent to petrochemical plants to produce other products such as plastics, because mercaptans frequently interfere with chemical processing. Mercaptans injected into gas do not create odors during burning, nor do they leave behind any troublesome residue.

Because mercaptans have a distinct, pungent odor, they are easily detected at 1% concentration in air. Gas and air mixed in this concentration are not hazardous, but an air and gas mixture containing 5% gas is explosive. By adding an odorant, it is possible to detect leaks or other unburned gas discharges before hazards develop.

PIPELINE CONSTRUCTION ON LAND

Design engineering determines:
- Definitive routing
- Pipe design and coating
- Design of components
- Power and controls systems
- Ancillary equipment

Before construction of a pipeline begins and depending on the commodity to be moved, extensive engineering studies and analyses of potential oil reservoirs and refined product markets occur before deciding to invest in a pipeline. Then, forecasts of long-term production or product demand are developed. Once that occurs, the oil company's transportation department develops a concept of how long and what size pipeline will meet the needs. Estimates of capital costs and operating expenses are made and the long-term rate of return is calculated. Because most large-scale pipeline projects are multimillion-dollar endeavors, management approval is solicited by presenting the conclusions derived from the economic evaluations. These conclusions include any factors that might influence changes in the economics, such as volume, costs, or other considerations.

In many large-scale, cross-country pipeline proposals, other carriers might also desire to move commodities over the same route. As a result, joint ventures where all parties share in the capital requirements and operating costs might be established. This approach usually results in a larger, more cost-effective pipeline for shippers and owners, and it reduces the risk to each participant.

Pipelines facilitate movement of petroleum commodities to markets, thus enabling the monetization of oil production (or refined products). Therefore, the pipeline proposal becomes a strategic asset for an integrated oil corporation. Such a project usually enjoys the support of the corporate affiliate being served.

Once management approves the project and the necessary funding, detailed design engineering begins to determine the following:
- Definitive routing
- Design of the pipe and its coating system

- Design of valves, flanges, fittings, pumps, and prime movers
- Design of instrumentation, controls, and SCADA system
- Switchgear, power facilities, and ancillary equipment

After the design of all equipment is completed, procurement of each item is consumated with special attention to cost and availability.

After the pipeline route is defined, right-of-way procurement teams begin to purchase rights from landowners along the route to construct, operate, and maintain a pipeline. Usually, governmental permits must be acquired from each level of government. This lengthy process includes environmental studies and formal application for permits for the facility's location, public safety impacts, and environmental provisions. Federal agencies usually involved in permitting include FERC, DOT, U.S. Army Corps of Engineers, Bureau of Land Management and others. After the permits are obtained and right-of-way is procured, a construction contract is secured through a bid process and the work of building the pipeline begins.

Assembling the Spread

The pipeline contractor assembles the *spread*. A spread is a stand-alone project that includes the manpower, equipment, and material needed to build the pipeline within the spread. Pipeline projects that are hundreds of miles (or kilometres) long might require several spreads to make them more manageable and to facilitate logistics.

A spread for an average project might have 200 to 300 workers and for a very large project, up to about 500 workers. The construction equipment needed depends on the size of the pipeline to be built and difficulty of the terrain. Stream crossings, marshes, bogs, heavily timbered forests, steep slopes, or rocky ground require different pieces of machinery. The pipeline contractor might rent rather than buy some of the machinery, because outfitting a large-diameter pipeline spread can be a multimillion-dollar undertaking.

The time and progress of construction projects within a spread vary depending on the pipe size and the construction environment. The distance between the *front end* (clearing stage) and the *back end* (cleanup stage) also vary depending on construction conditions and pipeline company specifications limiting the distance. A separation of 10 miles (16 kilometres) or more between front-end and back-end operations is not uncommon.

The tasks performed by a typical spread include clearing, grading the right-of-way, ditching, stringing, bending, welding, lowering in, backfilling, tie-ins, testing, cleanup, and commissioning.

Clearing Right-of-way

Right-of-way:
- Involves a strip of land to lay pipe
- Must be cleared and graded
- Provides a corridor for equipment to operate
- Results in a working surface to accommodate pipeline construction

After right-of-way is procured, clearing operations begin. The construction right-of-way usually involves a strip of land about 50 to 100 feet (15 to 30 metres) wide, depending on pipe size and terrain (fig. 4-1.49). Crews begin by opening fences; building gates, cattle guards, and bridges; then clearing and grading a corridor so the construction equipment can operate. Any trees inside the right-of-way are cut by the clearing crews, and the timber stacked for sale or given to the landowner. The remaining timber is cut and burned. In agricultural areas, it might be necessary to strip topsoil to a specified depth and stockpile it off to the sides of right-of-way. The crew typically uses bulldozers to removes boulders, brush, and other impediments that could interfere with construction. All this is done to prepare a working surface (roadway) to accommodate the construction equipment needed to lay the pipeline.

In rocky terrain, a machine equipped with a *ripper* extending several feet into the ground is used to loosen rocks for removal or grading. Blasting might be necessary in some rocky terrain.

Figure 4-1.49. A clear pipeline right-of-way

Some areas are uniquely challenging in terms of pipeline construction, such as the Arctic region. In such environments, pipeline routes must cross permanently frozen ground called *permafrost*, forests, snow-covered mountains, and tundra. For example, the TAPS runs through diverse terrain. Between the North Slope and Valdez, TAPS construction required special gravel and an insulated work pad to prevent the permafrost on the subsurface from degrading or melting. The special gravel road base provided insulation to protect the permafrost while the vehicles, equipment, and crew built the aboveground portion of the pipeline. About half of the 800-mile (1,287-kilometre) pipeline was laid aboveground in a zigzag pattern to allow for pipe expansion and contraction caused by extreme changes in temperature and to prevent damage to the permafrost (fig. 4-1.50).

Courtesy of the State of Alaska, Division of Oil and Gas

Figure 4-1.50. In this aboveground section of the Trans-Alaska Pipeline, the roadbed along the right-of-way supports working vehicles as well as the pipeline itself.

Ditching

Ditching, which is the process of digging the ditch to bury the pipe, is usually done with conventional equipment designed for subsurface conditions. In loose dirt or stable soil, a *wheel ditcher* is commonly used. The wheel ditcher's rotating toothed buckets pick up excavated dirt, called *spoil*, and pile it by the side of the ditch to use later as backfill (fig. 4-1.51). Certain rocky terrain requires a *rock ditcher* to cut through hard soil or rock, or pneumatically drilled holes to break up the rock. On some spreads, the crew uses track hoes or backhoes to dig through rock and to clear blasted rock from the trench.

The ditch must be at least 12 inches (30.5 centimetres) wider than the pipe diameter and deep enough to allow plowing and normal land use. The U.S. DOT regulations require a minimum of 30 inches (76 centimetres) of cover across farmland in normal soil and 36 inches (91 centimetres) in municipal areas.

Figure 4-1.51. A wheel ditcher leaves a neat spoil bank that aids in rapid backfilling.

Most pipeline ditching is handled with conventional equipment. However, in permafrost regions, aboveground sections of pipeline are often built on specially designed horizontal crossbeams mounted between pairs of *vertical support members (VSMs)*. Aboveground pipeline is surrounded by insulation panels made of metal-jacketed fiberglass with weatherproof expansion joints. Finned radiators atop the VSMs improve heat transfer between the atmosphere and the heat pipes to which they are attached (fig. 4-1.52). *Heat pipes*, 2 inches (5 centimetres) in diameter, keep the soil stable in permafrost areas by keeping heat from reaching the frozen ground. When ditching in unstable permafrost soil, a company might refrigerate a buried section of pipe to keep subsurface soils from melting. About 7 miles (11 kilometres) of the TAPS was constructed using this method.

Ditching is done using:
- A wheel ditcher with rotating tooth buckets
- A rock ditcher that cuts through hard rock
- Track hoes or backhoes to dig through and clear rock

Courtesy of Harvey Barrison

Figure 4-1.52. In aboveground construction, VSMs hold insulated pipe at various heights while special finned radiators and heat pipes draw heat away from the ground.

Stringing Pipe

Stringing is the process of delivering and distributing line pipe along the right-of-way (fig. 4-1.53). The pipeline contractor or a stringing subcontractor string the pipe. On many projects, the pipe is cleaned, primed, and coated with corrosion protection before delivery to the right-of-way. Coated pipe requires special handling to prevent damage to the coating and the beveled pipe ends.

To move pipe, a sling is formed with a cable threaded through a *boom*, which is a long arm attached to a side-boom tractor. Special curved aluminum plates at the end of the sling fit inside the ends of pipe to minimize contact with the coating and the beveled ends. Padded instruments might also be used to grab and move pipe. As pipe is lifted off a trailer or railcar, the equipment operator must evenly distribute the weight of the load to prevent the pipe from slipping, buckling, or dropping.

Figure 4-1.53. The pipeline contractor strings pipe joints along the right-of-way so they are accessible but do not obstruct spread equipment and work crews.

On jobs where the terrain is relatively flat and the road system allows, the pipe might be double-jointed before being strung along the right-of-way. *Double jointing* is the welding of two sections of pipe to form one piece approximately 80 feet (24.384 metres) long. The pipe-handling operator might use a spreader bar between the two lifting lines to prevent damage to these longer joints. Properly strung pipe ensures a successful assembly-line welding process and minimizes backward or forward movement of the pipe joints.

> Properly strung pipe ensures a successful assembly-line welding process and minimizes backward or forward movement of the pipe joints.

Bending Pipe

As ditching and stringing progress, the contours of the ditch are measured to determine how many degrees of bend must be put in the pipe to make it conform to the bottom of the ditch. The magnitude of this operation is governed by the terrain traversed by the pipeline. Often, many pieces of pipe must be bent to fit the ditch. Special equipment allows the pipe to be bent on location (fig. 4-1.54). This equipment includes a pipe bending machine or *bending shoe* attachment that works off a side-boom tractor and its winch. The bending shoe can be used on small-diameter pipe. Large-diameter pipe requires a *bending mandrel* on a bending machine. Each method keeps the pipe from buckling or wrinkling when bent. In some situations, special pipe bends called *hot bends* are premanufactured and shipped to the spread.

Figure 4-1.54. A pipe bending machine

Aligning and Welding Pipe

As the ditching and stringing activities progress, a crew, usually called the *pipe gang*, and the welders move onto the job to begin the pipe laying process. Before pipe is positioned for welding by the pipe gang, the pipe ends are cleaned and bevels are checked for damage. Side-boom tractors with winches lift the pipe into position and hold it in place so the crew can put wooden skids under it. *Line-up clamps* are used to align the pipe ends before welding. The clamps ensure that the circumference of the pipe ends match and proper spacing is maintained between the ends. The line-up clamps fit on the outside of small-diameter pipe and inside large-diameter pipe. When the clamps are set, the pipe is ready to be welded (fig. 4-1.55).

Figure 4-1.55. Preparing to weld

Pipe welding is a tightly specified and controlled process to make the welds stronger than the pipe itself. Based on the pipe's metallurgy, a welding procedure is developed by the pipeline company. The company considers all variables for acceptable welds based on *American Petroleum Institute (API)* standards. Each welder employed by the pipeline construction contractor must make a satisfactory weld on the specified pipe using the approved welding process (fig. 4-1.56).

In the production welding process during pipe laying, there are three basic types of welders usually identified as *stringer*, *hot pass*, and *cap*. The welds are inspected visually by company inspectors and with *nondestructive testing (NDT)*, usually by x-ray. Each day, inspection results are reviewed and any defective welds are cut out or repaired. Welders who continue to produce unacceptable welds are removed from the job. All pipeline welding and inspections are tightly specified in API standards, federal regulations, and pipeline company specifications.

Figure 4-1.56. Welders work on opposite sides of the pipe as they make the initial weld on two joints held together by an internal line-up clamp.

While manual arc welding is used most extensively in pipeline construction, automatic welding—namely, welding performed by preset machines—is used on large-diameter, heavy-wall-thickness pipe, particularly in offshore applications. This method of welding is gaining popularity with pipeline companies and their contractors.

Steel pipe corrodes when placed in the ground. To prevent metal corrosion, the pipe is coated with material to protect the metal. A well-designed pipe-coating system is the first line of defense in corrosion control. Three types of common pipe coatings are

Coating and Wrapping Pipe

Types of common pipe coatings:
- Fusion-bonded epoxy
- Enamel and tape
- Over-the-ditch tape

- *Fusion-bonded epoxy (FBE) coatings* are usually applied at the pipe manufacturing mill or coating plant. Epoxy coatings do not require an outer wrap. They are very resistant to handling damage and can withstand high operating temperatures such as those found in gas transmission lines.

- *Enamel coating* might also be applied at a coating plant. In other cases, enamel coatings and *tape coatings* can be applied to pipe while it is being laid, in a process called *line-travel-applied coating* or *over-the-ditch coating*. A self-propelled cleaning and priming machine moves along the top of the pipe, followed by a coating and wrapping machine. Coal tar enamels are particularly effective for line-travel-applied coating. The coating machine applies heated liquid enamel to the cleaned and primed pipe and then wraps the enamel-coated pipe with fiberglass, reinforced felt, and Kraft paper. The wraps protect the enamel coating while it hardens and when the pipe is lowered in the ditch.

Enamel coatings are most effective when the pipeline operating temperature range is between 30° F and 180° F (-1° C and 82° C).

- *Over-the-ditch tape* uses a machine to clean, prime, coat, and wrap the pipe. The taping machine with rolls of tape (polyethylene, polyvinyl, or other materials) mounted on spindles, wraps the tape in overlapping sections around the pipe as it moves along the line.

With any precoated pipe, welded joints, and coating damage must be cleaned, primed, and properly coated to ensure uniform protection of the entire pipeline. All coating applications must be carefully inspected before lowering in the pipe. In some situations, *concrete coated pipe* might be required for added protection from mechanical damage or as *negative buoyancy*. The added weight from the concrete ensures the pipeline will not float at water crossings.

Lowering in and Backfilling

With precoated pipe, after the joints are coated, the joined pipeline is picked up with side-boom tractors using cables, special slings, or padded devices to protect the coating. If pipe is lowered into the ditch in conjunction with coating and wrapping operations, then there is no need to lower the pipe to skids and pick it up later for final placement. When this burial technique is used in arctic permafrost environments, pipe is lowered into the ditch enclosed in a sheath of insulation placed over the coating. Special padding is placed in the ditch to minimize melting in the permafrost layer. Side booms with nonmetallic slings place the pipe safely into the ditch (fig. 4-1.57).

Figure 4-1.57. Side-boom tractors with correctly spaced slings lower pipe into the ditch.

Courtesy of Kinder Morgan

Copyright © The University of Texas at Austin—PETEX

After pipe has been lowered into the ditch, the crew replaces the soil in the ditch, covering the pipe (fig. 4-1.58). Contractors often use an auger fitted to the front of a bulldozer backfill machine to distribute the backfill evenly in the ditch. Backfilling requires breaking up rocky or frozen soil before returning it to the ditch to prevent it from damaging the pipe coating. Uneven distribution of backfilled soil can leave sections of the pipe unsupported, which can later cause damage to the pipe as settling takes place. In rocky areas, the pipe is often protected with backfill material that has been hauled in or by a shock-resistant covering call *rock shield*.

- Backfilling involves breaking up rocky soil before returning it to the ditch.
- Uneven distribution of backfilled soil can leave sections of pipe unsupported and cause damage.

Figure 4-1.58. Pipeline lowered in the trench.

Specialty and Tie-In Crews

As the spread progresses, any sections of pipeline requiring special construction techniques and equipment are bypassed. *Breaks* or bypassed sections are usually crossings at highways, railroads, waterways, swamps, and marshes. Breaks might also be needed to allow passage of livestock or vehicle traffic. At these locations, an adequate length of pipe is left behind by the pipe-laying crew to aid in completing the line.

Specialty or *tie-in crews* complete unfinished sections and connect them to the rest of the pipeline. The tie-in crew is a miniature spread with the necessary manpower, equipment, and material to complete the joining of these segments to make a continuous line. Unlike the assembly-line pipe laying of the main operation, the tie-in crew often faces difficult work due to constraints in positioning, aligning, welding, and placement at tie-in locations. At many highway, railroad, waterway, and preexisting pipeline crossings, a boring machine or horizontal directional drilling set-up might be required. Crews might need to set casing in which to place the carrier pipe to protect it under a crossing. These complicated operations require special lifting equipment and extra side-boom tractors to maneuver a difficult crossing. Crossings and steep terrain conditions also require skilled maneuvering by equipment operators to move and pull long sections of pipe into position.

One crossing construction technique used more and more involves placing pipe under an obstacle using horizontal directional drilling. A directional drilling rig makes a controlled pilot hole with its path shaped like an inverted arc under the feature being crossed (fig. 4-1.59). Guided by sensors, computers, and consoles, the crew follows the path of the pilot hole. After the pilot hole drill pipe reaches the other side of the crossing, a reamer is attached to the drill string along with the complete welded pipeline for the crossing. The entire drill string is pulled back through the pilot hole under the crossing while simultaneously reaming a hole large enough for passage of the crossing pipeline. After the crossing pipe is in place, it is tied into the rest of the pipeline.

Another method of crossing water such as ponds, lakes, and waterways is to attach flotation devices to the welded pipeline crossing section and float, carry, or pull the pipe across the water (fig. 4-1.60). The crew then removes the flotation devices and guides the sinking pipe into a pre-dredged ditch or into the bed of the water feature.

Special sections or fabrications might also be tied into the adjoining pipeline. Fabricated sections might include mainline valve settings, lateral or side connections, and pump station piping. These fabrications are often preassembled, welded, and tested prior to shipping to the spread where they are joined to the mainline. All tie-in operations, especially the welding, are inspected to ensure compliance with the pipeline company's specifications.

Figure 4-1.59. A boring machine pushes casing under a roadbed as its cutting head rotates just inside the front of the casing.

Figure 4-1.60. Flotation devices support sections of pipe during a river crossing.

Cleanup and Restoration

As construction progresses and backfill is completed, cleanup and restoration work follows. The land surface is restored as nearly as possible to its original condition (fig. 4-1.61). Fences are permanently repaired and any damage to landowner property is determined. Right-of-way agents make sure landowners are satisfied with the cleanup and payment for damages agreed upon. The right-of-way is left free of trees and brush to allow required visual inspection, usually by aircraft, after the pipeline is placed in operation.

Figure 4-1.61. After construction is completed, the pipeline is then backfilled using as much original dirt as possible, and the land is neatly restored so it can produce vegetation once again.

The last activities before project completion include cleaning and testing the new pipeline. Internal pipeline cleaning is usually done with an air-driven swab. The pipeline is tested by filling it with water or other test medium and pressure testing the finished line to a specific pressure to assure it meets regulatory and design requirements.

When all construction is completed to the satisfaction of the pipeline owners, the construction contractor turns over the pipeline to the owners, who in turn, commission it ready for operation.

Testing and Commissioning

Offshore pipelines in shallow depth have been used for some time. Modern technology has made it possible to lay pipelines in much deeper areas of the sea. Various types of pipe-laying barges are used in offshore pipeline construction. These include conventional *lay barges, bury barges, superbarges, semisubmersible barges,* and *reel barges.*

The pipeline industry has also developed advanced techniques for offshore pipeline operations in ice-laden arctic waters. Equipment that detects the presence of ice islands and pressure ridges is being used to reduce potential damage to pipelines caused by *ice scouring,* which is the abrasion of material in contact with moving ice in the ocean or other bodies of water. To protect the pipeline against ice scouring, it must be buried deeply, enough so that the top of the pipe cannot come in contact with any ice.

Pipelines that are constructed in permafrost near shorelines might also experience potentially damaging stress if the permafrost thaws. To minimize thawing in a permafrost layer and to reduce stress on the pipeline, a pipeline company might use one of the following methods:

- Place pipeline on special beds of granular material to maintain an insulating layer between the permafrost and pipeline.
- Artificially reduce the temperature of the oil at the processing facility.
- Raise the pipeline above the surface of the water on piles or artificial *berms.*
- Circulate refrigerant through cooling tubes in a jacket surrounding the pipeline.

OFFSHORE PIPELINE CONSTRUCTION

Conventional Lay Barges

Offshore lines are laid by pipe-laying barges, or lay barges (fig. 4-1.62). A lay barge is a complete seagoing plant that allows the pipeline to be assembled and laid continuously along the route, either on top of the ocean floor or in trenches on the seafloor. Depending on the project, a barge might be employed for several months. Support vessels supply these barges with pipe and construction materials as well as moving personnel and supplies they will need while on board.

Because barges have no drive power, an eight-point mooring system of cables and anchors is usually used to hold the lay barge in position and on a precise heading. The system also allows the barge to move by pulling itself along as anchor lines are reeled in and out. As the barge progresses, anchor-handling tugboats move the mooring system guided by a GPS (global positioning system).

A pipe barge brings line pipe from yards onshore to the lay barge where it is added to the pipeline. Welding, coating, and inspection are handled at stations, or work areas, along the length of the lay barge deck. The completed pipeline is lowered into the water by way of an inclined ramp and a *stinger* (fig. 4-1.63). The stinger, attached to the ramp, maintains the proper angle as the pipeline moves to the seafloor, thereby preventing any damage or deformity (fig. 4-1.64).

Figure 4-1.62. Welding, coating, and inspection are handled at stations on the lay barge.

Pipe-laying barges are used to construct offshore pipelines:
- Conventional lay barges
- Bury barges
- Superbarges
- Semisubmersible barges
- Reel barges

Courtesy of CRC Evans

Figure 4-1.63. The completed pipeline is lowered into the water by way of an inclined ramp and a stinger. The stinger, attached to the ramp, maintains the proper angle as the pipeline moves to the seafloor, thereby preventing any damage or deformity.

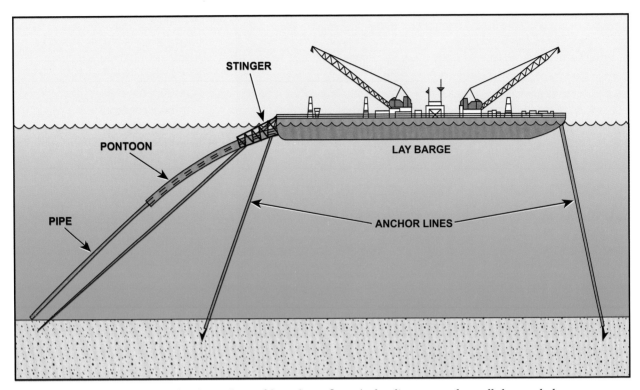

Figure 4-1.64. The stinger guides the pipeline safely to the seafloor. Anchor lines are used to pull the vessel along.

Offshore pipeline is precoated with a high-density cement to overcome buoyancy, allowing it to sink into place. In deep water, the crew might add an attachment called a *pontoon* to the stinger to prevent the concrete coating from cracking or the pipe from buckling. The crew floods the pontoon to lower the pipeline at an angle that will not overstress it. In deepwater pipe-laying operations, the crew will sometimes use a *tensioner* to maintain upward force in the pipe to keep the pipe from buckling under its own weight.

The method used to keep the pipeline on the bottom and lessen risk of damage varies with the topography of the seafloor. On rocky bottoms, the line might be fastened to the seafloor with pipeline anchors.

Subsea pipelines that might be harmed by fishing or other marine operations are laid in a *seafloor trench*. On softer bottoms, a bury barge, or *pipe-trenching barge*, with a sled is used for this operation (fig. 4-1.65). The sled is attached to the submerged pipeline and moves along the line on the seafloor. It uses a high-pressure jetting action to form a trench into which the pipeline will rest. The pipe is usually not covered at the time it is laid, because the movement of seawater eventually covers the pipeline with fill from the ocean bottom.

Bury Barges

A jet sled connected to the bury barge is attached to the submerged pipeline. It moves along the seafloor using high-pressure jets to make a trench for the pipeline.

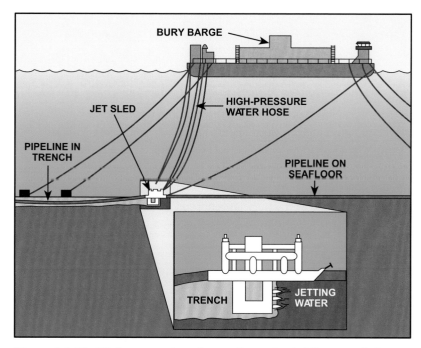

Figure 4-1.65. High-pressure jets of water from a jet sled dig a trench for a pipeline on the seafloor. The sled is operated from a bury barge as it moves forward by means of anchor lines.

Superbarges

Certain types of barges are specially designed to withstand rough seas and operate safely in deep water.

Designed for use in rough seas and deep water is a huge lay barge sometimes called a superbarge (fig. 4-1.66). It might be 650 feet (198 metres) long, 140 feet (43 metres) wide, and 50 feet (15 metres) deep. This barge can lay 80-foot-long (24-metre-long), double-jointed pipe in deep water without using a pipe-laying pontoon.

The superbarge can accommodate up to 350 people for extended periods of time. It can store as much as 20,000 tons (18,144 tonnes) of pipe. There are seven work stations for double-jointed pipe or nine work stations for 40-foot (12-metre) for automatic or manual welding of joints. It also includes a pipe-beveling station, two 125-ton (113-tonne) cranes, twelve 60,000-pound (27,216-kilogram) anchors, and a heliport.

Semisubmersible Barges

A semisubmersible lay barge operates similarly to a semisubmersible drilling rig. This type of lay barge is designed to minimize the effects of wave and wind action when operating in extremely rough waters. For example, a semisubmersible barge crew can lay pipe in the North Sea during 35-foot (11-metre) waves and 70-mile-per-hour (113-kilometre-per-hour) winds, a nearly impossible task with a conventional lay barge. The stability comes from the submerged portion of the vessel, which lowers the center of gravity and steadies the vessel against strong winds and waves.

Reel Vessel

On a reel vessel, whether a ship or a barge, pipe is welded together and spooled onto giant reels at onshore facilities and then loaded on a reel vessel (fig. 4-1.66). This pipe must be flexible enough to withstand reeling and unreeling without buckling or cracking.

In the early development of the reel vessel, pipe was a small gathering line about 2 inches (50 millimetres) in diameter. Now, reel vessels can lay pipelines up to 12 inches (30 centimetres) in diameter from a reel. Reels are designed with a large enough diameter so the curvature of the coiled pipe will not permanently deform the pipe.

Depending on the pipe diameter, spooled pipeline can be several hundred feet or metres to several miles or kilometres in length. It is unwound simply by moving the barge forward. The line unspools in a straight path. At the rear of the barge where the line extends into the water, large unspooling devices keep the line straightened. When one spool of line ends, the end is held above the water surface while welders join it to a new spool of line. The submerged line is then lowered and unspooling continues with the new reel.

Figure 4-1.66. A giant spool unreels continuous lengths for line pipe from a reel lay barge.

ECONOMICS AND SAFETY

Among the four modes of transport:
- Pipelines
- Water carriers
- Motor carriers
- Railroads

Pipelines are reported to be the safest overall mode of transporting oil and gas.

Economic and safety factors generally determine which method of transportation will be used to ship crude oil, petroleum products, and natural gas. The four modes of transportation used to move petroleum are pipelines, water carriers, motor carriers, and railroads, with pipelines reported as being the safest by the U.S. National Transportation Safety Board. From a fatality standpoint, oil pipelines are eighty times safer than motor carriers and three to five times safer than rail or water modes.

Pipelines are also the most economical mode of transporting oil and products as long as throughput remains relatively high. As an example of cost, 1 gallon (3.8 liters) of gasoline might be moved by pipeline from the Gulf Coast to New York City for as little as 2.5 cents per gallon. Since 1980, water carriers have had a slight edge over pipelines in crude oil transportation (Table 4-1.1). The increase in water-carrier use is partially due to increased shipments of crude by tankers from Valdez, Alaska, to U.S. mainland ports. Most petroleum products, however, are shipped by pipeline, with water carriers running a close second.

Natural gas is almost totally shipped by pipeline. However, natural gas is often brought from foreign sources as LNG. The LNG is shipped across the oceans and unloaded at LNG terminals, regasified, and then transported in gas transmission pipelines.

Each mode of petroleum transportation plays an important role in the profitable functioning of the petroleum industry (fig. 4-1.67). Motor carriers handle relatively small volumes to and from widely scattered locations. Rail carriers move small- to medium-range volumes over longer distances. High-volume concentrations of petroleum and petroleum products near waterways or seaports are moved economically by inland waterways or oceangoing vessels. Where large volumes require transportation over long distances for long periods of time, pipelines are used.

The petroleum transportation network in the United States is one of the most efficient in the world. However, even with a history of progress in innovation, improved safety, and reduced costs, future transportation challenges will need to be overcome. These challenges include:

- Constraints on the transportation network due to increased demand
- Shifting movement patterns
- Need for potentially large investments to reduce and eliminate constraints
- Need for more trained personnel at all levels
- Safety and environmental concerns based on heightened exposure risk of the extensive transportation network

Table 4-1.1
Modes Used for Petroleum Transportation

	Pipeline	Marine	Rail	Truck
Volumes	Large	Very large	Small	Large
Materials	Crude/Products	Crude/Products	Products	Products
Scale	2 ML+	10 ML+	100 kL	5-60 kL
Unit costs	Very low	Low	High	Very high
Capital costs	High	Medium	Low	Very low
Access	Very limited	Very limited	Limited	High
Responsiveness	1-4 weeks	7 days	2-4 days	4-12 hours
Flexibility	Limited	Limited	Good	High
Usage	Long haul	Long haul	Medium haul	Short haul

Source: Adapted from Ken Dymock (2007), Petro Canada, Chartered Institute of Logistics and Transport, Transportation and Outlook Conference

Figure 4-1.67. Transportation modes are evident at this ship channel.

LIQUEFIED NATURAL GAS

Transporting natural gas in large quantities is done either by pipeline or by converting the gas to liquefied natural gas, commonly referred to as LNG. Although pipeline transportation has played the dominant role globally, LNG is exceptionally competitive in the *transoceanic*, or long-distance, transportation of natural gas.

History of the LNG Industry

Although cryogenic (extremely low temperature) methods for gas liquefaction were developed in the late nineteenth century, early commercial efforts were directed toward *air liquefaction* and transportation. Many companies formed at that time, such as British Oxygen Company (BOC), Air Liquide, and Linde, which are familiar trade names today.

The natural gas industry noted the advantage of using liquefaction to reduce gas volume and vapor pressure for storing and transporting fluids. The first pilot plant for natural gas liquefaction was built in the United States in West Virginia in 1939. The results were so encouraging that in 1941, the first commercial LNG plant was completed in Cleveland, Ohio.

Over the next few years, relatively large, spherical LNG storage vessels were developed. In 1944, a large cylindrical LNG tank with an unusual base design failed due to inadequate knowledge of metallurgy at that time. The tank was built with 3.5% nickel that leaked and caused LNG discharge into the sewage system of a neighboring community. This resulted in a catastrophic explosion that demolished the entire community, caused 128 deaths, and halted LNG development for a decade.

After some study, a 9% nickel-steel metallurgical specification for the tanks was found to be adequate for LNG storage applications. The development of the LNG industry resumed, and this tank specification is still used today.

Since the LNG production, regasification, and safe storage technologies were successfully developed, the *peak-shaving* LNG industry has gained wide acceptance. LNG peak-shaving facilities are used for storing surplus natural gas to be used to meet requirements of peak consumption when needed, especially during winter.

Today, there are almost 100 peak-shaving LNG facilities across the United States. They are mainly located in the vicinity of natural gas consuming centers. Figure 4-1.68 shows the distribution of these facilities.

> The LNG industry has evolved since 1939. Today, nearly 100 peak-shaving facilities populate the United States.

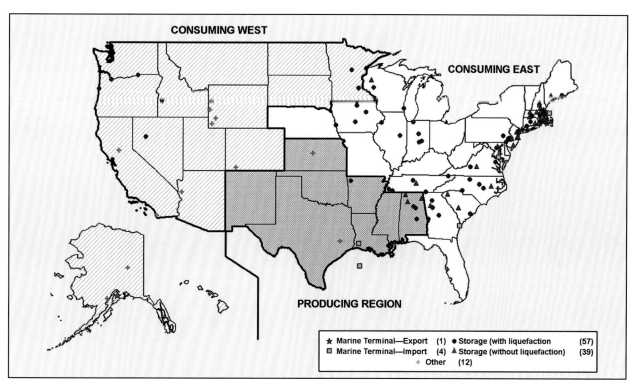

Source: Energy Information Administration, Office of Oil and Gas

Figure 4-1.68. Distribution of peak-shaving LNG facilities in the United States

These LNG facilities are an important element of the U.S. domestic natural gas distribution system and provide vital storage functions in addition to other underground storage facilities, such as *salt caverns*. Figure 4-1.69 shows a typical peak-shaving plant.

Although peak-shaving facilities are an important element in gas distribution systems, their capacities are factored into domestic gas inventories. The baseload LNG facilities play an important role in domestic natural gas balances. The modern-day LNG industry has evolved primarily into a cross-border, transoceanic transportation business.

LNG's commercial potential began to be realized only after the development of large oceangoing ships that could transport LNG over long distances. Natural gas pipelines are cost competitive for inland gas transportation. However, the transoceanic transport of LNG can outperform pipelines because cross-ocean pipelines are technically complex and cost prohibitive. Therefore, along with developing peak-shaving facilities, the natural gas industry also aimed to deliver large quantities of LNG to Great Britain. This region had a great demand for natural gas but was geographically isolated by the surrounding oceans.

Courtesy of Chicago Bridge and Iron Company

Figure 4-1.69. Typical peak-shaving LNG facility

Constock, a company in the United States, led the effort in developing specially designed LNG ships. A Constock ship made the first cross-Atlantic transport fully loaded with LNG. In 1959, the ship, the *Methane Pioneer*, sailed from Lake Charles, Louisiana, to Great Britain. This trip and the subsequent seven transports proved the feasibility of cross-ocean LNG transport. Since then, the baseload LNG industry has continued to make advances.

In the LNG shipping business, Constock, later called Conch, did not survive, but other companies such as Moss Rosenberg, Gaz Transport, and Technigaz continued the momentum and became familiar industry names.

The LNG development phase began in the early 1970s during the first energy crisis and was driven by Japan. As shown in figure 4-1.70, growth was steady at a relatively slow pace of 2.5% per year. The expansion phase of the LNG industry, about 4% to 5% per year, occurred in the early 2000s and is ongoing. Natural gas has become the fuel of choice due to its environmental advantages. Its driving force is the increased global demand for LNG. The expansion is further enhanced by dwindling U.S. domestic gas production prompting LNG imports to meet an increasing domestic demand.

LNG development:
- Began in early 1970s
- Growth was steady
- Accelerated growth in early 2000s
- Increased global demand today

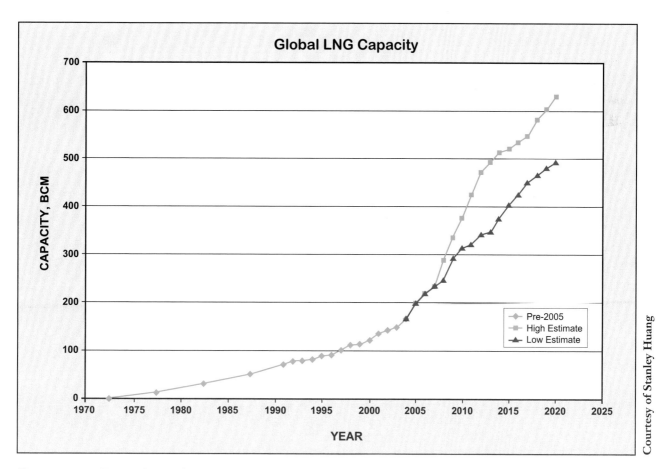

Figure 4-1.70. *Projected scale of LNG industry*

Courtesy of Stanley Huang

Links of the LNG Chain

A baseload LNG project consists of the following components:

- Gas production
- Pipeline transmission
- Liquefaction
- Shipping
- Regasification
- Sending out to local pipeline grid

The three components of liquefaction, shipping, and *regasification* are often referred to as the links of the LNG gas *monetization* chain. Monetization is the process of converting something, such as gas, into money. The full functioning of the monetization chain is closely connected to the individual links in sequence. When one link is broken, the whole monetary chain is broken.

The relationship between the liquefaction, shipping, and regasification components and their corresponding subsections is shown in the monetization process illustrated in figure 4-1.71.

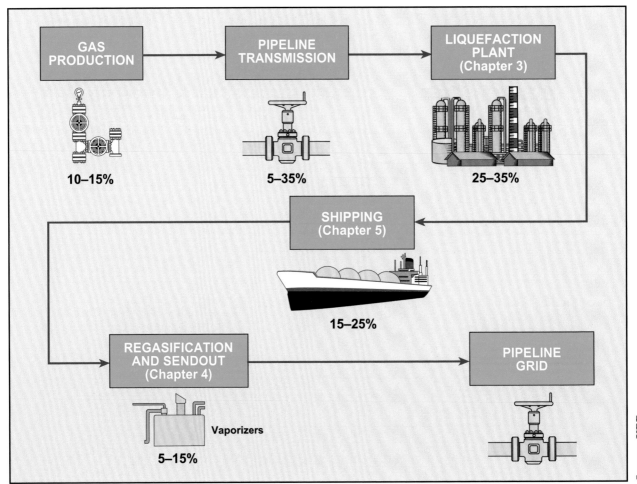

Figure 4-1.71. Components in LNG monetization chain

The process begins with the discovery of an abundant, but stranded, natural gas resource for which no local market exists or for high-value markets that are not easily accessible by pipeline. This stranded gas has no monetary value unless it is somehow moved to the marketplace by LNG transoceanic transport.

Gas Production

Depending on the geographic location of the gas field and availability of an adequate seaport, some pipeline connection might be required to get the gas to a seaport. Major gas fields are also found offshore and require transport via subsea pipeline to the liquefaction facility. It is not uncommon for such a pipeline to run for several hundred miles or kilometres.

Pipeline Transmission

Usually a natural gas liquefaction plant is built at the port location to prepare the gas for shipment. This is the first and most expensive link in the monetization chain and requires substantial financial investment.

Liquefaction

A fleet of LNG ships is required to transport LNG to receiving terminals closer to the target markets. Shipping is a critical part of an LNG project. It is the second link in the LNG chain and might represent the second largest financial investment.

Shipping

LNG receiving terminals serve three functions:

- Transferring LNG from ships to land LNG tanks
- Regasifying—or converting—the LNG to natural gas suitable for the local pipeline grid
- Delivering the gas to the grid at a specified time and in sufficient quantity

The regasification is the third link in the LNG monetization chain.

Regasification

The regasified gas is injected and sent out to the local pipeline system. There are various government and corporate regulations to ensure that the quality of the gas is interchangeable between local and imported gas production.

Send to Local Pipeline Grid

Baseload LNG Plant

Current industry practice uses three processes:
- Propane-mixed refrigerant liquefaction
- Optimized cascade
- Multi-fluid cascade

The liquefaction plant is the most financially expensive link in the entire LNG monetary chain. The *cryogenic liquefaction unit* needed to liquefy the natural gas in preparation for transport is the technical core of this link. In addition, there are other supporting units required in an LNG plant, such as gas sweetening, dehydration, NGL removal, and nitrogen rejection.

Although there are more than one hundred patents in the United States alone describing different processes for LNG liquefaction, only a handful of processes have been installed commercially. Among those installed, some have encountered operational and reliability challenges, and as a result, were never used again. Other processes have emerged only recently and are in the process of construction.

The following three processes are examples of current industry practices. The criteria for choosing a particular process usually includes its commercial success or perceived commercial potential. The three processes are:

- Propane-mixed refrigerant (C3MR) liquefaction process from Air Products
- ConocoPhillips Optimized Cascade[SM] Process (COPOC) from ConocoPhillips
- Multi-fluid Cascade (MFC®) from Linde

In terms of installed capacity, the basic *C3MR liquefaction process* licensed by Air Products is the most proven technology used today. It is used in the majority of LNG plants (about 75%) built to date and has a long history of safe and reliable operations. The cascade process accounts for about 20% of the global LNG capacity today. Together, the C3MR and COPOC processes account for about 95% of global LNG capacity (fig. 4-1.72). The Linde MFC process is a relatively new development. MFC is very similar to a classic cascade process in which pure component fluids are used in the refrigeration loops. The process uses a series of mixed refrigerant streams. The first refrigeration cycle is for precooling, the second is for liquefaction, and the third is for subcooling.

In a typical LNG plant, the storage tanks are the most visible objects of the entire plant. An LNG storage tank represents the most expensive single item in either production plants or receiving terminals. Careful and well-designed tank construction is critical. On average, after land preparations and commissioning, it could take 36 months to construct a tank. There are several types of LNG tanks. Figure 4-1.73 shows a comparison of three types of aboveground LNG tanks.

Courtesy of ConocoPhillips

Figure 4-1.72. Trinidad LNG plant where COPOC processes are performed

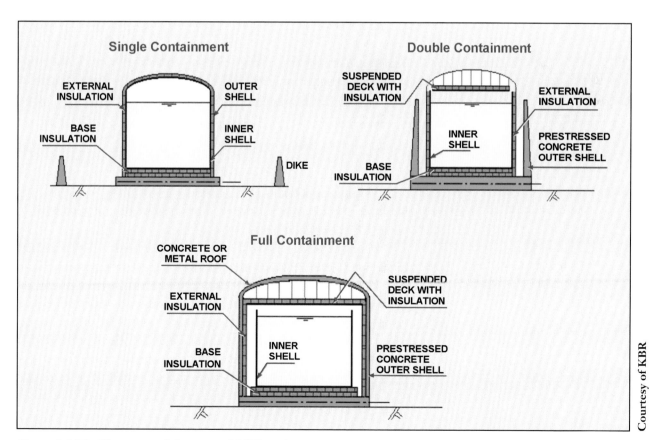

Courtesy of KBR

Figure 4-1.73. Three types of aboveground LNG tanks

Among the aboveground designs, the *single-containment tank* is the most popular type. In this design, there must be sufficient plot space available for earthen dykes to act as a secondary containment. The primary containment is the inner shell made of 9% nickel steel. If the inner shell should fail, liquefied gas will be held by the outer *bund wall*. A bund wall is a retaining wall that holds the contents of a tank in the event of a rupture. However, the gas vapors cannot be contained. Any vapors dispersed or flames radiating present serious hazards to people, equipment, and structures. Therefore, open land requirements around single-containment tanks are much greater than for those of other categories of containments.

Both *double-containment* and *full-containment tank* types provide constructed walls for secondary containment. The difference lies in the way vapors are handled. Double-containment tanks are only required to provide liquid tightness in case LNG spills from the inner tank. The outer wall provision significantly reduces the distance vapor might travel or flames might radiate if the inner tank fails. It also reduces the height of any flame and distance of any thermal radiation in the event of fire. For a full-containment tank, the outer tank can contain both the liquid and vapor, so if the inner tank fails, the outer wall contains the liquid and a portion of the vapor. A small amount of the vapor might be released through the tank relief vents.

LNG Receiving Terminals

The *receiving terminal* is the essential link between the LNG ships and the target pipeline grid. The terminal serves three vital functions:

- Receive and store ship-delivered LNG
- Regasify the LNG, with optional compositional adjustments
- Deliver the gas product into the local pipeline grid at a specified time and quantity

The storage capacity of a receiving terminal provides a supply buffer if inclement marine weather or other conditions interrupt delivery of the LNG for a number of days.

An LNG receiving terminal consists of several key components, including marine and unloading facilities, LNG storage tanks, LNG pumps, *boil-off gas (BOG)* facilities, LNG vaporizers, and a *send-out system*. Additionally, gas *odorization*, *caloric value* (a measure of heating value) control, and possible LNG road or rail loading facilities might be required. Due to the receiving terminal's relatively simple configuration, the storage tanks are the most prominent structures at the terminal (fig. 4-1.74). Also visible in figure 4-1.74 are two types of LNG containment systems on ships: spherical (Kvaener-Moss) and membrane.

> The LNG receiving terminal is the essential link between the LNG ships and the pipeline grid.

Courtesy of Cheniere Energy

Figure 4-1.74. Artist drawing of the Sabine Pass LNG, L.P. Regasification Terminal, in western Cameron Parish, Louisiana.

In the United States, the DOT regulates the transportation of LNG. In current commercial practice, there is minimum activity in the *spot market* where LNG is bought and sold for cash, so LNG ships are built based on a commitment basis, meaning each LNG project has its own dedicated LNG fleet.

Shipping is critical to the LNG monetization chain. The occasional transportation need created by spot-market activities can be met by searching for a ship that is available for an additional load in the desired time period. In the future, spot-market activities are expected to increase, and additional ships that are not committed should become available. Commercial LNG ships have different classifications, depending on LNG containment designs and pressure ratings.

The LNG industry is complex and growing. (For a more comprehensive explanation of LNG, refer to *LNG: Basics of Liquefied Natural Gas* [Huang et al., 2007] by PETEX.) References at the end of this section are helpful for researching more detailed information.

LNG Ships

SUMMARY

A complex system of tank trucks, rail cars, marine transportation, and pipelines supply methods of transporting and distributing petroleum products and natural gas from oilfields to refining and processing plants. Today, millions of barrels of crude oil, gasoline, fuel oils, and other petroleum products, along with billions of cubic feet of natural gas, are moved daily from wellheads to refineries—and from refineries to product terminals, onshore and offshore.

The chemical industry relies heavily on rail tank cars to transport petroleum-based chemicals used in manufacturing processes. Many chemicals are shipped from refineries and chemical plants to manufacturing centers for conversion into plastics, synthetic fibers, paints, and other products. Today, most liquefied petroleum gas moves through pipelines. But motor transportation still plays a key role in transporting petroleum and its derivatives, because carriers can respond to short lead times and can reach unconventional locations.

Some products, such as liquefied petroleum gas, require specifically designed refrigerated pressure tanks, often moved by barges. Where waterways exist, barges and tankers provide reliable transportation. A sophisticated communications network can locate vessels at any time.

Transporting natural gas in large quantities is done either by pipeline or by converting the gas to LNG. Although pipeline transportation has played the dominant role globally, LNG is exceptionally competitive in the long-distance, oceanic transportation of natural gas by cryogenic tankers.

Since World War II, pipelines to transport petroleum liquids have increased from 124,000 miles (200,000 kilometres) to more than 200,000 miles (322,000 kilometres) today. The coordination of shipments for liquid petroleum pipelines, whether for crude oil or refined products, is a critical function, because of the large volumes and high market value of the petroleum involved. Pipeline controllers handle key operations by remote control from a central control center linked to various locations via satellite and other communication links. Support services ensure accurate oil and gas measurement and tight quality control by following strict procedures and adhering to detailed industry standards. Modern technology has made it possible to lay offshore pipelines in much deeper areas of the sea. Various types of pipe-laying barges are used in offshore pipeline construction.

Economic and safety factors generally determine which method of transportation will be used to ship crude oil, petroleum products, and natural gas. Among the primary modes of transportation used to move petroleum, pipelines are reported as the safest by the U.S. National Transportation Safety Board.

REFERENCES

1. National Research Council (U.S.), Transportation Research Board, Committee for the Study of the Railroad Tank Car Design Process.

2. Petroleumhistory.org: Oil History.

3. Curt, B., "Marine Transportation of LNG", paper presented at Intertanko Conference, March 29 (2004).

4. Dimitroff, R., Chiu C.-H., "Methodology for LNG Liquefaction Technology Selection", paper to be presented in GasTech 2006, UAE, December 4–7 (2006).

5. Durr, C., Coyle, D., Patel, H., Cho, J. H., "Advanced Design of LNG Importing Terminals", paper presented at AIChE Spring Meeting, New Orleans, LA (2003).

6. Ffooks, R, "Natural Gas by Sea—The Development of a new Technology", 2nd Edition, Witherby & Co., London (1993).

7. Huang, S., Chiu, C.-H., Elliot, D., "LNG: Basics of Liquefied Natural Gas", published by Petroleum Extension Service of the University of Texas, Austin (2007).

8. McGuire, G., White, B., "Liquefied Gas Handling Principles on Ships and in Terminals", Witherby & Co., London (2000).

9. Mokhatab, S., Economides, M. J., "Process Selection Is Critical to Onshore LNG Economics", World Oil, issue of February (2006).

10. OGJ editor, "CERA Sees Strong LNG Growth, Mixed Commercial Success", Oil & Gas Journal, Issue of June 14 (2004).

11. Patel, H., Caswell, C., Durr, C., "North American LNG Terminals: Options?", Hydrocarbon Processing, issue of July (2005).

12. Scurlock, R.G., editor; "History and Origins of Cryogenics", Clarendon Press, Oxford (1992).

13. Sen, C. T., "World's LNG Industry Surges, Pushed by Confluence of Factors", Oil & Gas Journal, issue of June 27 (2005).

14. UK P&I Club, Web site publication, Issue 8, February 2005.

15. Yost, C., DiNapoli, R., "Benchmarking Study Compares LNG Plant Costs", Oil & Gas Journal, issue of April 14 (2003).

In this chapter:

- Structure of hydrocarbons in oil and gas
- Distillation and cracking processes
- Hydrotreating and blending fuels
- Petrochemical plant and processes
- Product marketing, sales, and distribution

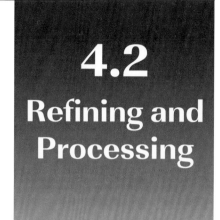

4.2
Refining and Processing

Collected crude oil and natural gas are of little use in their raw state. Their value lies in what is created from them—fuels, lubricating oils, waxes, asphalt, and petrochemicals.

To passersby, crude oil refineries and natural gas plants look like a strange conglomeration of towers and walls and a maze of pipes and tanks (fig. 4-2.1). In reality, a refinery is an organized and coordinated arrangement of equipment that separates the components in crude oil and gas and produces physical and chemical changes in them. These changes create salable products of the quality and quantity consumers want. Crude oil refineries and natural gas plants also include facilities to store crude oil and products and maintain equipment.

Figure 4-2.1. A refinery is an organized and coordinated arrangement of processes (called units) linked together with miles of pipe carrying crude oil in and products out. Pictured: Valero Corporation's Jean Gaulin Refinery in Quebec, Canada, has a capacity of 215,000 barrels per day.

Crude oil contains impurities
such as:
- Oxygen
- Nitrogen
- Sulfur
- Salt
- Water
- Trace metals

As *crude oil*, or *crude*, comes from the well, it contains hydrocarbon compounds and relatively small amounts of impurities such as oxygen, nitrogen, sulfur, salt, and water, plus traces of certain metals (primarily, nickel and vanadium). A *refinery* (crude oil) removes any substance from the crude oil that is not a hydrocarbon and breaks the oil down into various hydrocarbon components. Some of the components are further treated to give them more desirable properties. Finally, the resulting substances are sold as is or blended with fuel components produced internally (including biofuels), primarily for gasoline and diesel, and also for a multitude of other useful specialty products (fig. 4-2.2).

Likewise, natural gas is a mixture of hydrocarbon gases and impurities such as water, nitrogen, and carbon dioxide. A *natural gas processing plant*, or gas plant, removes impurities and separates out desired products from the gas.

Most refinery products are ready for consumers and industry to use. However, some go to petrochemical plants, where they are changed into chemicals used to manufacture an almost limitless number of products ranging from fertilizers to plastics.

Figure 4-2.2. Petroleum products are everywhere.

In the late nineteenth century, both crude oil and refined products were major exports of the United States. When the internal combustion engine was introduced in the early part of the twentieth century, demand for refined products grew enormously and sustained the refining industry.

The Standard Oil Company grew rapidly into one of the world's first and largest multinational corporations. The United States government required the company to break up into three separate companies in 1911:

- Standard Oil of New Jersey (Esso, later Exxon)
- Standard Oil Company of New York (Socony, later Mobil)
- Standard Oil of California (Socal, later Chevron)

These three companies, together with Royal Dutch Shell (Shell), the Anglo-Persian Oil Company (British Petroleum, later BP), Gulf Oil (later Chevron) and Texaco (later Chevron) were the dominant forces in refining business at the time.

Today, approximately 84 million barrels of oil are refined every day. There are 661 refineries worldwide of which about 116 are in the United States. Currently, the world's largest refining complex is in Jamnagar, India where over 1,240,000 barrels per day of crude oil are refined by *Reliance Industries headquarter in Mumbai, India* (fig. 4-2.3).

THE EARLY DAYS

TOP REFINERY CRUDE PROCESSING SITES IN THE WORLD		CRUDE CAPACITY (barrels per calendar day, b/cd)
1	Reliance, Jamngar, India	1,240,000
2	SK Corp., Ulsan, South Korea	817,000
3	GS Caltex Corp., Yeosu, South Korea	730,000
4	ExxonMobil Refining & Supply Co., Jurong, Singapore	605,000
5	ExxonMobil Refining & Supply Co., Baytown, Lousiana, USA	576,000
6	S-Oil Corp., Onsan, South Korea	565,000
7	Saudi Arabian Oil Co, Ras Tanura, Saudi Arabia	550,000
8	ExxonMobil Refining & Supply Co., Baton Rouge, Lousiana, USA	504,500
9	Hovensa LLC, St. Croix, Virgin Islands	500,000
10	Kuwait National Petroleum Co., Mina Al-Ahmadi, Kuwait	466,000
11	Shell Eastern Petrolem Ltd., Pulau Bukom, Singapore	462,000
12	Citgo Refining LLC, Lake Charles, Lousiana, USA	440,000
13	Marathon Oil USA Inc., Meraux, Lousiana, USA	436,000
14	Shell Nederland Raffinaderij BV, Pernis, Netherlands	404,000
15	Saudi Arabian Oil Co, Yanbu, Saudia Arabia	400,000
16	Saudi Arabian Oil Co, Rabigh, Saudi Arabia	400,000

Source: Oil and Gas Journal

Figure 4-2.3. World refineries by size (as of January 1, 2010)

The United States:
- Consumes about 25% of the world's crude oil production
- Produces 35% of its own oil needs

The largest companies producing petroleum liquids are not necessarily the largest refiners. The largest crude oil producer, Saudi Aramco, is one of the smaller refiners, refining only about 25% of its crude oil production and exporting about 75%. Exxon, Shell and BP refine almost twice as much crude oil as they produce. This is illustrated by refining numbers in the United States where approximately 25% (21 million barrels/day out of 84 million barrels/day) of the world's crude oil production is consumed (Table. 4-2.1).

The United States produces only 5 million barrels per day of crude oil and about 2.4 million barrels per day of gas condensate (liquids produced in association with natural gas). That means it produces only about 35% of its own oil needs (Table. 4-2.2). Canada and Mexico send another 3.8 million barrels/day of oil to the U.S., but the balance of nearly 10 million barrels/day must be imported from more distant countries such as Saudi Arabia.

Table 4-2.1
World Petroleum Supply and Demand

2009		2008	
Supply (millions of barrels/day) of:		*Supply (millions of barrels/day) of:*	
Crude	72.0	Crude	73.8
Other	12.0	Other	11.8
Total	**84.0**	**Total**	**85.4**
Demand (millions of barrels/day) of:		*Demand (millions of barrels/day) of:*	
Gasoline	21.6	Gasoline	21.4
Jet and Kerosene	6.2	Jet and Kerosene	6.5
Diesel	23.5	Diesel	24.0
Fuel Oil	8.9	Fuel Oil	9.5
NGLs and Other	23.8	NGLs and Other	24.2
Total	**84.0**	**Total**	**85.6**

Source: Valero Corporation

Table 4-2.2
U.S. Petroleum Supply and Demand

2009			
Supply (millions of barrels/day) of:		*Demand (millions of barrels/day) of:*	
Crude	14.4	Gasoline	9.0
Domestic	5.3	Jet and Kerosene	1.4
Imports	9.1	Diesel	3.6
NGL	2.7	Fuel Oil	0.5
Domestic	2.5	NGLs and Other	4.2
Imports	0.2	**Total**	**18.7**
Finished Product and Other Liquid Imports	1.8		
Total	**18.9**		

Source: Valero Corporation

Refining capacity in the United States is about 17.6 million barrels per day of crude oil. This means that the United States is refining approximately 10.2 million barrels per day of imported crude oil in addition to its own production. It also imports nearly 3.4 million barrels per day of refined products. This imbalance between the ability to refine vast quantities of crude oil and the lack of ready availability of refining raw material, or *feedstock*, is a driving force behind the refining industry's desire to be as effective and efficient as possible in designing and operating its facilities (figs. 4-2.4a and b).

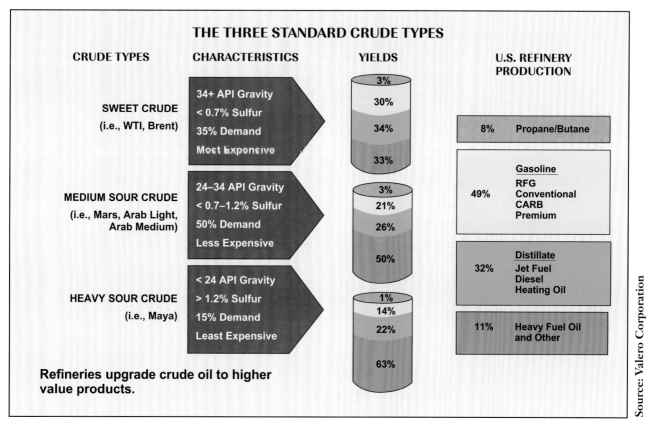

Figure 4-2.4a. Refineries upgrade crude oil to higher value products

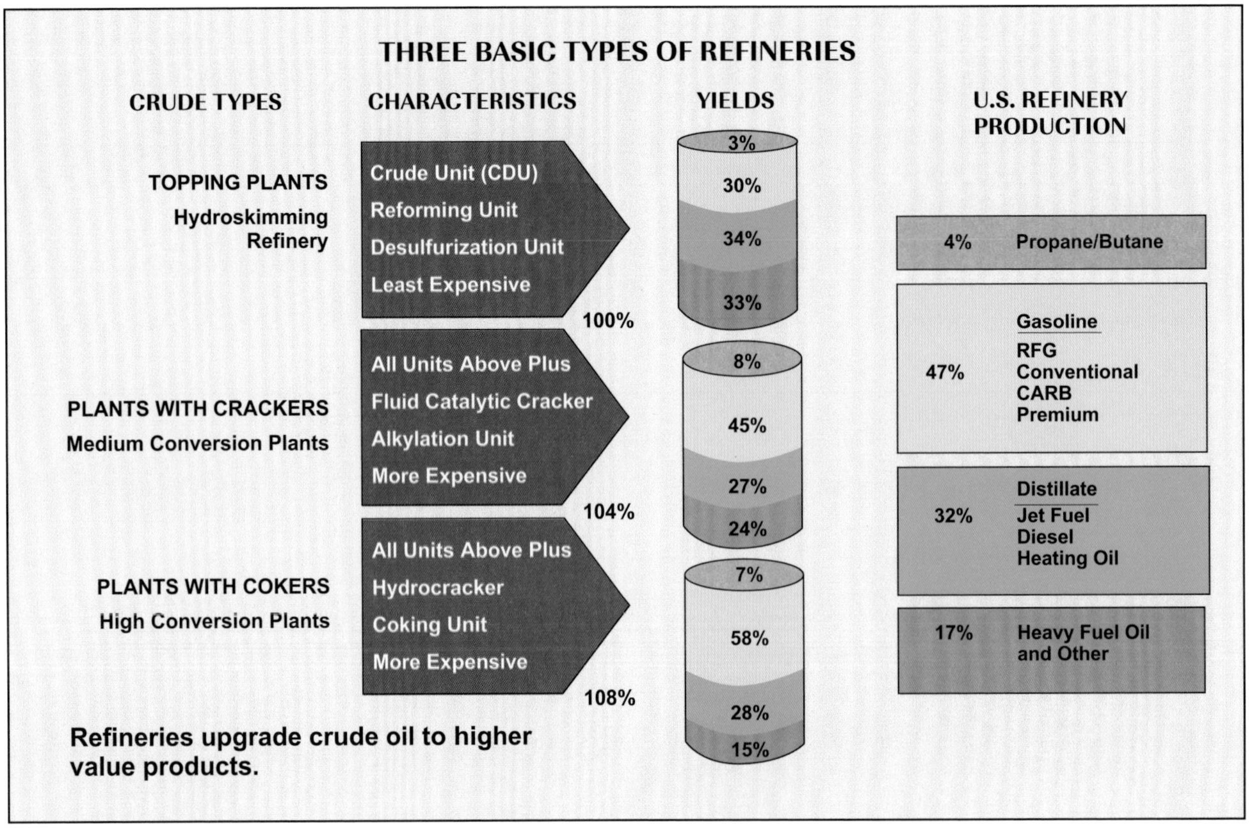

THREE BASIC TYPES OF REFINERIES

CRUDE TYPES	CHARACTERISTICS	YIELDS	U.S. REFINERY PRODUCTION

TOPPING PLANTS
Hydroskimming Refinery

Crude Unit (CDU)
Reforming Unit
Desulfurization Unit
Least Expensive
100%

3%
30%
34%
33%

PLANTS WITH CRACKERS
Medium Conversion Plants

All Units Above Plus
Fluid Catalytic Cracker
Alkylation Unit
More Expensive
104%

8%
45%
27%
24%

PLANTS WITH COKERS
High Conversion Plants

All Units Above Plus
Hydrocracker
Coking Unit
More Expensive
108%

7%
58%
28%
15%

Refineries upgrade crude oil to higher value products.

U.S. REFINERY PRODUCTION:
4% Propane/Butane
47% Gasoline RFG Conventional CARB Premium
32% Distillate Jet Fuel Diesel Heating Oil
17% Heavy Fuel Oil and Other

Source: Valero Corporation

Figure 4-2.4b. Refineries upgrade crude oil to higher value products

STRUCTURE OF HYDROCARBONS IN OIL AND GAS

Crude oil is a varying mixture of hydrocarbons, giving it specific characteristics such as:
- Color
- Viscosity
- Density
- Boiling point
- Ability to flow

In other parts of the oil industry, the word petroleum can refer to both crude oil and natural gas. But in the refining industry, *petroleum* refers only to crude oil—the heavier constituents that occur naturally in liquid form in the reservoir. The lighter constituents that occur naturally in gaseous form are simply called *gas*. A third, less common constituent is *natural gasoline*, which is in a gaseous state in the reservoir but emerges from an oilwell as liquid petroleum.

Crude oil and natural gas, as they are piped in from the reservoir, are mixtures of many different hydrocarbons ranging from light gases to asphalt *heavy pitch*, each with a unique chemical structure and properties. The crude oil varies in the type and amount of hydrocarbons and impurities it contains. The particular mixture determines characteristics such as color, viscosity, density, and boiling point. Some crude oils are light, flow easily, and make good gasoline (fig. 4-2.5). Others are heavy and thick and are excellent for producing asphalt. The refinery or gas processing plant does not separate each of these hydrocarbons. Instead, it refines or processes groups of hydrocarbons with similar chemical structures and physical characteristics.

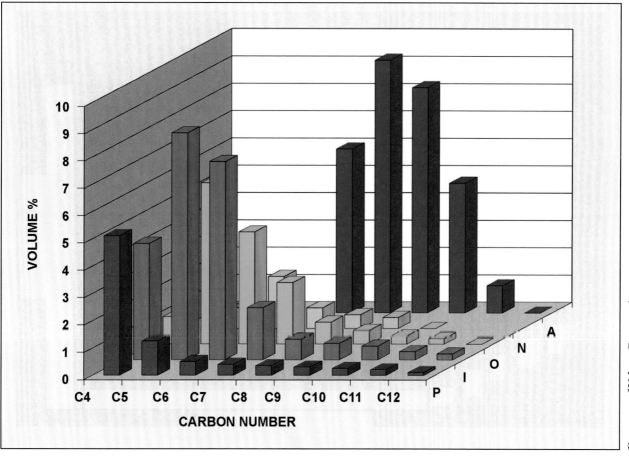

Courtesy of Valero Corporation

Figure 4-2.5. Hydrocarbon mix of gasoline. Bottom right: PIONA refers to paraffins, isomers, olefins, naphthenes, and aromatics.

Refineries and gas processing plants separate hydrocarbons into five types as shown in figure 4-2.5:

- (P) Paraffins
- (I) Isomers
- (O) Olefins
- (N) Naphthenes
- (A) Aromatics

All of these compounds are arrangements of carbon and hydrogen atoms, and sometimes they include other elements such as oxygen, sulfur, and trace metals.

Paraffins

- Paraffins are chemically stable compounds with names ending in "ane."
- Isomers result from paraffins having at least four carbon atoms in arrangement.
- Aromatics contain a ring of six carbon atoms with fewer hydrogen atoms.

Paraffin hydrocarbons make up natural gas and a substantial portion of crude oil (fig. 4-2.6). The simplest paraffin is *methane*, the main ingredient of natural gas. A molecule (a group of atoms bonded together) of methane has one carbon atom attached to four hydrogen atoms. The other hydrocarbons in the paraffin group are chains of carbon atoms with attached hydrogen atoms. Examples are *ethane* and *propane*, also components of natural gas. Each carbon atom can bond, or attach, to four other atoms, and each hydrogen atom can bond with one other atom.

Paraffins always have names ending in *ane*. Chemically, they are very stable compounds. The paraffin group is large, varying in number of carbon atoms from one to ninety or more. Chemists express the number of carbon and hydrogen atoms in each hydrocarbon by a formula. For example, the formula for ethane is C_2H_6, meaning that each molecule is made up of two carbon atoms and six hydrogen atoms.

Hydrocarbons with few carbon atoms (C_1 to C_4) are light in weight and are gases under normal atmospheric pressure. Hydrocarbons with more carbon atoms are heavier and are either liquid or solid under atmospheric pressure. As the number of carbon atoms increases, the boiling point also increases. More heat must be applied to change the hydrocarbon from a liquid or solid to a gaseous state. Paraffins are also known as saturated hydrocarbons because they contain the maximum ratio of hydrogen to carbon.

Isomers

Paraffins with four or more carbon atoms can have more than one arrangement of atoms resulting in an *isomer*. All the carbon atoms can form a single straight chain, but the probably of a straight chain is less likely as the number of carbons increases; the result is some of the carbon atoms form branches attached to the main chain. *Butane*, for example, has two forms: *normal*, or *n-butane* (straight chain), and *iso*, or *i-butane* (branched chain). Isobutane is known as an *isomer* of normal butane because i-butane has exactly the same formula but a different arrangement of atoms (fig. 4-2.6). This difference is important because isobutane boils at a temperature different from normal butane, causing different chemical reactions in the refinery. The larger the paraffin molecule, the more isomers it can have.

Other paraffins include *pentane* (C_5H_{12}), *hexane* (C_6H_{14}), *heptane* (C_7H_{16} and has an Octane of 0), *octane* (C_8H_{18} and has an Octane of 100), *nonane* (C_9H_{20}), and *decane* ($C_{10}H_{22}$). Because paraffins and isomers have the greatest possible number of hydrogen atoms, they are called *saturated hydrocarbons*.

Aromatics

Aromatic hydrocarbons, like naphthenes, contain a ring of six carbon atoms, and like olefins, have double and single bonds and so have fewer hydrogen atoms (fig. 4-2.6). This type of structure is known as a benzene ring. The most important aromatics in refinery production are the BTXs—*benzene*, *toluene*, and *xylene*. Aromatics occur naturally in crude oil. Refinery and petrochemical plant processes also create them.

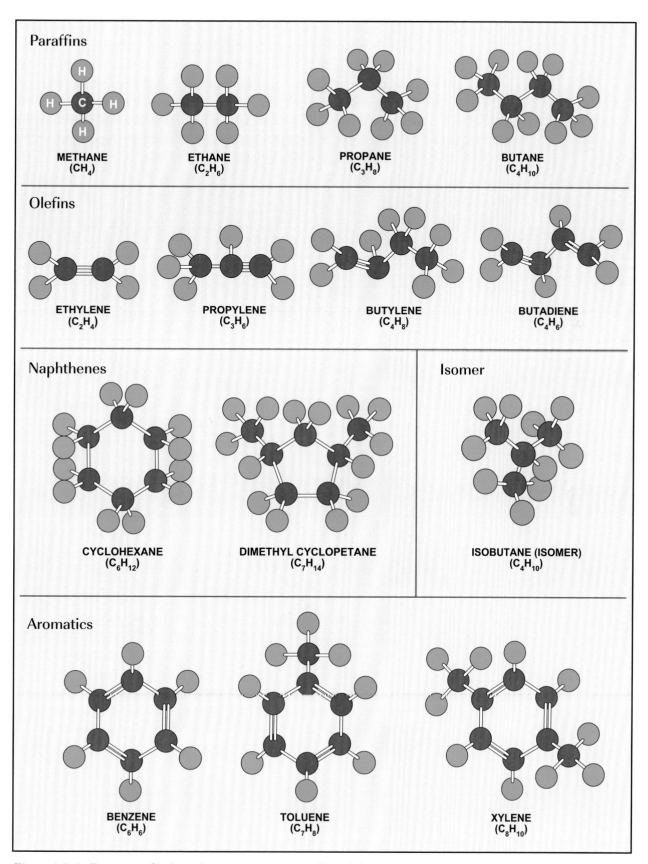

Figure 4-2.6. Four types of hydrocarbon structures are paraffins, olefins, napthenes, and aromatics.

Naphthenes

The carbon atoms of *naphthenes* form rings rather than chains, so naphthenes are called ring *compounds* or *cycloparaffins* (fig. 4-2.6). Hydrocarbons in this group have names that begin with the prefix *cyclo* to indicate the ring structure. An example is *cyclohexane*, a hydrocarbon often occurring in natural gasoline. The carbon rings of naphthenes contain all the hydrogen atoms they can, so naphthenes are chemically stable. They occur naturally in crude oil and have properties similar to the paraffins.

Olefins

Like paraffins and isomers, *olefins* are chains of carbon atoms with attached hydrogen atoms (fig. 4-2.6). However, olefin chains do not have the greatest possible number of hydrogen atoms. If two hydrogen atoms are missing, two carbon atoms in the chain will form a *double bond* to make up for the deficiency. An example is *ethylene*, an important petrochemical. If four hydrogen atoms are missing, the carbon chain will have two double bonds (an example is *butadiene*, another petrochemical). Olefins with one double bond have names ending in *ylene* or *ene*, and olefins with two double bonds have names ending in *adiene*. Other common olefins are *propylene* and *butylene*.

Olefins are known as *unsaturated hydrocarbons* because of their hydrogen deficiency. Because the carbon atoms of olefins are always seeking to attach their empty bonds to other atoms, olefins are unstable and are easily used to make new chemical compounds. They do not occur naturally in crude oil but are formed in the refinery by the breakdown of larger hydrocarbon molecules. Olefins are very useful in creating certain refinery products and petrochemicals.

- Naphthenes are ring compounds with names beginning with "cyclo."
- Olefins are chains of carbon atoms with attached hydrogen atoms.
- Other elements might include oxygen, nitrogen, sulfur, and metals.

Other Elements

Anywhere from 2% to 50% of the molecules in a crude oil might contain oxygen, nitrogen, sulfur, and metals. Oxygen content can be as high as 2 percent, and nitrogen content as high as 0.8 percent. Sulfur content ranges from traces to more than 5 percent. If a crude contains appreciable quantities of sulfur or sulfur compounds, it is called a *sour crude*; if it contains little or no sulfur, it is called a *sweet crude*. Trace metals contained in crude oil include sodium, magnesium, calcium, strontium, copper, silver, gold, aluminum, tin, lead, vanadium, chromium, manganese, iron, cobalt, nickel, platinum, uranium, boron, silicon, and phosphorus. Of these metals, nickel and vanadium occur in the greatest quantities.

Today, many processes are available to refine crude oil (fig. 4-2.7). Which processes a refinery uses depend partly on the content and quality of the crude oil it receives, partly on consumer demand, and partly on existing plant facilities and the economics involved in changing them. Not all refineries produce all products or serve all markets.

However, every refinery begins the processing by separating crude oil into different components, called *fractions* or *cuts*—groups of hydrocarbons with the same boiling-point range and similar properties. Next it breaks down or rearranges the molecules of some of the separated fractions and separates them again. The final process is to blend the refined hydrocarbons into mixtures that have desirable qualities for certain purposes. These processes convert virtually all of the crude oil into salable products in amounts the market demands.

REFINING CRUDE OIL

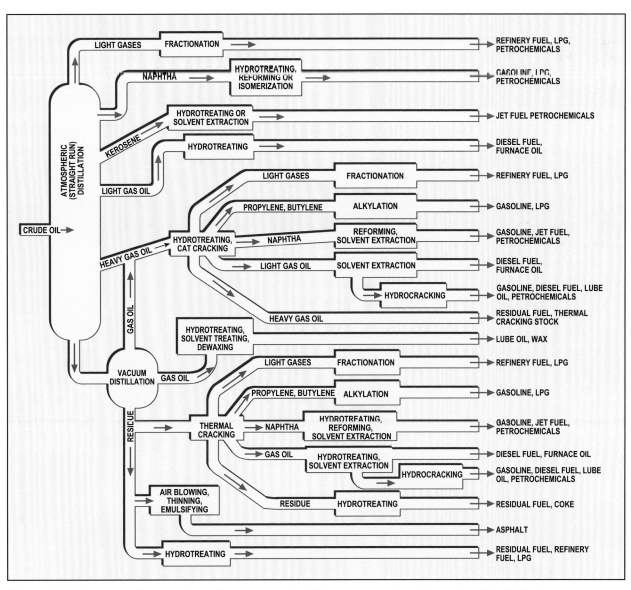

Figure 4-2.7. A variety of processes is used to convert crude oil into many products, beginning with distillation.

Assays

Before a crude can be processed, it must be evaluated in a process called an *assay*. An assay determines exactly what hydrocarbons and impurities are present and in what amounts. The reasons for assaying include:

- To plan the processing of the crude into desirable products
- To detect changes over time in an oil whose properties are known (As crude oil from a given field is produced, the quality can change over time.)
- To compare the crude with the crude of competitors and assess its market value

An assay classifies crude oil as:
- Paraffin-base
- Asphalt-base
- Mixed-base

The completeness of the crude oil assay depends on the purpose. A few routine tests may be enough to monitor changes in well-known crude oils, but planning a refinery operation to process a large quantity of a new crude oil requires a full-scale evaluation.

A complete assay may evaluate the whole crude for properties such as API gravity (density), viscosity (resistance to flow), and sulfur content. Or just certain cuts may be evaluated for properties important to the products they will yield.

Classifications

An assay classifies a crude oil in one of three groups, based on the composition of its components: paraffin-base, asphalt-base, and mixed-base:

- *Paraffin-base crude* oil contains mostly paraffin hydrocarbons in its heavier fractions. It is a good source of paraffin wax, quality motor lubrication oils, and high-grade kerosene.
- *Asphalt-base crude* oil contains mostly asphaltic hydrocarbons in its heavier fractions. Asphalt is a dark solid or semisolid containing carbon, hydrogen, oxygen, sulfur, and sometimes nitrogen. This type of crude is particularly suitable for making high-quality gasoline and roofing and paving materials.
- *Mixed-base crude oils* occur when the heavier fractions of some crude oils contain considerable amounts of both paraffin and asphalt. Virtually all products can be obtained from mixed-base crude oils, although at lower yields than from the other two classes.

Refinery processes have also developed in response to changing market demands for certain products (fig. 4-2.8 and table 4-2.3). Before the automobile, the primary product of refineries was kerosene for lamps and home heating. With the advent of the internal-combustion engine, the main job of refineries became the production of gasoline and diesel fuel. At first, a process called fractional distillation was the only method of producing gasoline. However, the amount of gasoline and diesel fuel that could be produced from crude oil using only distillation was soon insufficient to satisfy consumer demands (fig. 4-2.9).

Refining Processes

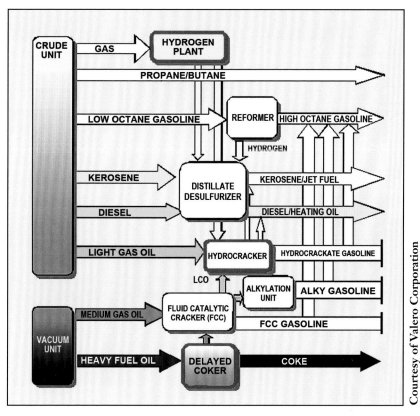

Figure 4-2.8. A simplified depiction of a refinery's key processes

Table 4-2.3
Refinery Processes

Feed	Process (also called Unit)	Primary Output
Crude oil	Atmospheric distillation unit (CDU)	Gases (C2 and lighter), propane and butane, straight-run naphtha, kerosene, diesel, gas oil, and atmospheric residue
Atmospheric residue	Vacuum distillation unit (VDU)	Light vacuum gas oil (LVGO), heavy vacuum gas oil (HVGO), unfinished wax, and vacuum residue
Gases (C2 and lighter)	Amine treating	Dry sulfur-free gas (usually consumed by the plant process units) and hydrogen sulfide (H_2S)
Propane and butanes	Sweetening and drying	Propane and butane sales or butane blended into winter grades of gasoline
Sraight-run naphtha	Naphtha hydrotreater (NHT)	Isomerization and reforming units
Butane, pentanes, and hexanes	Isomerization unit (ISOM)	Isobutane, light gasoline component for blending (C5 and C6 isomers)
Straight-run kerosene	Sweetening, drying and/or hydrotreating (KHT)	No. 1 burning oil, commercial jet fuel, kerosene, military jet fuels (JP-4, 5, or 6)
Straight-run diesel	Diesel hydrotreater (DHT)	No. 2 burning oil or road-grade diesel
Gas oil, LVGO, and HVGO	Gas oil hydrotreater (GOHT)	Sulfur-free gas oil, fluid catalytic cracking unit feed, hydrocracker feed, lube plant feed, no. 5 fuel oil for sale
Atmospheric residue	Reside fluid catalytic cracker (RFCC)	Gases (C2 and lighter with olefins), C3s and C4s mixed paraffins and olefins, pryrolis naphtha, light cycle oil, slurry oil, no. 6 oil or carbon black for sales
Atmospheric residue	Reside hydrotreater (RHT)	Fluid catalytic cracker feed or reside hydrocracker feed
Vacuum residue	Coker (atmospheric thermal cracker)	Gases (C2 and lighter with olefins), C3s and C4s mixed paraffins and olefins, cracked naphtha, cracked kerosene, cracked diesel, cracked gas oil, and coke for sales
Vacuum residue	Propane deasphalter (PDA)	Gas oil for FCC and asphalt for road repair
LVGO, HVGO, and waxes	Lube oil plant	Finished greases, waxes, and lube oils
Cracked and pryrolis gasoline	Gasoline hydrotreater	Gasoline components with less that 30 ppm sulfur for blending
Gas oil, LVGO and HVGO	Hydrocracker	Gasoline component for blending, kerosene, and diesel for sales
Gases and naphtha	Hydrogen plant	Hydrogen for use in hydrocrackers and hydrotreaters
Hydrotreated naphthas	Reforming unit	Hydrogen, propane, butane, isobutene, and gasoline component for blending
C3 and C4 olefins and isobutane	Alkylation unit	High-octane gasoline component for blending, propane, and butane for sales
Gasoline blend components	Gasoline blender	Regular, mid-grade and premium gasoline less ethanol to send to gasoline rack for distribution with ethanol blend into delivery truck
Hydrogen sulfide (H_2S)	Sulfur unit	Elemental sulfur for sales
Waxes	Solvent extraction	Lube oil and finished wax
Slurry oil	Carbon black plant	Carbon black
Hydrogen sulfide (H_2S)	Acid plant	Multiple grades of fresh sulfuric acid
C3 and C4 olefins	Petrochemical plant	Plastics, nylons, materials for rugs, etc.

Source: Valero Corporation

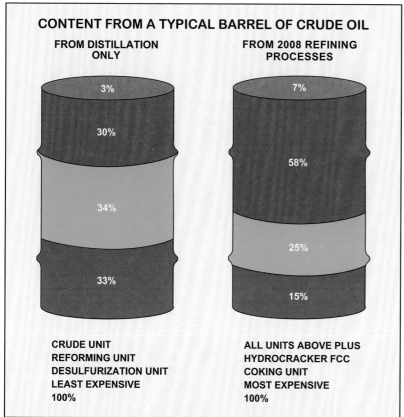

CONTENT FROM A TYPICAL BARREL OF CRUDE OIL

FROM DISTILLATION ONLY

3%
30%
34%
33%

CRUDE UNIT
REFORMING UNIT
DESULFURIZATION UNIT
LEAST EXPENSIVE
100%

FROM 2008 REFINING PROCESSES

7%
58%
25%
15%

ALL UNITS ABOVE PLUS
HYDROCRACKER FCC
COKING UNIT
MOST EXPENSIVE
100%

Processes that rearrange hydrocarbon molecules for gasoline and diesel:
- Fluid catalytic cracking
- Hydrocracking

Source: Valero Corporation

Figure 4-2.9. An important job of refineries today is the conversion of oil at "the bottom of the barrel" into gasoline and other more marketable products.

At the same time, refineries had more heavy hydrocarbons than they needed for making lubricating oils and other types of fuel. So refineries began to look for ways of chemically converting a part of the heavier oils into gasoline and diesel fuel. Two types of processes were developed:

- Fluid catalytic cracking
- Hydrocracking

These processes rearrange or rebuild hydrocarbon molecules primarily for gasoline and diesel. The other products from these two processes came to have many other uses as well.

Fractional Distillation

Every refinery begins the processing of crude oil by separating it into different cuts or fractions by distillation (figs. 4-2.10 and 4-2.11). This is called *fractional distillation*, or *fractionation*, and the products may be called *distillates*.

Distillation is quite simple in principle—it is like turning water into steam in a teakettle. When the water is heated, it vaporizes into steam and escapes from the kettle. If the spout of the teakettle had a transparent cup over it, you could see the steam condensing on the inside of the cup and dripping down the sides as water. Because crude oil is a mixture of hydrocarbons that boils, or vaporizes, at different temperatures, heating it to a certain temperature allows one fraction to boil off while others remain liquid (fig. 4-2.12).

Refineries use two types of distillation: atmospheric and vacuum.

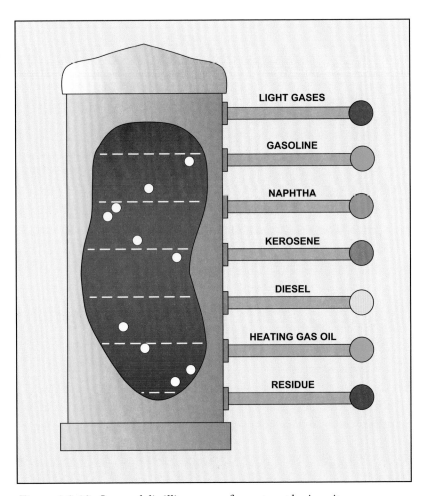

Figure 4-2.10. Internal distilling process from atmospheric unit

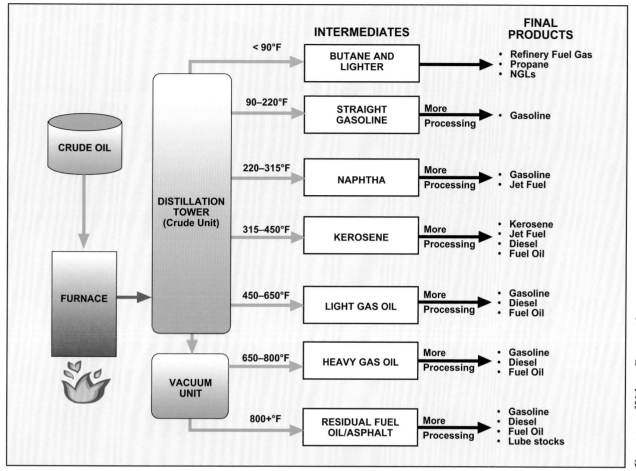

Figure 4-2.11. Basic refining concepts

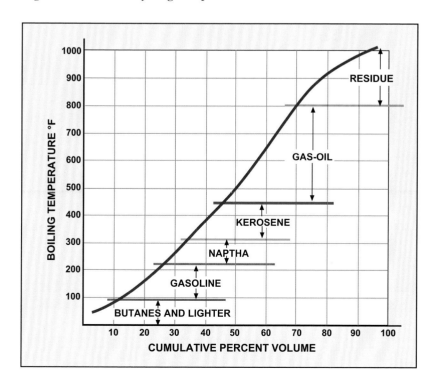

Figure 4-2.12. Distillation curve chart showing the boil-off temperature of crude oil components

Atmospheric Distillation

Atmospheric distillation uses a distilling column with
- Slotted trays through which liquid flows and vapor rises
- Pipes that direct liquids to high and low trays

In atmospheric distillation, the process takes place at atmospheric (normal) pressure in a piece of equipment known as a *distilling column*. The distilling column is a tall cylindrical steel tower (fig. 4-2.13a and b).

Inside the tower, flat steel trays are welded to the sides every few feet (fig. 4-2.14). The trays have holes and slots in them so that liquid can flow down through them and the vapor can rise. Pipes called *downcomers* direct the liquids from higher trays to lower ones. To begin, crude oil is heated to a temperature at which some of the hydrocarbons vaporize, and the resulting mixture of vapor and liquid is piped into the distilling column. The liquid flows to the bottom of the column and is removed. The vapor rises, passing through perforated *bubble caps* on the trays (fig. 4-2.15). As the vapor rises, it cools and condenses, becoming a liquid that settles on the trays. Heavier hydrocarbons condense more quickly and settle on lower trays, and lighter hydrocarbons remain in the vapor state longer and condense on higher trays. The liquid fractions are drawn from the trays and removed from the distilling column. The lightest hydrocarbons remain gaseous and pass out through the top of the column.

Courtesy of Chevron

Figure 4-2.13. Lines (a) carry the distilled cuts from different heights to the distillation tower (b).

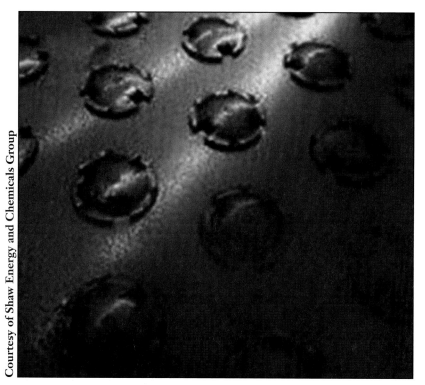

Courtesy of Shaw Energy and Chemicals Group

Figure 4-2.14. Flexitrays

Drilling columns are a complex maze of trays and downcomers that heat the crude to remove the steam and filter it out of the column.

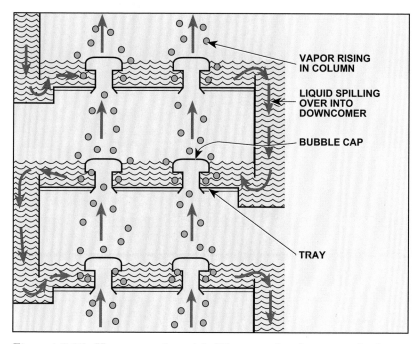

VAPOR RISING IN COLUMN

LIQUID SPILLING OVER INTO DOWNCOMER

BUBBLE CAP

TRAY

Figure 4-2.15. Vapor passes through bubble caps and settles on trays in the distilling column.

- Light distillates include naptha and kerosene.
- Middle distillates include light and heavy gas oils.

The distillates coming out from atmospheric distillation are useful in their new state, or they may be blended with other substances or processed further (table 4-2.4). For further processing, the gases go to a gas processing plant in the refinery to be fractionated again. Light distillates include naphtha and kerosene. Naphtha is used to make gasoline and petrochemicals. (This naphtha is not the same as certain commercial solvents popularly known as naphthas.) Kerosene is used to make jet fuel. Middle distillates include light and heavy gas oils. Light gas oils are made into diesel fuels and furnace oils (heating oil). Jet, diesel, and furnace fuels are sometimes called distillate fuels. Heavy gas oils are often cracked into lighter molecules (see below) to produce naphtha and other products. The unvaporized residue left after atmospheric distillation, containing the heaviest hydrocarbons, usually goes to a vacuum distillation column for further fractionation.

Table 4-2.4
Temperatures at which Common Fractions are Produced

Temperatures	Fractions
< 90°F	Butanes and lighter
90–220° F	Gasoline
220–315° F	Naphtha
315–450° F	Kerosene
450–800° F	Gas-oil (including diesel)
800° F and higher	Residue

Distillation at atmospheric pressure does not work for separating heavy hydrocarbons with boiling points of 900° F (482° C) and higher into fractions. The high temperatures required to vaporize them instead cause the molecules to break down into smaller molecules. To prevent this, the heated residue, or *residual oil*, from the atmospheric distillation column goes to a vacuum distillation tower (fig. 4-2.16). As the name implies, this tower creates a partial vacuum, which means that the pressure inside it is lowered. At a lower pressure, the residual oil's boiling point is lower, which allows the hydrocarbons to vaporize at lower temperatures and separate into fractions. Vacuum distillation separates light and heavy gas oil from the *bottoms*, the heaviest residue.

Light and heavy gas oils are further processed to produce products ranging from gasoline and distillate fuels to lubricating oils. Depending on its content, the bottoms will be processed to make fuels, asphalt, sealants, lubricating oils, wax, and coke.

Vacuum Distillation

Vacuum distillation separates the light and heavy oils, which are further processed to make:
- Fuel
- Asphalt
- Sealant
- Lubricating oil
- Wax
- Coke

Courtesy of Valero Corporation

Figure 4-2.16. This Port Arthur refinery in Texas contains a vacuum distillation unit that fractionates residual oil into, light vacuum gas oil, heavy vacuum gas oil, waxes and asphalt and other products. The heater preheats the feed under vacuum condition to keep the molecule from cracking thermally before it goes to the vacuum distillation column.

Cracking

Heavier hydrocarbons from the "bottom of the barrel" have limited markets and, therefore, are not very useful in their natural state. *Cracking* breaks down the heavy residues into lighter products such as gasoline and distillate fuels. Unlike distillation, which just separates hydrocarbons from each other, cracking is a chemical process that breaks long, heavy molecules into lighter, shorter ones. Cracking processes include catalytic cracking, thermal cracking, and hydrocracking.

Catalytic Cracking

Catalytic cracking, or *cat cracking*, uses a catalyst in a chemical reaction that converts gas oils and cracked gas oil obtained from atmospheric and vacuum crude oil distillation, coker distillation, propane deasphalting unit and residue hydrotreaters, which might be hydrotreated prior or after these processes, to produce primarily a gasoline component for blending and cycle oil for diesel (fig. 4-2.17). A *catalyst* is a substance that affects the speed of the reaction without itself being chemically changed or used up. The catalyst may be in the form of small pellets or a powder. Today, powders are more common. Because the catalyst behaves like a fluid when mixed with the gas oil, the method is also known as *fluid catalytic cracking*.

Figure 4-2.17. Cat crackers break down gas oils into lighter, more useful products.

Courtesy of Valero Corporation

Cat cracking produces gasoline, light gases, olefin compounds, cracked gas oils, a liquid residue called cycle oil, and a solid carbon residue known as coke. Cycle oil is usually recycled through the reaction chamber to break it down further. Coke is a solid that coats the catalyst and must be removed by burning so that the catalyst can be used again. One use for coke is as a fuel for in situ combustion. The other hydrocarbon products of the cracking reaction are sent to a fractionator to be separated, and most of them undergo further processing elsewhere in the refinery before they are ready for sale.

A few refineries now use a heavy oil cracker (HOC) to upgrade residues into unleaded gasoline and other products in demand. This large fluid catalytic cracking unit consists of a main fractionator, catalyst storage hoppers, vapor lines, heaters, and a bank of coolers. The fractionator has a regenerator at the bottom for removing water from the hydrocarbons and a reactor on top for catalytic cracking.

Thermal cracking uses heat to break down the bottoms from vacuum distillation and sometimes the heavy gas oils resulting from catalytic cracking (fig. 4-2.18). The lighter hydrocarbons produced by thermal cracking can be made into distillate fuels and gasoline. The heavy residue that remains is converted into a semiliquid residual oil or into coke. Two common types of thermal cracking are viscosity breaking, or visbreaking, and coking.

> Cracking breaks down the heavier residues into lighter product through:
> - Catalytic cracking
> - Thermal cracking
> - Hydrocracking

Thermal Cracking

Figure 4-2.18. Texas City thermal cracking operations

Courtesy of Valero Corporation

Thermal cracking has two forms:
- Visbreaking—a mild method
- Coking—a more aggressive method

In *visbreaking*, a relatively mild form of cracking, a furnace heats the feedstock for a short period of time. Using high pressure and immediately quenching, or cooling, the cracked products prevent coke from forming. Then the pressure is lowered, allowing the lighter hydrocarbons to vaporize. They go to a fractionator to be separated. Part of the heavy residue is recycled back to the reaction vessel for further breakdown.

In *coking*, a more severe form of thermal cracking, the feedstock is heated and sent to insulated vessels called coke drums, where it remains under high heat for an additional period of time. The lighter cracked products vaporize and leave through the top of the coke drum, and the heavier hydrocarbons form solid coke. Periodically, high-pressure water jets into the coke to break it up so it can be removed from the drum.

The products of thermal cracking include both saturated and unsaturated light gases, naphtha, gas oil, and residual oil or coke. The lighter products are of low quality and are usually upgraded by further processing before being sold. Cracked gases and naphtha are converted to gasoline. Gas oil can be used as distillate fuel or can be converted to gasoline and other products. Coke is heated to drive off water and is crushed. Coke is used in the manufacture of electrodes, graphite, and carbides, along with fuel blended with coal to produce electricity.

Hydrocracking

Whenever gas oils produced by catalytic and thermal cracking are not needed to make distillate fuels, they can be converted to high-grade gasoline by hydrocracking. *Hydrocracking* is catalytic cracking in the presence of hydrogen. The extra hydrogen adds hydrogen atoms to, or *hydrogenates*, the cracked hydrocarbon molecules. Hydrocracking is also a treating process, because the hydrogen combines with contaminants such as sulfur and nitrogen, allowing them to be removed.

A gas-oil feed is mixed with hydrogen, heated, and sent to a reactor vessel containing a catalyst in a bed (a fixed-bed catalyst), where cracking and hydrogenation take place. The excess hydrogen is separated from the cracked products and recycled to the reactor. The products go to a fractionator to be separated. Residue from the first reaction is mixed with hydrogen, reheated, and sent to a second reactor for further cracking under higher temperatures and pressures.

In addition to a large quantity of *hydrocrackate*—cracked naphtha for making gasoline—hydrocracking yields light gases useful as fuel for the refinery or for alkylation and as components for high-quality fuel oils, lubrication oils, and petrochemical feedstocks.

Some of the hydrogen for the hydrocracking process is a byproduct left over from reforming, but usually *steam methane reforming*, a series of chemical reactions that extract hydrogen from steam and methane (natural gas), must supply additional hydrogen.

A refinery can use several chemical processes to rearrange hydrocarbon molecules or to build new molecules to produce high-quality gasoline, jet fuel, and petrochemicals. Common processes are isomerization and reforming.

Rearranging Hydrocarbon Molecules

Olefins such as propylene and butylene are *byproducts* (a side product of a process to produce a main product) of catalytic and thermal cracking from the FCC, RFCC and coker process. In the refining industry, *alkylation* refers to the chemical combining of these light molecules with isobutane to form larger branched-chain molecules (isoparaffins) that make high-octane gasoline. This process occurs in an alkylation unit (fig. 4-2.19).

Alkylation

Courtesy of Total Planète Energies

Figure 4-2.19. An alkylation plant is capable of producing 9,200 barrels per day of alkylate.

In the alkylation unit, olefins and isobutane are first mixed with an acid catalyst and cooled. They react to form liquid gasoline components known as alkylates. The reaction also produces some n-butane, isobutane, and propane, which are pressurized until they are liquid and then stored in dome-shaped tanks (fig. 4-2.20). After the reaction, the acid catalyst settles out of the liquid and is drawn off to be reused. The remaining liquid is treated to neutralize remaining traces of acid, and the products are separated in a series of distillation columns. The isobutane is recycled as a feedstock, and the butane and propane can be sold as liquid petroleum gas.

Courtesy of Valero Corporation

Figure 4-2.20. These tanks store n-butane, isobutene, and propane until they are needed as a feedstock or are sold. Their spherical shape gives them strength to contain the high pressure necessary for storing liquefied petroleum gas.

Isomerization

In the refining industry, *isomerization* is a chemical process that rearranges straight-chain hydrocarbons (paraffins) into hydrocarbons that have branches attached to the main chain (isoparaffins).

One use for isomerization is to create extra isobutane for use in alkylation. Catalytic cracking and hydrocracking produce the isobutane needed as a feedstock for alkylation. But if a refinery does not have a hydrocracker, it may use an isomerization unit to produce isobutane from normal butane by isomerization. Normal butane is mixed with a little hydrogen and a chloride, and the resulting reaction, in the presence of a catalyst, forms isobutane. Other products of this reaction include normal butane and a small amount of lighter gases, which are separated in a fractionator. The lighter gases are used as fuel for the refinery, and the normal butane is recycled as a feedstock.

Another use for isomerization is to improve the performance of straight-run pentanes and hexanes as a feedstock for blending gasoline. *Straight-run* products are those produced by the initial distillation process. Pentanes and hexanes are the lighter components of gasoline. Isomerization improves gasoline quality by converting these hydrocarbons to their higher-octane isomers. *Octane* in this instance is a classification of gasoline—a higher-octane gasoline has better anti-knock properties. The process is the same as for butane. The hydrocarbons react with hydrogen and chloride in the presence of a catalyst, and the reaction products are separated. Again, the light gases are used as refinery fuel, and the normal pentane and hexane are recycled as feedstocks.

> Common hydrocarbon reconstruction uses isometric and reforming techniques:
> - Isomerization rearranges both paraffins and isoparaffins.
> - Reforming upgrades naphthas into high-octane gasoline and petrochemical feedstocks.

Catalytic Reforming

Catalytic reforming is a process for upgrading naphthas into high-octane gasoline and petrochemical feedstocks. The feedstock can be naphthas from straight-run distillation, thermal cracking, or hydrocracking. Naphthas are hydrocarbon mixtures containing many paraffins (chain molecules) and naphthenes (ring molecules). Reforming converts a portion of these compounds to isoparaffins and aromatics, which make a higher-octane gasoline. Aromatic compounds are also an important feedstock for the petrochemical industry.

> Reforming uses heat, pressure, and a catalyst to bring about desired chemical reactions.

Reforming uses heat, pressure, and a catalyst to bring about the desired chemical reactions (fig. 4-2.21). Of the several ways of exposing the naphtha to the catalyst, the most common method is to send the naphtha through a series of reactors with fixed catalyst beds. There it is mixed with hydrogen, which helps to prevent coke from forming on the catalyst bed. Hydrogen does this by combining with free carbon to form carbon monoxide and carbon dioxide.

Each reactor in the reforming series has a different temperature and pressure in order to promote a specific chemical reaction. Reaction products include hydrogen, light gases, and *reformate*—a liquid mixture of hydrocarbons. Hydrogen is separated from the other products by cooling, part is recycled as feed, and the remainder is used as a feedstock for hydrocracking. The gases are separated from the reformate in a fractionator and used as refinery fuel or as a feedstock for other plant operations.

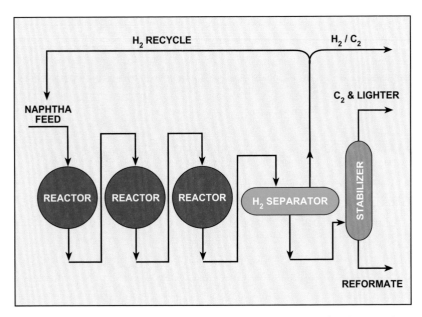

Figure 4-2.21. Catalytic reforming boosts the octane rating of hydrotreated naphtha.

Solvent extraction is the use of a solvent to selectively dissolve a particular compound and remove it from a mixture of hydrocarbons. The method is especially useful when all the hydrocarbons in the mixture have the same boiling point and so cannot be separated by distillation. Solvent extraction has many applications in the refining industry. It is used most often to improve the burning qualities of fuels, to refine lubricating oils and waxes, and to recover aromatic hydrocarbons for use as gasoline components or petrochemicals. The propane deasphalting unit is common in plants that do not have cokers. Propane or butane or a mix of both propane and butane can be used at the solvent.

Although there are many types of solvent extraction, the basic steps for all of them are the same. A solvent is selected that will dissolve only the *extract*, which is the substance that is to be separated from the *raffinate* (the remaining mixture). In a contacting tower, the solvent is thoroughly mixed with the feedstock, so that the solvent contacts and dissolves all of the extract. The extract solution is separated from the raffinate by settling, precipitation, cooling, and filtering, or by other means. Next, distillation or evaporation separates the solvent from the extract, and the solvent is recycled to the contacting tower. The raffinate contains traces of solvent, which must also be removed by distillation or other means.

Kerosenes and gas oils used to make jet, diesel, and burner fuels often contain aromatic hydrocarbons, sulfur, nitrogen, metallic compounds, and other substances that smoke when they are burned. Solvent extraction removes these hydrocarbons, which improves the burning quality of the fuels. Solvent extraction also improves the *cetane number* of diesel fuel, a measure of its ability to self-ignite. Today, kerosene is often hydrotreated to meet the ultra-low sulfur fuel requirements of diesel.

Hydrocarbons used to make lubricating oils and waxes often contain substances that interfere with desirable product qualities. Solvent extraction methods such as deasphalting, treating, dewaxing, and deoiling can remove these substances and make good lubricating oils and waxes from almost any crude oil. *Deasphalting* is the removal of asphaltic substances that tend to form carbon deposits when lubricating oils are heated. It is an alternative to removing asphalt by vacuum distillation. *Solvent treating* is the removal of aromatics, naphthenes, and olefins that decrease the stability of a lubricating oil's viscosity under temperature changes and cause gummy deposits to form. *Dewaxing* removes waxes so that a lubricating oil will flow better at low temperatures. Wax that has been separated from lubricating oil is *deoiled* to remove traces of oil and compounds with a low melting point.

Solvent Extraction

Improving Fuels

Making Lubricating Oils and Waxes

BTX Recovery

A third use of solvent extraction is the recovery of the aromatic compounds benzene, toluene, and the xylenes—commonly known as *BTX recovery*. These aromatics are separated from reformed naphtha and used as stock for gasoline blending or sold as petrochemical feedstocks.

Treating

Treating either removes contaminants from crude oil or converts them into harmless compounds. Treating is often necessary to improve the qualities of refinery feedstocks and finished refinery products, to prevent damage to expensive catalysts and refining equipment, and prevent environmental pollution. Sometimes treating may occur as a side benefit of a refinery process meant for other purposes. Examples of this are hydrocracking and solvent extraction. Other treating processes include dehydration and desalting, hydrotreating, and sulfur recovery. Today, all refiners are hydrotreating the gasoline and diesel streams to meet environmental standards (fig. 4-2.22).

Treating methods that remove and convert contaminants:
- Dehydration and desalting
- Hydrotreating
- Sulfur recovery

Courtesy of Valero Corporation

Figure 4-2.22. Hydrodesulfurization is a catalytic chemical process widely used to remove sulfur from natural gas and from refined petroleum products. Pictured above is an ultra-low sulfur diesel (ULSD) unit in Quebec.

Salts, which are impurities in some crudes, break down during refinery processing and foul and corrode the equipment. They must be removed, along with any water in the crude, at the beginning of refinery processing, before distillation takes place. When the salts are suspended in the water, they can be removed by heating the oil and allowing the water-salt solution to settle out (fig. 4-2.23). However, if the oil and water are in the form of a stable emulsion that resists separation, chemicals or an electric current must be used to break the emulsion and allow the water-salt solution to separate from the oil.

Dehydration and Desalting

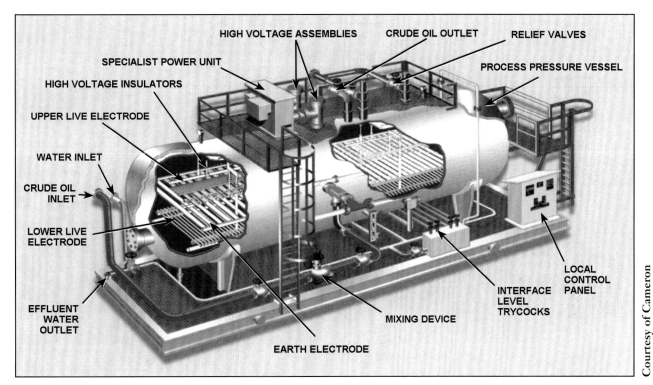

Figure 4-2.23. Desalter vessel internals (TriGridmax™ unit)

Hydrotreating

Hydrotreating is a method of removing sulfur, nitrogen, and metals from crude oil fractions (fig. 4-2.24 and fig. 4-2.25). It is used to treat straight-run naphthas, kerosenes, and gas oils; thermally cracked fractions; and residual fuel oils. Nearly all refinery streams are hydrotreated at least once to produce products that meet environmental standards.

Hydrotreating is similar to hydrocracking. The feed is mixed with a stream of hydrogen, heated, and sent to a reactor where a series of chemical reactions takes place in the presence of a fixed-bed catalyst. The hydrogen combines with nitrogen and sulfur to form ammonia and hydrogen sulfide, and metals are deposited on the catalyst. The reaction conditions for hydrotreating are less severe (temperatures and pressures are lower) than for hydrocracking, because the purpose is to remove contaminants rather than to crack large hydrocarbon molecules.

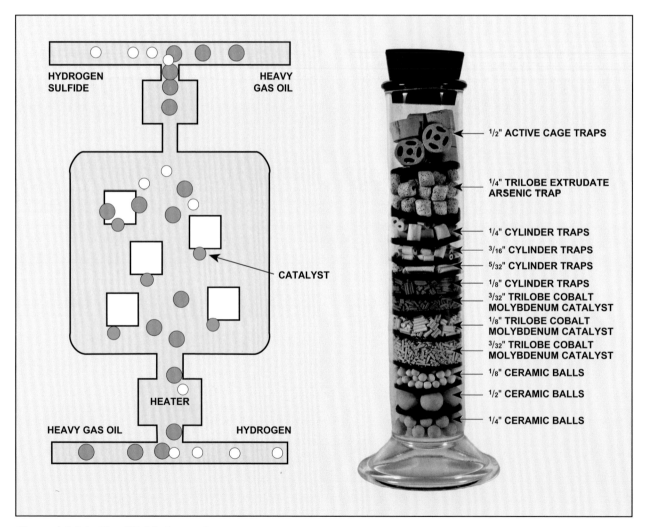

Figure 4-2.24. Simplified hydrotreating reactor

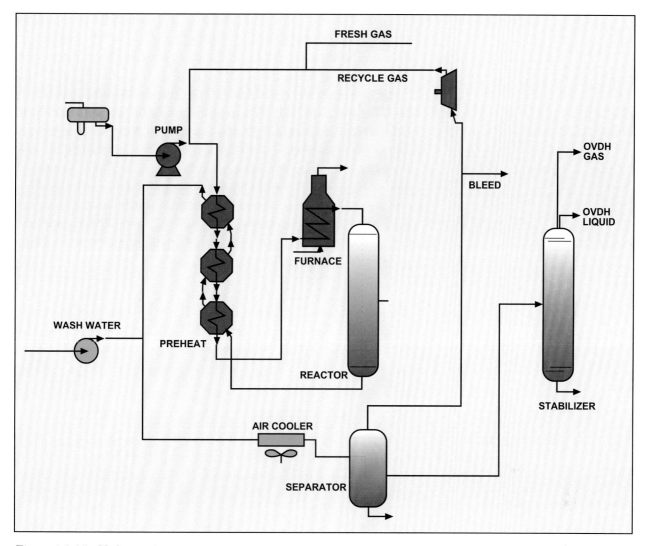

Figure 4-2.25. Hydrotreating process

However, a certain amount of cracking and olefin saturation does take place. Heavier oils, in particular, have to undergo more chemical breakdown of the molecules in order to free contaminants from the molecules that contain them. In the case of kerosene hydrotreating, molecular changes are beneficial because they improve the burning qualities of diesel fuel. After hydrotreating, the reaction mixture is separated from the remaining hydrogen and sent to a fractionator to separate the oil from the contaminant and hydrocarbon gases.

Sulfur Recovery

Hydrogen sulfide, the highly poisonous gas sometimes contained in natural gas or created by hydrotreating, can be converted into elemental sulfur. Sulfur is useful because it can be converted into ammonium thiosulfate, a fertilizer.

The most widely used and reliable process for sulfur recovery is the *Claus process*. In this process a furnace heats the hydrogen sulfide in the presence of a controlled amount of oxygen. Most of the hydrogen sulfide reacts chemically with the oxygen to form sulfur and water, but some of the hydrogen sulfide forms sulfur dioxide. The sulfur dioxide is sent to a series of two or three catalytic converters, which convert it into a sulfur vapor and water. The vaporous sulfur is cooled and sent through a condenser to change it into a liquid state. The liquid sulfur is then drained into a heated tank and stored until it is ready to be pumped into tank trucks or cars for delivery.

Other Methods

A number of other chemical and physical methods have been used for treating. They include washing oil with caustic (basic) or acidic solutions, exposing the oil to adsorbent clays, and oxidating (adding oxygen to) oil with catalysts. Many of these methods have been largely replaced by hydrotreating.

Blending and Using Additives

After crude oil has been refined into useful products, many of these products are further improved either by adding small amounts of other substances to modify their properties or by blending hydrocarbons with different characteristics. Blending is particularly important in refining gasoline, diesel fuel, furnace oils, and residual fuel oils.

After refining crude oil into products, many products can be further improved by:
- Adding substances to modify properties
- Blending hydrocarbons with different characteristics

The gasolines produced by straight-run distillation, catalytic cracking, hydrocracking, reforming, alkylation, and gas processing (see following) have different hydrocarbon contents and performance qualities. Refineries blend them into intermediate grades of products to blend with ethanol to meet US federal regulations at the wholesale distribution point. The components are blended to perform well under varying weather conditions, altitudes, and engine compressions to meet market demands. For example, the temperature at which it vaporizes is important. A gasoline has to vaporize enough to ignite in a cold engine but not enough to cause vapor-lock stalling in hot weather. It has to have an octane that prevents it from knocking or self-igniting. In modern refineries, computer operators make the complex calculations needed to plan production of the required amounts and types of gasoline components (fig. 4-2.26).

Gasoline

Courtesy of Valero Corporation

Figure 4-2.26. Operator looking at blending board. Computers are used to calculate the proper blend to meet the customer's specifications, to open and close the valves of lines leading to equipment on the plant site, and to automatically gauge storage tanks on the site.

Diesel Fuel

Diesel fuel is blended from straight-run light gas oils, cracked gas oils, and kerosene. All of these blends are hydrotreated today to meet the ultra low sulfur specification for road diesel which is 15 ppm. It must have a minimum cetane number that allows it to self-ignite readily, just the opposite of the antiknock quality needed in gasoline. Several grades are sold; the premium grades allow better cold starts and smoke less when burning.

Furnace and Residual Fuel Oils

Oils destined to be burned in furnaces for residential and commercial heating are blended from straight-run and cracked gas oils.

Residual fuel oils, burned in industrial and ship boilers, are made from the residue of vacuum distillation and thermal cracking. These oils must be able to flow at the temperatures at which they are commonly used and must not vaporize enough to form mixtures with air that could start an accidental fire. Residual fuels are blended with heavy gas oils to make them pour more easily and to reduce sulfur content to acceptable levels (if they have not been hydrotreated). Figure 4-2.27 shows a hydrotreater for residual fuel.

Courtesy of Valero Corporation

Figure 4-2.27. A residual fuel hydrotreater

PETROCHEMICALS

Although most petroleum products are used as energy sources, such as gasoline for cars, fuel oil for boats and ships, and natural gas for heating and fuel, petroleum components also provide the raw material for the manufacture of petrochemicals. A *petrochemical* is a chemical substance produced commercially from feedstocks derived from crude oil or natural gas. Consequently, many petrochemical plants are integral parts of large refining complexes and are often subsidiaries of major oil companies.

Types of Petrochemicals

The basic job of most petrochemical plants is to turn crude oil fractions or their cracked or processed derivatives into feedstocks that will ultimately be used in the manufacture of a host of other products, from liquid detergent to the plastic bottle containing it (fig. 4-2.28). These feedstocks fall into three groups, based on chemical composition and structure—aliphatic, aromatic, and inorganic.

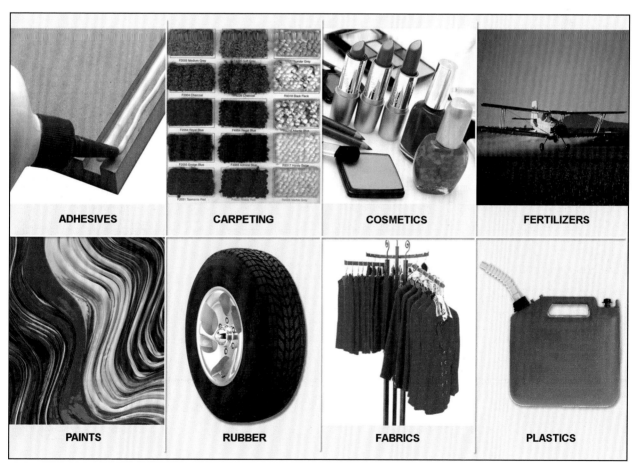

ADHESIVES CARPETING COSMETICS FERTILIZERS

PAINTS RUBBER FABRICS PLASTICS

Figure 4-2.28. Petrochemicals satisfy the fundamental needs of modern life. They help supply the carpeting, plastic soda bottles, clothing, fertilizer, tires, paints, pharmaceuticals, cosmetics, and the list goes on and on.

Aliphatic Petrochemicals

> Paraffins and olefins makeup over half the volume of all petrochemicals produced.

Aliphatic petrochemicals are straight-chain hydrocarbons, either saturated (paraffins) or unsaturated (olefins). They make up over half the volume of all petrochemicals produced. Two major olefin feedstocks are ethylene and propylene. They are produced from hydrocarbons by thermal cracking in the presence of steam, a process known as *steam cracking*. The hydrocarbons used as raw materials range from natural gas to naphtha to gas oil. Ethylene in turn can be chemically converted to several other important feedstocks such as polyethylene, ethylene glycol, vinyl chloride, and styrene. Similarly, propylene can be used to make feedstocks such as polypropylene and isopropyl alcohol. These petrochemicals ultimately go to factories that make plastics, solvents, synthetic rubbers, and synthetic fibers. Other aliphatic petrochemicals include methanol, made from natural gas; and butadiene, derived from butanes and butylenes (C_4 hydrocarbons). Methanol is used to make resins, polyester fibers, and solvents. Butadiene is used to make rubber, resins, and plastics.

Aromatic Petrochemicals

Aromatic petrochemicals are unsaturated hydrocarbons with six carbon atoms in a ring. Major aromatic feedstocks include benzene, toluene, and the xylenes. A large portion of toluene is chemically converted to benzene, the most widely used aromatic feedstock. Aromatic petrochemicals are used to make plastics, resins, fibers, and elastomers.

Inorganic Petrochemicals

Inorganic petrochemicals include sulfur and ammonia. These substances do not contain carbon compounds and can be produced from nonhydrocarbon sources. Nevertheless, they are considered to be petrochemicals because the primary raw materials for their manufacture are substances derived from petroleum refining. Carbon black, made from natural gas, is used to manufacture synthetic rubbers, printing ink, and paint. Sulfur, produced from hydrogen sulfide and other sulfur compounds, is used to make sulfuric acid, which in turn is used in the manufacture of steel, fertilizer, paper, and other chemicals. Ammonia, synthesized from natural gas and naphtha, is an important feedstock for the manufacture of fertilizers, fibers, and plastics.

Since each petrochemical plant is designed to convert particular petroleum fractions or other substances into specific petrochemicals, each plant uses different processes, procedures, facilities, and auxiliary operations (fig. 4-2.29). To get an insight into a petrochemical plant, consider the operation of a hypothetical plant that manufactures two basic plastics—polyethylene and polypropylene.

A Petrochemical Plant

Figure 4-2.29. Ethylene petrochemical plant

Courtesy of Shaw Energy and Chemicals Group

Petrochemical plants produce polyethylene and polypropylene to make thousands of products, such as:

- Appliance and automotive parts
- Moldings
- Battery cases
- Luggage
- Bottles
- Plastic toys
- Transparent food wrappers
- Plastic containers
- Construction materials

Situated in the heart of oil country where miles of pipelines crisscross underground and barges ply the waterways, this hypothetical plant uses several basic raw materials derived from petroleum or natural gas. From these materials, the plant manufactures polyethylene and polypropylene, which are used to make thousands of products such as appliance and automotive parts, moldings, battery cases, luggage, bottles, plastic toys, transparent food wrappers, plastic containers, and a wide range of construction materials (fig. 4-2.30).

Courtesy of Rhewum GmbH

Figure 4-2.30. Polyethylene is used to make a host of products.

The plant operates twenty-four hours a day, seven days a week. Although the chemical processes themselves are complex, they involve the application of familiar principles: controlled temperature, pressure, and time, and sometimes the presence of a catalyst and a solvent. All operations take place in a labyrinth of pipes, valves, silos, and towers powered by heavy equipment controlled by elaborate instruments, and monitored by trained technicians (fig. 4-2.31). The plant is organized in three systems: the olefin units, the polymer units, and the supporting facilities.

Courtesy of Elliot Company

Figure 4-2.31. This high-powereed centrifugal compressor is an example of the huge yet precise equipment in a petrochemical plant.

Olefin Units

Olefin units—or petrochemical refinery—use liquefied ethane and propane and distillates as raw materials to make products.

The primary job of the *olefin units* is to provide ethylene and propylene for the polymer units (polyethylene and polypropylene units), as well as for sale to other chemical or plastic producers. The olefin units, sometimes referred to as a petrochemical refinery because of their wide range of products, also produce butadiene, butylenes, hydrogen, and aromatics for use in the manufacture of other chemicals or gasoline products. These coproducts are sold to other chemical producers or used as feedstocks for other plants operated by the hypothetical company.

The olefin units use liquefied ethane and propane and distillates such as natural gasoline and naphtha as raw materials. These hydrocarbons spend a brief period in a furnace where they are thermally cracked under high temperatures in the presence of steam. The resulting products are sent to a fractionator to be separated (fig. 4-2.32).

Other processes used in the olefin units include catalytic conversion of acetylenes, cryogenic separation of hydrogen, and adsorption. Catalytic reforming of straight-run naphtha produces aromatics. When the naphtha is passed over a catalyst such as platinum, it forms ring compounds with no double bonds. These compounds are changed into aromatic compounds by *dehydrogenation*—removing some of the hydrogen so the carbons will form double bonds.

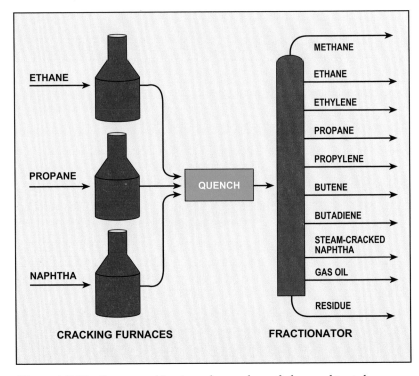

Figure 4-2.32. Steam cracking is used to produce ethylene and propylene.

In the plant's *polymer units*, propylene and ethylene are combined into larger molecules (*polymerized*) to make polypropylene and polyethylene. The reaction takes place in a liquid solvent in the presence of a catalyst. After the polymers have been formed, they are removed from the reactor and sent to a purification facility to remove the catalyst and the solvent. The powdered product is blended with additives and sent through an extruder to form pellets (fig. 4-2.33).

Polymer Units

Courtesy of Plastic Options

Figure 4-2.33. Polypropylene is extruded into small bb-size pellets in its finished form.

Quality control technicians perform extensive laboratory tests to maintain quality during each phase of plant processes. Technicians check polyethylene and polypropylene pellets for proper content and consistency. If they meet the specifications, the pellets are prepared for shipping.

Supporting Facilities

Plant operations are designed to conserve energy, air, and water. On-site water-treatment facilities purify and recirculate water used to cool the process units. Only steam is allowed to rise from the plant's cooling towers and units. The steam is odorless, contains no contaminants, and rapidly disperses into the atmosphere. The intermittent discharge of waste hydrocarbon gas from the processing units—a potential source of air pollution—is burned in a flare system from tall, derricklike structures. Engineers design processing units to make full use of the energy consumed, and often the hydrocarbons created as byproducts are recovered and used as fuel.

Companion Plant Linked closely with the operation of this Tex-Chem plant, the company runs another plant nearby. Using feedstocks from plant No. 1, Tex-Chem's plant No. 2 produces specialty chemicals and petrochemical intermediates for the manufacture of other products (table 4-2.5).

Table 4-2.5
Some Petrochemicals, Feedstocks, and Final Products

Feedstock	Petrochemical	Typical Final Products
Styrene	Polystyrene	Cups and glasses, phonograph records, radio and TV cabinets, furniture, luggage, telephones, ice chests, lighting fixtures
Paraxylene	Terephthalic acid (TPA), dimethyl terephthalate (DMT)	Polyester fibers used to make wearing apparel, tire cords; polyester film used to make electronic recording tape, photographic film, cooking pouches, specialty packaging items
Metaxylene	Isophthalic acid (IPA)	Fiberglass-reinforced auto bodies, surfboards, snow-mobile housings, outboard motor covers, cooling fans, vaulting poles, many paints and coatings
Propylene	Polypropylene	Appliance parts, bottles, safety helmets, disposable syringes, battery cases, construction materials, feed bags, carpet backing

Planning for future refinery capabilities is complicated by the fact that it takes two or more years to construct and power up a major new refining plant. A company must expect to make enough profit over the life of the refinery to justify the amount of capital required to build it. Smaller investment projects at existing refineries might include increased dock facilities, environmental protection facilities, or new storage areas.

New government regulations might require extensive restructuring on the part of some refineries. An example is the effect of the changeover to unleaded gasoline ordered by the Environmental Protection Agency (EPA) beginning in 1984. Most U.S. refineries were able to meet this deadline, but as EPA rules have become more stringent, upgrades proved too costly for many small refineries and so they closed.

REFINING CAPACITY

New EPA regulations sometimes require extensive, costly restructuring of refineries to meet stringent environmental requirements.

The task of distributing petroleum products from processing plants and refineries to the final consumers is complex and costly, taking into consideration the combined costs of product storage and handling, transportation, and delivery. Consumer products, such as gasoline and home heating oil, are usually sent directly from the refinery via pipeline, tanker, barge, or railroad to an installation terminal. From the terminal, products are transported to bulk plants serving smaller communities or directly to service stations, airports, homes, or businesses.

A refining company might supply its own service stations and other company-brand outlets. The terminal's owning company might contract with a *jobber* (an independent middleman) to act as a wholesale agent for that brand of product in a given trade area. A jobber might also own a retail outlet that resells the product from the terminal. Independent service station owners might purchase their fuels from terminals or from jobbers, and jobbers might purchase propane to deliver to rural homes.

Products Sales and Distribution

Environmental Considerations

The environmental concerns in regard to refineries are twofold. First, the refining processes themselves use a lot of water for cooling and other purposes and emit toxic gases and dust. Both water and air emissions must be treated before release from the refinery. Second, increasingly strict regulation of fuel emissions forces refineries to manufacture cleaner-burning gasoline and other petroleum-based fuels. Petrochemical plants have many of the same problems as refineries when it comes to controlling water and air pollution caused by the manufacturing processes.

Water Quality

When water is discharged from a refinery or petrochemical plant (*effluent water*), it must be pure enough to meet the demands of local and state water quality boards, the EPA, and other regulatory agencies. Refineries use chemical treatment tanks, holding ponds, and oil-degrading bacteria to remove contaminants such as hydrogen sulfide, ammonia, phenols, and salts from the water (fig. 4-2.34).

In effluent water storage tanks, hazardous wastes settle on the bottom, so the contents must be separated into water, oil, and solids. The water is recycled through the refinery's treatment plant where any oil is recovered for reuse. Then the water is centrifuged and heated to separate out the solids that are to be disposed of in a landfill. Because disposal is costly, refineries try to separate out as much oil and water as possible.

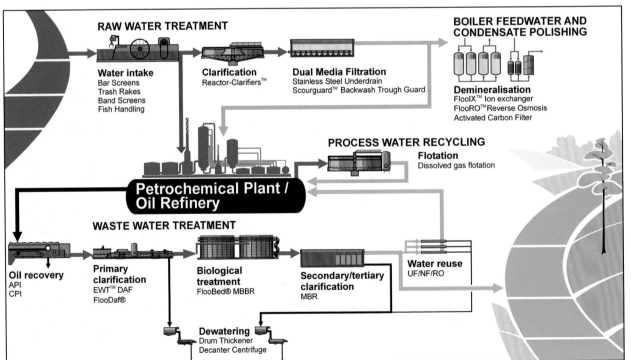

Fig. 4-2.34. Water treatment and recycling to and from a petrochemical plant or oil refinery

Courtesy of Eimco Water Technologies

Toxic air emissions that are of particular concern to refineries are *volatile organic compounds (VOCs)*. These refer to the light fractions of petroleum that evaporate at atmospheric temperature and pressure, such as benzene (table 4-2.6). They cause smog and ozone formations near the ground.

Dust is another problem in refineries. Petroleum coke dust can blow off in air or run off in water. It is a health hazard for workers and can interfere with machinery. Coke contains metals such as vanadium, copper, iron, and nickel. The dust is made up of fine particles that are easily airborne and repel water. For this reason, spraying plain water does not control the dust. Chemicals are added to spray water to enable better wetting properties so the dust particles will stick to the water droplets. This system has successfully reduced dust inside and outside facilities.

Other air pollution controls include floating roofs on storage tanks that eliminate space for vapor buildup, periodic checks for leaks along storage tank walls, vapor collection systems, scrubbers to remove sulfur from combustion gases, and electrostatic precipitators to collect dust.

Because vehicle emissions are among the most significant and widespread air pollution problems, standards for them have become increasingly strict. Lead as an additive to boost octane was phased out in the 1970s, gas volatility in summer temperatures were reduced in 1989, and low-sulfur diesel fuel was mandated in 1993. Starting in 2004, the EPA required trucks and buses to lower emissions.

Refiners continue to seek processes that will produce higher-quality, lower-sulfur fuels and gasoline from lower-quality crudes. Today, biofuels, primarily ethanol, are being added to the gasoline and diesel fuels. Refiners are investing in this technology and the equipment to reduce the imports of crude to the United States. Forecasts indicate that the crudes of the future will be progressively heavier with higher sulfur content. Some crudes also contain much higher concentrations of metals. At the same time, environmental restrictions force reduced sulfur in fuel oils, and safety concerns remain a high priority in achieving the best product for consumers and the environment.

Air Quality

Table 4-2.6
Petroleum Constituents

Listed by Decreasing Volatility
1-Pentene
(n) Heptane
(n) Hexane
(n) Pentane
Toluene
Benzene
Ethylbenzene
(o) Xylene
Naphthalene
Phenanthrene
Phenol
Benz (a) Anthracene
Benzo (a) Pyrene

SUMMARY

Crude oil refineries and natural gas plants take products in their natural state, refine and distill them, and store them before distribution to an end user. Crude oil is comprised of various hydrocarbon compounds and impurities including nitrogen, sulfur, salt, and water. Likewise, natural gas is also a formation of hydrocarbon compounds and impurities such as water, nitrogen, and carbon dioxide.

In the early twentieth century, the U.S. government forced the conglomerate of Standard Oil to break into three separate companies. Today, these three companies produce 84 million barrels of refined oil every day.

In the refining industry, petroleum is divided by the heavier constituents (crude) and the lighter constituents (gas). Refineries and gas processing plants separate the hydrocarbons into five separate categories: paraffins, isomers, olefins, naphthenes, and aromatics. The goal of refineries is to separate hydrocarbons and impurities from petroleum and prepare the products for sale.

Many processes are used to refine crude oil. First, the hydrocarbons are evaluated and the oil is classified. The refining process depends on the results of this initial assay. Fractional distillation begins the refining process, and this might be done in a number of ways, depending on the type of crude oil being refined. Heavier sediments are processed through a vacuum, where impurities are pulled from the crude and distilled to a lighter form. Crude oil can be further refined using a solvent to dissolve particular hydrocarbons that have the same boiling point as the product and cannot be heated. Products produced by solvent extraction are lubricating oils and waxes and kerosene and gas oils used to make jet, diesel, and burner fuels. Some processes used to treat crude oil products are hydrotreating, dehydrating and desalting, and sulfur recovery.

Petroleum products are generally used for energy sources, but there are components of the petroleum that are used to make petrochemicals. The petrochemicals produced from feedstock and derived from petroleum make common, everyday products such as plastic bottles and tires. Petrochemical plants also manufacture two basic plastics—polyethylene and polypropylene.

Planning and operating a refinery is a timely and expensive process. The plants are highly regulated by the EPA, which can mandate certain modifications to the plant. Water and air quality are of utmost importance to the industry, the government, and the general public.

In this chapter:

- Functions of gas processing plants
- Natural gas liquids and cryogenic recovery
- Absorption and adsorption processes
- Fractionation to produce salable products

4.3
Gas Processing

$\mathbf{A}$s late as the 1930s, natural gas leaving the wellhead had to reach a market nearby or else be burned off, or *flared*. Huge amounts of natural gas have been flared in the United States. Flaring is still a common practice in remotely located oilfields when gas cannot be reinjected into the reservoir for gas lift or used locally as fuel. With the advent of gas pipelines (commonly called *transmission lines*), gas transport trucks, and field processing facilities for gas, gas production in the United States and elsewhere has become an industry in itself.

Natural gas straight from the well is processed in the field. The processing includes the removal of water, impurities, and excess hydrocarbon liquids as required by the sales contract. It also includes the control of delivery pressure. When it is economical to gather the gas from several wells to a central point, an operator may build a gas processing plant to do the same work as separate facilities next to each well would do. Often, these gas plants dehydrate the gas and remove hydrogen sulfide. In addition, they generally separate hydrocarbon mixtures or individual hydrocarbons from natural gas and recover sulfur and carbon dioxide.

In general, the larger the gas processing plant, the more economical it is to operate (fig. 4-3.1). However, large plants must be near fields that provide large volumes of natural gas. In recent years, manufacturers have developed portable skid-mounted plants to provide efficient, relatively inexpensive gas processing for smaller fields.

In addition, refineries have facilities to process the gases resulting from crude oil distillation, cracking, and reforming. Refinery gas processing provides fuel gas (methane, ethane, and ethylene) to power refinery operations. Refineries also separate individual natural gas liquids (NGLs), which may be used to make fuel products or may be sent to an alkylation unit for further processing.

Courtesy of Dominion

Figure 4-3.1. A typical gas processing plant

RECOVERING NGL MIXTURES

One function of a gas processing plant is to recover mixtures of natural gas liquids. NGLs include propane, butane, and natural gasoline. The four processes for doing this are straight refrigeration, cryogenic recovery, oil absorption, and dry-bed adsorption. In *absorption*, the molecules of one substance penetrate the inner structure of another, the way a sponge soaks up a liquid. In *adsorption*, one substance is attracted to and held onto the surface of another, as dust particles stick to flypaper.

The simplest way to produce NGLs is to cool natural gas until it becomes liquid. Smaller gas processing plants, particularly portable, skid-mounted plants that produce from 10 to 20 million cubic feet (2.8 to 5.6 million cubic metres) of product per day, often use straight refrigeration. Several designs are available; all of them use refrigerants such as Freon or propane (fig. 4-3.2).

Straight Refrigeration

Courtesy of Elliot Company

Figure 4-3.2. Gas turbine-driven propane refrigeration compressor in a natural gas plant

Cryogenic Recovery

Cryogenic recovery processes are used in most of the newer gas processing plants. *Cryogenics* is a branch of physics that relates to producing and studying the effects of very low temperatures. Cryogenic processes use high pressures and extremely low temperatures to recover most of the ethane (90% to 95%) as well as all of the propane and the heavier hydrocarbons.

Because cryogenic processes use temperatures lower than -150° F (-101° C), they require special equipment and techniques. The construction materials must not become brittle in low temperatures, and cold boxes enclose and insulate the processing equipment. Control valves and pumps have extended shafts so that they can be located inside the cold box while motors on the outside operate them. The inlet gas requires special treating to remove contaminants before it can enter the cryogenic equipment. Salt water, wax, dirt, scale, iron sulfide, and oil carried over from wellhead separators and compressors will clog the heat exchangers and stop the flow of fluids. Water must be reduced to less than one part per million.

Two types of cryogenic recovery are used: the expander process and cascade refrigeration.

Expander Processing

The most commonly used cryogenic method is the *expander process* (fig. 4-3.3). After being treated, the dry, clean inlet gas is cooled. Under high pressure, the gas enters the separator chamber of an expander-compressor (fig. 4-3.4), where it expands and cools further. As the inlet gas cools, the NGLs condense and are separated from the methane vapor.

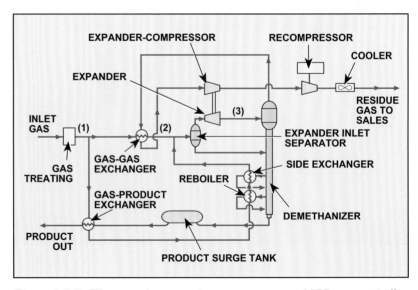

Figure 4-3.3. The expander process is one way to recover NGLs cryogenically.

Figure 4-3.4. An expander compressor used for cryogenic natural gas plants made for the El Wastani Field Development Project in Egypt

Because some methane remains dissolved in the NGLs, the liquid is then sent to a demethanizer to remove the methane. The demethanizer works similarly to a distillation column. It heats the liquid until some of it vaporizes and rises through the column. As the vapor contacts cold liquid descending from above, heavier hydrocarbons condense to liquid again, but the methane vapor continues to rise and leaves from the top. When separate, the methane is compressed to the proper pressure for sale, cooled, and delivered to its destination. The NGLs are piped to a fractionation facility to be separated into individual components.

Four processes for recovering NGL mixtures:
- Straight refrigeration
- Cryogenic recovery
- Oil absorption
- Dry-bed absorption

Cascade Refrigeration

Refrigerants used to separate methane from NGLs in cascade refrigeration are:
- Propane
- Ethane or ethylene

Cascade refrigeration uses two-stage refrigeration to separate methane from the NGLs. In the first stage, the treated inlet gas is cooled in heat exchangers by residue gas (methane that has already been separated) and then by a refrigeration system using propane as the refrigerant. In the second stage, residue gas and a refrigeration system using ethane or ethylene as the refrigerant cool the inlet gas further. The inlet gas, now at a temperature of -120° F (-84° C) or lower, enters a separator where the NGLs condense and separate from the methane vapor. As in expander processing, some of the methane remains dissolved in the liquid, so the liquid goes to a demethanizer for further separation.

Cascade refrigeration can also be used to liquefy methane. This requires three stages of refrigeration, with propane, ethylene, and methane as the refrigerants. Temperatures must be below -200° F (-129° C).

Oil Absorption

Oil absorption is a process used by older gas processing plants and by many gas plants in refineries. It may work alone or with refrigeration. Without refrigeration, oil absorption recovers about 70 percent of the propane and all of the butane and heavier hydrocarbons. With refrigeration, the process can recover about 50 to 75 percent of the ethane and all of the propane and heavier hydrocarbons.

The oil absorption process has three steps: NGL recovery, methane removal, and separation of the absorbent from the NGLs (fig. 4-3.5). Usually, a combination of refrigeration and oil absorption is used in the first step. The absorbent is a hydrocarbon liquid called *lean oil*. When the lean oil absorbs the heavier hydrocarbons, it is called *rich oil*. A refrigerant such as ammonia, Freon^{TM}, or propane cools both the inlet gas and the lean oil to a temperature between 0° F and -40° F (-18° C and -40° C). Since this step liquefies some of the methane along with the desired NGLs and methane is not a desirable component, the next step (the rejection step) removes methane from the NGL-rich oil mixture. Most plants use a device called a *rich-oil demethanizer (ROD)* to separate the methane. In the final step, the NGLs go to a fractionator to separate them from the rich oil. Exposed to steam or hot oil, the NGLs vaporize and flow out the top of the fractionator. The rich oil then becomes lean oil again and flows out the bottom to be recycled to the first step.

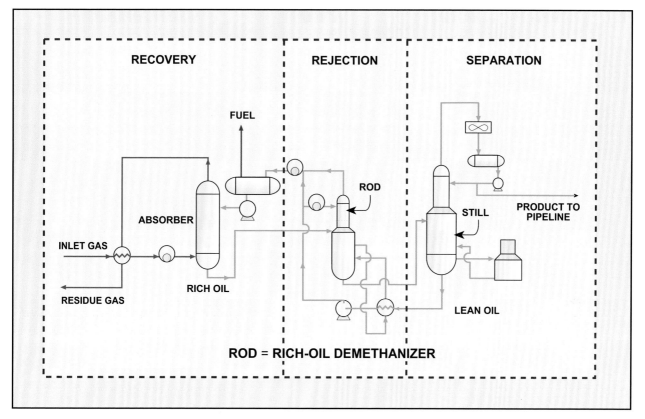

Figure 4-3.5. The oil absorption process consists of NGL recovery, methane rejection, and separation of the absorbent.

Dry-bed adsorption can be used not only to dehydrate natural gas but also to remove some of the heavier hydrocarbons in order to prevent them from condensing in pipelines during transmission. The natural gas passes over a bed of solid desiccant, which adsorbs some of the NGLs and separates them from the gas stream (see Chapter 5 for more detail). This process can recover 10% to 15% of the butane and 50 to 90 percent of the natural gasoline. Operators primarily use it to ensure that the NGL content of natural gas meets the specifications of the gas sales contract.

Dry-Bed Adsorption

FRACTIONATION OF NGLS

Fractionators for NGLs require:
- A large number of trays in the tower
- Substantial heat input by the reboiler
- Heat removal by the reflux and condenser

Fractionation, or fractional distillation, separates a mixture of NGLs into salable individual products. Just as in fractionation of crude oil, NGLs can be separated because they have different boiling points. The process uses fractionation towers with reboilers and reflux equipment (fig. 4-3.6). A reboiler supplies heat to the system, while the reflux equipment returns the condensed stream to the column to cool it further. The hydrocarbon components usually separated in a fractionation plant are ethane, propane, isobutane, normal butane, pentane, and a remaining mixture of heavier hydrocarbons (pentane and higher).

The NGL products are separated in a series of fractionation towers, the lighter product being removed first (fig. 4-3.7). Fractionators are usually named for the main product being separated, known as the overhead or top product because it comes from the top of the fractionator. A deethanizer, for example, produces ethane as the top product, and a depropanizer produces propane.

Because individual NGL products have boiling points that are close together, they are difficult to separate. Fractionators for NGLs require a large number of trays in the tower, a substantial heat input by the reboiler, and heat removal by the reflux and condenser.

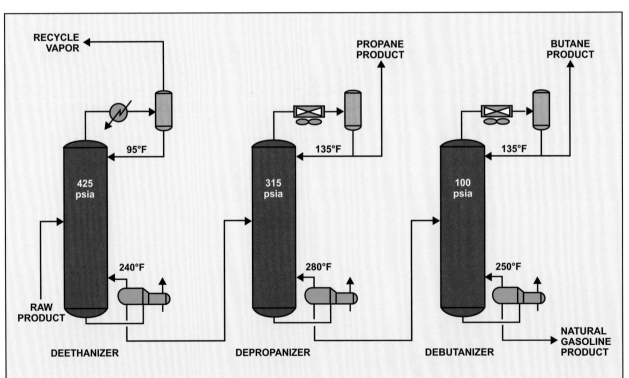

Figure 4-3.6. Example of a fractionation plant used to produce three products

Source: GPSA Engineering Data Book, 12th edition

Figure 4-3.7. Fractionation plant

Courtesy of Linde Group

Natural gas from the field must be processed by removing water, impurities, and excess hydrocarbon liquids, and the delivery pressure must be controlled. Gas processing plants are used to recover mixtures of natural gas liquids. This can be done by one of four methods: straight refrigeration, cryogenic recovery, oil absorption, or dry-bed absorption. The simplest of these methods is straight refrigeration, where natural gas is cooled until it becomes liquid. The second method, cryogenic recovery, uses high pressure and low temperature to recover ethane, propane, and the heavier hydrocarbons from natural gas. Oil absorption uses lean oil to absorb heavier hydrocarbons in NGLs. Dry-bed absorption involves passing natural gas over a bed of solid desiccant to separate NGLs from the gas stream. NGLs can then be further processed through fractionation. Fractionation uses the different boiling points of NGLs to separate the mixture. The ultimate goal is to distribute each part of the NGLs as individual products.

SUMMARY

PART 5
The Changing Market

The Authors

ECONOMICS

Rick Bobigian

President and Chief Executive
Black Pool Energy

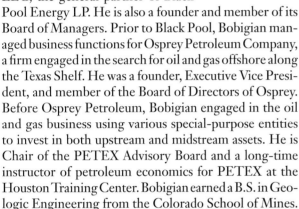

Rick Bobigian is President and Chief Executive of Black Pool Energy GP LLC, the general partner of Black Pool Energy LP. He is also a founder and member of its Board of Managers. Prior to Black Pool, Bobigian managed business functions for Osprey Petroleum Company, a firm engaged in the search for oil and gas offshore along the Texas Shelf. He was a founder, Executive Vice President, and member of the Board of Directors of Osprey. Before Osprey Petroleum, Bobigian engaged in the oil and gas business using various special-purpose entities to invest in both upstream and midstream assets. He is Chair of the PETEX Advisory Board and a long-time instructor of petroleum economics for PETEX at the Houston Training Center. Bobigian earned a B.S. in Geologic Engineering from the Colorado School of Mines.

ENVIRONMENTAL CONCERNS

Joe Ibanez

Chief Executive Officer
SAGE Environmental Consulting

Joe Ibanez has nearly 15 years of experience in the environmental field. He is currently a partner and key principal at Sage Environmental Consulting, LP. His broad experience covers hazardous waste and water issues, focusing on Clean Air Act regulations. Ibanez has worked extensively with all sectors of the oil and gas industry in preparing and negotiating complex permitting projects. He has completed environmental audits and helped multiple facilities implement environmental management systems. This experience has enabled him to directly interface with industry and local, state, and federal agencies (such as the Texas Commission on Environmental Quality and EPA Region 6) to solve technical and regulatory problems.

Along with participating in technical reviews and regulatory negotiations on projects, Ibanez participates in providing leadership and strategic planning for Sage and helped develop and implement a company-wide performance measurement system focused on generating and managing sustainable growth. Ibanez has a Chemical Engineering degree from The University of Texas at Austin.

ENERGY OPTIONS

Michael Webber

Instructor and Associate Center Director
The University of Texas at Austin

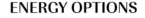

Michael Webber is Associate Director of the Center for International Energy and Environmental Policy, Co-Director of the Clean Energy Incubator, and Assistant Professor of Mechanical Engineering at The University of Texas at Austin. He is on the Board of Advisors of Scientific American and has authored more than 125 articles, columns, and book chapters. He has given more than 150 lectures, speeches, and invited talks in the last few years, including testimony for a U.S. Senate hearing, keynotes for scientific conferences, and lectures at the United Nations. Michael holds four patents and is an originator of the Pecan Street Project, a multi-institutional public-private partnership in Austin to create the smart electricity and water utilities of the future. He earned B.A. and B.S. degrees in Liberal Arts and Aerospace Engineering from UT-Austin and a M.S. and Ph.D. degrees in Mechanical Engineering from Stanford University.

INDUSTRY SAFETY

Jim Johnstone

President and Co-founder
Contek Solutions

Jim Johnstone, a 30-year veteran of the oil and gas business, has worked with various companies to implement management systems and set up exemplary safety programs. He has led process hazard reviews, implemented behavioral-based training programs, conducted safety training, led safety compliance initiatives and investigated incidents. Johnstone began his career with ARCO (now BP) and later became responsible for all its process safety and support of environmental health and safety regulatory compliance for worldwide operations. He has participated in numerous technical committees and authored technical content, including safety publications for the American Petroleum Institute. He holds a B.S. in Mechanical Engineering from Washington State University and a Certified Safety Professional certificate from the Board of Certified Safety Professionals. Johnstone is a member of the Society of Petroleum Engineers, American Society of Safety Engineers, and American Society of Mechanical Engineers.

- Supply chain businesses that create new supplies of oil and gas
- Supply creation companies and how they operate
- Factors in investment decision-making
- Calculating rates of return to evaluate prospects
- Predicting future commodity prices

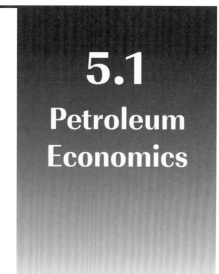

5.1
Petroleum Economics

Conventional supplies of crude oil and natural gas are, by definition, extracted from reservoirs in the sedimentary rocks by means of wells drilled and equipped to flow or lift raw materials to the surface. Upon reaching the surface, these raw materials are partially processed at the well site to remove contaminates such as saltwater and poisonous and inert gases and solids. Next, these partially processed raw materials are transported from the well site via pipeline, barge, ship, or truck to a refiner for crude oil or a natural gas processing facility for natural gas (figs. 5-1.1 and 5-1.2). These raw materials are converted into finished and semi-finished products to be sold and consumed.

Figure 5-1.1. Crude oil refinery

Figure 5-1.2. Gas processing facility

Unconventional supplies of—
- Crude oil, extracted using mining techniques
- Natural gas, extracted using drilling wells

Unconventional supplies of crude oil and natural gas differ from *conventional supplies* in three ways:

- Method of extraction
- Cost of extraction
- Processing methods following extraction

Unconventional supplies of crude oil are extracted using mining techniques. It is generally more expensive and disruptive to the Earth's surface to extract unconventional deposits of crude oil and refine that raw material into finished products. Examples of unconventional crude oils are tar sands, ultra-heavy crudes, oil shale, biofuels, gas-to-liquids, and coal-to-liquids.

Unconventional supplies of natural gas are commonly extracted using wells and differ from conventional supplies, because the natural gas is recovered from reservoir rocks—such as sandstone, shale, and coal—that are characterized by very low permeability. These rocks are sometimes called *tight gas sands*. Low permeability or tightness impairs *radial flow* from the reservoir rock to a wellbore and thus, requires technology to extract supplies in quantities that are economic.

Radial flow is the method by which crude oil, natural gas, and water move from the reservoir rock to the wellbore. For example, think of the wellbore as the hub of a wheel and the spokes of the wheel as the flow paths for the fluids in the reservoir to move from their storage location in the wellbore. The smaller the flow path, the more energy or pressure it takes to move the flow. In tight rocks, the flow paths are tiny and often discontinuous, so it takes technology to connect the wellbore to the boundaries of the reservoir. Technologies used in extraction are hydraulic fracturing, long-reach horizontal drilling, or both.

This chapter focuses on the economic considerations of creating new conventional supplies of crude oil and natural gas.

The business model for supply creation of crude oil and natural gas is comprised of three distinct but dependent business units:

- Upstream
- Midstream
- Downstream

Table 5-1.1 highlights the attributes of each business unit. The metaphor of a stream is used to describe the flow of events in the supply chain from concept to finished product.

The *Upstream Business Unit* starts the entire process. It is defined as exploring, exploiting, and producing crude oil and natural gas from conventional reservoirs. This unit drills wells to find and produce this raw material.

The *Midstream Business Unit* is defined as the processing of natural gas produced from wells. This unit removes contaminants from the raw natural gas produced from the wells and delivers the methane and natural gas liquids to downstream business units via gas and liquid pipelines.

The *Downstream Business Unit* is defined as the process of refining, distributing, and marketing unfinished and finished products. The refiners buy crude oil from producers and make products such as motor fuels and other carbon-hydrogen-based products. The pipelines and local distribution companies buy processed natural gas, which is now methane (CH_4), and distribute this product to customers to burn for heat or electricity. Downstream Business Units also include the petrochemical plants that buy semi-finished products to make into chemical products and plastics.

THE ECONOMICS OF CREATING NEW SUPPLIES

Business Model Overview

Table 5-1.1
Supply Chain Business Units

Business Unit	Upstream	Midstream	Downstream
Business Activity	Exploration and production	Pipelines, transportation, and gas processing	Raw material refining, finished product distribution, such as gasoline, diesel, and chemicals, and marketing
Revenue Generation	Revenue is units produced multiplied by commodity prices for crude oil and natural gas.	Revenue is units transported multiplied by the transportation fee.	Revenue is units refined into finished products multiplied by the wholesale and retail prices.
Revenue Volatilty	Revenue fluctuates with commodity prices. Revenue is highly volatile as crude oil and natural gas prices fluctuate.	Revenue is relatively stable compared to Upstream and Downstream Business Units. Volatility is in throughput volume, which can shrink as supply creation shrinks.	Revenue is less volatile relative to Upstream Business Units; however, raw material costs fluctuate with commodity prices of crude oil and natural gas shrinking or expanding profitability.

The principal differences between each business unit is the work each performs, the way each makes revenue, and the risks associated with these endeavors. Revenue is universally defined as units produced and sold multiplied by the prevailing wholesale or retail product price. In the supply chain, wholesale and retail prices are determined by the buyers and sellers participating in certain physical delivery markets, contracts, and futures markets.

An explanation of the functions of each business unit follows.

Upstream Business Units

> Revenue is critical to each business unit. Each unit must invest a portion of annual cash flow to create new supplies or maintain the existing physical infrastructure that supports supplies.

Upstream Business Units produce and sell crude oil and natural gas at market price or at a predetermined contractual price. Its revenue is calculated by multiplying barrels of crude oil or cubic feet of natural gas produced from a well or wells times the price paid for each product. The buyer is, most often, a Downstream Business Unit in the case of crude oil and a Midstream Business Unit in the case of natural gas. Generally, crude oil is sold to and purchased by a refiner on a term contract where the price paid is tied to a mutually agreeable *crude oil index*, such as *West Texas Intermediate* or *Brent*. There are many other indexes available around the world. The choice of index is a function of geography. Natural gas is also sold on a term contract either to a pipeline owner or a natural gas processor. The contract term varies with pipeline, geography, and capital costs to connect a well, platform, or facility. The price paid by the purchaser is tied to an index such as *Henry Hub*, or in the absence of an index, to a contract price. Regardless of the index or the product, the price the producer receives is net of the transportation costs to move the crude oil or natural gas from the well to the refinery or distribution point, respectively.

Midstream Business Units

Midstream Business Units process, treat, transport, and handle natural gas in exchange for a fee and or a percent of the liquids value removed from the natural gas processed. The arrangement is much like a toll. The Midstream Business Unit uses pressure- and temperature-control equipment to remove the natural gas liquids and make methane. In that manufacturing process, liquids—also known as natural gas liquids (NGL), such as ethane (C_2H_6), propane (C_3H_8), butane, natural gasoline, and other substances such as carbon dioxide (CO_2) and sulfur (S_2)—are extracted from the natural gas. Its revenue is calculated by multiplying the cubic feet of natural gas processed times a contractual fee, plus a percentage of the market value of the NGL and other by-products.

Downstream Business Units buy crude oil, NGLs, and natural gas from Upstream and Midstream Business Units. They use them as raw material or feedstock and make finished and semi-finished products. These products are then distributed and consumed by individuals or residential, commercial, industrial, and electrical-generation processes. Downstream Business Unit revenue is calculated by multiplying the number of gallons, barrels, and cubic feet times the wholesale price. The wholesale price is volatile as is the retail price.

Downstream Business Units

Revenue is the life blood of each business unit. Management focuses on revenue creation and profitability and must forecast future income statements, balance sheets, and statements of cash flow. All forecasts start with projecting revenue for one to five years or longer. The strength of any revenue forecast is simply the correctness of units produced and sold and the price received for each unit.

Revenue

To stay in business, all business units must invest a portion of annual cash flow as new capital to either create new supplies of crude oil and natural gas or maintain the existing physical infrastructure of transportation, processing, and refining. The amount of that annual investment is, of course, dependent on many factors. Most importantly, the reinvestment decision is based upon the amount of cash flow from operations and available cash from financing activities. In addition, *macroeconomic* and market forces of demand, supply, and price greatly influence the decision to invest capital in creating new supplies and the amount of capital invested.

Integrated and Independent Energy Companies

Supply creation companies might be further classified for revenue and financial purposes as either integrated, independent, or hybrid companies.

An *integrated company* is one that operates in all three business units and consolidates the financial results of each business unit into one balance sheet, income statement, and cash flow statement. Examples of integrated energy companies include all of the *super majors* and many of the *National Oil Companies*.

An *independent company* operates exclusively in one of the three business units. Its financial statements reflect the financial results of that business unit. Independent energy companies abound in North America.

As in every classification, there are exceptions or *hybrids*, but the exceptions are a small percentage of companies operating in the supply-creation business. The hybrids are companies where one business unit dominates revenue generation while there are also pieces of a second business unit contributing revenue. To illustrate this concept, some Upstream Business Units are independents and own natural gas pipelines or process natural gas at various processing plants, while others own and operate petrochemical plants and, thus, become a hybrid company.

Knowing that a company is structured as either an integrated, independent, or hybrid company is important in understanding how that company:

- Generates revenue
- Makes a profit
- Invests to create new supplies
- Makes investment decisions
- Is influenced by economics

For example, at any given time, the revenue of an Upstream Business Unit is greatly dependent on the market price of crude oil and natural gas. As prices fluctuate, revenue fluctuates. Specifically, as market prices decline, revenue declines unless production increases. Conversely, as prices increase, revenue increases as long as production does not decline.

A side effect of higher crude oil and natural gas prices is to increase revenue in the Upstream Business Unit and increase costs to the Downstream Business Unit. Higher upstream prices increase the operating costs of the Downstream Business Unit because the cost of the raw materials has increased. If the Downstream Business Unit is unable to pass on the additional costs to the consumer in the form of higher finished product prices, its profit will shrink.

The Upstream Business Unit is where crude oil and natural gas are produced. It is also the place where new wells are drilled and new supplies of crude oil and natural gas are created. This business unit is comprised of all individuals, private companies, publicly traded corporations, National Oil Companies, and governments that explore for and produce crude oil and natural gas as their core business.

Upstream companies create revenue by producing and selling crude oil, natural gas, and related byproducts. These business units produce a product that is finite and depleting. As a result of this phenomenon, the upstream business model requires companies to make annual capital investments to create new supplies or otherwise go out of business. The primary goal of a capital program for the Upstream Business Unit is to find enough new crude oil and natural gas deposits to replace its annual production and to add more reserves to the total remaining reserves owned by the company.

Upstream Business Units create new conventional supplies by simply drilling new wells to find, produce, and sell crude oil, natural gas, and associated products. It is a simple business notion, but its execution is difficult. The key action phrase in the business plan is "drill new wells to find." The questions are: How does the task of drilling wells come about? How is it financed? And what motivates the financing?

Before a new well is drilled, most Upstream Business Units employ a formal, rigorous evaluation process designed to minimize mistakes and maximize profitability. In previous sections of this book, readers learned about the processes and functions of geology, geophysics, leasing, and drilling through production, transportation, and refining. This section integrates those disciplines into a financial and economic framework to show readers how and why new supplies are created. The evaluation process involves several technical, economic, and financial tasks, specifically involving the following steps:

- **Step 1: Prospect Generation.** A *prospect* is an idea. It is a geologic idea of where technical specialists think crude oil and natural gas might be trapped in a reservoir within the Earth's subsurface. The prospect might be created by anyone, just as it was done in the formative years of exploration. However, in the modern era of exploration, the prospect idea is usually created by an interdisciplinary technical team comprised of a geologist, geophysicist, and engineers who work on a geographical area of interest. Their job is to identify the opportunity using maps and cross-sections to calculate the amount of crude and oil and natural gas contained in the reservoir trap, determine the production rate, and estimate the investment.

Creating New Supplies

Upstream Business Units create new supplies by simply drilling new wells to find new conventional supplies—a simple notion but not a simple task.

> The evaluation process includes:
> Step 1: generating the prospect
> Step 2: securing the leases and
> permits
> Step 3: appraising the prospect
> Step 4: deciding whether to
> invest

- **Step 2: Lands, Leasing, and Permits to Drill.** Permission is always required before drilling wells in certain lands both on-shore and offshore. Such permission is commonly a contractual arrangement between the mineral owner and the Upstream Business Unit desiring to drill the well. The permission process is the same throughout the world. The Upstream Business Unit must identify the owner of the minerals, whether it is an individual, company, or country, and negotiate a *Lease Agreement, Exploration Agreement,* or *Production Sharing Agreement.* Fundamental to the majority of such contracts is a key concept: The Upstream Business Unit invests all the capital and takes all the financial and operational risks to explore and develop a prospect over a finite time period in exchange for an agreed percentage of all crude oil and natural gas produced and sold from the endeavor. In North America, that percentage is typically in the range of 75% to 80% of the production for the life of the well. Commonly, the lease will have three to five years to begin the process of drilling the initial well on the property. Elsewhere, the sharing ratio is negotiated and might range from as little as a fee for services and a right to refine and process the production to a return of capital and an even sharing of production.

- **Step 3: Appraisal of the Prospect.** Before a well is drilled, it is appraised to determine the capital to be invested and the future net revenue. The capital to be invested is the sum of the estimated cost to drill an appraisal well and, if successful, the estimated cost to equip the well for production. Important elements of the prospect appraisal are, among other factors:
  - Likelihood of success
  - Estimated volume of crude oil and natural gas (reserves)
  - Estimated ultimate recovery, which is expected units of production
  - Estimated costs to drill the appraisal well and, if successful, to equip the well for production
  - Estimated commodity prices for crude oil and natural gas
  - Future gross and net revenue

- **Step 4: Management's Decision to Invest.** Making a decision to invest is the last step in the prospect approval process and the drilling of a new well. This is the step where management has:
  - Evaluated the technical merit of the prospect
  - Assigned risk factors to the processes of drilling, completion, reserves, production, and market price for the commodity to be produced
  - Evaluated the economic merit of the prospect
  - Calculated the return on capital to be invested
  - Decided to invest or not invest in the prospect idea

Each year, around the globe, tens of thousands of new wells are drilled and billions of dollars are invested by integrated, independent, and hybrid companies in search of new supplies of crude oil and natural gas. The principal objective of these investments is to create new supplies profitably. The other assumption is that the demand for crude oil and natural gas will consume new supplies.

How are the decisions made about whether to invest in drilling new wells to create new supplies? How are the wells selected? And, what information is required to properly analyze those prospects and decisions?

In a capitalistic society and for-profit industries, most decisions to invest are made by management comparing project costs to future revenue and calculating the project rate of return. This pre-investment analysis is done to grade projects and help management make the best decisions on how to allocate money. Investment analysis is the process of evaluating the technical merits of any revenue-producing projects or prospects using science, engineering, and financial modeling. These techniques and methodologies are used to assess and predict future performance, future revenue, and profit potential.

Once a project is ready for evaluation, it is first evaluated technically and then modeled financially. Table 5-1.2 demonstrates the format of a simplified financial model. Figure 5-1.3 calculates the cash flows and then compares the sum of the cash flows to the total cost.

Investment Decision-Making

Table 5-1.2
Simplified Financial Model of Cash Flow

	Year 0	Year 1	Year 2	Year 3	Year 4
Revenue – Costs		2,000,000 -200,000	2,000,000 -200,000	2,000,000 -200,000	2,000,000 -200,000
Gross Income – DD&A – Income Tax		1,800,000 -360,000 -430,000	1,800,000 -360,000 -430,000	1,800,000 -360,000 -430,000	1,800,000 -360,000 -430,000
Net Income		1,010,000	1,010,000	1,010,000	1,010,000
Cash Flow		1,470,000	1,470,000	1,470,000	1,470,000
Investment	-5,000,000				

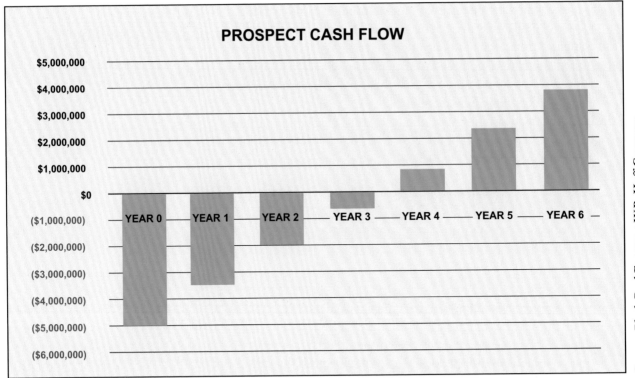

Figure 5-1.3. Graphical presentation of project cash flow

Completing Table 5-1.2 produces the:

- **Investments in the project at time zero (T0).** This is the total expenditure of creating the revenue-producing asset, such as the total drilling and completion costs, for a new well. Usually, these expenditures are made within twelve to eighteen months, but there are projects, such as deepwater drilling ventures where the investment period exceeds this time period.
- **Annual cash flow.** This is the amount of money left when expenses are subtracted from revenue.
- **Cumulative cash flow for the life of the project.** This is the sum of the annual cash flow and the value compared to the total amount of money invested.

In the table, the following definitions apply:

- *Revenue* is units produced and sold, multiplied by price.
- *Costs* are expenditures associated with operating the asset created by the investment.
- *Gross Income* is income generated from operations, such as a producing well
- *DD&A* is depletion, depreciation, and amortization, which is a non-cash item.
- *Net Income* is Gross Income less DD&A and Income Tax.

- *Cash Flow* is Net Income plus DD&A.
- *Investment* is the capital spent to develop the project.

In this example, notice that $5,000,000 was invested in the first year and there was no revenue. Figure 5-1.3 shows the amount as a negative cash flow in Year 1. As cash flow is created from operations of the asset in Year 1 and beyond, the cash flow repays the investment. If there is no revenue as in the case of a failed well, then the investment is lost.

The next step is calculating project rate of return. This is calculated by comparing the investment (I) with the sum of the annual cash flows. A simplified equation is shown here and in this example, where I = $5,000,000 and the Sum of the Cash Flows = $5,880,000. Note that this equation is a simplified illustration of the method to calculate *rate of return (ROR)*, and this calculation does not consider the *time value of money*. Generally, money is less valuable in the future. Thus, for projects greater than one year in duration, the money received in Year 1 and beyond is worth less than it is today, so it must be reduced in *relative value*. Considering the time value of money is beyond the scope of this discussion.

> ROR gives management a measurement tool to compare projects to each other to help decide whether to spend capital on the investment.

Calculating ROR

> Rate of Return (ROR) = (Sum of Cash Flow-I)/I

where

Sum of Cash Flow = $1,470,000 + $1,470,000 + $1,470,000
                          + $1,470,000 = $5,880,000

I = $5,000,000

To solve this equation for ROR

$$\text{ROR} = \frac{5,880,000 - 5,000,000}{5,000,000} = 17.6\%$$

ROR is now the measuring tool that allows management to compare one project to another. ROR and internal rate of return (IRR) are similar calculations that seek the interest rate generated by the investment when compared to the present value of the future cash flows. Most Upstream Business Units establish minimum required ROR or hurdle rates to deem the investment acceptable.

The decision to invest in new projects is based on the ability to maximize value through the spending of capital, and it assumes the capital is available within the company or at attractive rates if sought outside the company.

For ROR, calculate:
- (I) Investment, which, in this case, is the amount of money required to drill a well and, if successful, to complete and equip the well for production
- (SCF) Sum of Cash Flow, which, in this case, is the sum of cash flows generated from the new well

Therefore, before making a decision to drill a new well, the technical and financial teams must complete all of the categories of Table 5-1.3 to calculate annual cash flow and ROR.

For the Upstream Business Units, the categories are more fully defined under Table 5-1.3. The table is blank now, but it will be completed in later discussions within this chapter of the book.

Table 5-1.3
Blank Spreadsheet for Upstream Business Unit Prospects
Question: How is this data obtained?

	Year 0	Year 1	Year 2	Year 3	Year 4	Year 5	Year 6	Year 7	Year 8	Sum
Revenue										
Royalty										
OPEX										
G & A										
Gross Income										
DD&A										
Tax										
Net Income										
CashFlow										
Investment										

The following defines and describes the revenue and expense categories for Upstream Business Units:

- **Revenue** is defined as units of crude oil and natural gas produced and sold, multiplied by a commodity price. The revenue units of production are barrels of crude oil and thousand cubic feet of natural gas. The price of each produced unit is more fully explained later in this chapter.

- **Royalty Expense** is also known as *cost of goods sold (COGS)*. This is the amount of each unit produced that is retained by the mineral owner pursuant to a lease agreement. It is generally 20% to 25% and is treated as an expense.

- **Operating Expense** (*OPEX*) is defined as the annual cost to operate a well or wells. These expenses are fixed and variable. They are directly associated with the cost of producing crude oil and natural gas from the well or wells created by the investment. This category includes expenditures such as *severance taxes*, *ad valorem taxes*, personnel, transportation, utilities, materials, parts, third-party services, and regulatory costs.

- **General and Administrative Expense** (*G&A*) are the re-occurring costs associated with operating the company and are classified as indirect expenses. This category of expense usually includes all expenditures that are not spent directly on a well or wells. They include personnel, office rent, communication, travel, legal, and other administrative expenditures. G&A is an allocation of corporate overhead to each revenue-producing well or property.

- **Gross Income** is defined as Revenue less Royalty less OPEX less G&A.

- **Depletion, Depreciation, and Amortization Expense (DD&A)** is the allocation of costs or reduction in value over the useful life of an asset. It is calculated using *generally accepted accounting practices (GAAP)*. DD&A is a non-cash capital cost deduction taken before calculating income tax. As the acronym implies, the company has purchased equipment, goods, and services used in drilling and equipping wells to create new supplies of crude oil and natural gas. This includes seismic licenses, geologic information, computers, leases, tangible equipment, and intangible goods and services—all of which deplete, depreciate, and amortize over time. This allowance lowers taxable income and thus lowers income taxes, allowing the business unit to retain more of its revenue. The intent of this provision is to encourage companies to reinvest in replacing assets that are depleted through production, depreciated through wear and tear, amortized through use, or are less valuable with time. Specific to Upstream Business Units, this feature allows companies to internally finance the cost of drilling new wells, replace production, and create new supplies of crude oil and natural gas. More complete definitions are as follows:

  - **Depletion** is the process of recording decreases in the value of minerals such as, crude oil and natural gas, coal, water, precious metals, and all other minerals that deplete when harvested. This is calculated as a decimal fraction where the numerator is the units produced and sold in a year and the denominator is the total units in the reservoir when the well was placed in service.

> In Upstream Business Units, DD&A allows companies to internally finance the cost of drilling new wells, replace production, and create new supplies of crude oil and natural gas.

- **Depreciation** is the process of recording decreases in the value of physical property such as buildings, industrial plants, machinery, vehicles, and land. Depreciation is calculated using methods such as straight line, declining balance, or double-declining balance. The method selected relates to the expected years of service or life of certain machines, equipment, or property.

- **Amortization** is the process of recording decreases in the value of nonphysical property such as term-limited-rights of leases, lands, and copyrights. Amortization is calculated using methods that reduce the value with time. For example, a five-year license is amortized (reduced in value) at the rate of 20% per annum.

• **Tax Expense** is tax on income and is calculated according to the business structure and applicable tax rate of the company.

• **Net Income** is defined as Gross Income less DD&A less Tax

• **Cash Flow** is defined as Net Income plus DD&A and is the after-tax annual free cash available for use by the company. Upstream Business Units typically allocate or budget a percentage of Cash Flow to be invested in new wells and associated equipment necessary to sustain or grow the business unit's assets and revenue. Depending on the capital structure of a business unit—a partnership, limited liability company, or regular corporation—Cash Flow will also be allocated to pay shareholders, retire debt, and reinvest in creating new supplies of crude oil and natural gas.

• **Investment Capital** (I) is defined as the cash required to drill the initial test well and to equip it for production. This cash is either surplus cash or borrowed cash to be invested in the activities of the business unit.

Now that the key components of economic analysis, investment decision-making, and ROR for any prospect have been discussed, these questions arise: How is it all applied to a specific prospect? Where do we get the data to complete Table 5-1.3?

The input data is obtained from the work papers created by the technical and finance teams working on the prospect evaluation. It is important to note that prospect generation and evaluation is a collaborative, interdisciplinary effort incorporating geology, geophysics, engineering, and finance. These teams perform many parallel tasks. The entire process is designed to present the prospect to management and solicit a decision to invest money in drilling the new well.

Parallel tasks include:

- **Calculating reserves**: What do the experts expect to find; that is, what is the size of the petroleum reserves and expected recovery?

- **Leasing**: Is the lease available and what will it cost?

- **Estimating the cost to drill**: What will it cost to drill this well to the depth of the hydrocarbon reservoir to test the geologic idea or prospect?

- **Estimating the cost to complete and equip**: If successful, what will it cost to complete and equip the well?

The foundation of prospect evaluation is estimation and measurement. For example, if one wants to know the amount of crude oil and natural gas thought to be trapped in a reservoir, one would estimate it by measuring the surface area, the thickness, and the amount of pore space of the reservoir. To find out the amount of crude oil and natural gas to be produced annually, one would estimate it by measuring the reservoir pressure, making assumptions about the quality of the reservoir rock properties, and create a production schedule. There are many other estimations and measurements required to evaluate the technical and economic merit of a prospect before it is approved and drilled. These will be discussed later when a specific prospect is evaluated. At this point, readers are now aware that:

- A well will not be drilled without this evaluation process and a calculated ROR.

- The entire evaluation process is founded on estimation and measurement.

Prospect Generation and Evaluation

Estimation and measurement are the foundation of the evaluation process. Drilling will not take place until a prospect is evaluated and rate of return is calculated.

The prospect-generation team prepares the support documentation to explain the prospect to management. The team wants to drill a well. They know that to get the money to drill the initial test well, they must sell the idea to management and convince them to allocate the money to drill. The team also knows that, within a company, there are other technical teams creating prospects that need money to drill an appraisal well; meaning, there is competition for a fixed or budgeted amount of money. There are two parts to the sales process. First, the team members must convince management of the prospect's technical merit, and second, of its economic merit. The capital will likely be awarded to the prospect with the highest *risked rate of return*. The concept of risk goes hand in hand with the processes of estimation and measurement. Risk assessment deals with what can go wrong. In estimating reserves, units of production, commodity prices, and operational hazards many things can and do go wrong. Mistakes generally result in smaller reservoir deposits, lower units of production, and higher costs. The same is true for estimating future commodity prices. They are often wrong, resulting in prospects that are not economical to drill.

The technical merit explanation addresses the logic, reasoning, evidence, and science supporting the geologic idea and the foundation of the subsurface trap, which is the targeted reservoir. The team will also qualify and quantify risk-related issues of reservoir size and thickness, reservoir rock properties of porosity and permeability, sealing trap boundaries, expected drilling and completion problems, expected ranges of production rates, and surface environment.

The economic merit explanation addresses the investment capital needed to drill, equip, and produce the initial test well and the assumptions used in the calculation of:

- Future gross revenue
- Operating cost
- Net income
- Cash flow
- Rate of return

The cash flow calculation assumes the initial test well finds the targeted reservoir and is, as theorized, full of crude oil and natural gas. It also assumes the initial test well is successfully completed and equipped for production within the estimated cost to drill, complete, and equip the initial test well for production. Future gross revenue is calculated by estimating barrels of crude oil and cubic feet of natural gas to be produced daily, monthly, and annually and total production throughout the life of the reservoir.

There are many variables and possible outcomes to address in analyzing the risk of finding and producing crude oil and natural gas. Risk assessment is an important part of technical evaluation before drilling. Therefore, every step of the way, the technical team must think about risk and qualify and quantify that risk. They know that management will ask about it, and the teams must have answers.

The most significant risk assessment is to quantify the likelihood that crude oil and natural gas are in the targeted reservoir. The reservoir is often located thousands of feet below the Earth's surface and, because it cannot be seen, touched, or felt, the team conceptualizes the reservoir's shape and size.

When an appraisal well is drilled to test the concept, there are many possible outcomes, and management will want to know the odds of encountering each one. To name a few, some possible outcomes are:

- The **best case**, where the well is successful in finding crude oil and natural gas and is equipped for production.

- The **worst case**, where the well is unsuccessful and is abandoned after drilling.

- The **most difficult case**, where the well is marginally successful by finding crude oil and natural gas but not in the quantity theorized by the technical team in its presentation to management. For example, the original prospect idea might estimate the reservoir thickness as 100 feet (30.48 metres) thick, but when drilled and evaluated, it might be only 50 feet (15.24 metres) thick. This change in thickness affects the total volume of crude oil and natural gas reserves and could make the prospect uneconomic to complete and produce. This outcome is known as a technical success but an economic failure. Historically, much capital has been spent completing and equipping marginal wells in hopes that prices will rise to make them economic.

The best method to illustrate this process is to actually evaluate a prospect from prospect generation to the calculation of one well's ROR.

The prospect evaluation procedure is universal and used by most Upstream Business Units around the world. This discussion focuses on one prospect. It is important to understand that the methodology is the same whether one prospect or thousands are evaluated. The methodology focuses on evaluation of both technical and economic merit. The prospects that are drilled are those that exhibit the greatest ROR for the money invested.

In appraising a well, possible outcomes are considered:
- The best case—oil and gas are found and can be produced
- The worst case—no oil and gas can be produced
- The most difficult case—oil and gas are there but are hard to reach economically

---

The variables in evaluating a prospect are the prospect itself and the ROR, taking into account:

- Prospects vary in many ways—geographical location, reservoir target depth, reservoir properties, risk, and economic attributes.

- Depth of investigation, the rigorous estimation of all categories of risk, and the commodity prices used in calculating revenue.

An understanding of these steps and procedures allows one to fully understand industry-standard prospect evaluation.

As stated earlier, the primary goal of any technical and financial prospect evaluation is calculating ROR. To do this, one must know the investment and estimate the sum of the annual cash flow generated by the well or wells to be drilled. The investment is the sum of costs required to drill, test, complete, and equip the wells for production. This estimate is made in present time with the expectation of accuracy.

The sum of the annual cash flow is solved by calculating revenue, subtracting operating costs, DD&A, and taxes and adding back the DD&A. This is best accomplished by completing Table 5-1.3. Completing Table 5-1.3 helps guide readers through the steps of evaluation and identifies the data necessary to complete the spreadsheet. The next steps necessary to complete this table are to:

- **Calculate reserves-in-place**, which results in the volume of crude oil and natural gas stored in the targeted reservoir.

- **Calculate the estimated ultimate recovery**, which results in the volume of crude oil and natural gas to be recovered by the well to be drilled. Recovered reserve volumes are less than the volume of reserves-in-place.

- **Create a production schedule**, which documents the units of crude oil and natural gas to be produced.

- **Create a product price schedule** for crude oil and natural gas that ranges from the beginning to the end of the reserve life.

The data is obtained from measuring and estimating prospect data.

Example: Fundamentals of Petroleum #1 Well

The technical team has generated a prospect idea and they want to drill it. In this example, the prospect is named Fundamentals of Petroleum #1 (FOP #1). The proposed well site is located 5 miles (8 kilometres) off the Texas coast near the city of Corpus Christi in the United States (fig. 5-1.4). The well will be drilled in 54 feet (16.46 metres) of water using a jackup-style drilling rig (fig. 5-1.5).

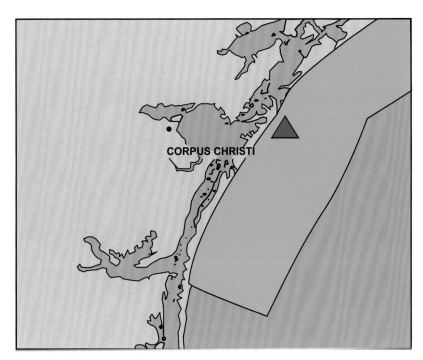

Figure 5-1.4. Prospect area map

Figure 5-1.5. Typical jackup rig used to drill the proposed well off the Texas coast

If crude oil and natural gas are found in economic quantities, the well will be equipped with a single-well production platform similar to the one shown in figures 5-1.6, 5-1.7, and 5-1.8.

The team has proposed drilling a well to reach a sandstone reservoir 10,000 feet (3,048 metres) below sea level that is believed to contain natural gas and condensate. Members of the team estimate it will take 30 days to drill and evaluate the well. If successful, they estimate a platform and pipeline can be installed for this single well in 180 days (fig. 5-1.9). The estimated costs are $12,025,000. The investment capital is compiled as follows:

- Prospect generation cost = $300,000
- Leasing cost = $225,000
- Drilling cost to appraise the reservoir = $4,000,000
- Completion costs = $2,250,000
- Facilities, platform, and pipeline costs = $5,250,000

Figure 5-1.6. Well awaiting production deck and facilities

Figure 5-1.7. Installing production deck and facilities

Figure 5-1.8. Production deck and facilities installed

Figure 5-1.9. Pipeline installation

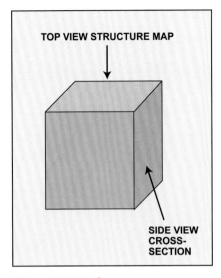

Figure 5-1.10. Structure map to demonstrate the prospect idea

The team explained that the capital at risk is the prospect generation, leasing, and drilling costs, which total $4,525,000. If the well fails to find the reservoir as expected, then there will be no revenue and this money will be lost. In the event of a success, the additional costs to continue are approximately $7,500,000 and comprise completion, facilities, platform, and pipeline costs.

To show the geologic idea, the team uses two principal displays: a structure map and a cross-section display. A structure map is a top view of the reservoir map. A cross-section is a side view. These views are shown by the cube in figure 5-1.10.

Figure 5-1.11 shows a structure map of the subsurface from the top view of the reservoir. This map is created using geology, geophysics, and data from other wells in the vicinity that were drilled and produced before. This map uses color to identify areas of trapped natural gas. Note that on this map, there are three areas of similar color:

- **Area A** is a reservoir with three older offset wells (1, 2, and 3) that were drilled, completed, and produced by another company.
- **Area C** has two older offset wells (4 and 5) that were also drilled and produced by another company.
- **Area B** is undrilled and is the proposed location for FOP #1, the new well to be drilled. The star indicates the proposed location.

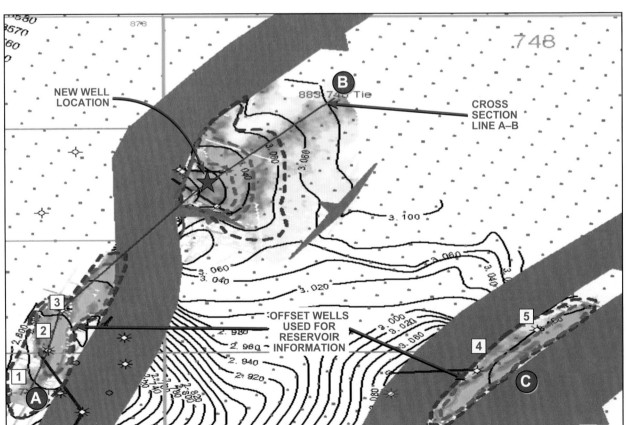

Figure 5-1.11. Subsurface structure map

Fig. 5-1.12 is a cross-section that shows a side view of the subsurface strata drawn using 3D seismic. Note the red line labeled A on the lower left and B on the upper right. This line is the line of cross-section and it slices the reservoir along the line, dividing Areas A and B and exposing the layered strata.

There are several points of interest on cross-section A-B, such as:

- The seismic *wiggle traces* show bedding patterns that appear like layers of strata.

- The position of FOP #1 is superimposed on the seismic cross-section.

- The target reservoir is shown.

- The positions of the three older offset wells are identified by 1, 2, and 3.

The technical team explains that this prospect was developed using modern and recently compiled 3D seismic data. The interpretation of the 3D seismic data showed that Areas A, B, and C exhibit a color pattern that indicates the presence of natural gas in the reservoir trap. Areas A and C were drilled and produced prior to gathering the 3D seismic, whereas Area B is undrilled and therefore prospective.

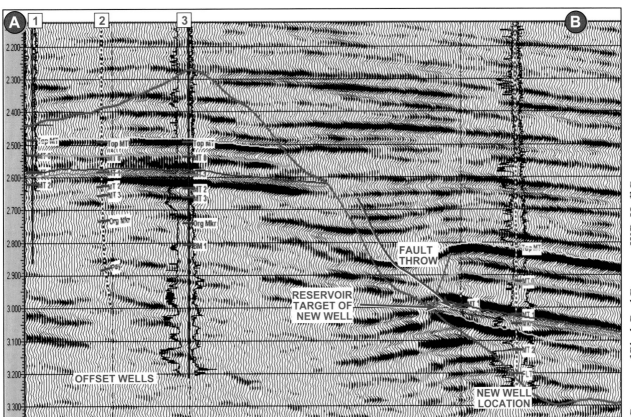

Figure 5-1.12. Seismic cross-section

The team's confidence in their geologic and geophysical interpretations in figures 5-1.11 and 5-1.12 arises from five older offset wells that were drilled, completed, and produced with similar seismic indicators of natural gas hydrocarbons. These older offset wells labeled Wells 1-5 in figure 5-1.11 provide valuable information about the reservoir rock properties such as, porosity and permeability, reservoir pressures, expected units of production, and total reserves. Further, these five wells produced natural gas and condensate in economic quantities, and that fact is reassuring to the technical team because:

- The color pattern is indeed an indicator of natural gas.
- The fault (in brown) is a sealing fault.
- The risk of failure is lessened.

Calculating Reserves and Estimated Ultimate Recovery

Estimating the *reserves-in-place* for FOP #1 requires calculation. Reserves-in-place are defined as the amount of natural gas and condensate stored in the reservoir rocks. Calculating reserves is a technically complicated process involving subsurface pressure, drive mechanisms, temperature, phase relationships, reservoir rock properties, and other radial flow characteristics. For the sake of FOP #1 in this text, a rudimentary volumetric formula is used to illustrate the process.

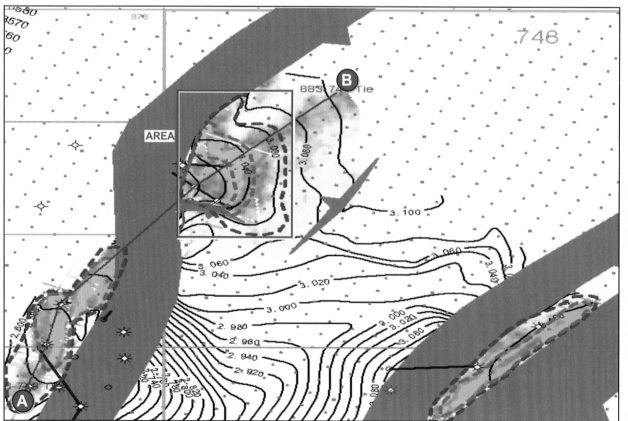

Figure 5-1.13. Calculating reservoir area

Courtesy of Black Pool Energy, a W.R. Huff Company

The equation is:

$$Reserves\text{-}in\text{-}Place = Area \times Thickness \times Porosity$$

The data for the calculations is obtained as follows:

- **Step 1:** Calculate rock volume, which is the reservoir area multiplied by reservoir thickness:

$$Rock\ Volume = Length \times Width \times Thickness$$

Note: This information is located on figs. 5-1.13 and 5-1.14.

- Figure 5-1.13 contains a rectangular box around the target reservoir. The purpose of this box is to show surface area of the reservoir trap, which is calculated by multiplying length by width. Typically, this shape is irregular and the area will be calculated using a *planimeter* (an instrument that measures the area by tracing the boundaries of the shape).

- Figure 5-1.14 shows a rectangular box around the target reservoir. The purpose of this box is to demonstrate reservoir thickness. Typically, thickness is estimated using any well logs from nearby wells, such as Wells 1-5, and seismic.

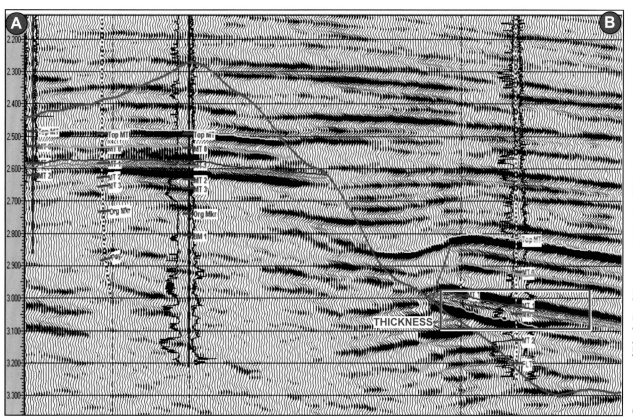

Figure 5-1.14. Calculating thickness

Calculating reserves and recovery:
Step 1: calculate rock volume.
Step 2: calculate or estimate pore space.
Step 3: calculate estimated ultimate recovery.

- **Step 2:** Natural gas and condensate are stored in the pore spaces within the reservoir rock. To calculate or estimate pore space, actual data obtained from offset wells is most often used. In the example of FOP #1, the porosity data is obtained from reading the well logs of the older offset Wells 1–5. In the event there were no offset wells from which to gather reservoir rock data, pore space is estimated using geologic data. In this example, the reservoir rock is sandstone and its porosity ranges from 20% to 30%; therefore, an average porosity of 25% will be used. The equation now looks like this:

Reservoir Volume = Length × Width × Thickness × Pore Space

- **Step 3:** Next is a calculation of the *estimated ultimate recovery*, which is the amount of natural gas likely to be produced during FOP #1's useful and economic life. Note that a well will not produce all of the natural gas stored in the pore spaces of the reservoir, so the above equation must be modified to address that fact. A *recovery factor (RF)* is required to account for the many inconsistencies of reservoir rocks, water saturation, and inefficiencies of reservoir rocks in radial flow. The RF addresses variances in pressure, temperature, and permeability, and this factor is generally limited to the geographic area of the wells. This example calculates the RF and then compares it to the ranges experienced by the older offset Wells 1–5. The actual calculation is beyond the scope of this text, but for FOP #1, one would calculate a RF of 80%. The equation would look like this:

Estimated Ultimate = Length × Width × Thickness ×
Recovery   Porosity × RF

Now that the reserve volume has been calculated and the ultimate recovery of natural gas has been estimated, the next step is to create a daily, monthly, and annual production schedule. Figure 5-1.15 is an illustration of a production schedule for units of natural gas to be produced and sold. This graph is a production schedule for a *depleting pressure reservoir*, which is defined as a reservoir that loses energy with every unit of natural gas produced. It shows daily units of production that remain constant throughout the year but decline from year to year. The data used to create the production schedule in this example was obtained from five offset wells.

At this point, two key tasks are completed in the process of calculating future revenue from FOP #1. These completed tasks are:

- Calculated estimated ultimate recovery
- Scheduled units of natural gas production

The next step is to select the present and future commodity price for the natural gas.

Creating a Production Schedule for FOP #1

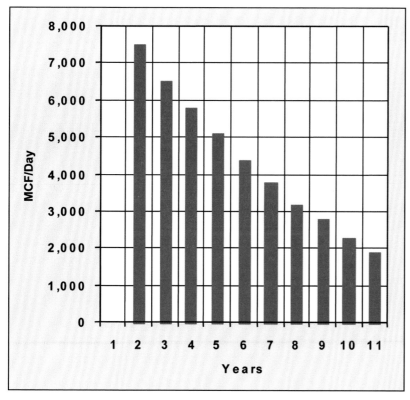

Figure 5-1.15. Production forecast

Selecting Commodity Prices

The prognosis is that FOP #1, if successful, will produce mostly natural gas with small amounts of condensate—a light specific-gravity crude oil—for about eleven years. To calculate revenue, the economic team must prepare a natural gas price forecast for Year 1 through Year 11. Selecting a price today is easy because the market information is current and reliable. Selecting a price eleven years from today is another issue, because no one can select a price with any degree of reliability. In fact, selecting a price for Year 2, even though it is relatively near in time, is not much easier than selecting a price for Year 11, but the price in Year 2 can seriously affect the revenue and the rate of return calculation. This phenomenon is the result of the front-end loading of production, as noted in figure 5-1.15.

There are many resources to help identify a natural gas price for FOP #1, among them:

- Company policies
- Banks
- Financial institutions
- Consultants
- Commodity indexes
- Commodity futures markets

There are also many experts to offer well-founded and economically sound advice on future prices for commodities in general, and natural gas, specifically. The majority of those forecasts will be wrong because no one knows the future, and therefore, no one can know the upcoming changes that will influence commodity prices up or down.

To remove the uncertainty of future prices, most Upstream Business Units establish a set of crude oil and natural gas prices for the start of the project and into the future. This set of prices is a baseline and is called a *price deck*. Price decks change over time with changes in the cash and *futures markets*, so price decks can be updated frequently. Regardless of the frequency of change, the company stipulates that all prospects will use the published price decks in effect at the time of the prospect valuation so that all prospects are compared on as similar a basis as possible.

Predicting future commodity prices is very difficult because so many economic variables influence price. Commodity prices are the weakest link in any valuation process. The confidence in the predicted price wanes the further into the future that prices must be predicted. For example, figure 5-1.16 shows the variance in historic natural gas prices during the past eleven years. The average actual price during this timeframe was $3.42 per thousand cubic feet (MCF) produced and sold, and the range was approximately $1.25 to $9.21 per MCF. The graph also shows a recent three-year history of $6.42, $6.97, and $9.21 per MCF. Future pricing is difficult to model, therefore future price decks tend to average prices annually. Some variables that effect price are:

- Supply and demand balances, both regionally and globally
- Weather
- Innovations and conservation
- Politics

In the case of FOP #1, payment for units produced and sold is based on the Henry Hub Index. This is a geographical index that handles the sale of most natural gas arriving from wells producing offshore. The price received is the daily or monthly Henry Hub Index, less the cost of transportation from the well to the designated sales point. Generally, the producer receives the Henry Hub Index price less $0.30 per MCF, which is deducted for transportation and treating. It is the producer's responsibility to build the pipeline at the producer's sole expense to bridge the distance from the well to the designated tie-in point. The cost of the pipeline was included in the investment (I).

Variables affecting price:
- Supply and demand balances
- Weather
- Innovations
- Conservation
- Politics

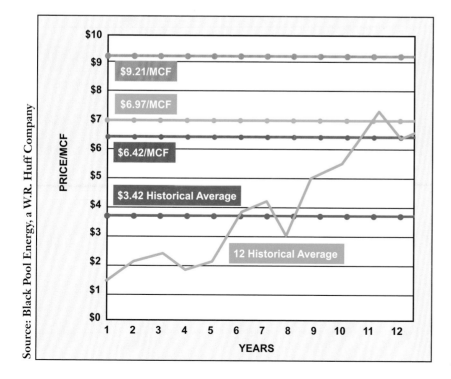

Figure 5-1.16. Natural gas price forecast

Once a price deck is selected, calculating revenue is simple. To do so, select the average daily rate from the production schedule and multiply it by 365 days in a year and the commodity price from the price deck. Table 5-1.4 shows the financial model complete with revenue, expenses, and cash flow. Thus far, there has been little discussion of expenses, because expenses are more predictable and tend to follow or rely heavily upon revenue. For example, two major expenses are the cost of goods sold and taxes. Such calculations are based on percentages of revenue. In the financial model, those expenses are calculated as percentages of revenue. In addition, operating costs are more predictable as historical cost data, such as the data obtained from the five older offset wells, and provide reliable estimates.

The weakness of any financial model is the revenue calculation, and the weakest link in the revenue calculation is future commodity prices.

Table 5-1.4
Completed Spreadsheet for Upstream Business Unit Prospects

	Year 0	Year 1	Year 2	Year 3	Year 4	Year 5	Year 6	Year 7	Year 8	Sum
Revenue		$8,464.500	$7,335,900	$6,545,880	$5,755,860	$4,740,120	$4,288,680	$3,498,660	$3,047,220	$43,676,820
Royalty		($2,116,125)	($1,833,975)	($1,636,470)	($1,438,965)	($1,185,030)	($1,072,170)	($874,665)	($761,805)	($10,919,205)
OPEX		($677,160)	($586,872)	($523,670)	($460,469)	($379,210)	($343,094)	($279,893)	($243,778)	($3,494,146)
G & A		($169,290)	($146,718)	($130,918)	($115,117)	($94,802)	($85,774)	($69,973)	($60,944)	($873,536)
Gross Income		$5,501,925	$4,768,335	$4,254,822	$3,741,309	$3,081,078	$2,787,642	$2,274,129	$1,980,693	$28,389,933
DD&A		($1,692,900)	($1,467,180)	($1,309,176)	($1,151,172)	($948,024)	($857,736)	($699,732)	($609,444)	($8,735,364)
Tax		($1,447,430)	($1,254,439)	($1,119,345)	($984,252)	($810,561)	($733,364)	($598,271)	($521,075)	($7,468,736)
Net Income		$2,361,596	$2,046,716	$1,826,301	$1,605,885	$1,322,493	$1,196,542	$976,126	$850,174	$12,185,833
CashFlow		$4,054,496	$3,513,896	$3,135,477	$2,757,057	$2,270,517	$2,054,278	$1,675,858	$1,459,618	$20,921,197
Investment	($12,025,000)									

Assumptions:
1. Production days averaged 330 days per year.
2. Pricing is $3.42 per MCF—based on 11-year average. Hold prices constant.
3. Royalty is 25% of revenue.
4. OPEX includes manpower, taxes, and all miscellaneous expenses.
5. DD&A is a percentage based upon units produced.
6. Tax is calculated as 38% of gross income less DD&A.
7. Cash flow is net income plus DD&A.

Now, all the data necessary to complete the financial model spreadsheet is available to calculate reserves, prepare a production schedule, and develop a commodity price schedule (Table 5-1.4).

Completing the Financial Model and Calculating Cash Flow

This completed financial model gives the sum of the cash flows. Now it is time to calculate FOP #1's ROR.

To complete the example, the next step is to calculate the ROR for FOP #1. This calculation is exactly like the earlier one where the investment (I) and the sum of the cash flows (SCF) are used to calculate a decimal fraction. The decimal fraction is converted to a percentage to arrive at the ROR for one set of parameters.

Calculating Rate of Return for FOP #1

Calculating ROR

Rate of Return (ROR) = (Sum of Cash Flow-I)/I

where

Sum of Cash Flow = $20,921,197

I = $12,025,000

To solve this equation for ROR

$$ROR = \frac{20,921,197 - 12,025,000}{12,025,000} = 73.9\%$$

In financial modeling, ROR is usually calculated for three cases: the best case, the most likely case, and the worst case. Table 5-1.4 is the most likely case and yields a 73.9% ROR because the Sum of the Cash Flow exceeds the Investment by $8,896,197. Remember that this calculation did not account for the time value of money as that concept is beyond the scope of this content. Each case has a defined set of assumptions, which vary within a range of values. Typical value variations are within the following key areas:

- **Reserves.** Reserves are calculated using varying area, thickness, and porosity.
- **Estimated Ultimate Recoveries** (EURs). EURs are varied by lowering or increasing the units of production over the productive life of the well.
- **Commodity Prices.** As established earlier, commodity prices will vary into the future. In the case of FOP #1 and the information in figure 5-1.16, $3.42 per MCF was the historical average Henry Hub Index price with a range of $1.25 to $9.21 per MCF. It would make sense to model cash flow using a flat $3.42 per MCF for the life of the well. This model and ROR could be a worst case or a most-likely case. It would also make sense to model the cash flow at a current price.

In the end, a range of cash flows will be created and an array of RORs will be calculated, and these ROR will be used by management to decide whether to invest.

SUMMARY

The economics of creating new supplies focuses on business and revenue models for Upstream, Midstream, and Downstream Business Units of operation. Critical data begins with economic evaluation from the beginning of the prospect, or geologic idea, of where the crude oil and natural gas might be stored in the Earth's subsurface. The process continues through the steps necessary to make a decision to invest money in creating new supplies by drilling, completing, and equipping a new well. Estimation and measurement are necessary to calculate reserves, production, and future revenue from income-producing investments. Completing Table 5-1.3 is a key step in creating the financial model associated with economic evaluation. ROR calculation and analysis is the deciding factor regarding which prospects will be drilled and tested.

Along the way in the economic evaluation process, there are many unknowns that must be estimated or measured to complete the ROR calculation. Of all the inputs of economic evaluation, commodity prices are the least accurate and thus, can make the most difference to such evaluation.

Commodity prices can be very volatile. For Upstream and Downstream Business Units that want to dampen the volatility by setting a price for the crude oil or natural gas they will receive, in the case of Upstream, or pay, in the case of Downstream, it is possible to purchase a commodity price *hedge* in the futures markets or from a third party. These are very complex financial and contractual arrangements that vary with contract terms such as:

- Set periods of time, such as one month to several years
- Specific volumes of crude oil or natural gas that the company putting on the hedge will guarantee to deliver and/or purchase
- Commodity prices for the term of the hedge contract

Most companies use hedges at a point in time in their business life to protect or stabilize revenue.

Changes in the price that Upstream Business Units receive for the sale of crude oil and natural gas directly influence investment decisions to create new supplies. It is a perception or realization that higher or lower commodity prices will yield corresponding ROR and therefore, corresponding investment decisions. For example, in a rising price environment, future revenue and investment will increase, provided production volumes are static. Conversely, in a declining price environment, future revenue and investment will decline.

The following relationship of price and supply illustrates this point.

- As the price (P) of crude oil and natural gas goes up, the investment (I) increases, the number of working drilling rigs (DR) increases, the number of new producing wells (W) increases, and the overall supply (S) increases.

> Price ↑ Investment ↑ Drilling Rigs ↑ Wells ↑ Supply ↑

- As the price (P) of crude oil and natural gas goes down, the investment (I) decreases, the number of working drilling rigs (DR) declines, the number of new producing wells (W) declines, and the overall supply (S) declines.

$$P\downarrow I\downarrow DR\downarrow W\downarrow S\downarrow$$

The length of time it takes for this relationship to change from increasing prices to decreasing prices is a *business cycle*. These cycles range in duration from months to years.

This relationship explains the economically confounding affects of volatile prices. For example, in a declining price environment investment diminishes and a number of working drilling rigs are idled, creating a snowball effect for those vendors that provide goods and services to the process of creating new supplies. Some of those affected are vendors -suppliers of location construction, casing and tubing, fuels, trucking, work boats, drilling mud, bits, directional services, well logging, downhole tools, wellheads, production tank batteries, and facilities construction. In this example, everyone's revenue declines.

Predicting future commodity prices is an important function in economic evaluation and in the process of creating new supplies. It is a difficult task to get it right, but nevertheless it must be done.

REFERENCES

1. Economic Evaluation and Investment Decision Methods, Franklin J. Stermole and John M. Stermole, Eighth Edition, ISBN 1-878740-03-2
2. Merriam-Webster Dictionary
3. Dictionary of Finance and Investment Terms, Third Edition, ISBN 0-8120-4631-5

- Laws and regulations to protect human health and the environment

- Exploration and production waste disposal

- Cleanup methods for blowouts and spills

- Refining processes that minimize environmental impact

- Equipment and controls to promote workplace safety

5.2
Environmental, Health, and Safety Concerns

Petroleum products are everywhere. Many of the common household items we use every day contain petroleum. Unfortunately, the recovery, transport, processing, and use of petroleum are fraught with potential hazards to human health and the Earth's ecology. For example, exploration, drilling, and production use toxic chemicals that can pollute the air, water, and ground to yield a product that might be very useful but is also poisonous to most living things. Producing and transporting petroleum products pose risks of fire, explosions, and pollution. Similarly, refining it produces still more noxious chemicals that must be changed into harmless compounds or disposed of in harmless ways (fig. 5-2.1).

For these reasons and because of its size and importance to the economy, the petroleum industry is subject to much criticism. Various environmental groups monitor the industry and publicize dangers and potential dangers they find or suspect. Oil companies face a great public relations challenge in regard to their adverse impact to the environment.

Figure 5-2.1. Recovery, transport, processing, and use of petroleum have potential hazards to human health and the Earth's ecology.

Although disasters have brought new laws, new technologies, and innovative practices, the public usually hears most about the damage done to people and the environment. The oil and gas industry cannot prevent all accidents, but it can do its part to ensure the safety of people and the environment. The industry can also have an effect on consumer opinion by publicizing its efforts to comply with environmental and safety laws and educate the public about how it operates responsibly.

Because environmental and safety regulations affect many aspects of the petroleum industry, companies are continuously researching ways to comply with laws and remain profitable. New technologies can sometimes bring unexpected benefits in recycling and efficiency.

This chapter presents information about some of the laws and regulations that currently govern the petroleum industry's practices related to environmental, health and safety concerns. Examples of environmental impacts and methods used by the drilling, production, transportation, and refining sectors to reduce the harmful effects of petroleum operations, processes, and products will be presented and discussed. This text also examines how the petroleum industry strives to protect the health and safety of its workers.

> Environmental impacts are managed and reduced by:
> * New laws
> * New technologies
> * Innovative industry practices

U.S. LAWS AND REGULATIONS

The oil industry in the United States is regulated by federal and state government laws allowing numerous agencies to oversee aspects regarding pollution and risk to human health and safety. Such regulation has helped protect the environment and reduce unsafe practices. Petroleum-related companies in the United States must comply with these laws, and successful companies routinely explore ways to produce and process petroleum more cleanly and efficiently while achieving profits.

Beginning in the 1970s, federal laws authorized the U.S. Environmental Protection Agency (EPA) and other agencies to draw up rules in the form of regulations. Some regulations directly protect the quality of water, air, and land. Some protect the health and safety of employees, surrounding communities, and plant and animal life. Others regulate the use of hazardous chemicals and disposal of hazardous waste. All the following regulations affect the oil industry:

* *Clean Air Act:* Authorizes the EPA to set standards for air quality and regulate emissions of pollutants into the air. *Criteria air pollutants* include ozone, carbon monoxide, sulfur dioxide, lead, nitrogen dioxide, and particulates. Criteria pollutants are those that can harm your health and the environment and cause property damage. Oil and gas exploration, drilling, production, and processing produce air emissions such as dust from road construction, site clearing, mud mixing, along with exhaust from combustion sources such as diesel engines, heaters, boilers, and other process equipment (fig. 5-2.2). Opera-

Figure 5-2.2. Smokestacks are often used to cool the exhaust from combustion sources and to provide better air dispersion of emitted pollutants.

tions also produce hydrogen sulfide (H$_2$S) from sour gas plants, treatment facilities, and from drilling into or producing from formations that contain H$_2$S. Many oil and gas operations also store materials in storage tanks that contain and emit *volatile organic compounds (VOCs)*, which are a precursor to ozone formation in the atmosphere. Some of the most visible EPA regulations pertain to motor vehicle emissions into the air. Changing standards for the formulation of gasoline have affected refinery operations over the past two decades including the removal of lead, methyl *tert*-butyl ether, and the reduction of sulfur often contained in gasoline. More information can be found at www.epa.gov/air/caa.

- *Clean Water Act:* Charges the EPA with regulating pollutant discharges into surface waters (fig. 5-2.3). Some petroleum industry discharges are sewage, hot water, drilling fluids, drill cuttings, and produced wastewater. Other discharges include pollutants washed into water resources by storms, deck drainage from offshore units, blowout prevention fluids, and any fluids containing chemicals, suspended solids, or oil. To prevent and clean up pollution, this act requires all onshore facilities with potential to discharge oil or other pollutants into navigable waters to abide by the *Spill Prevention, Countermeasures and Control (SPCC) Plan*. The SPCC requires predictions of the type and quantities of petroleum that might be released if equipment fails. This includes descriptions of prevention equipment, pre-

Preventative U.S. laws and regulations include:
- Clean Air Act
- Clean Water Act
- Safe Drinking Water Act
- Oil Pollution Act
- Outer Continental Shelf Act

Figure 5-2.3. Operators of offshore rigs must follow EPA regulations concerning any discharges of waste into water.

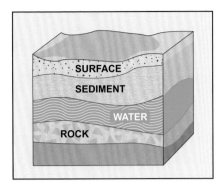

Figure 5-2.4. An aquifer is a stratum of rock, sand, or gravel that holds enough water to supply wells or springs often used as a source of drinking water.

The EPA regulates SPCC plans for onshore spills while the Oil Pollution Act creates guidelines for offshore spills.

ventative training, notification procedures, descriptions and handling of past spills, and prevention plans. More information can be found at www.epa.gov/watertrain/cwa.

- **Safe Drinking Water Act:** Protects underground waters. Almost half of the people in the United States get their drinking water from underground aquifers (fig. 5-2.4). Under this law, the *Underground Injection Control (UIC)* program regulates injection wells for waste disposal. The petroleum industry uses injection wells to dispose produced water into depleted oil formations below drinking water sources, inject produced water from the reservoir back into the producing zone, inject fluids for enhanced recovery, and store hydrocarbons. Petroleum operations can contaminate drinking water if abandoned wells are not properly plugged, the casing is faulty, or fluids are accidentally injected into an aquifer. As a result, UIC has specific requirements for constructing wells and performing casing and cementing, plugging and abandoning; for the types of substances and volume and pressure that can be injected; and for the mechanical integrity of the well. More information can be found at www.epa.gov/safewater.

- **Oil Pollution Act:** Provides guidelines for offshore spill plans. This act was enacted by the U.S. Congress in response to large tanker spills. In 1988, 46 million gallons (174 million litres) were spilled in U.S. waters in 16,000 reported incidents. In the same way that EPA requires onshore facilities to have an SPCC plan for spills, the Oil Pollution Act authorized the Minerals Management Service (now the Bureau of Ocean Energy Management, Regulation, and Enforcement) to create guidelines for offshore spill plans. Under these guidelines, owners and operators of onshore and offshore vessels and facilities must have contingency plans for containing and recovering a disastrous spill. The Oil Pollution Act regulates owners and operators of drilling units, pipelines, storage units such as tanks, and any other facility that could potentially discharge oil or gas into federal waters. More information can be found at www.epa.gov/emergencies/content/lawsregs.

- **Outer Continental Shelf Lands Act:** Authorizes the U.S. Secretary of the Interior to grant mineral leases and regulate oil and gas activities on the Outer Continental Shelf, which consists of all lands under offshore waters within U.S. jurisdiction (fig. 5-2.5). Leases here often require the exploration and development company to plan measures to protect the environment, train its employees in environmentally safe operations, and dispose of its wastes in a safe manner. More information can be found at www.boemre.gov/aboutboemre/ocs.

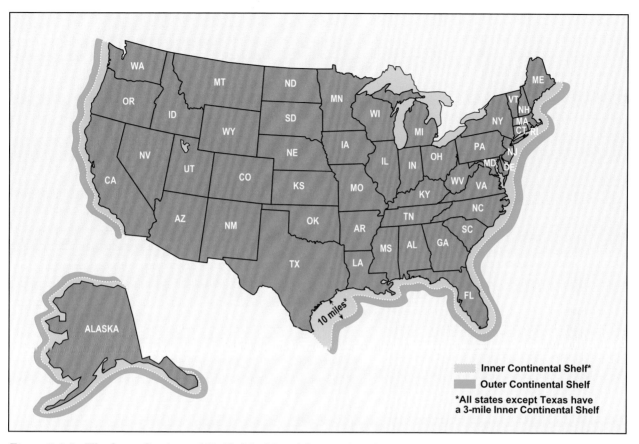

Figure 5-2.5. The Outer Continental Shelf of the United States is leased to petroleum companies by the U.S. Department of the Interior.

- ***Occupational Health and Safety Act:*** Established the Occupational Safety and Health Administration (OSHA) to regulate safety and health in the workplace. An OSHA guideline that affects the petroleum industry is the *Hazard Communication, or "Employee Right-to-Know" Standard* that guarantees employees the right to know about chemical hazards on the job and how to protect themselves from those hazards. Employers must list hazardous materials, label them, and train employees in their proper handling (fig. 5-2.6). Another OSHA regulation, the *Hazardous Waste Operations and Emergency Response Standard*, requires employers to protect workers who respond to emergencies involving hazardous wastes. More information can be found at www.osha.gov.

- ***Migratory Bird Treaty Act:*** Covers five multinational treaties that protect migrating birds. Provisions that concern the petroleum industry cover birds injured in pits or open-topped tanks that contain oil, oil products, caustic chemicals, or poisonous contaminants such as boron or arsenic. More information can be found at www.animallaw.info/statutes.

Figure 5-2.6. Waste disposal containers must be clearly labeled according to OSHA regulations.

> State and local entities have imposed additional and often more stringent regulation to the adopted federal law.

- **Endangered Species Act:** Protects species on the *List of Endangered and Threatened Wildlife and Plants*. Once a species is on the list, all federal agencies must ensure that federal actions will not harm the listed species or their habitats. Although oil companies are not federal agencies, they often drill on federal lands and are therefore subject to this act. More information can be found at www.fws.gov/endangered.

- **Toxic Substances Control Act:** Regulates the manufacture, processing, distribution, use, and disposal of chemicals. The EPA maintains a list of chemicals that are used, or were once used, in commerce. No facility can manufacture an unlisted chemical. Industries that use these chemicals must report where and how much they use or produce. Naturally occurring chemicals are exempt, which means a pipeline company need not report oil transported from the well to the refinery. However, refineries must report the production of toxic chemicals from oil such as benzene, toluene, and xylene. More information can be found at http://www.epa.gov/lawsregs/laws/tsca.

- **Resource Conservation and Recovery Act:** Monitors the disposal of hazardous wastes. Most wastes from exploration, drilling, and production operations are exempt from this law, but the same materials produced or used during transportation or refining are not exempt. For example, unused fracturing fluids or acids, refinery wastes, caustic or acid cleaners, and pipeline waste must be disposed of in proper containers, labeled, and shipped to a special disposal facility. More information can be found at http://www.epa.gov/lawsregs/laws/rcra.

Since the 1970s, many states and local jurisdictions adopted the federal laws and have imposed additional regulations—which, in some cases, are more stringent than the federal requirements—that also govern the industry on the protection of the environment and risks to human health and safety.

INTERNATIONAL LAWS AND TREATIES

There are several international laws and treaties regarding safety and pollution prevention. Among them are:

- The *Safety of Life at Sea Treaty* and *Oil Spill Preparedness and Response Treaty* created in response to the Titanic ship disaster of 1912.
- The *Environment Act* in 1995 passed by Great Britain that gives the environment secretary authority to draft standards.
- The *European Community* works with the industry to create standards for European producers and refiners.

- The Norwegian industry and energy minister created joint campaigns to solve Norway's offshore environmental problems with fishing and petroleum industries and environmentalists.

- The *Kyoto Protocol* was established through the United Nations Framework Convention on Climate Change as an international agreement aimed at fighting global warming by reducing *greenhouse gases (GHG)*. Although the United States has not currently signed the protocol, the EPA has recently passed new regulations through the Clean Air Act that require the mandatory reporting of GHG emissions from industries, including the oil and gas industry.

The following sections of this chapter focus on some examples of environmental hazards and methods used by the drilling, production, transportation, and refining industries to reduce the harmful effects of petroleum operations, processes, and products.

> International laws protecting the environment:
> - Safety of Life at Sea
> - The Environmental Act
> - The Kyoto Protocol

A *closed-loop drilling system* recirculates drilling mud, making a *reserve pit* unnecessary. A reserve pit contains buried drilling wastes, specifically mud and cuttings. Pit burial is a low-cost, low-technology method where wastes do not need to be transported away from the well site. Various regulations exist regarding reserve pits. Some require the operator to reclaim the site after drilling, use an impermeable lining, or dispose of the liquids off site (fig. 5-2.7). The advantages of a closed-loop system are that it lowers construction and reclamation costs and uses less water. The solids that remain after drilling can sometimes be reused to line irrigation ditches, feedlots, and landfills, if chemical additives in the mud are minimal.

EXPLORATION AND PRODUCTION ENVIRONMENTAL IMPACTS

Closed-Loop Drilling System

Courtesy of Bret Boteler, EnerMax, Inc.

Figure 5-2.7. Water pits used for drilling fluids

Synthetic-Based Drilling Fluid

Onshore drilling uses water-based muds while offshore uses oil-based muds as drilling fluids. Synthetic muds cut costs and are reusable and recyclable.

Spent drilling fluids and cuttings comprise the largest quantity of waste from exploration and drilling (fig. 5-2.8). Their impact is especially significant offshore where muds that do not meet EPA standards must be barged away for disposal on land. EPA standards prohibit the discharge of oil or mud with a high content of particulates, cadmium, or mercury, for example. No drilling mud or cuttings can be discharged within 3 miles (4.8 kilometres) of any shore.

Drilling fluids are generally either water-based or oil-based. Onshore drilling operations usually use water-based muds, but offshore horizontal drilling often requires muds that are oil-based. Oil-based muds have greater impact if disposed of onsite. Oil and cuttings obstruct oxygen to the sediment where they are dumped, and recovery is slow. At many drill sites in the North Sea, cuttings lie in huge piles 100 to 150 feet (30 to 45 metres) high and 200 feet (60 metres) across. Oil-coated sand and pebbles smother bottom-dwelling life, and oil can leach out more than couple of miles or kilometres from the site. If the mud and cuttings are not dumped onsite but transported offsite, moving them can pollute the air and use energy, disposal threatens groundwater, and worker safety is at risk during loading and unloading.

Since 1990, mud suppliers have offered nontoxic, biodegradable, *synthetic-based muds (SBMs)* to address the high costs and problems of disposing of mud offshore. SBMs are reusable and recyclable, so the quantity of spent mud and cuttings is lower. It also allows faster drilling, especially in horizontal wells common in offshore drilling. Faster drilling reduces air emissions from the prime movers. Although SBMs cost more than oil-based muds, tests have shown that SBMs are also less toxic.

Figure 5-2.8. Oil floating on top of drilling fluids that have been returned to the surface.

Courtesy of Bret Boteler , EnerMax, Inc.

Copyright © The University of Texas at Austin—PETEX

Russian companies have developed chemical additives for drilling mud from the waste of other industries. Following the collapse of the Soviet Union, the usual sources for such chemicals were located outside of Russia and, as a result, they became expensive to import. In searching for a new source for these chemicals, researchers looked at industrial wastes and byproducts that contained the raw components for drilling mud additives. Some of the wastes used were cake from sewage disposal plants, starches from expired biological materials, and byproducts of the metallurgical, perfume, vitamin, and microbiology industries (figs. 5-2.9 and 5-2.10).

Mud Additives from Waste

Courtesy of Bret Boteler, EnerMax, Inc.

Figure 5-2.9. Mud chemicals to be used as additives

Figure 5-2.10. A derrickhand wearing personal protective equipment adds dry components to the mud.

Blowouts

Effects of onshore spills can be minimized using skimmer ships, booms, anchored barriers, and sand-filled barricades.

A blowout is the uncontrolled release of crude oil and/or natural gas from an oilwell after pressure control systems have failed. In addition to the initial explosion and the possibility of fire, blowouts can cause a toxic cloud of H_2S and other poisonous gases such as benzene, depending on the well formation. These gases can sometimes accumulate close to the ground, especially in low spots, if not burned. H_2S is colorless, corrosive, and flammable and produces sulfur dioxide when it burns. In low concentrations, the gas smells like rotten eggs and can quickly deaden the sense of smell and cause severe problems and death if one is exposed to high enough concentrations. The gas kills by paralyzing the nerve centers that control breathing (for more information, see *Chapter 2.2: Well Control and Chapter 2.3: Drilling Safety*). Benzene is a flammable, colorless, slightly sweet smelling gas that is known to be a carcinogen. To reduce the potential environmental and health impacts from these chemicals, an operator might decide to ignite the stream to convert these poisonous gases to less hazardous substances during a blowout.

In April 2010, the *Deepwater Horizon* drilling rig, owned by British Petroleum (BP) and located in the Gulf of Mexico just offshore of the Louisiana coast, experienced a blowout resulting in the largest offshore oil spill experienced in U.S. history. The blowout caused an explosion that killed 11 platform workers and injured 17 others (fig. 5-2.11). After sinking, the platform left a seafloor oil gusher flowing at 35,000 to 60,000 barrels of crude oil per day, resulting in a total oil spill estimated at well over 125,000 million gallons. This total amount is greater than 10 times the 1989 Exxon Valdez oil spill.

Source: U.S. Coast Guard

Figure 5-2.11. Water supply vessels combat the fire on the Deepwater Horizon while the U.S. Coast Guard searches for missing workers.

Like the Exxon Valdez spill, the BP oil spill has had extensive environmental impact on marine and wildlife habitats, devastating the Gulf of Mexico fishing and tourism industries. However, much of the onshore impacts have been minimized so far using the response plans and techniques used during the Exxon Valdez oil spill cleanup. There have been enormous efforts to stem the flow at the wellhead for months while crews continued working to protect hundreds of miles of beaches, wetlands, and estuaries along the northern Gulf coast, using skimmer ships, floating containment booms, anchored barriers, and sand-filled barricades along shorelines. Based on how recent the BP oil spill is in conjunction with the publication of this chapter, the full extent of the environmental impacts from the spill is not yet known.

> To date, the April 2010 offshore blowout represents the largest oil spill in U.S. history, killing 11 people and gushing up to 60,000 gallons per day.

Spills from Tankers

In 1989, the Exxon Valdez tanker rammed into a reef and spilled an estimated 11 million gallons (41.6 million litres) of crude oil near Alaska. Aside of the recent BP oil spill in the Gulf of Mexico, this has become known as one of the largest spills in U.S. history and one of the largest ecological disasters of all time. The spill killed plants and animals across 2,000 miles (3,220 kilometres) of shoreline and 500 miles (805 kilometres) out to sea, devastating fishing, hunting, tourism, and recreation in the area (fig. 5-2.12).

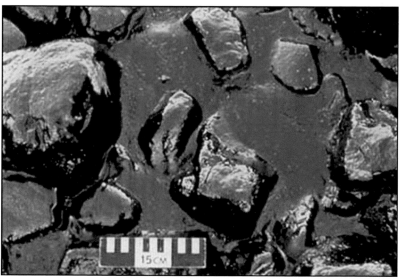

Source: National Oceanic and Atmospheric Administration, U.S. Department of Commerce

Figure 5-2.12. Pooled oil from the Exxon Valdez *sitting between rocks on the shore. Most of the spilled oil decomposed. Cleanup crews recovered about 14%, 13% sank to the seafloor, and about 2% remained on the beaches. Today, very little oil remains.*

After the Valdez oil spill, international oil companies formed the Marine Spill Response Corporation to improve cleanup endeavors and response time.

The Valdez spill presented logistical, technical, and scientific challenges never before encountered. Many people and organizations participated in its containment and cleanup. An Alaskan spill-response firm, Alyeska Pipeline Service Company, responded immediately, and the U.S. Coast Guard oversaw the cleanup. Exxon was responsible for directing and paying for the cleanup. The Alaska Department of Environmental Conservation had jurisdiction over water quality and fisheries. Many volunteers—fishers, conservationists, and residents—donated equipment, expertise, and time to help keep the oil away from salmon hatcheries and parts of the shore.

Since the spill, response plans for remote offshore areas have greatly improved. Several international oil companies have funded the *Marine Spill Response Corporation (MSRC)*. Numerous firms and cooperatives have formed in the aftermath. These groups are designed to deal with spills from tankers, platforms, rigs, and pipelines off the U.S. mainland, Hawaii, U.S. Virgin Islands, and Puerto Rico. The Alyeska Pipeline Service Company does the same for Alaska by keeping an arsenal of boats, booms, and skimming equipment ready for a spill emergency. In addition, a cottage industry of cleanup consultants has arisen.

The number and frequency of oil spills have decreased significantly in the last 30 years. Despite an increase in sea trade in the past two decades, the number of crude oil spills from tankers is significantly fewer than in previous years.

Prevention

Single-hulled vessels are twice as likely to produce a spill than double-hulled vessels.

The U.S. Coast Guard, the entity that creates guidelines for offshore safety, reports that human error is the main cause of maritime accidents. According to the Coast Guard, fatigue, inadequate pilot-bridge coordination, and inadequate technical knowledge are the primary reasons for accidents. In the offshore oil industry, human error is a particular danger when operating drilling rigs or navigating tankers through rough seas in narrow bays, especially in the North Sea and offshore Alaska. Preventing accidents depends, in part, on training and improved technologies. Prevention is critical because spills are not only devastating to the environment and those who make their living from regions affected by spills, but also because oil is most difficult to clean up in bad weather.

An engineering solution used to help prevent spills when accidents occur is the application of *double hulls* for oil tankers, although their usefulness has been questioned. In 1995, the double-hulled vessel, the Borga, collided with rocks off the coast of South Wales and spilled no oil. In 1996, the single-hulled Sea Empress struck the same rocks and spilled about 77,000 tons (70,000 tonnes) of oil.

To be effective, response to a spill must occur fast and before the oil reaches shore and weathers. The first challenge is detecting the location of the spill. This is usually done visually from ships or aircraft, which means the response team is limited by darkness, fog, and rain.

The first action is to send special response vessels with extra deck space for helicopters, booms, boom boats, and skimming systems to the area. These vessels also have oil and water separators and storage capacity for the captured oil.

A *boom* (fig. 5-2.13), which is a long floating fence, is towed slowly by a boom boat to enclose the spill or to protect part of the shore. A boom only works where the waves are no more than 2 to 3 feet (60 to 90 centimetres) high and in winds no stronger than 15 to 20 knots. Waves on the Outer Continental Shelf, for example, are routinely higher, so the effectiveness of booms is limited to calm seas.

Cleaning Up the Sea

Source: U.S. Coast Guard., Photo by Petty Officer 1st Class John Masson

Figure 5-2.13. A boom is a flexible air-filled bag that prevents spilled oil from spreading further.

Response to a spill must occur before the oil reaches shore and weathers. The first action is to send special response vessels.

A *skimmer* is like a huge vacuum cleaner (fig. 5-2.14). Skimmers work only in oil that is floating on the top of the water—called an *oil slick*—and only in calm seas. The crews need airborne spotters to direct them to the center of the slick. They also need a location and equipment to offload the captured oil.

Rough seas begin to convert crude and water into an emulsion called a *mousse*. If response is fast enough to reach the spill before the mousse forms, it can be burned or dispersed using chemicals. Burning can be a good solution in remote areas where logistics prevent other types of quick response. Burning removes 50% to 90% of the oil as long as it has not been emulsified from wave action. As happens with leaks and soil contamination, the volatile fractions evaporate. After this occurs, the oil will not burn. Burning is dangerous because it releases toxic gases into the air.

Using a *dispersant* to break down the oil into tiny drops requires specific conditions. Weather and sea conditions must be energetic enough to mix the oil and dispersant but not so rough that aircraft carrying the application equipment cannot fly. The dispersant must be applied repeatedly and no longer works after the oil weathers into a mousse. The use of dispersants is controversial because some are more toxic than oil to marine life. Chemicals such as gelling agents, sinking agents, demulsifiers, and burning agents can be dropped by aircraft at the site and used as dispersants.

Source: National Oceanic and Atmospheric Administration, U.S. Department of Commerce

Figure 5-2.14. The skimmer and boom swing over the side of the boat to enclose and suck up the oil.

Waves and tides often bring spilled oil onshore and then wash it out to other shores. It is dangerous to wildlife because of its toxicity. The washed-up oil can smother plants and destroy the ability of animal fur and bird feathers to retain heat (fig. 5-2.15).

Oil onshore can be removed manually with shovels, buckets, and absorbent materials. Some cleanup teams have used high-pressure hot water to wash the oil from between rocks or low-pressure cold water to return the oil to the water for skimming or collection (fig. 5-2.16).

In time, patches of asphalt and tar develop onshore after the volatile factions have evaporated and the oil has weathered. The final effort might apply a chemical fertilizer to stimulate the growth of natural oil-degrading bacteria, as described in the section on cleaning contaminated soil. The top layers of soil can be removed with a backhoe and then fertilizer applied, or the fertilizer can be tilled into the soil.

In 1978, a cleanup of a marsh in Brittany, France, which had been heavily contaminated from an oil spill, demonstrated that cleaned-up sections recovered more slowly than the sections left alone. Efforts to remove the oil by scraping off the top layer of soil and uprooting plants, combined with damage done by people trampling the marsh, actually did more harm than good. Such accusations have been leveled at the well-publicized Valdez cleanup.

Cleaning Up the Shore

Courtesy of the State of Louisiana

Figure 5-2.15. Wildlife such as the birds can suffocate when covered with oil.

Source: U.S. Coast Guard, photo by Petty Officer 3rd Class Patrick Kelley

Figure 5-2.16. Health, Safety, and Environment (HSE) workers were contracted to clean up oil on the beaches in Port Fourchon, Louisiana, in May 2010 following the Deepwater Horizon/BP oil spill.

Cleaning Up Shallow Waters

Cleanup in shallow waters can be more problematic because response vessels are often too large and have too deep a draft to enter the area. At one time, oil in shallow waters was dealt with by letting it wash onshore and then cleaning it up. Barges mounted by trailer to transport by truck can navigate the water in places such as Galveston Bay, Texas, in the United States.

After a spill in Galveston Bay in 1990, the response team used a containment boom and skimming equipment to collect approximately 30% of the oil. Oil-degrading bacteria were used to break down 85% to 100% of the remaining spill. Shallow-draft, flat-bottomed boats traveled to the marsh areas carrying the bacteria in dry form. The crew mixed the bacteria with seawater and sprayed the mixture into the marsh through fire hoses with pumps.

Hazards to Cleanup Workers

The workers and volunteers who clean up ocean spills are exposed to hazardous materials and conditions. Inhaling gases, getting chemicals on the skin, and ingesting petroleum products are potential dangers. In addition, exposure to the environment and weather can cause sunburn, cold or heat can contribute to illness, insects can cause bites and stings, and loud equipment can cause hearing injuries. There is also the risk of fire and drowning. A well-organized cleanup effort provides protective clothing and gear as well as a safe place for workers to eat, drink, and receive first-aid treatment. Further information about response to marine accidents and cleanup can be found at The Oil Spill Working Group (OSWG) Web site at www.ipieca.org.

Pipeline and Transportation Environmental Impacts

Pipelines carrying both crude oil and petroleum products, such as natural gas, operate under the U.S. Department of Transportation. A pipeline is considered a closed system. However, product sampling and routine station operations expose petroleum to the air and people to the petroleum. For this reason, the U.S. *Occupational Safety and Health Administration* (OSHA) and EPA are also involved in regulating pipeline companies.

Other than routine hazards, the main environmental concerns related to petroleum pipelines are potential leaks and spills. Pipelines can develop leaks or breaks due to damages from excavation (digging) or corrosion (fig. 5-2.17). Heavy rains and flooding can expose pipelines that have been safely buried. This happened in Houston, Texas, in 1994, when flooding exposed lines buried for 30 years. Debris propelled by flooding water damaged the lines and caused them to spill crude and refined products into the San Jacinto River. In the same month, rains washed out a dam in the Russian Arctic and caused crude to spill from a pipeline. Whenever a leak or spill occurs, fire is always a danger, as is vaporization of the exposed petroleum or migration of petroleum into our drinking water supplies underground.

Courtesy of Tekscent Pipeline

Figure 5-2.17. Detecting a leak in an underground pipeline.

While spills are easy to spot, the main difficulty with pipeline leaks is detecting them, especially those containing natural gas, which is not visible to the naked eye. There are many systems used to detect leaks. The effectiveness of such systems is often measured by how small a leak they can detect and how quickly. Systems might include temperature-sensing pipes to detect thawing in permafrost areas, flow meters to measure flow rate, transmitters to measure the pressure at pump stations and at several valve sites, or thermal imaging devices such as *infrared (IR)* cameras. IR cameras have become increasing popular in the petroleum industry because they can accurately detect small gas leaks quickly while covering a broad area (fig. 5-2.18).

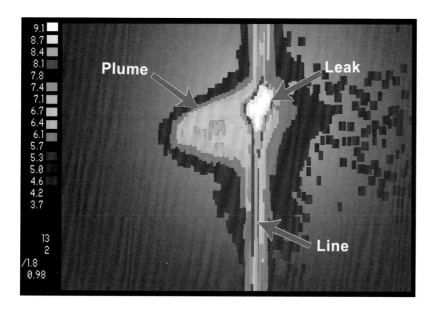

Figure 5-2.18. Accurately detecting leaks in pipelines can be costly and difficult. However, with the use of thermal imaging devices (a representation), this process can become more efficient and effective in detecting leaks.

Detection methods for natural
gas leaks:
- Temperature-sensing pipes
- Flow meters
- Transmitters
- Thermal imaging devices
- Infrared cameras

Many pipeline companies use thermal imaging or laser devices attached to aircraft to inspect their pipelines, in addition to regular *pigging* operations. Pigging is the practice of using pipeline inspection gauges or *pigs* to perform various operations on a pipeline including, but not limited to, physical inspection of pipelines for corrosion or cracks.

The transportation of petroleum products also includes operations in-between production and processing or in-between processing and the distribution of products, such as storage terminals and/or natural gas transfer stations. Terminals involve the storage and sometimes loading of products such as crude oil, liquid natural gas, and other petroleum products. Other than potential spills, environmental impacts related to these operations include VOC air emissions from the storage tanks and loading operations. Depending on their volatility, the emissions from these operations might require control using a combustion device to destroy the associated VOC emissions.

Natural Gas transfer (compressor) *stations* are commonly used to transport natural gas under pressure via a complex network of pipelines designed to quickly and efficiently transport natural gas from its origin to areas of high natural gas demand. Equipment such as compressor engines, turbines, or motors are used to compress the natural gas from one station to the next. Compressor stations can also include other related ancillary operations such as condensate storage and loading, dehydrators to remove water from the natural gas, and simple natural gas condensate separation equipment. Depending on the sulfur content of the natural gas being transported, some stations include equipment used to remove sulfur to prevent corrosion (namely, amine, and sulfur recovery units). Environmental impacts related to compressor stations include potential spills and air emissions generated from the process equipment described above. For example, engines and turbines commonly burn natural gas or diesel to operate, resulting in combustion pollutants such as nitrogen oxides, sulfur dioxide, carbon monoxide, particulates, formaldehyde, and other VOCs. VOC emissions from the storage of condensate or wastewater at the compressor station might occur. In fact, depending on the amount of condensate entrained in the natural gas being transferred, flashing might occur. Flashing is the partial vaporization of natural gas condensate that occurs when reducing its pressure from a high-pressure to a low-pressure environment. Sulfur dioxide and H_2S emissions can occur when there are high concentrations of sulfur in the natural gas being handled, sometimes referred to as sour gas. If necessary, sour gas may be burned using a combustion device called a flare before being emitted to the atmosphere.

The environmental concerns related to refineries involve water quality, air emissions, and waste management. Refining crude oil into marketable products such as diesel, jet fuel, and gasoline is a complex and integrated process involving multiple process units and associated equipment. The refining processes directly and indirectly generate wastewater, storm water run-off, wash water, sewage, and other process-related wastes that must be properly managed to minimize their impacts on the environment. Furthermore, many of the refining process equipment generate air emissions that must be recaptured or treated before being released into the atmosphere.

Increasingly strict regulation of fuel emissions forces refineries to manufacture cleaner-burning gasoline and other petroleum-based fuels. Petrochemical plants have many of the same challenges as refineries when it comes to controlling water and air pollution caused by the manufacturing processes.

Refining Environmental Impacts

When water is discharged from a refinery or petrochemical plant (*effluent water*) in the United States, it must be pure enough to meet the demands of local and state water quality boards, the EPA, and other regulatory agencies. Refineries often use chemical treatment tanks, holding ponds, and oil-degrading bacteria to remove contaminants such as H_2S, ammonia, phenols, and salts from the refinery's wastewater (fig. 5-2.19).

In effluent water storage tanks, hazardous wastes settle on the bottom, so the contents must be separated into water, oil, and solids. The wastewater is then removed and recycled through the refinery's wastewater treatment plant where any oil is recovered for reuse. The water is centrifuged and heated to separate out the solids that are to be disposed of in a landfill. Because disposal is costly, refineries try to separate out as much oil and water as possible.

Water Quality

Courtesy of Siemens Water Technologies Corp.

Figure 5-2.19. A bioreactor uses microorganisms to remove impurities from the water.

In some cases, refineries operate and use *underground injection control wells* to dispose of contaminated waters including, but not limited to, storm water runoff, sewage, and wash water generated during the maintenance of equipment.

Air Quality

Environmental concerns relating to refining:
- Water quality
- Air quality

Given their size and complexity, most refineries are major sources of emissions for all criteria pollutants including ozone, carbon monoxide, sulfur dioxide, lead, nitrogen dioxide, and particulates. Refineries are also known to emit many of the EPA's original 188 named *Hazardous Air Pollutants (HAPs)*, such as benzene, toluene, and xylene (Table 5-2.1). Many of these pollutants are VOCs which refer to the light fractions of petroleum that evaporate at atmospheric temperature and pressure. VOCs and nitrogen oxides react in the atmosphere to form smog and ozone formations near the ground.

Emission sources commonly found at most refineries include, but are not limited to:

- Combustion sources—used to heat materials, produce steam and/or control or reduce other VOC emissions sources at the refinery
- Storage tanks—used to store raw materials and final products
- Cooling towers—used to cool hot water used in heat transfer exchangers throughout the refinery
- Engines—used to compress refinery gases or power certain equipment
- Loading racks—used to load products into trucks, railcars, ships, or barges
- Process vents—from sulfur recovery units and fluidized catalytic cracking units
- Equipment leaks—from piping and instrumentation components
- Petroleum coke or catalyst handling
- Wastewater treatment facilities

Many of these sources require controls to help minimize their environmental impacts. For example, particulate (dust-like) emissions generated from handling petroleum coke or catalysts can be a health hazard for workers and can interfere with machinery. Coke and certain catalysts containing metals such as vanadium, copper, iron, and nickel might require spraying with water or other chemicals to reduce their ability to become airborne because they stick to the water droplets. This system has successfully reduced particulates inside and outside facilities.

Other air pollution controls include floating roofs on storage tanks that eliminate space for vapor buildup, periodic checks for equipment leaks using emission monitors, vapor collection systems, scrubbers to remove sulfur from combustion gases, and electrostatic precipitators to collect particulates.

Table 5-2.1.
EPA's Original List of HAPs

CAS Number	Chemical Name	CAS Number	Chemical Name	CAS Number	Chemical Name
75070	Acetaldehyde	106467	1,4-Dichlorobenzene(p)	108316	Maleic anhydride
60355	Acetamide	91941	3,3-Dichlorobenzidene	67561	Methanol
75058	Acetonitrile	111444	Dichloroethyl ether (Bis(2-chloro-ethyl)ether)	72435	Methoxychlor
98862	Acetophenone			74839	Methyl bromide (Bromomethane)
53963	2-Acetylaminofluorene	542756	1,3-Dichloropropene	74873	Methyl chloride (Chloromethane)
107028	Acrolein	62737	Dichlorvos	71556	Methyl chloroform (1,1,1-Trichloroethane)
79061	Acrylamide	111422	Diethanolamine		
79107	Acrylic acid	121697	N,N-Dimethylaniline	78933	Methyl ethyl ketone (2-Butanone)*
107131	Acrylonitrile	64675	Diethyl sulfate	60344	Methyl hydrazine
107051	Allyl chloride	119904	3,3-Dimethoxybenzidine	74884	Methyl iodide (Iodomethane)
92671	4-Aminobiphenyl	60117	Dimethyl aminoazobenzene	108101	Methyl isobutyl ketone (Hexone)
62533	Aniline	119937	3,3'-Dimethyl benzidine	624839	Methyl isocyanate
90040	o-Anisidine	79447	Dimethyl carbamoyl chloride	80626	Methyl methacrylate
1332214	Asbestos	68122	Dimethyl formamide	1634044	Methyl tert butyl ether
71432	Benzene (including benzene from gasoline)	57147	1,1-Dimethyl hydrazine	101144	4,4-Methylene bis(2-chloroaniline)
		131113	Dimethyl phthalate	75092	Methylene chloride (Dichloromethane)
92875	Benzidine	77781	Dimethyl sulfate		
98077	Benzotrichloride	534521	4,6-Dinitro-o-cresol, and salts	101688	Methylene diphenyl diisocyanate (MDI)
100447	Benzyl chloride	51285	2,4-Dinitrophenol		
92524	Biphenyl	121142	2,4-Dinitrotoluene	101779	4,4'-Methylenedianiline
117817	Bis(2-ethylhexyl)phthalate (DEHP)	123911	1,4-Dioxane (1,4-Diethyleneoxide)	91203	Naphthalene
		122667	1,2-Diphenylhydrazine	98953	Nitrobenzene
542881	Bis(chloromethyl)ether	106898	Epichlorohydrin (l-Chloro-2,3-epoxypropane)	92933	4-Nitrobiphenyl
75252	Bromoform			100027	4-Nitrophenol
106990	1,3-Butadiene	106887	1,2-Epoxybutane	79469	2-Nitropropane
156627	Calcium cyanamide	140885	Ethyl acrylate	684935	N-Nitroso-N-methylurea
105602	Caprolactam*	100414	Ethyl benzene	62759	N-Nitrosodimethylamine
133062	Captan	51796	Ethyl carbamate (Urethane)	59892	N-Nitrosomorpholine
63252	Carbaryl	75003	Ethyl chloride (Chloroethane)	56382	Parathion
75150	Carbon disulfide	106934	Ethylene dibromide (Dibromoethane)	82688	Pentachloronitrobenzene (Quintobenzene)
56235	Carbon tetrachloride				
463581	Carbonyl sulfide	107062	Ethylene dichloride (1,2-Dichloroethane)	87865	Pentachlorophenol
120809	Catechol			108952	Phenol
133904	Chloramben	107211	Ethylene glycol	106503	p-Phenylenediamine
57749	Chlordane	151564	Ethylene imine (Aziridine)	75445	Phosgene
7782505	Chlorine	75218	Ethylene oxide	7803512	Phosphine
79118	Chloroacetic acid	96457	Ethylene thiourea	7723140	Phosphorus
532274	2-Chloroacetophenone	75343	Ethylidene dichloride (1,1-Dichloroethane)	85449	Phthalic anhydride
108907	Chlorobenzene			1336363	Polychlorinated biphenyls (Aroclors)
510156	Chlorobenzilate	50000	Formaldehyde		
67663	Chloroform	76448	Heptachlor	1120714	1,3-Propane sultone
107302	Chloromethyl methyl ether	118741	Hexachlorobenzene	57578	beta-Propiolactone
126998	Chloroprene	87683	Hexachlorobutadiene	123386	Propionaldehyde
1319773	Cresols/Cresylic acid (isomers and mixture)	77474	Hexachlorocyclopentadiene	114261	Propoxur (Baygon)
		67721	Hexachloroethane	78875	Propylene dichloride (1,2-Dichloropropane)
95487	o-Cresol	822060	Hexamethylene-1,6-diisocyanate		
108394	m-Cresol	680319	Hexamethylphosphoramide	75569	Propylene oxide
106445	p-Cresol	110543	Hexane	75558	1,2-Propylenimine (2-Methyl aziridine)
98828	Cumene	302012	Hydrazine		
94757	2,4-D, salts and esters	7647010	Hydrochloric acid	91225	Quinoline
3547044	DDE	7664393	Hydrogen fluoride (Hydrofluoric acid)	106514	Quinone
334883	Diazomethane			100425	Styrene
132649	Dibenzofurans	7783064	Hydrogen sulfide*	96093	Styrene oxide
96128	1,2-Dibromo-3-chloropropane	123319	Hydroquinone	1746016	2,3,7,8-Tetrachlorodibenzo-p-dioxin
		78591	Isophorone		
84742	Dibutylphthalate	58899	Lindane (all isomers)	79345	1,1,2,2-Tetrachloroethane

Table 5-2.1. (cont.)
EPA's Original List of HAPs

CAS Number	Chemical Name	CAS Number	Chemical Name	CAS Number	Chemical Name
127184	Tetrachloroethylene (Perchloro-ethylene)	1582098	Trifluralin	0	Beryllium Compounds
		540841	2,2,4-Trimethylpentane	0	Cadmium Compounds
7550450	Titanium tetrachloride	108054	Vinyl acetate	0	Chromium Compounds
108883	Toluene	593602	Vinyl bromide	0	Cobalt Compounds
95807	2,4-Toluene diamine	75014	Vinyl chloride	0	Coke Oven Emissions
584849	2,4-Toluene diisocyanate	75354	Vinylidene chloride (1,1-Dichlo-roethylene)	0	Cyanide Compounds[1]
95534	o-Toluidine			0	Glycol ethers[2]
8001352	Toxaphene (chlorinated cam-phene)	1330207	Xylenes (isomers and mixture)	0	Lead Compounds
				0	Manganese Compounds
120821	1,2,4-Trichlorobenzene	95476	o-Xylenes	0	Mercury Compounds
79005	1,1,2-Trichloroethane	108383	m-Xylenes	0	Fine mineral fibers[3]
79016	Trichloroethylene	106423	p-Xylenes	0	Nickel Compounds
95954	2,4,5-Trichlorophenol	0	Antimony Compounds	0	Polycylic Organic Matter[4]
88062	2,4,6-Trichlorophenol	0	Arsenic Compounds (inorganic including arsine)	0	Radionuclides (including radon)[5]
121448	Triethylamine			0	Selenium Compounds

NOTE: For all listings above that contain the word "compounds" and for glycol ethers, the following applies: Unless otherwise specified, these listings are defined as including any unique chemical substance that contains the named chemical (i.e., antimony, arsenic, etc.) as part of that chemical's infrastructure.

[1] X'CN where X = H' or any other group where a formal dissociation may occur. For example KCN or Ca(CN)2

[2] Includes mono- and di- ethers of ethylene glycol, diethylene glycol, and triethylene glycol R-(OCH2CH2)n -OR' where n = 1, 2, or 3 R = alkyl or aryl groups R' = R, H, or groups which, when removed, yield glycol ethers with the structure: R-(OCH2CH)n-OH.

[*] Polymers are excluded from the glycol category.

[3] Includes mineral fiber emissions from facilities manufacturing or processing glass, rock, or slag fibers (or other mineral derived fibers) of average diameter 1 micrometer or less.

[4] Includes organic compounds with more than one benzene ring, and which have a boiling point greater than or equal to 100 ° C.

[5] A type of atom which spontaneously undergoes radioactive decay.

Source: U.S. Environmental Protection Agency

The passive soil-gas technique identifies:
- Volatile organic compounds
- Chlorinated hydrocarbons
- Contaminants in water and soil

Because vehicle emissions are among the most significant and widespread air pollution problems, standards for their fuel have become increasingly stringent as demonstrated by these changes:

- Lead as an additive to boost octane was phased out in the 1970s.
- Gas volatility in summer temperatures was reduced in 1989.
- Low-sulfur diesel fuel was mandated in 1993.
- Low-sulfur gasoline was mandated in 2000.
- Starting in 2004, the EPA required certain trucks and buses to lower emissions.

Refiners continue to seek processes that will produce higher quality, lower sulfur fuels and gasoline from lower quality crudes. Today, biofuels, primarily ethanol, are being added to gasoline and diesel fuels. Refiners are investing in this technology and the equipment to reduce the imports of crude to the United States. Forecasts indicate that the crudes of the future will be progressively heavier with higher sulfur content. Some crudes also contain much higher concentrations of metals. At the same time, environmental restrictions force reduced sulfur in fuel oils, and safety concerns remain a high priority in achieving the best product for consumers and the environment.

Soil and groundwater can become contaminated with oil and hazardous chemicals from breaks in pipelines, spills from trucks, or leaks from aboveground or underground tanks or refinery storage facilities. The *passive soil-gas technique* is a way to identify the presence of volatile organic compounds, chlorinated hydrocarbons, semi-volatile organic compounds, and other contaminants in groundwater, surface water, and soils. The technique maps areas of suspected pollution, such as where the contaminants are headed, and whether they come from multiple sources. It also identifies complex mixtures of contaminants. The technique is useful in the Arctic region, in tropical and desert environments, and in bottom sediments because the information collected offsets the influence of variations in temperature, barometric pressure, and moisture. It is also inexpensive and provides quality data.

Methyl *tert*-butyl ether (MTBE) was commonly produced at refineries and used as an oxygenate additive for gasoline prior to 2000. However, in 2000, the EPA set out a plan to phase out the use of MTBE in the United States over four years, because MTBE gives water an unpleasant taste at very low concentrations, and thus can render large quantities of groundwater non-potable, if contaminated. For the past decade, ethanol has been used as a safer alternative oxygenate additive for gasoline.

A number of ways exist to clean, or *remediate*, contaminated soil to safely leave it in place or reuse it as fill. Some methods are described in the following text.

In a process called *volatilization*, or *soil venting*, workers place slotted pipes down into the soil (fig. 5-2.20). The slotted pipes meet a horizontal pipe at the surface attached to a fan that blows out, creating a partial vacuum in the soil. As a result, the oil *volatilizes*, or evaporates, and passes into the slotted pipes, then flows to a treatment unit on the surface.

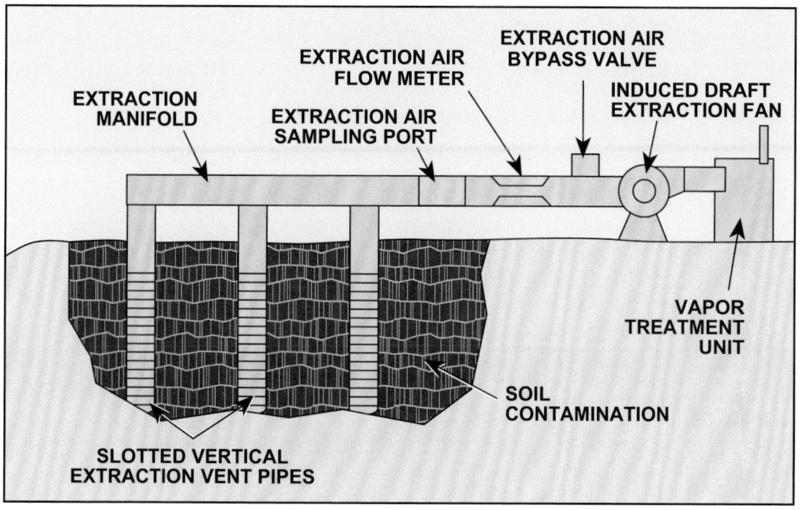

Detecting Contaminated Water and Soil

Cleaning Contaminated Soil

Mechanical Methods

EXTRACTION AIR BYPASS VALVE
EXTRACTION AIR FLOW METER
EXTRACTION MANIFOLD
EXTRACTION AIR SAMPLING PORT
INDUCED DRAFT EXTRACTION FAN
VAPOR TREATMENT UNIT
SOIL CONTAMINATION
SLOTTED VERTICAL EXTRACTION VENT PIPES

Figure 5-2.20. A blower extracts the volatile components from soil contaminated with oil.

Cleaning contaminated soil
uses:
- Mechanical methods
- Biodegradation
- Recycling
- Passive methods

Volatilization is a limited form of remediation. Only the lighter fractions of the oil volatilize and are removed. The process is ineffective in removing metals and nonvolatile compounds.

In *leaching*, a chemical is mixed with water and added to the soil (fig. 5-2.21). The chemical collects or reacts with the contaminant as the mixture soaks downward through the soil. Before it reaches the water table, the mixture is collected, usually using recovery wells. Next, the recovered water mixture must be purified by fractionation, centrifugation, solvent extraction, or some other means, all of which are not totally effective at purification.

Hydrocarbons are volatilized or encapsulated in hardened soil. Contaminated soil can be treated with heat or electricity. In thermal treatment, the soil is excavated and incinerated. This method requires air pollution control systems and disposal of the remaining ash or soil. A *vitrification treatment* applies electricity to the soil to melt it, taking the soil one to two weeks to cool. However, this process generates gases that must be treated.

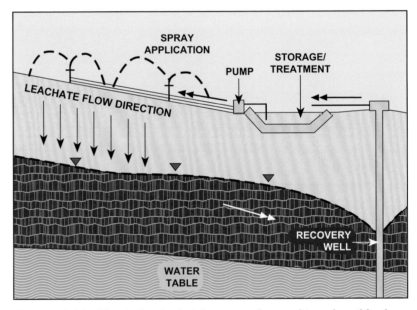

Figure 5-2.21. Chemicals mixed with water and sprayed into the soil leach contaminants from the soil and into a recovery well.

A wide variety of bacteria break down petroleum hydrocarbons, essentially by eating them. In addition to hydrocarbons, these bacteria need oxygen and water. A reclamation company can promote the action of such bacteria by mixing fertilizer with water and spraying or irrigating the soil. An oxygen source, such as hydrogen peroxide, can be added to the water, or the soil can be tilled periodically to supply oxygen to the bacteria. This process of *biodegradation* is similar to composting.

Where the water table is close to the surface, providing a ready water source, biodegradation is economical without moving the soil (fig. 5-2.22). At other sites, the reclaiming operator, or *reclaimer*, might remove the soil and place it on a lined pad. Such biodegradation methods can take several months.

To hasten biodegradation, the reclaimer might excavate the contaminated soil and pile it on a plastic liner with layers of crisscrossed slotted pipes every 1 to 2 feet (30 to 60 centimetres). Then fertilizer is added between rows of pipes, and black plastic that absorbs heat is used to cover the pile. The heat volatilizes the lighter hydrocarbons and speeds biodegradation of the rest of the hydrocarbons. The pipes carry away the produced gases and can also be used to add air to the pile. In a few months, the reclaimer can return the soil to the site as fill.

Biodegradation

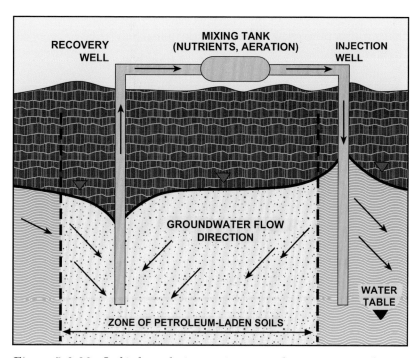

Figure 5-2.22. In biodegradation on site, groundwater is pumped to the surface, fertilizer is added, and then the groundwater is returned to the soil.

Recycling

If an asphalt plant is nearby, the reclaimer might transport contaminated soil there to be added to the asphalt. Because of the high heat involved in producing asphalt, the lighter fractions volatilize, and the rest becomes part of the asphalt. There are concerns that some contaminants such as leaded gasoline might leach out of the asphalt during use.

Passive Methods

If environmental regulations allow, the company responsible for the contaminated soil might do nothing but test it periodically to see if the site cleans up on its own by means of natural biodegradation, volatilization, *photolysis* (degradation by light), leaching, and adsorption. Liners or impermeable caps might be used to contain the contaminated soil to prevent contaminants from migrating due to rain.

FROM THE ENVIRONMENT TO THE INDIVIDUAL—HEALTH AND SAFETY

Laws governing refining and drilling are designed to improve safety and protect workers as well as the environment.

Regulations and treaties are in place not only to protect the environment and public welfare, but to also ensure the safety of individuals working in the oil and gas industry. Often, the two go hand in hand. The protection of one informs and improves the protection of the other. The previous sections outlined the environmental impacts of oil and gas and some of the methods used to minimize damage. The following sections outline the impact on humans and their safety needs in the workplace.

"Safety first" is a highly recognizable safety slogan in most work environments. No employer wants personnel injured on the job. Companies recognize that injuries are costly in terms of medical treatments and liability for injured workers as well as lost productivity. Losing employees to injuries also means that crews might have to function short-handed or risk substituting less-experienced workers in specialized roles. There are many laws and regulations governing safety. If ignored, companies face paying large fines and possible legal prosecution. Over the past decade, OSHA has increased enforcement against the oil and gas industry, particularly the refining and petrochemical sector.

Each year, more than 100 people are killed in the oil and gas industry due to industrial accidents. The industry engages in various construction activities and uses large machinery to do so. Such activities are spread out over a large area. These facts require workers to drive frequently and also handle oil and natural gas, two potentially flammable and explosive products. Dangers exist in almost all job functions.

An analysis of fatal injuries among oil and gas workers in the United States between 2003 and 2007 reveals these primary sources of injury:

- 28.7% from highway crashes
- 20.7% from being struck by an object
- 8.3% from explosions
- 7.8% from being caught in moving machinery
- 6.8% from falling
- 5.7% from electrocution
- 5.5% from fire
- 3.8% from aircraft crash
- 12.7% from other causes

Source: SPE 121 056 "Injury Risk among Oil and Gas Extraction Workers by Company Type and Size," R.D. Hill and P.D. Somervell

INDUSTRY WORKPLACE SAFETY

Industry Incidents

OSHA regulates safety in the workplace and has increased enforcement, specifically in the oil and gas industry.

Reducing Injuries

The most effective way of reducing industry injuries and incidents is to understand the risks involved with all work activities (fig. 5-2.23). Risk is defined as a combination of frequency and severity.

If one reduces the frequency of driving a car, then there is a reduction in the likelihood of a motor vehicle accident. Using the driving example again, crash data shows the severity of an injury is also reduced if the car travels at a slower speed—for example, driving 10 miles per hour (16 kilometres per hour) instead of 60 miles per hour (97 kilometres per hour). Obviously, workers can reduce risk of injury in a car crash if they drive less frequently and at lower speeds.

The same is true for oilfield injuries. Risk to employees can be minimized if the frequency and severity of a dangerous event are reduced. There are three critical ways to reduce risk to workers:

- Designing safe equipment
- Enforcing controls
- Wearing protective gear

Figure 5-2.23. Workers on oil rigs are exposed to numerous hazards.

Courtesy of Ensco International

The first step in making the workplace safe is to design safe facilities and processes. This means that facilities, wells, rigs, and roads must have safety features and protection devices to ensure the safety of all workers. An example might be installing a handrail to prevent workers from falling off of an elevated walkway or platform. In the same way, pressure vessels, pipe, pumps, and equipment must be designed with safety devices such as relief valves to release dangerous pressure. Safety design might include basic actions such as building a platform with stairs next to a pressure gauge so workers do not have to climb on piping to obtain pressure readings.

Resources that provide guidelines and protections regarding safe design include:

- **Codes and standards:** Many codes and standards have been developed by organizations such as the *American Petroleum Institute* (www.api.org), the *American Society of Mechanical Engineers* (www.asme.org), and the *National Fire Protection Association* (www.nfpa.org). These codes and standards can be used as guidelines when building new facilities and to help identify design problems after a facility is built. OSHA also has equipment standards that must be followed when designing a facility.

- **Hazard analysis:** A hazard analysis is often conducted on a plant to determine what could go wrong. Each item of equipment is scrutinized by a team of engineers and operations personnel to ensure the facility remains safe in all circumstances. Pressure rates, liquid levels, and temperatures are all examined in detail to ensure the facility is safe in the event of unexpected equipment problems or improper worker judgment, such as turning the wrong valve.

- **Past history or experience:** Another effective tool is using knowledge of past history and experience to help ensure equipment is safe. Many operators have vast experience operating equipment and can offer operating details to improve the safety design of new facilities and ensure old facilities are modified correctly to prevent injuries.

Equipment Designed for Safety

Designing safe equipment reduces workplace injuries. Equipment must include safety devices to ensure worker protection.

Administrative Controls

Guidelines for safe facilities and processes are kept through resources such as:
- Codes and standards
- Hazard analysis
- Past history of equipment safety

Administrative controls can be defined as safety policies, regulations, supervision, schedules, and training designed to improve safety (fig. 5-2.24). Most companies have written safety policies that guide decisions about their safety programs. A sound policy statement should be endorsed by management, be relevant to the specific workplace, and be accepted and enforced in practice.

Safety manuals generally contain information about the company's safety program, rules, and work procedures. Safety rules usually instruct workers on using *personal protective equipment (PPE)* and address job planning and *job safety analysis* (JSA). The manual might also contain specific procedures for common tasks, such as digging and trenching, confined space entry, and *lockout/tagout* of energized equipment.

Courtesy of SignPro

Figure 5-2.24. Proper signs help reinforce potential danger areas in the workplace.

Personal Protective Equipment

Photo by MC2 Sandra M. Palumbo, U.S. Navy

PPE, or personal protective equipment, is often viewed as a last resort of controls to protect workers from risk. PPE is used to prevent employee injuries or illnesses resulting from contact with physical, chemical, electrical, mechanical, or other such workplace hazards (fig. 5-2.25). For most workers, PPE often includes a hard hat, steel-toed shoes, and safety glasses. Under certain circumstances, it might also include flame-resistant clothing, a face shield, goggles, gloves, vest, earplugs, respirator, and a fall-protection harness.

Figure 5-2.25. PPE helps prevent employee injuries or illnesses due to physical, chemical, electrical, or mechanical hazards.

The Occupational Safety and Health Act of 1970 resulted in 24 states among the United States operating their own OSHA-approved safety and health programs. The state programs are equally as stringent as the federal program and might contain additional requirements. The oil and gas industry is generally covered by either General Industry (29 CFR 1910) requirements or Construction (29 CFR 1926) requirements. See the section on U.S. Laws and Regulations for more information on the Occupational Safety and Health Act.

OSHA requirements cover everything from the proper type of oil storage vessels to training requirements for employees. Additionally, the *General Duty Clause* states that each employer must furnish a worksite free from recognized hazards that cause, or could cause, injury or illness. Fundamentally, OSHA requires the employer take the lead and be held accountable for any safety deficiencies.

There are several types of records that companies must maintain. The records do not have to be submitted to OSHA but must be available to an OSHA inspector. Each company must keep records of workplace injuries and illnesses. Each company must also complete an annual *Summary of Work-Related Injuries and Illnesses* (OSHA 300A) form and post it from February 1 to May 1 of each year. This form and other information can be found on the OSHA Web site at www.osha.gov. Certain OSHA standards require records be kept on employee exposures to toxic substances and hazards, employee physical examination reports, and employment records. An employer is required to report to OSHA within 8 hours of the accident all work-related fatalities and multiple hospitalizations that involve three or more employees.

OSHA may conduct an inspection if there is imminent danger, a fatality, complaints, or because of referrals from other agencies. Inspectors may also conduct follow-up inspections to verify that unsafe conditions have been corrected or to conduct planned inspections of high-priority sites. Generally, the inspector will present credentials, conduct an opening conference, tour the site, and hold a closing conference.

Citations for any violations are categorized as other-than-serious, serious, willful, repeated, and failure to abate. Penalties rise in cost depending on the category of violation.

Safety Regulations

The law protects safety in the workplace via international administrative controls such as PPE and JSA, while also guarding workers on a federal level through OSHA.

Organizing a Safety and Health Program

The Management Systems Approach is a method regulating safety protocol and holds superiors accountable to ensure the safety of all employees.

Clean safety records and strong programs are usually the result of an entire company working as a team to promote safety (fig. 5-2.26, 5-2.27, and 5-2.28). Executives, managers, supervisors, and workers must know and exercise their roles to insure the safety of everyone. One successful means of compliance is having a management-supported program of basic safety expectations, often referred to as the *management systems approach* to safety. Elements of effective safety and health programs include:

- Making information available about risks and hazards to affected employees
- Identifying hazards and taking measures to prevent accidents
- Evaluating changes to equipment, procedures, and personnel for their impact on safety
- Ensuring operating procedures are in place to deal with start-up, normal, or emergency situations
- Establishing safe workplace practices and documenting them in a safety manual
- Conducting safety training for all employees
- Purchasing the right equipment and maintaining it to ensure it operates safely
- Conducting pre-startup reviews to make sure each job can be performed safely
- Ensuring emergency procedures are in place in case an accident happens
- Reporting and investigating all accidents to prevent recurrence
- Conducting safety audits to insure worksite safety and compliance with company polices and regulatory requirements

Courtesy of Ensco International

Figure 5-2.26. Checking the safety of electrical equipment

Figure 5-2.27. Monitoring the control system to ensure safe operations of a facility

Figure 5-2.28. All workers should receive training in safe work practices.

Checking for Hazards

Hazards that could lead to accidents must be identified before they can be controlled. For example, a potentially flammable gas must first be determined as leaking before actions can be taken to prevent sparks that could ignite vapors.

There are many ways to check a job site for hazards (fig. 5-2.29). Two of the most common methods are conducting a JSA (job safety analysis) and conducting a *checklist inspection*.

The JSA provides training to employees just before performing a job and gives pre-job instructions for irregular jobs. The JSA also investigates ways to perform a job more safely. All members of the job crew need to provide input during the process of a JSA. The process comprises three key steps:

1. Record the sequence of job steps or actions.
2. Identify potential hazards for each job step.
3. Record a recommended action or procedure to prevent hazards from causing an accident.

The checklist approach is also frequently used, and companies often create their own instruments. If a company does not have a checklist, one can be obtained from OSHA. Checklists are an effective way of self-auditing the work site. Workers evaluate their own work areas, whether an office or in the field. Checklists are available to address requirements for ladders, walking surfaces, cranes, office ergonomics, and so on.

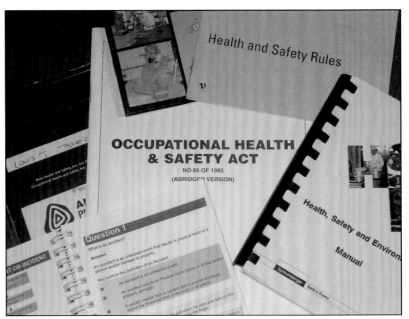

Figure 5-2.29. Procedures manuals and checklists assist in checking job site hazards.

The purpose of conducting accident investigations is to prevent a recurrence. All incidents must be investigated, regardless of the number of injuries (or lack of injuries) or amount of property damage.

During the course of an investigation, the facts, timelines, direct causes, and contributing factors are explored and documented. Interviews with each affected individual are conducted as soon as possible.

Often, accidents result from what is commonly referred to as a domino effect. The root cause can be defined as the initiating cause in a chain of unfortunate events. For example, a worker might cut a hand with a knife while opening a box. The investigation would seek to determine the root cause of the incident. In this example, the cause might be lack of proper training, or a PPE assessment that had not been completed for this task, or lack of a tool maintenance program.

Methods to prevent similar accidents based on the investigation's results are promptly communicated to other workers so everyone can learn from the incident.

Investigating Accidents

Workplace safety incorporates two methods:
- PPE, referring to physical safety
- JSA, training the employee in safe practices

All states within the United States have enacted *Workers Compensation* laws (www.workerscompensation.com). Benefits to an injured worker include income, medical payments, and rehabilitation, regardless of fault.

Companies benefit from the laws because they reduce personal-injury litigation. Employers are usually required to carry Workers Compensation insurance for their employees. Insurance rates depend on the number of accident claims by the employer over a given time period. As with most insurance, safer companies pay lower premiums. That means companies can save money by implementing effective safety programs that reduce injuries.

Treatment for industrial injuries is often managed by the company's Workers Compensation insurance carrier and not the employee's personal health insurance provider. In most cases, workers injured on the job do not incur out-of-pocket expenses. However, they must understand they are being treated under Workers Compensation, which is an entirely different system than personal health insurance.

Workers Compensation

Workers Compensation is not a form of personal health insurance. Workers are only covered by the employer's provider.

Incident Rates

Total recordable case rate or *days away from work frequency* refer to the incident rate of a company or portion of that company. Recordable work-related injuries and illnesses include:

- Death
- Loss of consciousness
- Days away from work cases
- Restricted activity or job transfer
- Medical treatment beyond first aid

Case incident rates hold companies accountable for the quality of their safety program as well as measure the improvement of programs over time.

Incident rates are calculated based on number of work-related injuries or illnesses for a given number of full-time employees. Most incident rates are *normalized* for 100 workers. For example, if there was one recordable injury for a company that had exactly 100 workers, then the total recordable case rate would be one for that company. The rate would be two for a company with 50 full-time employees and only one recordable injury for the year.

Incident rates are used to determine Workers Compensation insurance rates and to indicate the quality of a company's safety program. These rates are also used by companies to determine if their safety program is improving over time and to compare their performance to other companies or to national averages. Some companies use incident rates as a factor when considering contractors to hire.

Industrial Hygiene

Industrial hygiene helps prevent work-related sickness, impaired health, or discomfort. Examples of factors an *industrial hygienist* would examine are:

- Chemicals in the workplace
- Physical impacts such as noise, vibration, radiation, or extreme temperatures
- Ergonomic conditions such as improperly designed tools or workstations
- Biological factors such as exposure to viruses or bacteria

Some key hygiene areas of the oil and gas industry include heat exhaustion and exposure to noise, chemicals and benzene, *naturally occurring radiation*, and poisonous gases such as H_2S.

An industrial hygiene program might involve an industrial hygienist taking samples and readings to determine risk to workers' health. One tool used to determine chemical exposure takes atmospheric samples using a small device strapped to a worker's belt. The device is then analyzed to determine if the worker was exposed to dangerous quantities of chemicals during the testing period.

An industrial hygienist recommends corrective steps to reduce or prevent exposures. These measures might include engineering controls, administrative controls, or PPE to reduce exposure to harmful substances or conditions.

The oil and gas industry commonly employs contractors to perform many construction, drilling, workover, and maintenance jobs. Often, the nature of contracting work puts contractors at risk of injury. Operating companies have joint responsibility with contractors to make sure worksites are safe.

Operating companies bear responsibility to inform contractors of any hazards. They must also inspect the site for potential hazards, implement a system to correct hazards, and make sure the contractor follows safe practices (fig. 5-2.30).

The contractor must inform its employees of any existing hazards, take precautions to avoid creating hazards, and work with the operating company to correct hazards. Most operators have contractor selection criteria that address safety considerations. Operators will often ask for a document of the contractor's safety program and incident rates, as well as the contractor's *experience modification rate* and training program. This information helps the operator determine if the contractor has an effective safety program, acceptable incident rates, and proper training for its employees.

Contractor Safety

Figure 5-2.30. Contractors must have well-documented, positive safety records to be considered to work on drilling and production operations.

Proper Training

Effective safety programs require proper personnel training. Training might include discussing new PPE requirements or conducting a JSA.

A good safety program ensures workers are trained in safety. The type of training, supporting materials, and frequency generally depends on the type of work performed or the hazards to which the workers are exposed.

Some training might be given to all personnel at a company. For example, all employees might receive training on emergency procedures, PPE requirements, or proper reporting of injuries. There are also certain regulatory requirements, such as training workers on the role of OSHA.

Most training depends on the type of work and equipment a company uses. Safety professionals often develop a training matrix based on potential hazards a worker might encounter. Using a matrix or other aid helps employers track if employees have been properly trained.

Training can take place in a classroom environment and in the field (fig. 5-2.31). Workers might be asked to demonstrate knowledge in hands-on activities or with a written test to assess comprehension. A successful training program should document the instruction each employee receives. Generally, training records are centrally kept and are subject to inspection by company or OSHA personnel.

Figure 5-2.31. Training programs ensure employees maintain a safe workplace.

Safety meetings are an effective means to heighten awareness of potential hazards or risks (fig. 5-2.32). A *tailgate meeting* usually occurs at the beginning of a job or shift. Such meetings provide an opportunity to discuss possible hazards expected that day, review recent incidents, or conduct a JSA to facilitate the day's work.

Most companies hold group meetings every month to discuss safety issues affecting a broad group of employees. Topics might include new PPE requirements, changes in operating procedures, or updates to regulatory requirements. Some companies might also conduct safety training at these group meetings.

Another tactic is holding *safety stand downs*, which are large group safety meetings called as needed, such as following a major incident or near incident. The purpose of these meetings is to heighten safety awareness on a particular topic or promote discussion about a recent accident.

Safety Meetings

Courtesy of Contek Solutions

Figure 5-2.32. Company safety meeting in progress

Emergency Planning

Each worksite needs an emergency plan in the event of an accident. The plan should include emergency telephone numbers for an ambulance, the fire department, the police, and local hospitals. Workers must know proper protocols to be used in an emergency.

Additionally, plans must be developed to determine each worker's role during a fire, explosion, or natural disaster such as a flood, tornado, hurricane, or earthquake. Plans should include how to notify company management and safety staff members, especially if a worker has been injured. Usually, an incident investigation team is assembled after an incident to determine how to avoid a repeat event.

Special Requirements

Facilities that have over 10,000 pounds (4.5 tonnes) of a flammable or hazardous substance might be subject to special requirements under federal regulations. Such facilities are required to implement a comprehensive management program that integrates technologies, procedures, and management practices under OSHA regulations with a goal to improve safety at the facility. *Process Safety Management* has fourteen elements covering topics such as process safety, operating procedures, training, maintenance, audits, incident investigations, and contractor responsibilities.

Larger facilities might also be required to develop a *Risk Management Plan* under EPA regulations. Such plans deal primarily with impact on the public or areas outside plant boundaries. Scenarios involving fires, blasts, and release of a toxic substances are modeled to determine if a potential incident at a facility could impact the public.

SUMMARY

Every day brings new challenges for the petroleum industry. These include the way a company responds to the human and environmental hazards of working with oil and gas. There are many methods and regulations to help protect human health and the environment and prevent damaging incidences. It does not matter whether a facility is on land or offshore, the company running the exploration, drilling, or production of petroleum has responsibility for safety. This responsibility covers the method of drilling a company chooses to use, how it transports petroleum products, or how it prevents and responds to incidents. Operating according to the international and federal standards in place is the means by which companies can rise to these challenges. However, companies must do more than obey laws. They must adapt to ever-changing conditions in the field (for example, weather) and in the public arena (for example, perceptions of non-industry groups and individuals).

REFERENCES

1. *E&P Onshore Operations Safety Handbook*, First Edition, API, Washington DC (December 2008).

2. *§1910.119 Process Safety Management of Highly Hazardous Chemicals*, 29CFR Part 1910.119

3. Fairfax, Richard, *OSHA Letter of Interpretation to Mr. C. Morgan*, July 17, 2006 (Can be found online at: http://www.osha.gov/pls/oshaweb/owadisp.show_document?p_table=INTERPRETATIONS&p_id=25498)

4. "Training Requirements in OSHA Standards and Training Guidelines," U.S. Department of Labor, OSHA 2254, (1998 [Revised])

5. *Accident Prevention Manual for Business and Industry, Administration & Programs*, Eleventh Edition, National Safety Council, Itasca Illinois (1997)

6. *RP 74, Recommended Practice for Occupational Safety for Onshore Oil and Gas Production Operation*, First Edition, API, Washington DC (Reaffirmed 2007)

7. *RP 75, Recommended Practices Development of a Safety and Environmental Management Program for Outer Continental Shelf (OCS) Operations and Facilities*, Fourth Edition, API, Washington DC (2004)

8. *RP 76, Contractor Safety Management for Oil and Gas Drilling and Production Operations*, Second Edition, API, Washington DC (2007)

9. Hill, R.D., Conway, G.A., and Somerveil, P.D.: "Injury Risk Among Oil and Gas Extraction Workers by Company Type and Size," Proc., 2008 SPE Americas E&P Environmental & Safety Conference, San Antonio (2008)

10. *Safety on the Rig, Unit I Lesson 10*, Fourth Edition, Petroleum Extension Service, Austin Texas (1999)

11. *2007 Summary of Occupational Incidents (US Land Totals)*, IADC ASP Program, International Association of Drilling Contractors, Houston Texas (2008)

12. U.S. Department of Labor, OSHA. Retrieved 5/15/2009, from http://www.osha.gov/dep/industry_profiles/p_profile-138.html

13. U.S. Department of Labor, OSHA. Retrieved 5/15/2009 from http://www.osha.gov/recordkeeping/new-osha300form1-1-04.pdf

In this chapter:

- Petroleum and other energy sources
- Challenges and priorities
- Critical technologies of the future
- Nontechnical solutions

Petroleum is only one source of energy. People and countries care about energy because it is relevant to many sectors across societies. Many sources are used to supply that energy. The world uses a mix of oil, coal, natural gas, nuclear, and other alternatives, in order of decreasing magnitude. The world's use of fuels includes slightly less oil and slightly more traditional *biomass*, such as wood or cow dung, than the United States, but other than that has a similar mix. In the United States, petroleum is the leading fuel source, followed by natural gas, coal, nuclear, hydropower, and other renewable energy (fig. 5-3.1).

A *British thermal unit (Btu)* is equal to the energy of about one standard kitchen match. In 2004, the United States reportedly used one billion million Btus a year. A *quad* is 1 quadrillion Btus, or 1×10^{15} Btus. In 2004 alone, total energy use was approximately 445 quad for the world's consumption and 100 quad for consumption in the United States. Since then, global consumption has increased to approximately 500 quad in 2008, while consumption in the United States has stayed about the same.

The information presented in this chapter reflects the viewpoints of the author and is based on his extensive research and professional experience.

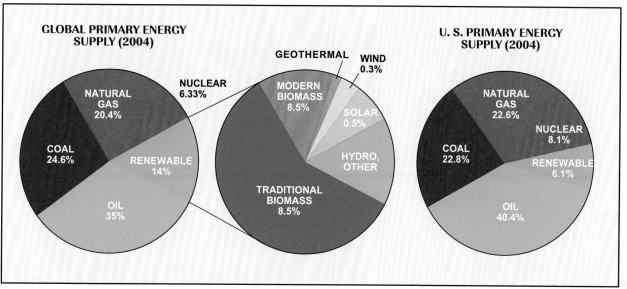

Source: U.S. Department of Energy, Energy Information Administration

Figure 5-3.1. The global (left and middle) and United States (right) energy mix is diverse, although fossil fuels satisfy more than 80% of the world's primary energy resources.

In 2008 in the United States, petroleum was responsible for:
- About 96% of fuel consumption in the transportation and electricity sectors
- Less than 2% of electricity generation

Various sectors are responsible for this energy consumption, including:

- Transportation
- Electricity
- Industry
- Residential
- Commercial

Figure 5-3.2 compares 2007 fuel consumption in the transportation and electricity sectors of the United States. In the pie chart on the right, petroleum for transportation accounts for 96%, making up the largest portion. The remaining 4% comes from sources such as ethanol and compressed natural gas. The pie chart on the left shows the fuel mix for electricity, which is diverse and almost completely powered by domestic sources, with approximately half of its fuel from coal, then natural gas, nuclear, *renewables*, and finally, petroleum. While petroleum was responsible for up to 17% of electricity generation in the United States in the 1970s, its use has dropped to less than 2% today. Consequently, the popular notion that conserving electricity (for example, by turning off lights), or bringing more renewable sources online such as wind and solar power, will displace petroleum does not make sense. Because these sectors are mostly independent from each other, there is minimal connection between electricity use and petroleum consumption. However, if transportation should become powered by electricity, then these two sectors will be joined and petroleum consumption for transportation could be reduced.

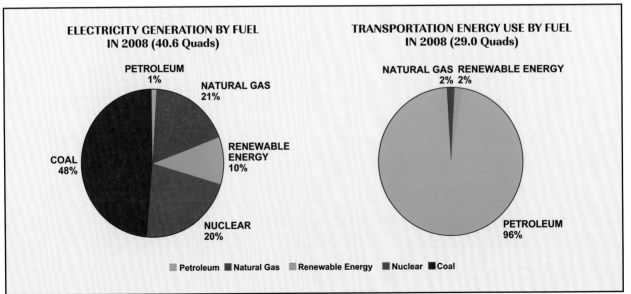

Source: U.S. Department of Energy, Energy Information Administration

Figure 5-3.2. The fuels for electricity generation (left) in the United States are diverse, with coal providing about half. By contrast, transportation (right) is almost completely fueled by petroleum.

As a nation, the United States consumes the most overall energy. Among larger nations, it is the largest consumer of energy per person, although some smaller, energy-rich nations such as Iceland or Qatar consume more energy per person than the United States. It is likely that China passed the United States in total annual *greenhouse gas (GHG)* emissions in 2007 or 2008, but such tallies carry large uncertainties and so it is difficult to know for certain.

This large energy consumption has many positive benefits and negative impacts. Among the positive benefits are the enabling effects energy has on transportation, mobility, industry, and the economy. Many people historically associate energy consumption with societies that are affluent and have a higher quality of life. And while it's true that low energy consumption correlates very well with poverty, high energy consumption does not linearly correlate with affluence or high quality of life. For example, some countries such as Russia and Saudia Arabia do not have the scale of economic activity to match the scale of their energy consumption. Despite their high energy consumption, residents of the United States rank thirty-eighth in life expectancy and thirteenth in quality of life worldwide (Table 5-3.1).

ENERGY CONSUMPTION

Table 5-3.1
Countries and Total Energy Use

Rank	Energy Use (Quad)	Annual Energy Use Per Capita (MMBtu)	Life Expectancy at Birth (years)	Quality of Life
1	**United States (99.9)**	Canada (427.2)	Japan (82.6)	Canada
2	China (73.8)	**United States (334.6)**	Hong Kong (82.2)	Switzerland
3	Russia (30.4)	Australia (276.9)	Iceland (81.8)	Norway
4	Japan (22.8)	Belgium (265.1)	Switzerland (81.7)	Luxembourg
5	India (17.677)	Saudi Arabia (255.0)	Australia (81.2)	Sweden
6	Germany (14.6)	Finland (252.7)	Spain (80.9)	Australia
7	Canada (14.0)	Netherlands (250.9)	Sweden (80.9)	Iceland
8	France (11.4)	Sweden (245.8)	Israel (80.7)	Italy
9	United Kingdom (9.8)	Russia (213.9)	Macau (80.7)	Denmark
10	Brazil (9.6)	Taiwan (200.6)	France (80.7)	Spain
—	—	—	—	—
13				**United States**
—	—	—	—	—
38			**United States (78.2)**	

Listing of countries according to their total energy use (in quadrillion Btu, or quads), per capita energy use (for countries with a population greater than 5 million; in million of Btu, or MMBtu), life expectancy at birth (in years) and quality of life. Based on 2004 and 2005 data. Source: U.S. Department of Energy, Energy Information Administration; Population Division of the Department of Economic and Social Affairs of the United Nations Secretariat; and *The Economist: The World.*

> While the amount of today's emissions is important, the concerns about global climate change are the result of cumulative GHGs emitted over the last few hundred years.

Although Americans consume much more energy than do other industrialized countries, they do not live any longer and do not appear to experience a higher quality of life, according to sources. The question arises: Is this an opportunity for the United States or other countries to consider a new approach to energy? How can people get all the benefits of energy consumption while mitigating some of the downside risks?

The drawbacks of large consumption include significant environmental, economic, and national security impacts. For example, as of the date of this book's publication, the United States and China are the leading annual emitters of GHGs (source: USEIA. *World Carbon Dioxide Emissions from the Use of Fossil Fuels*. International Energy Annual 2005, 2007; cited 26 October, 2007). While the amount of today's emissions is important, the concerns about global climate change are the result of cumulative GHGs emitted over the last few hundred years. Over this timeframe, the United States is far and away the leading emitter, having produced about 30% of all emissions since the mid-nineteenth century, far ahead of Europe, China, India, and other major emitters combined (fig. 5-3.3).

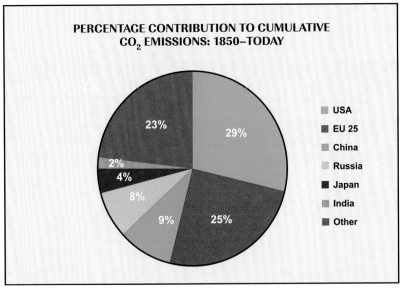

Figure 5-3.3. The percentage contribution to cumulative CO₂ emissions, 1850-2005, from different countries or regions reveals the United States to be the dominant historical contributor of CO₂ emissions to the atmosphere. Although China might have passed the United States in annual emissions, its total emissions over the last 150 years is less than one-third the size of U.S. emissions.

Other environmental impacts from high energy consumption (fig. 5-3.4) include:

- Air pollution from sulfur oxides, nitrogen oxides, and other toxics that can cause respiratory problems
- Water pollution, including the risk of thermal pollution; for example, from the rejection of cooling water from power plants. Also contamination from oil spills and ash ponds
- Land disturbances from mining, energy crop production, and storage of waste
- Cumulative effects of GHG emissions, which many experts consider to be inducing global climate change

The economic impacts include the effects of energy prices on the broader economy, particularly in an era of generally increasing prices and greater volatility. With finite resources, depletion and geological constraints invite concerns about having a sufficient abundance of energy to meet a nation's goals for a prosperous, vibrant economy. In addition, there are national security concerns about the vulnerability of supplies to intentional disruption. It's important to note here that these issues are not endured by the United States alone, but rather are typical of the experience of other major consuming nations.

Figure 5-3.4. High energy consumption causes impacts to the environment.

ENERGY CHALLENGES

The existing global energy system has several challenges that are expected to worsen if the current fuel mix remains the same while energy consumption grows. These challenges can be categorized into three main impact areas:

- Environmental
- Economic
- Security

Environmental Impact

The current energy system has extensive impacts on the environment (fig. 5-3.5). Impacts to land include:

- Acreage for power plants and collecting fuels such as coal, crops for biomass, and collectors for solar and wind energy
- Water used in power plants for cooling—the number-one cause of water withdrawals in the United States—and for agricultural production of energy crops
- Risk of oil spills, leaked nuclear radiation, or other contaminants getting into the water supply
- Air impacts caused by emissions of particles and gases that affect human health and induce climate change, acid rain, and smog
- Escalating concerns about carbon emissions

Figure 5-3.5. To deliver electricity, power plants must draw significant resources to distribute energy.

Energy imports can be expensive. For example, every day, the United States imports 14 million barrels of oil at a price ranging from $50 to $140 per barrel, creating a large trade deficit that exceeded a half trillion dollars in 2008. While this sum is significant, it is generally accepted that the imported oil is cheaper than equivalent volumes of domestically produced oil. Natural gas imports add billions of dollars more to the deficit. At an individual level, energy expenditures are a substantial portion of personal budgets as higher energy prices show up in the prices of food, plastic, chemical products, and pharmaceuticals. A new record was made in 2006 with the average family paying $2,227 for gasoline (fig. 5-3.6). This record was shattered again in 2007 and 2008. Notably, because electricity markets are almost entirely domestic, very little electricity crosses national boundaries.

Economic Impact

Figure 5-3.6. Gasoline prices directly impact households in terms of behavior. Transportation continues to be the largest sector of energy use.

Security Impact

- Analysts predict that U.S. energy consumption will increase steadily and the fuel mix will remain about the same.
- Expectations are driven by population and economic growth projections, but trends can shift with changes in policies and behaviors.

The energy system also has an impact on national security. For example, countries in the headlines are intertwined with the world's energy system:

- Iraq has the second largest reserves of conventional petroleum in the world.
- Iran is a major oil producer and exporter and has publicly expressed its desire to build nuclear weapons.
- North Korea would also like to build nuclear power plants.
- Nigeria's oil producing delta is in a state of open rebellion, largely due to the uneven distribution of oil wealth within the country.
- China has growing energy consumption and constructs one or two new coal power plants every week, which do not conform to environmental standards defined by developed nations, and subsequently have much higher levels of CO_2 emissions.
- Russia temporarily became the largest oil producing country in 2008 and has the world's largest reserves of natural gas. Russian pipelines control the flow of significant volumes of natural gas into central Europe. The oil-rich countries of the Caspian area have few routes to market that do not flow through Russia.

All of these challenges are present today. By moving forward without implementing a change in energy strategy, these problems will likely worsen.

ANALYST PROJECTIONS

Analysts in the U.S. Department of Energy expect American consumption to increase steadily over the next twenty years (fig. 5-3.7). However, according to many mainstream predictions, the fuel mix is not expected to change much, even if renewable sources continue showing swift adoption rates. The fundamental drivers of these expectations for increasing energy demand are population growth and economic growth. While these projections offer a useful assessment of continuing business as usual, the energy fate of the U.S. population is by no means restricted to these trend lines. For example, figure 5-3.8 shows different projections released annually, with 2030 consumption projected to vary from as high as 134 quads (based on 2006 projections) to as low as 113 quads (based on 2009 projections).

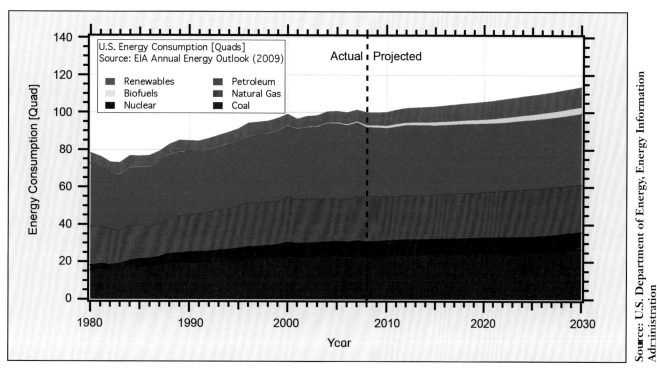

Figure 5-3.7. Projections reveal expectations for continued growth in overall energy consumption in the United States with little substantive change to the overall fuel mix, despite aggressive growth for renewable power. Note: liquids includes biofuels.

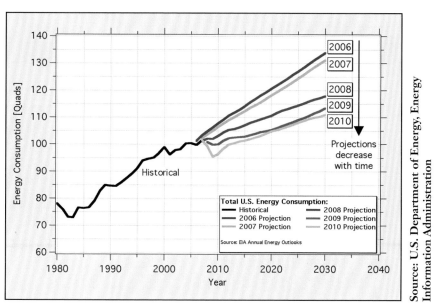

Figure 5-3.8. Projections show expectations for continued growth in overall energy consumption. However, the projected energy consumption in 2030 varies from as high as 134 quads (from the 2006 projection) to as low as 111 quads (from the 2010 projection). This range reveals the difficulty in making accurate projections for energy consumption.

Energy Attitudes

Confused attitudes about energy inhibit the ability to formulate effective policy. There are many examples that prove this point, the most telling of which is how China's growing demand for energy was often blamed for high oil prices during the 2006–2009 time period.

Newspaper articles, commentaries, pundits, and letters to editors often decry that The People's Republic of China bears responsibility for higher prices. Trusted media outlets often point to China's (and the rest of Southeast Asia's) surging demand for oil as largely responsible for run-ups in energy prices. One of the reasons China is assigned so much blame is because Chinese oil consumption has been rising at an amazing rate over the last decade. In 2008, China demanded 4.2 million more barrels of oil every single day than it did in 1996. Although Chinese domestic oil production has increased to meet some of that demand, in 2008, China still imported 3.7 million more barrels every single day from the world markets than in 1996, making imports about half of its total consumption and helping to drive up world oil prices (fig. 5-3.9)

Over the exact same time span, U.S. oil demand rose as well, and its imports of oil from the world markets went up 3.7 million barrels every day between 1996 and 2007. In 2008, the United States imported about three-fifths of its petroleum and more than 3.5 times as many barrels of

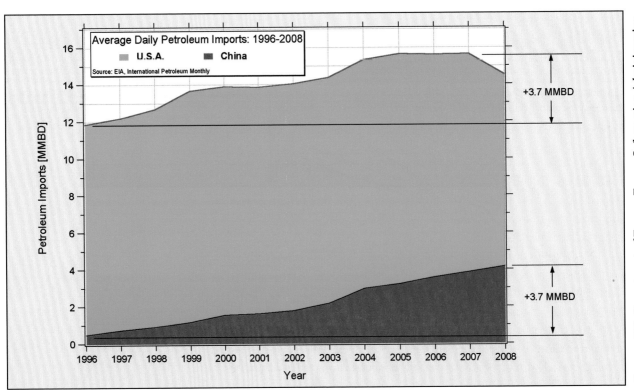

Figure 5-3.9. The average daily petroleum imports in millions of barrels per day (MMBD) for the United States and China have shown similar patterns of growth over the last 12 years. U.S. petroleum imports grew 3.7 MMBD between 1996 and 2007 before dropping to about 1 MMBD in 2008 in the face of high prices. China's petroleum imports similarly grew 3.7 MMBD between 1996 and 2008. Overall, U.S. consumption and imports of petroleum are 2.5 and 3.5 times larger than China's, respectively.

oil in total than China, while its total consumption (including domestically produced petroleum) is about 2.5 times larger. These staggering differences occurred despite having a population one-fourth the size. Thus, U.S. imports of oil from the world make America's demand just as responsible for high prices as China's. Notably, U.S. imports dropped by approximately one *million barrels per day (MMBD)* in 2008 because of a spike in oil prices, which triggered conservation domestically, whereas Chinese imports continued to grow.

This example demonstrates the impact of current mindsets regarding growing demand for imported oil and which demand is acceptable. If each country considers their own consumption to be okay but another country's consumption to be the problem, then making progress toward a collaborative energy future will be difficult.

Confusion in the United States also exists about whether oil prices should be high or low. High prices are good for energy companies and increase employment in energy-producing locations such as Texas in the United States. High prices are also favorable for energy-producing allies such as Saudi Arabia and Norway. Also, high prices are great for the environment because they encourage conservation and adoption of alternative fuel sources. High prices also free companies to fund research to develop more sophisticated energy technologies. Therefore, high prices are good.

However, low prices are also good. They are good for consumers to keep energy affordable, which is important for social justice considerations. And, low prices are also good for the U.S. foreign policy stance toward energy-producing countries such as Iran. Low prices discourage research of new technologies and encourage overconsumption. Recoverable reserves decrease significantly when oil prices are low because entities cannot afford to develop them.

The lack of consensus about whether prices should be high or low is in contrast to the opinion of the European Union (EU), which has a longstanding consensus that prices should be high. Those high prices together with higher population density have enabled the EU to make progress with its conservation efforts.

A sensible energy policy moving forward would tolerate higher energy costs but only in conjunction with incentives, technology investments, and market innovations to neutralize the net effect on consumers. For example, consumers are not likely to mind if gasoline prices double as long as car fuel economy also doubles, making the net cost per mile traveled the same. As utility executives know well, consumers care a lot about the total amount of their monthly electricity and gas bills. If price per kilowatt hour were doubled and overall consumption were halved, then the total bill would be left the same, and few customers might notice.

Achieving this kind of rational energy policy requires consensus. As long as differences in opinion regarding fundamentals on energy policy continue, progress will be slow.

> Future energy policy should tolerate higher energy costs in conjunction with:
> - Incentives
> - Technology investments
> - Market innovations

ENERGY TRADEOFFS

An important approach to solving energy problems is to consider the energy options in terms of tradeoffs. Unfortunately, there are no clear-cut choices. Some choices, while good for addressing one need, have drawbacks regarding another need. The following is an example of such a dilemma.

Question: Paper or Plastic?

Consider the following common scenario. Shoppers checking out at many grocery stores are often asked whether they want a paper or a plastic bag to hold their groceries. The answer might seem simple, but it is actually quite complex.

Plastic is beneficial because it is reusable, compact, and consumes very little material. Also, plastic does not use paper pulp, so no trees need be harvested for its fabrication. But plastic bags can be a bad choice because they are not biodegradable, they float into ecosystems, and they use primary energy resources (fig. 5-3.10).

Paper is beneficial because it is reusable, renewable, and biodegradable. However, it can be a bad choice because it uses more materials and is made of biomaterials. Making paper involves harvesting trees.

So, what is the answer? Canvas can be an answer, because it is reusable for many years, it will not float away, and it is renewable and biodegradable. However, it is the most expensive of the three options and requires a fundamental behavioral change on the part of consumers.

This question is a typical energy riddle. There are only two options presented when a different, third option exists. Often, typical media coverage and political approaches simplify the energy problem into a choice between two options without noting there are additional options available.

Figure 5-3.10. Paper or plastic? Both have distinct advantages and disadvantages in terms of environmental considerations.

In looking at tradeoffs, it is important to examine priorities. For example, to explore its energy options, the United States seeks to balance the three priorities outlined earlier: economy, environment, and security. The ideal U.S. energy solution:

- Is sufficiently abundant such that it enables the U.S. economy to prosper

- Does not pollute the environment beyond U.S. capacity to clean up

- Does not undermine U.S. security by introducing vulnerabilities into the system of energy delivery, and does not enrich countries with interests counterposed to the United States

These three priorities are essentially the criteria by which to measure options for energy policy moving forward (fig. 5-3.11).

The challenge is that many fuels or energy technologies that might be considered for solving the energy problem only satisfy one or two of the three criteria.

For example, the United States has the largest coal reserves in the world where coal is domestically abundant. There are extensive reserves, and coal is inexpensive to produce. However, coal is dirty and carbon intensive. Therefore, it satisfies the economic concerns and national security concerns of the United States, but it does not satisfy its environmental concerns. *Bioenergy* (in the form of biomass or liquid fuels) is domestically produced, but it is currently not abundant and is potentially bad for the environment. The United States has other domestic resources that are aligned with the environment, namely solar and wind. They are both abundant in terms of raw resources but are generally unavailable where people reside. This means their availability is not guaranteed as needed. So, these domestic sources satisfy only two of the three priorities.

Finding ways to bridge these gaps is the key to finding a viable energy solution.

Balancing Priorities

The ideal energy solution:
- Is sufficiently abundant
- Does not pollute the environment
- Does not undermine U.S. security

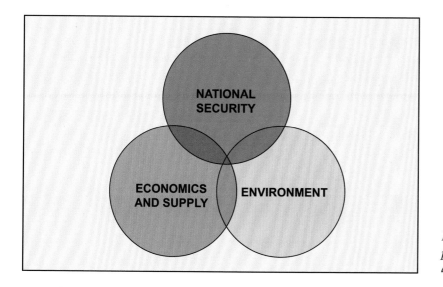

Figure 5-3.11. Three energy policy priorities: national security, economics and supply, and the environment.

ENERGY TECHNOLOGIES OF THE FUTURE

The critical energy technologies of the future are those that address the energy problem while balancing the three key priorities.

Defining Critical Technologies

Many of the fuels or energy technologies that might be considered for solving the energy problem only satisfy one or two of the three key priorities. There are abundant domestic resources—coal, biomass, solar, and wind—but they are all problematic in one way or another. Critical technologies are those that allow either development of domestic resources in an abundant and environmentally friendly manner or the import of clean and abundant energy from "friendly" nations. Technologies that can bridge the gaps and enable win-win situations are the critical technologies of the future.

Green Energy Transition

There are four critical technologies that facilitate overcoming barriers to a green energy transition:

- Energy storage, both large and small scale
- Carbon capture and sequestration
- Supergrids
- Next-generation biofuels

All four have their merits, promises, and drawbacks.

Small-Scale Electricity Storage

Energy storage can be effective on two scales. On a small scale, energy storage enables *electrified transportation*. Electrified transportation is valuable because it can be powered by abundant domestic resources (or uranium imported from Australia or Canada) and thereby offset the use of imported petroleum. That is, electrified transportation, enabled by breakthroughs in small-scale energy storage, allows the use of fuels produced domestically or from friendly nations to displace petroleum, thereby averting the security vulnerabilities induced by the transportation sector.

In addition, it is easier to lessen the size or severity of the environmental impact of about 1,500 power plants with electrified transportation than it is to manage impact from the tailpipes of more than 200 million petroleum-fueled vehicles. In this way, by shifting the air quality impacts of transportation from the tailpipe to the smokestack, the problem of controlling emissions is simplified and easier to manage.

The key parameters that determine readiness of small-scale energy storage for use are *gravimetric density* (energy storage per unit mass) and *volumetric density* (energy storage per unit volume).

The challenge for small-scale energy storage for transportation is that it must compete with liquid fuels. Gasoline, diesel, and other liquid fuels have exceptional storage capabilities. They also have excellent power densities, which means their energy can be stored in a compact, lightweight way. As shown in Table 5-3.2, conventional approaches to electricity storage, including batteries, must still achieve an order of magnitude of improvement to displace liquid fuels in a significant way.

Table 5-3.2
Technologies, Energy, Use, and Impact

Technology	Volumetric Energy Density (MJ/m³)	Gravimetric Energy Density (kJ/kg)	Capacity
Inductor	10	2	Small
Capacitor	40	40	Small
Battery: Lead-Acid	30	180	Small
Flywheel	200	200	Small
Battery: NiMH	360	270	Small
Battery: Lithium	1080	540	Small
Gasoline	35,000	44,000	Small
Ethanol	24,000	24,000	Small
Hydrogen	0.000001	120,000	Small
Pumped Hydro	0.001	0.001	Large
Compressed Air Energy Storage	10-20	N/A	Large

Different fuels and storage devices store energy, each with a particular volumetric and gravimetric energy density. Liquid fuels are particularly good at storing energy, which makes it challenging to find a replacement for their use. (Values derived from a variety of standard sources and references.)

Large-Scale Electricity Storage

Large-scale electricity storage is also valuable because it enables greater use of intermittent renewable sources. Intermittency is a limiting factor of domestic renewable sources such as wind and solar. Using storage to mitigate this intermittency by storing power when excess wind or sunlight is available, to release later when both are unavailable, will allow for much greater penetration of both renewable sources.

The key parameters that determine widespread use are volumetric density, energy storage per unit volume, and total volume or total capacity. The two basic schemes for large-scale energy storage in use today are *compressed air energy storage (CAES)* and pumped *hydroelectric energy storage*, both of which have been deployed in limited fashion. Other options being deployed include flow batteries and other novel electrochemical storage configurations.

Carbon Capture and Sequestration

Carbon capture and sequestration (CCS) is another critical technology. CCS basically enables the use of abundant domestic solid fuels such as coal and oil shale to make electricity and liquid fuels. Because shale and coal are abundant, they remain attractive options for displacing imported liquid fuels, and thus, are appealing from economic and national security perspectives. However, because of concerns about higher GHG emissions per unit of useful energy harvested, their production is not expected to grow quickly. Consequently, by developing a way to minimize the carbon emissions of these sources—for example, by capturing and sequestering the carbon—these fuels can be tapped to offset imported petroleum without concerns of amplifying GHG emissions.

There are two key questions in considering CCS:

- What is the best capture method?
- What is the best approach to sequestration once the CO_2 has been captured?

Regarding the best capture method, one option is post-combustion capture, which includes stripping CO_2 out of smokestack gases (fig. 5-3.12). One challenge with this approach is that the stack gases are comprised of many species, several of which (for example, water vapor and nitrogen) are harmless and abundant. As a result, it will be necessary to design a system that can discriminately capture the CO_2 while allowing the bulk of other gases to pass through unfiltered.

To accomplish this goal, *carbon scrubbers* use solutions that contain chemicals such as chilled ammonia or methanolamine that tend to bind with CO_2. Therefore, when flue gases are bubbled through the solutions, they scrub out the CO_2. After capturing the CO_2 in an absorber system using one of these working fluids, the CO_2 can be removed in a device called a *stripper* (because it strips off the CO_2 from the absorbent) and then used for enhanced oil recovery, or sequestered. One drawback is that the current designs for carbon capture require significant heat inputs for the stripper, and therefore, are a significant drag on the overall power plant efficiency. This is due to the heat siphoned off for carbon capture instead of power generation. For example, capturing 90% of the emitted carbon with these scrubbers can lower power output by 30% because of the diverted steam power.

Other approaches such as *oxy-combustion* help drive up the relative portion of the stack gases comprised of CO_2, which makes the capture process simpler, even though more energy is required up front to make the oxygen used for combustion. Also, the use of *integrated gasification combined cycle (IGCC)* power plants might make carbon separation easier. By beginning with gasification of the coal, the unwanted carbon flows in a mixture of carbon monoxide with hydrogen. Because the relative *atomic diameters* and *molecular masses* are very different for CO and H_2, it is much simpler to separate out the gases.

Figure 5-3.12. CO_2 from smokestacks and refineries can be captured and permanently injected in the ground.

Determining the best approach for capturing carbon and advancing the system will be an important research question for years to come (fig. 5-3.13). Capturing the CO_2 is only half the problem; it will also need to be sequestered. Among the options is to sequester CO_2 geologically underground in liquid form, to inject CO_2 into the oceans, or to capture CO_2 and embed it into products such as drywall. One inventor even turned the captured carbon into baking soda, from which he made chocolate chip cookies. Putting this into humorous perspective, while baking soda is indeed a useful commodity, capturing one billion tons of carbon would produce a significant amount of baking soda. This could potentially cause worldwide baking soda prices to collapse and lead to the creation of more cookies than could possibly be consumed by humanity.

Finding the most economic, sustainable, and feasible mix of carbon capture and sequestration approaches remains one of the critical technology barriers of the future.

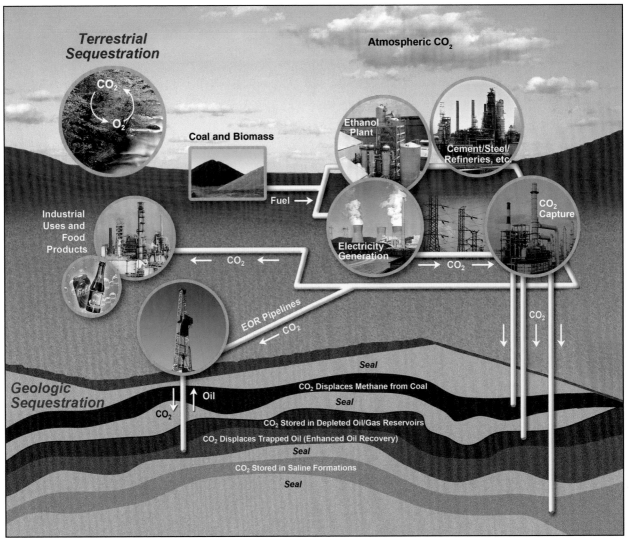

Figure 5-3.13. Carbon sequestration cycles

Source: U.S. Department of Energy, Office of Fossil Energy

The third critical technology is the *supergrid*, which is a super-efficient grid operating over long distances. Supergrids are a critical technology because they can connect remote sources of renewable power with locations of demand. The premise is that it is always windy and sunny somewhere, and if those locations can be connected to the places that need the wind and sun, then there will always be renewable energy available. We can also use supergrids to connect remote large-scale storage systems with locations of demand and with sources of intermittent renewable power.

Supergrids

Wind energy has been a success story so far. The benefits of wind are that it is profitable and there are no emissions. However, there are several problems:

Wind Energy

- Wind is intermittent, which affects its overall capacity factor. The wind can periodically shut off for days at a time and without much warning.
- The general profile of wind power throughout the day often does not match up with peak demand. For example, mid-continental wind in the United States is strongest at night in the winter and spring (when there is already excess capacity), and weakest on hot, dry, still afternoons (when it is needed most). This phenomenon is typical for other locations worldwide.
- The wind often blows more where people do not live. To illustrate, the windiest corridors on the American continent happen to have the lowest overall population density (see figs. 5-3.14 and 5-3.15), though this mismatch also occurs globally.

The experience with wind in continental Asia and Europe is similar in terms of availability and general profile. However, off-shore wind, while more difficult and expensive, tends to have better availability that matches up with peak power demand. While offshore wind is just now beginning to be developed in the United States, coastal resources in the UK, Spain, and Denmark are good examples of performance and costs. Unfortunately, some of the best European wind resources are off the western cost of Scotland, far from the demand centers such as Berlin and Paris.

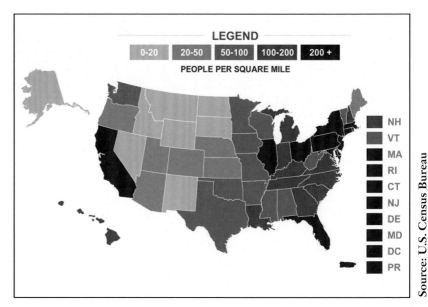

Source: U.S. Census Bureau

Figure 5-3.14. Map of population density of the United States by state (from the 2000 U.S. Census).

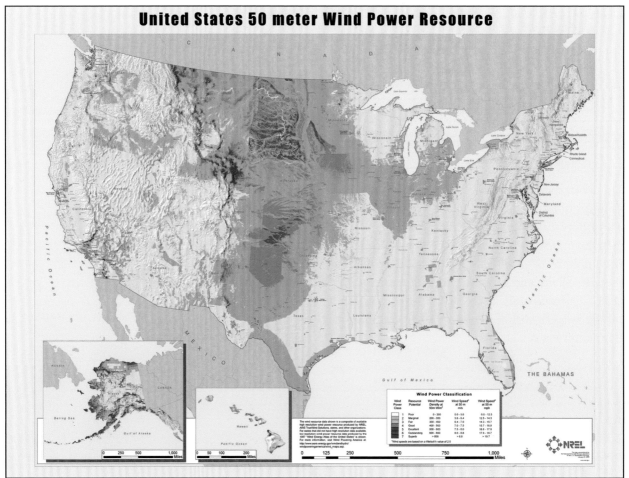

Source: U.S. Department of Energy, National Renewable Energy Laboratory

Figure 5-3.15. This map of wind resources at 50 miles (80 kilometres) above the Earth's surface in the United States shows that wind resources are generally located away from population centers.

The story of solar power is similar to wind, in that the fuel is free, renewable, and inexhaustible. However, it is also plagued with intermittency challenges. The good news is the profile of solar matches better with peak demand (in that demand is usually higher during the day) than it does with continental wind. The days with highest summer demand also tend to be sunny days throughout much of the nation, and the profile is more predictable than for wind. Solar—like wind—is land intensive, but its dual-use nature is different. Wind can enjoy dual use (for example, power generation and cattle ranching), while solar can be put into dual use over a much smaller area with urban rooftops. Breakthroughs include more efficient direct conversion to electricity, more efficient *concentrating solar power* to create steam, and cost-effective *photovoltaic manufacturing*.

Solar is also like wind in that its greatest potential in the United States is in the south and southwest regions in states like Texas, New Mexico, and Arizona. While these states have some large load centers in their major cities, the areas of greatest population density (and therefore power demand) in the nation are in the eastern half of the United States and on the West Coast (fig. 5-3.16). Europe's greatest solar irradiation is in the southern part of the continent, in countries such as Greece and Italy. Other solar-rich areas include the Sahara desert, Australian Outback, and northern Mexico, all of which have low population densities and are removed from the load centers such as Berlin, Moscow, and Johannesburg.

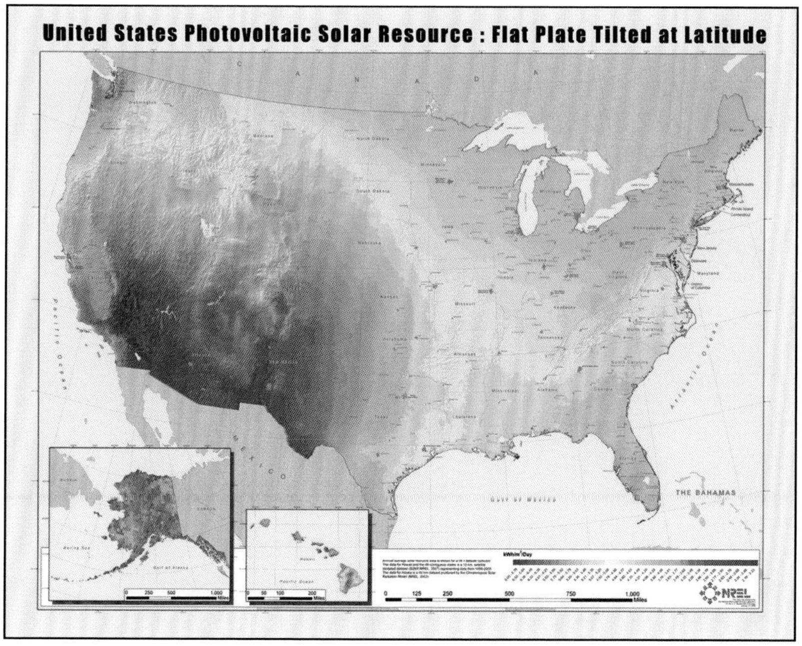

Solar Energy

United States Photovoltaic Solar Resource : Flat Plate Tilted at Latitude

Source: U.S. Department of Energy, National Renewable Energy Laboratory

Figure 5-3.16. A map of solar photovoltaic insolation shows a phenomenon similar to that of wind in that solar resources are generally located away from population centers in the United States, with the exception of large southwest cities in Arizona, Nevada, and California.

Combining these renewable sources—wind and solar—with super-efficient grids means that these remote sunny and windy places can be connected to distant demand centers (fig. 5-3.17). This would serve to offset fossil fuels from closer power plants and could give desolate or underserved areas a new revenue stream. Furthermore, if grids are combined with large-scale storage, the intermittency problems can be mitigated by connecting remote solar or wind with remote storage. For example, imagine Irish wind connecting with Norwegian pumped-hydroelectric reservoirs for backup and load leveling before selling power to Germany. In the same way, intermittent wind and solar in the United States could connect with remote storage to sell the power back to the grid during periods of high demand. With the right kind of technology, Saharan sunshine could be powering London, though the technical and financial hurdles remain tremendous.

Figure 5-3.17. Wind and solar energy farms around the world help supply renewable energy options.

Next-generation biofuels are also a critical technology of the future because they allow for abundant domestic supply of energy with a much lower carbon footprint than conventional liquid fuels. *First-generation biofuels* such as corn-based ethanol and soy-based biodiesel each have significant challenges, including water intensity, use of fossil fuels, and limits on production. For example, the expectation is that corn-based ethanol can produce at most 15 to 20 billion gallons per year in the United States, which is about 10% of today's 140 billion gallons per year consumption of reformulated gasoline and 40 billion gallons per year of diesel consumption. Thus, biofuels are not expected to achieve the desired abundance to meet economic objectives globally. In addition, water and fertilizer use inspires complaints that these biofuels, despite their uptake of CO_2 during photosynthesis, introduce significant environmental impacts. Other complaints emerge from the competition between food (corn and soy) and fuel, with demands for biofuels contributing to higher food prices and competition for arable land. Notably, by contrast, Brazil has a sugar cane climate and is the other large producer of ethanol. Brazilian production of ethanol from sugar cane, which is largely harvested manually, has a much higher yield per acre and is self-seeding. Ethanol was federally mandated in Brazil in 1972, and all light vehicles use it exclusively.

As of 2010, ethanol in the United States has only been profitable because of federal, state, and local subsidies. The challenge is to develop biofuels that can be made from nonfood feedstocks, without freshwater irrigation, on nonarable land, and without the intensive inputs of fossil fuels such biofuels would be able to directly displace petroleum, would largely use existing infrastructure to reduce GHG emissions, and would have the abundance desired for economic purposes.

Some of the feedstocks for biofuels that might meet these criteria include *cellulosic* sources such as grasses and wood for ethanol production and algae for biodiesel production (fig. 5-3.18).

Next-Generation Biofuels

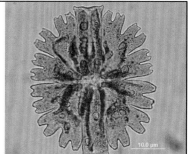

Figure 5-3.18. Algae are resilient and easy to grow in both brackish and fresh water.

Algae are particularly compelling for a variety of reasons:

- Algae are very resilient, having grown for billions of years, whether wanted or not. In fact, algae are the primary source for today's petroleum. Dead algae from many millions of years ago have been pressurized by geological forces over time to create petroleum.

- Unlike many biofuel sources, algae are known to produce high-quality oils if processing time is sped from millions of years to days or hours.

- In addition to nutrients, algae need just three primary ingredients to grow: sunlight, CO_2, and water.

- Because they do not need high-quality soils, algae production does not compete for arable land.

- While algae production is water-intensive, because many oil-producing strains grow in brackish or saltwater, competition for freshwater can be avoided.

- Algae's productivity, possibly as high as 3,000 gallons (12,000 litres) of oils per acre per year, is five times more productive than palm oil, which is currently the world's leading source of biodiesel.

- Algae can be grown in open systems using ambient CO_2, or they can be used as another method for post-combustion carbon capture. By siphoning off a portion of CO_2-rich flue gases in smokestacks, algae growth can be enhanced in controlled systems. This form of carbon capture does not lead to sequestration, as CO_2 is released when the algae-based fuels are burned. However, because the CO_2 was released as the consequence of two uses (electric power generation plus liquid fuels combustion), it lowers the overall contributions to CO_2 in the atmosphere.

Figuring out how to make next-generation biofuels in an economically sustainable way and at sufficient scale remains a critical technical challenge in solving the energy problem.

While many people acknowledge that an energy problem exists, they often claim that technology is the solution. This faith in technology alleviates the responsibility from people as energy consumers. Rather than change personal habits and behaviors, many people believe we simply need better technology.

This attitude toward technological solutions is reflected in some governmental policies and decisions about where to invest money. For example, approximately 80% of energy-related research and development funding from the U.S. government over the last few decades was for new sources of energy supply as opposed to ways to reduce energy demand.

Energy technologies improve year after year with steady progress, but breakthroughs are rare. Consequently, waiting for a breakthrough to solve the energy problem is not sound energy policy. When considering how to address the energy problem, it is quite possible that nontechnical solutions will be more effective and available sooner than new technologies.

Nontechnical solutions might include:

- Behavioral shifts
- Cultural shifts
- New policies
- Innovative markets

Behavioral and cultural shifts include a society-wide emphasis on reducing energy consumption, carpooling, purchasing nonpolluting products, and so on. Innovative markets are working toward ideas like real-time pricing, environmental dispatching, and including environmental impacts and national security implications along with the energy choices. It is possible that all these nontechnical solutions could have greater impact than technological solutions. To solve the energy problem, investments in technology are needed. At the same time, it is important to recognize that technological fixes alone might not be sufficient or available in time, so it is critical to include nontechnical pathways to a solution.

Nontechnical Solutions

SUMMARY

How can we get all the benefits of energy (mobility, prosperity, industry) without the downside risks (pollution, national security vulnerabilities and depletion)? We might need new critical technologies to pave the way. Critical technologies are those that enable the abundant, domestic production of clean sources of energy, or enable energy trade with friendly nations. Four critical technologies—electricity storage, carbon capture and sequestration, supergrids, and next-generation biofuels—can open the way for the United States and other countries with similar energy concerns to use their domestic resources more fully without hitting environmental limits. In the end, however, these technologies might need to be implemented hand-in-hand with new markets, policies, and consumer behaviors.

REFERENCES

1. USDOE, *International Energy Outlook 2006*. 2006, U.S. Department of Energy, Energy Information Administration.

2. UN, *World Population Prospects: The 2006 Revision*. 2006, Population Division of the Department of Economic and Social Affairs of the United Nations Secretariat.

3. *The Economist Intelligence Unit's quality-of-life index*, in *The Economist: The World in 2005*. 2006.

4. USEIA. *World Carbon Dioxide Emissions from the Use of Fossil Fuels*. International Energy Annual 2007 [cited 2007 26 October 2007]; Available at: http://www.eia.doe.gov/emeu/iea/carbon.html.

5. Houser, T., et al., *Leveling the Carbon Playing Field: International Competition and US Climate Policy Design*. 2008.

6. USEIA, *December 2008 International Petroleum Monthly*. 2008, U.S. Department of Energy, Energy Information Administration.

7. USEIA, *Annual Energy Outlook 2007: With Projections to 2030*. 2007, U.S. Department of Energy, Energy Information Administration.

8. Goldemberg, J., *Ethanol for a Sustainable Energy Future*. Science, 2007. 315.

9. USEIA, *Annual Energy Review 2007*. 2008, U.S. Department of Energy, Energy Information Administration.

10. USEIA, *Annual Energy Outlook 2008: With Projections to 2030*. 2008, U.S. Department of Energy, Energy Information Administration.

11. USEIA, *Annual Energy Outlook 2009: With Projections to 2030*. 2009, U.S. Department of Energy, Energy Information Administration.

12. USEIA, *Annual Energy Outlook 2006: With Projections to 2030*. 2006, U.S. Department of Energy, Energy Information Administration.

13. USDOI, *National Atlas*. 2009, U.S. Department of Interior.

14. USDOE, *United States Wind Resource Map*. 2008, U.S. Department of Energy, National Renewable Energy Laboratory.

15. USDOE, *PV Solar Radiation Map*. 2004, U.S. Department of Energy, National Renewable Energy Laboratory.

16. Smil, V., *Energy at the Crossroads*. 2005, Cambridge, MA: MIT Press.

17. USDOE, *International Energy Outlook 2009*. 2009, U.S. Department of Energy, Energy Information Administration.

Figure		Owner	Web site
1-1.1	A cross section of the Earth shows its inner and outer cores, the mantle, and the crust.	The University of Texas at Austin, PETEX	www.utexas.edu/ce/petex
1-1.2	The relative positions of the continents as they have changed over the past 225 million years	Public Domain. U.S. Geological Survey.	www.usgs.gov
1-1.3	Oceanic crust is heavier than continental crust.	The University of Texas at Austin, PETEX	www.utexas.edu/ce/petex
1-1.4	Geologic formations of crust are exposed above the surface as shown in Carbon Creek in Grand Canyon National Park in Arizona (United States).	Photo by Dr. Richard G. Baker, University of Iowa, Department of Geoscience	www.uiowa.edu
1-1.5	The Mid-Atlantic Ridge is an example of two plates moving apart, forming new oceanic crust as lava rising from beneath the plates hardens.	The University of Texas at Austin, PETEX	www.utexas.edu/ce/petex
1-1.6	Along the Pacific coast, the North and South American continental plates are forcing the Pacific plate downward.	The University of Texas at Austin, PETEX	www.utexas.edu/ce/petex
1-1.7	This photo of the Sheep Mountain Anticline shows deformation of the Earth's crust by the buckling of layers into folds.	Christopher Zahm	www.beg.utexas.edu
1-1.8	Geologists group folds into anticlines and synclines.	The University of Texas at Austin, PETEX	www.utexas.edu/ce/petex
1-1.9	Geologists further divide anticlines and synclines by how the folds tilt.	The University of Texas at Austin, PETEX	www.utexas.edu/ce/petex
1-1.10	A dome might be elongated or circular and some have an intrusive core of salt or other type of rock that pushes up the surrounding rock.	The University of Texas at Austin, PETEX	www.utexas.edu/ce/petex
1-1.11	A basin is a broad inward dipping feature often tens to hundreds of kilometres across.	Redrawn with permission from Nova Science Publishers, Inc.	www.novapublishers.com

Figure		Owner	Web site
1-1.11 (cont.)		From: *Coalbed Natural Gas: Energy and Environment*, K. J. Reddy, Editor/Author; ISBN 978-1-61668-036.	
1-1.12	This view of the San Andreas Fault in California shows a distinct fault line.	Public Domain. U. S. Geological Survey.	www.usgs.gov
1-1.13	Several common types of faults are normal dip slip, reverse or thrust dip slip, lateral or strike slip, overthrust, and growth faults.	The University of Texas at Austin, PETEX	www.utexas.edu/ce/petex
1-1.14	Two landscape features formed by faults are the graben and the horst.	The University of Texas at Austin, PETEX	www.utexas.edu/ce/petex
1-1.15	Geologic time	Copyright © Geology.com. All rights reserved.	www.geology.com
1-1.16	The weight of overlying sediments and water compacts sediments along with minerals in water creates different cements that alter the rock.	The University of Texas at Austin, PETEX	www.utexas.edu/ce/petex
1-1.17	Contact and regional metamorphism.	The University of Texas at Austin, PETEX	www.utexas.edu/ce/petex
1-1.18	The rock cycle changes rocks from one type to another.	The University of Texas at Austin, PETEX	www.utexas.edu/ce/petex
1-1.19	Abundant sea life helped form petroleum beneath the ocean floor.	Public Domain. Energy Information Administration, U. S. Department of Energy, 2005.	www.eia.doe.gov
1-1.20	Increasing pressure also causes temperatures to increase.	Modified and republished with permission of Gulf Coast Association Geological Society Transactions. Source: Figure 10 in McKenna, T. E., 1997, *Fluid Flow and Heat Transfer in Overpressured Sediments of the Rio Grande Embayment, Gulf of Mexico*: Gulf Coast Association of Geological Societies Trans., v. 47, p. 351-366.	www.gcags.org
1-1.21	As the rock reaches a temperature of 150°F, the kerogen begins recombining with hydrocarbon molecules.	Source: W.W. Norton & Company Inc., Publisher, *Earth: Portrait of a Planet*, 3rd Edition (Fig. 14.5 from page 49) Author: Stephen Marshak	www.wwnorton.com
1-1.22	When reservoir rock is magnified, its porosity can be seen.	The University of Texas at Austin, PETEX	www.utexas.edu/ce/petex
1-1.23	When reservoir rock is magnified, its porosity can be seen.	Source: (top) F. Jerry Lucia, Bureau of Economic Geology (BEG), The University of Texas at Austin; (bottom) Shirley Dutton, BEG, The University of Texas at Austin	www.beg.utexas.edu
1-1.24	A rock is permeable when the pores are connected.	The University of Texas at Austin, PETEX	www.utexas.edu/ce/petex
1-1.25	Basic types of hydrocarbon traps, including anticlinal, fault, unconformity, and impermeable barriers, such as shale surrounding sandstone.	The University of Texas at Austin, PETEX	www.utexas.edu/ce/petex

Figure		Owner	Web site
1-1.26	Common types of structural traps are fault, anticlinal, and dome plug traps.	The University of Texas at Austin, PETEX	www.utexas.edu/ce/petex
1-1.27	Oil accumulates in a dome-shaped structure and an anticlinal type of fold structure.	The University of Texas at Austin, PETEX	www.utexas.edu/ce/petex
1-1.28	A nonporous salt mass has formed dome-shaped traps in overlying porous rocks.	The University of Texas at Austin, PETEX	www.utexas.edu/ce/petex
1-1.29	Discontinuous peripheral traps form around a piercement salt dome.	The University of Texas at Austin, PETEX	www.utexas.edu/ce/petex
1-1.30	Gas and oil are trapped in a fault trap—a reservoir resulting from normal faulting or offsetting of strata.	The University of Texas at Austin, PETEX	www.utexas.edu/ce/petex
1-1.31	Structure contour maps show simple and compound faulting.	The University of Texas at Austin, PETEX	www.utexas.edu/ce/petex
1-1.32	A change of permeability within a rock layer can form a trap.	The University of Texas at Austin, PETEX	www.utexas.edu/ce/petex
1-1.33	Common types of stratigraphic traps	The University of Texas at Austin, PETEX	www.utexas.cdu/cc/pctcx
1-1.34	Oil is trapped under an unconformity.	The University of Texas at Austin, PETEX	www.utexas.edu/ce/petex
1-1.35	Lenticular traps are often formed in buried river sandbars.	The University of Texas at Austin, PETEX	www.utexas.edu/ce/petex
1-1.36	When hydrocarbons are layered in a reservoir, the water is on the bottom and the gas on the top.	The University of Texas at Austin, PETEX	www.utexas.edu/ce/petex
1-1.37	Bottom water is below the petroleum in a reservoir, and edgewater is at the edge of the oil zone.	The University of Texas at Austin, PETEX	www.utexas.edu/ce/petex
1-1.38	Wetting water usually coats the grains of the reservoir rock.	The University of Texas at Austin, PETEX	www.utexas.edu/ce/petex
1-1.39	Solution gas stays in solution until a well is drilled into the reservoir.	The University of Texas at Austin, PETEX	www.utexas.edu/ce/petex
1-1.40	Free gas forms a gas cap.	The University of Texas at Austin, PETEX	www.utexas.edu/ce/petex
1-1.41	When the petroleum reservoir has a connection to the surface, the pressure is considered normal.	The University of Texas at Austin, PETEX	www.utexas.edu/ce/petex
1-1.42	Abnormal pressure can occur in formations outcropping higher than the rig elevation.	The University of Texas at Austin, PETEX	www.utexas.edu/ce/petex
1-2.1	Landsat photos such as this are received by remote sensing systems and processed by computers.	Public Domain. U.S. Geological Survey.	www.usgs.gov
1-2.2	Seeps are located either updip or along fractures.	The University of Texas at Austin, PETEX	www.utexas.edu/ce/petex
1-2.3	Oil and gas naturally rise towards the Earth's surface wherever there is a way up as it did in New Zealand.	Simon Nathan	www.teara.govt.nz

Figure		Owner	Web site
1-2.4	Seismic exploration takes geophysicists into the jungles of India and the freezing plains of Alaska.	Top: Copyright © Geophysical Institute of Israel. All rights reserved. Bottom: Copyright © CGGVeritas/ Dominique Lecuivre Productions. All rights reserved.	Top: www.seis.mni.gov Bottom: www.aapg.org
1-2.5	A seismic section indicates boundaries between formations.	The Moroccan Ministry of Energy and Mines and Vanco Energy. Provided by the U.T. Bureau of Economic Geology.	www.beg.utexas.edu
1-2.6	A 3D seismic image is a cube that shows the types of rock, their depths, and whether a trap with hydrocarbons is present.	The Moroccan Ministry of Energy and Mines and Vanco Energy. Provided by the U.T. Bureau of Economic Geology.	www.beg.utexas.edu
1-2.7	4C seismic sensor for deep-water geophysical exploration	Photo by Trond Sørem. Copyright © SeaBed Geophysical. All rights reserved. Source: The Norwegian Design Council.	www.norskdesign.no
1-2.8	Engineers have developed mechanical impactors and vibrators to create seismic waves that penetrate down into rock layers to be recorded on the surface.	Redrawn with permission from Cobalt Exploration.	www.cobaltexploration. com
1-2.9	The Thumper drops a 6,000 pound steel slab (surrounded by safety chains to warn personnel) 9 feet to strike the earth and create shock waves.	Public Domain. National Energy Technology Laboratory.	www.netl.doe.gov
1-2.10	The Vibroseis truck has a vibrator mounted underneath it that creates low-frequency sound waves.	Copyright © Industrial Vehicles International, Inc. All rights reserved.	www.geosys.co.jp
1-2.11	Geophysical vessels can log hundreds of thousands of miles of geophysical data.	Copyright © Tesla Offshore. All rights reserved.	www.teslaoffshore.com
1-2.12	Seismic operations at sea use sound to create shock waves that have reflections that are picked up by hydrophones.	The University of Texas at Austin, PETEX	www.utexas.edu/ce/petex
1-2.13	Onboard computers allow geologists to analyze the seismic data as it comes in.	Copyright © WesternGeco. All rights reserved.	www.westerngeco.com
1-2.14	A well log is examined for indications of the presence of hydrocarbons and other fluids in a formation.	Provided by the Government of South Australia PIRSA	www.petroleum.pir.sa. gov.au
1-2.15	SP and resistivity logs record natural and induced electrical currents.	Redrawn with permission from Kansas Geological Survey, The University of Kansas.	www.kgs.ku.edu
1-2.16	An acoustic (sonic) log is a curved line that moves horizontally to show the speed of the sound waves and vertically to show the depth.	Copyright © Geophysics and Geology Branch of the California Department of Transportation. All rights reserved.	www.dot.ca.gov
1-2.17	This technician is marking the well core to maintain the order in which pieces came out of the ground.	Copyright © CO2CRC. All rights reserved.	www.co2crc.com
1-2.18	This coring bit drills out a slender column of rock.	Copyright © Corpro. All rights reserved.	www.corpro-group.com

638

Figure		Owner	Web site
1-2.19	This stratigraphic cross section shows the presence of sand at various depths over an area of several thousand feet.	The University of Texas at Austin, PETEX	www.utexas.edu/ce/petex
1-2.20	A structure contour map shows the depth of a formation from the surface.	Copyright © Kentucky Geological Survey. All rights reserved.	www.uky.edu
1-2.21	Isopach maps show the thickness of formations based on microlog surveys.	Public Domain. U.S. Geological Survey.	http://pubs.usgs.gov
1-2.22	Vertical cross section	Redrawn with permission from U.S. Geological Survey. From Brocher, T.M., McCarthy, J., Hart, P.E., Holbrook, W.S., Furlong, K.P., McEvilly, T. V., Hole, J.A., and BASIX Working Group, 1994, Seismic Evidence for a Possible Lower-Crustal Decollement Beneath San Francisco Bay, Science, v. 265, p. 1436-1439.	www.usgs.gov
1 2.23	Geoscientists rely on computerized images to indicate whether and where to drill.	Photo by Trond Sørcm. Copyright © SeaBed Geophysical. All rights reserved. Source: The Norwegian Design Council.	www.norskdesign.no
1-2.24	Maps integrate data to provide clear pictures of geological features.	Copyright © Shell International Ltd. All rights reserved.	www.shell.com
1-2.25	Computer operators can enhance Landsat, seismic, and other graphics to create three-dimensional images in color to highlight certain features.	Copyright © Central Petroleum Ltd. All rights reserved.	www.centralpetroleum.com
1-2.26	A block diagram represents a section of the Earth showing subsurface strata and surface topography.	The University of Texas at Austin, PETEX	www.photos.com
1-3.1	In most oil-producing nations outside the United States, the mineral rights are owned and controlled by the government.	The University of Texas at Austin, PETEX	www.utexas.edu/ce/petex
1-3.2	Of the produced oil worldwide, most rights to the mineral resources are in the hands of central governments.	The University of Texas at Austin, PETEX	www.photos.com
1-3.3	Oil and gas production on federally owned land in the United States from 1996–2001	Public Domain. U.S. Department of the Interior.	www.doi.gov
1-3.4	A Texas General Land Office bid application or mineral lease of state land.	Copyright © State of Texas General Land Office. All rights reserved.	www.glo.state.tx.us
1-3.5	Map showing land ownership in the state of Alaska	Copyright © World Resources Institute. All rights reserved.	www.wri.org
1-3.6	Management of U.S. federal government lands	O'Connor Center for the Rocky Mountain West, 2002	www.crmw.org
1-3.7	Government owned offshore land in the United States	The University of Texas at Austin, PETEX	www.utexas.edu/ce/petex
1-3.8	Government mineral-ownership map of Pinedale Resource Management site in Pinedale, Wyoming	Public Domain. U.S. Bureau of Land Management, August 2002.	www.blm.gov

639

Figure		Owner	Web site
1-3.9	An oil, gas, and mineral lease in Texas (United States)	Copyright © American Association of Professional Landmen. All rights reserved.	www.landman.org
1-3.10	A landman's job	The University of Texas at Austin, PETEX	www.utexas.edu/ce/petex
1-3.11	Deed records in courthouse establish property ownership.	The University of Texas at Austin, PETEX	www.utexas.edu/ce/petex
1-3.12	County records show unbroken chain over time.	Public Domain. Bureau of Land Management, U. S. Department of the Interior.	www.blm.gov
1-3.13	Sample runsheet mapping the ownership of mineral rights.	Copyright © Ted W. Walters and Associates, LLP. All rights reserved.	www.twalters.com
1-3.14	An 1835 land patent in Ralls County, Missouri, signed by U.S. President Andrew Jackson	Public Domain. Bureau of Land Management, Government Land Office Records.	www.blm.gov
1-3.15	Abstract of title traces the history of ownership of a property	The University of Texas at Austin, PETEX	www.utexas.edu/ce/petex
1-3.16	Hurricane Katrina in the Gulf of Mexico, August 28, 2005, resulted in force majeure delays for the petroleum industry.	Public Domain. United States Department of Commerce, NOAA.	www.noaa.gov
1-3.17	A farmout on two blocks of Libyan oil and gas basins was acquired by Canadian Occidental Petroleum Ltd. from Bula Resources (Jersey) Ltd., Dublin.	Redrawn with permission from Oil and Gas Journal, Volume 95, Issue 42, October 20, 1997.	www.ogj.com
2-1.1	Oilwells in Baku, Azerbaijan, in the late 1800s	Copyright © Brita Asbrink Collection. All rights reserved.	Not available
2-1.2	Edwin L. Drake and his friend Peter Wilson in front of the historic Drake well in 1861	The Drake Well Museum, Pennsylvania Historical and Museum Commission	www.drakewell.org
2-1.3	Wall cake stabilizes the drilling hole.	The University of Texas at Austin, PETEX	www.utexas.edu/ce/petex
2-1.4	The 1901 Lucas well is estimated to have flowed about 2 million gallons of oil per day.	Photo by John Trost	www.wikimedia.org
2-1.5	Cable-tool rig	Photo by Carla Jensen, Odessa, TX	www.redbubble.com
2-1.6	A drill bit	Copyright © Baker Hughes Incorporated. All rights reserved.	www.bakerhughes.com
2-1.7	Cable-tool drilling rig and derrick	Photo by Walter Eskridge	www.okhistory.org
2-1.8	Rotary drilling at Spindletop revolutionized the drilling industry.	The University of Texas at Austin, PETEX	www.utexas.edu/ce/petex
2-1.9	A typical 1920 oilfield of drilling and production operations	The University of Texas at Austin, PETEX	www.utexas.edu/ce/petex
2-1.10	Drilling fluid, or mud, circulates down through the pipe, out through the bit, and back up the hole.	The University of Texas at Austin, PETEX	www.utexas.edu/ce/petex
2-1.11	A rotary rig	The University of Texas at Austin, PETEX	www.photos.com

Figure		Owner	Web site
2-1.12	Closeup of metals taken with a high-powered microscope: etched cast iron microstructure (left) and alloy steel 4140 quenched and tempered martensite (right)	Copyright © EPI Materials Testing Group. All rights reserved.	www.epimtg.com
2-1.13	Example of a stress vs. strain curve	Redrawn with permission from EPI Materials Testing Group.	www.epimtg.com
2-1.14	Corroded pipe (A) and magnified corrosion pits (B)	Copyright © EPI Materials Testing Group. All rights reserved.	www.epimtg.com
2-1.15	It takes a well-trained, highly skilled crew to run a drilling operation.	Texas A&M University—Integrated Ocean Drilling Program	www.iodp.tamu.edu
2-1.16	Modern land rig	The University of Texas at Austin, PETEX	www.utexas.edu/ce/petex
2-1.17	Modern offshore rig	The University of Texas at Austin, PETEX	www.utexas.edu/ce/petex
2-1.18	Schematic of rotary land rig with drill stem and bit on the bottom of the drilling hole.	The University of Texas at Austin, PETEX	www.utexas.edu/ce/petex
2-1.19	Similar to the action of a drilling winch, a windlass hoists a bucket with water from a well.	The University of Texas at Austin, PETEX	www.utexas.edu/ce/petex
2-1.20	The hoisting system of a rotary rig is shown without the derrick.	The University of Texas at Austin, PETEX	www.utexas.edu/ce/petex
2-1-21	A derrick has four distinct legs.	The University of Texas at Austin, PETEX	www.photos.com
2-1.22	A mast being transported.	Copyright © National Oilwell Varco. All rights reserved.	www.nov.com
2-1.23	Transocean's Discoverer Spirit drillship with dual-activity derricks	Copyright © Transocean. All rights reserved.	www.deepwater.com
2-1.24	This supply reel mounted on the derrick floor supplies wire rope for the rig.	The University of Texas at Austin, PETEX	www.utexas.edu/ce/petex
2-1.25	Drilling line passes through the sheaves (top) and the traveling block (bottom).	(top) Copyright © National Oilwell Varco. All rights reserved. (bottom) The University of Texas at Austin, PETEX	www.nov.com www.utexas.edu/ce/petex
2-1.26	A deadline anchor on the rig's substructure holds the deadline in place.	(left) Copyright © National Oilwell Varco. All rights reserved. (right) The University of Texas at Austin, PETEX	www.nov.com www.utexas.edu/ce/petex
2-1.27	The drawworks on the rig floor contains the drum and other equipment in a steel housing unit.	Copyright © National Oilwell Varco. All rights reserved.	www.nov.com
2-1.28	The drilling line on the drawworks	Copyright © National Oilwell Varco. All rights reserved.	www.nov.com
2-1.29	The driller's console controls the power, transmission, and brakes of the hoisting system.	Copyright © National Oilwell Varco. All rights reserved.	www.nov.com
2-1.30	Makeup cathead attached to a catshaft	Copyright © National Oilwell Varco. All rights reserved.	www.nov.com
2-1.31	Tongs	Copyright © National Oilwell Varco. All rights reserved.	www.nov.com

Figure		Owner	Web site
2-1.32	An air hoist moves heavy equipment around the rig floor.	The University of Texas at Austin, PETEX	www.utexas.edu/ce/petex
2-1.33	Schematic of rotary table equipment from the surface to the bottom of the hole	The University of Texas at Austin, PETEX	www.utexas.edu/ce/petex
2-1.34	The hook on the bottom of the traveling block is about to be latched onto the bail of the swivel.	(left) Copyright © National Oilwell Varco. All rights reserved. (right) The University of Texas at Austin, PETEX	www.nov.com www.utexas.edu/ce/petex
2-1.35	The kelly passes through the kelly bushing, which fits into the master bushing of the rotary table.	The University of Texas at Austin, PETEX	www.utexas.edu/ce/petex
2-1.36	Various designs of slips have gripping dies that keep pipe and casing from falling into the hole.	(left) Copyright © National Oilwell Varco. All rights reserved. (right) The University of Texas at Austin, PETEX	www.nov.com www.utexas.edu/ce/petex
2-1.37	With the drill string in the slips, the top drive is hoisted into position to pick up a new stand of pipe.	The University of Texas at Austin, PETEX	www.utexas.edu/ce/petex
2-1.38	Floorhands set the lower end of the stand of pipe off to one side of the rig floor.	The University of Texas at Austin, PETEX	www.utexas.edu/ce/petex
2-1.39	Crewmembers latch onto drill pipe with breakout tongs.	Bret Boteler. Copyright © EnerMax, Inc. All rights reserved.	www.enermaxinc.com
2-1.40	Drill collars racked in front of drill pipe on the rig floor	The University of Texas at Austin, PETEX	www.utexas.edu/ce/petex
2-1.41	Tool joints are threaded connections like the pin-ends in this photo.	Copyright © International Rig and Equipment. All rights reserved.	www.iretrading.com
2-1.42	Tool joints have a pin connection and a box connection.	Copyright © MSI Oilfield Products. All rights reserved.	www.msiproducts.com
2-1.43	Roller cone and diamond bits	Copyright © Baker Hughes Incorporated. All rights reserved.	www.bakerhughes.com
2-1.44	Each cone of a roller cone bit rotates on its axis.	The University of Texas at Austin, PETEX	www.utexas.edu/ce/petex
2-1.45	Each cone rotates on ball and roller bearings or journal bearings or both.	Copyright © Bit Brokers International, Ltd. All rights reserved.	www.bitbrokers.com
2-1.46	The circulating system consists of a number of components, all of which serve to get mud down the hole and back to the surface.	The University of Texas at Austin, PETEX	www.utexas.edu/ce/petex
2-1.47	The mud pump pumps drilling fluid into the hole.	The University of Texas at Austin, PETEX	www.utexas.edu/ce/petex
2-1.48	Drilling rig floor	Dr. Tom Dunkley Jones	www.imperial.ac.uk
2-1.49	A shale shaker removes cuttings carried to the surface by the mud.	Copyright © ICDP, GFZ Potsdam. All rights reserved.	www.icdp-online.de
2-1.50	Additional circulating equipment can include a degasser, desilter, and desander, located over the mud pits downstream from the shaker.	The University of Texas at Austin, PETEX	www.utexas.edu/ce/petex
2-1.51	Three diesel engines power this rig.	The University of Texas at Austin, PETEX	www.utexas.edu/ce/petex

Figure		Owner	Web site
2-1.52	Three diesel engines and the compound send power to the drawworks and mud pumps.	The University of Texas at Austin, PETEX	www.utexas.edu/ce/petex
2-1.53	This diesel engine drives an alternating current electric generator.	The University of Texas at Austin, PETEX	www.utexas.edu/ce/petex
2-1.54	Controls in the SCR house where AC electricity is converted to the correct DC voltage for the many DC motors powering this rig.	The University of Texas at Austin, PETEX	www.utexas.edu/ce/petex
2-1.55	SCR electrical power system diagram	Recreated. Source: National Oilwell Varco.	www.nov.com
2-1.56	Motor-driven drawworks	The University of Texas at Austin, PETEX	www.utexas.edu/ce/petex
2-1.57	Powerful electric DC traction motors driving the drawworks	The University of Texas at Austin, PETEX	www.utexas.edu/ce/petex
2-1.58	Reserve pit	The University of Texas at Austin, PETEX	www.utexas.edu/ce/petex
2-1.59	A concrete pad to support the substructure surrounds this cellar.	The University of Texas at Austin, PETEX	www.utexas.edu/ce/petex
2-1.60	This rathole is storing the kelly when it is not being used.	The University of Texas at Austin, PETEX	www.utexas.edu/ce/petex
2-1.61	A mast is raised to the upright position using the drawworks.	The University of Texas at Austin, PETEX	www.utexas.edu/ce/petex
2-1.62	This heavy-lift vessel is transporting this rig to its offshore location.	The University of Texas at Austin, PETEX	www.utexas.edu/ce/petex
2-1.63	Making a connection with a kelly	The University of Texas at Austin, PETEX	www.utexas.edu/ce/petex
2-1.64	Making a connection with a top drive	The University of Texas at Austin, PETEX	www.utexas.edu/ce/petex
2-1.65	While tripping out with a rotary table system, the kelly and related equipment rest in the rathole.	The University of Texas at Austin, PETEX	www.utexas.edu/ce/petex
2-1.66	The open elevator has a latch and comes in several sizes and weight ratings.	The University of Texas at Austin, PETEX	www.utexas.edu/ce/petex
2-1.67	Standing on the monkeyboard high in the mast, the derrickhand guides a stand of pipe into the fingerboard.	The University of Texas at Austin, PETEX	www.utexas.edu/ce/petex
2-1.68	Several centralizers and scratchers are installed on the casing to aid in cementing.	The University of Texas at Austin, PETEX	www.utexas.edu/ce/petex
2-1.69	The guide shoe is made up on the bottom of the first joint of casing to go into the hole.	The University of Texas at Austin, PETEX	www.utexas.edu/ce/petex
2-1.70	Casing stacked for use in this drilling operation.	The University of Texas at Austin, PETEX	www.utexas.edu/ce/petex
2-1.71	The crew runs surface casing into the hole.	Texas A&M University—Integrated Drilling Program. Photo from Expedition 327 by William Crawford.	www.iodp.tamu.edu

Figure		Owner	Web site
2-1.72	This diagram of a casing cementing job shows the route of the slurry as well as the role played by the various cementing accessories.	The University of Texas at Austin, PETEX	www.utexas.edu/ce/petex
2-1.73	After the cement hardens, tests indicate whether the cement has bonded with no voids between the casing and hole.	The University of Texas at Austin, PETEX	www.utexas.edu/ce/petex
2-1.74	Crewmembers making a connection	The University of Texas at Austin, PETEX	www.photos.com
2-1.75	Using a top drive, the crew stabs and makes up the joint of drill pipe and the motor turns the drill stem and the bit.	The University of Texas at Austin, PETEX	www.utexas.edu/ce/petex
2-1.76	An Iron Roughneck™ spins and bucks up joints with built-in equipment.	The University of Texas at Austin, PETEX	www.utexas.edu/ce/petex
2-1.77	Intermediate casing fits inside the surface casing, and the production casing fits inside the intermediate casing.	The University of Texas at Austin, PETEX	www.utexas.edu/ce/petex
2-1.78	Cuttings retrieved from the shale shaker are examined by the mud logger.	Public Domain	www.wikimedia.org
2-1.79	Drillers running wireline to measure formation properties and record, or log.	The University of Texas at Austin, PETEX	www.utexas.edu/ce/petex
2-1.80	An electric log is one type of log that helps determine whether oil and gas are present in a drilled formation.	Source: National Energy Technology Laboratory	www.netl.doe.gov
2-1.81	Measurement while drilling system	Redrawn with permission from Halliburton.	www.halliburton.com
2-1.82	Schematic of the mud siren technique of MWD/LWD data transmission	Copyright © Schlumberger. All rights reserved.	www.slb.com
2-1.83	Data from downhole being decoded into digital form for display and recording at the surface in an Anadrill logging unit	Copyright © Black Viper Energy Services. All rights reserved.	www.blackviperenergy.com
2-1.84	Bottomhole assembly cross-section, side view	Redrawn with permission from GE Oil and Gas. Source: GE Energy—DOE award DE-FC26-05NT15487.	www.ge.com
2-1.85	Bottomhole assembly cross-section, top view	Redrawn with permission from GE Oil and Gas. Source: GE Energy—DOE award DE-FC26-05NT15487.	www.ge.com
2-1.86	Integrated LWD/MWD measurement system in coiled tubing drilling bottom-hole assembly	Redrawn with permission from GE Oil and Gas. Source: GE Energy—DOE award DE-FC26-05NT15487.	www.ge.com
2-1.87	This small magnetometer can sense the relationship of the well azimuth to the Earth's magnetic field.	Copyright © Wellog. All rights reserved.	www.wellog.com
2-1.88	Final assembly area: 6.75-inch and 4.75-inch resistivity collars in process	Source: GE Energy—DOE award DE-FC26-05NT15487	www.ge.com
2-1.89	Seadrill SSETR or semisubmersible self-erecting tender rig	Copyright © SeaDrill Asia Limited. All rights reserved.	www.seadrill.com

Figure		Owner	Web site
2-1.90	The first mobile drilling rig was a posted barge submersible designed to drill in shallow water.	The University of Texas at Austin, PETEX	www.utexas.edu/ce/petex
2-1.91	Types of MODUs	The University of Texas at Austin, PETEX	www.utexas.edu/ce/petex
2-1.92	When flooded, the bottles cause a bottle-type submersible to rest on the seafloor.	The University of Texas at Austin, PETEX	www.utexas.edu/ce/petex
2-1.93	A concrete island drilling system features a reinforced concrete caisson with a steel base.	The University of Texas at Austin, PETEX	www.utexas.edu/ce/petex
2-1.94	The hull of a jackup is raised well above the water surface before drilling begins.	The University of Texas at Austin, PETEX	www.utexas.edu/ce/petex
2-1.95	An inland barge rig at work	The University of Texas at Austin, PETEX	www.utexas.edu/ce/petex
2-1.96	The Deepwater Pathfinder drillship travels to a remote drill site.	Copyright © Transocean. All rights reserved.	www.deepwater.com
2-1.97	Dynamic positioning systems use global positioning systems (GPS) and hydro-phones to measure the vessel's position and send computer-controlled commands to thrusters to hover over the wellhead.	The University of Texas at Austin, PETEX	www.utexas.edu/ce/petex
2-1.98	Dynamic positioning systems have computerized controls on board the vessel.	Copyright © Ebbe Holsting. All rights reserved.	www.menkent.dk
2-1.99	A semisubmersible drilling unit floats on hulls that are flooded and submerged just below the water surface.	Copyright © Transocean. All rights reserved.	www.deepwater.com
2-1.100	A column-stabilized semisubmersible rests below the waves and waterline while drilling.	The University of Texas at Austin, PETEX	www.utexas.edu/ce/petex
2-1.101	A self-contained platform such as the Thunderhorse in the Gulf of Mexico (pictured)houses drilling and production equipment and facilities for the crew.	Copyright © BP p.l.c. All rights reserved.	www.bp.com
2-1.102	Constructed on its side, and loaded onto a transportation and installation barge, this jacket will be towed offshore and launched at the installation site, and set using a derrick barge.	Copyright © McDermott International Inc. All rights reserved.	www.jraymcdermott.com
2-1.103	A large crane hoists a deck section onto the jacket.	The University of Texas at Austin, PETEX	www.utexas.edu/ce/petex
2-1.104	A concrete gravity platform is so heavy that gravity holds it in place.	Copyright © Arup. All rights reserved.	www.arup.com
2-1.105	These steel-caisson platforms rest in the Cook Inlet of Alaska.	Public Domain. U.S. Coast Guard, photo by PA1 Sara Francis.	www.cgvi.uscg.mil
2-1.106	This relatively light weight jacket of a guyed-tower platform is supported by several guy wires and clump weights.	The University of Texas at Austin, PETEX	www.utexas.edu/ce/petex
2-1.107	Steel tendons are kept in tension by the buoyancy of the platform on a tension-leg platform.	The University of Texas at Austin, PETEX	www.utexas.edu/ce/petex

Figure		Owner	Web site
2-1.108	The Genesis spar platform in the Gulf of Mexico	Copyright © Chevron. All rights reserved.	www.chevron.com
2-1.109	Deviated wells can reach places conventional straight wells cannot.	Copyright © Lone Star Securities. All rights reserved.	www.lonestarsecurities.com
2-1.110	Several directionally drilled wells can tap multiple reservoirs.	The University of Texas at Austin, PETEX	www.utexas.edu/ce/petex
2-1.111	Qatar's largest offshore oilfield: Al Shadeen	Copyright © Maersk Oil. All rights reserved.	www.maerskoil.com
2-1.112	Some of the applications of directional wells	The University of Texas at Austin, PETEX	www.utexas.edu/ce/petex
2-1.113	A long section of a horizontal well can pass through the oil in the reservoir.	The University of Texas at Austin, PETEX	www.utexas.edu/ce/petex
2-1.114	This horizontal well reaches several oil-containing vertical fractures.	The University of Texas at Austin, PETEX	www.utexas.edu/ce/petex
2-1.115	Drill collars placed at the end of the drill string in a horizontal well would not add weight to the bit.	The University of Texas at Austin, PETEX	www.utexas.edu/ce/petex
2-1-116	Here, the drill collars are below the vertical section of pipe and above the horizontal section.	The University of Texas at Austin, PETEX	www.utexas.edu/ce/petex
2-1.117	Mud motor section showing the flow path and the shaft (rotor) and housing (stator).	João Luiz Vieira	www.halliburton.com
2-1.118	Bent sub	Joao Luiz Vieira	www.halliburton.com
2-1.119	Steerable motor	João Luiz Vieira	www.halliburton.com
2-1.120	Three-dimensional well	Copyright © Halliburton. All rights reserved.	www.halliburton.com
2-1.121	Push-the-bit rotary steerable	João Luiz Vieira	www.halliburton.com
2-1.122	Point-the-bit rotary steerable	João Luiz Vieira	www.halliburton.com
2-1.123	Types of multilateral well architectures	Copyright © Halliburton. All rights reserved.	www.halliburton.com
2-1.124	Multilateral wells TAML classification	Copyright © Halliburton. All rights rights reserved.	www.halliburton.com
2-1.125	Limits of mud density in a well	Copyright © Weatherford International. All rights reserved.	www.weatherford.com
2-1.126	In some wells, the pore pressure approaches the fracture pressure.	Copyright © Weatherford International. All rights reserved.	www.weatherford.com
2-1.127	Static mud column versus pumping mud column with lost circulation	Bill Rehm	Not available
2-1.128	Controlling bottomhole pressure with surface choke and RCD	Bill Rehm	Not available
2-1.129	Constant circulating sub	Bill Rehm	Not available
2-1.130	Underbalanced setup showing compressors, oil storage, and flare line	Copyright © Weatherford International. All rights reserved.	www.weatherford.com
2-1.131	Different gas volumes in a gaseated hole	Bill Rehm	Not available

Figure		Owner	Web site
2-1.132	Gaseous systems: methods of adding gas (A) parasite string, (B) bull heading, (C) jet sub, and (D) dual-casing string	Bill Rehm	Not available
2-1.133	Different foam volumes	Bill Rehm	Not available
2-1.134	Since SAGD drilling techniques were introduced, production efficiencies have increased in heavy oil reserves.	Copyright © Halliburton. All rights reserved.	www.halliburton.com
2-1.135	Skid-mounted compressors furnish the high-pressure air used on this rotary rig for drilling.	The University of Texas at Austin, PETEX	www.utexas.edu/ce/petex
2-1.136	A keyseat	The University of Texas at Austin, PETEX	www.utexas.edu/ce/petex
2-1.137	A. A free-point indicator locates stuck pipe. B. Diagram showing forces at work during differential sticking.	The University of Texas at Austin, PETEX	www.utexas.edu/ce/petex
2-1.138	A backoff connector is used on stuck pipe inside the washover pipe to keep the drill pipe from falling when freed.	The University of Texas at Austin, PETEX	www.utexas.edu/ce/petex
2-1.139	An overshot and spear are two commonly used tools for retrieving fish.	Copyright © Logan Oil Tools Incorporated. All rights reserved.	www.loganoiltools.com
2-2.1	A blowout and resulting fire at Greenhill Well in Timbalier Bay, Louisiana	Public Domain. National Oceanic and Atmospheric Administration (NOAA).	www.noaa.gov
2-2.2	Blowouts are dangerous, destructive, and avoidable if warning signs are recognized by watchful workers.	(top) Copyright © Great White Pressure Control. All rights reserved. (bottom) The University of Texas at Austin, PETEX	www.greatwhitepressure control.com www.utexas.edu/ce/petex
2-2.3	Hydrostatic pressure in a wellbore holds back formation pressure.	The University of Texas at Austin, PETEX	www.utexas.edu/ce/petex
2-2.4	Typical land BOP stack	The University of Texas at Austin, PETEX	www.utexas.edu/ce/petex
2-2.5	Types of annular blowout preventers: Hydril GL, Hydril GK small, Hydril GX	Copyright © GE Oil and Gas. All rights reserved.	www.geoilandgas.com
2-2.6	Cutaway diagram of a pipe ram	The University of Texas at Austin, PETEX	www.utexas.edu/ce/petex
2-2.7	A subsea BOP	Copyright © Cudd Well Control. All rights reserved.	www.cuddwellcontrol.com
2-2.8	Choke manifold	Copyright © Cudd Well Control. All rights reserved.	www.cuddwellcontrol.com
2-2.9	A positive adjustable choke with tungsten carbide wear surfaces	Copyright © Cameron. All rights reserved.	www.c-a-m.com
2-2.10	Remote choke panel with hydraulic module	Copyright © Electro-Flow Controls Ltd. All rights reserved.	www.electroflowcontrols. com
2-2.11	Quality well control training is not only essential for rig workers but also important for all personnel involved in various aspects of drilling and production operations.	The University of Texas at Austin, PETEX	www.utexas.edu/ce/petex

Figure		Owner	Web site
2-3.1	Drilling rigs present potential hazards for all workers on site.	The University of Texas at Austin, PETEX	www.utexas.edu/ce/petex
2-3.2	Blowouts such as this can release hazardous gas that can quickly harm workers.	The University of Texas at Austin, PETEX	www.utexas.edu/ce/petex
2-3.3	Handrails are essential safety devices on all drilling rigs.	The University of Texas at Austin, PETEX	www.utexas.edu/ce/petex
2-3.4	**Don't**: Some rig workers perform risky tasks high above the rig floor but safety harnesses should be worn and not left on deck.	The University of Texas at Austin, PETEX	www.utexas.edu/ce/petex
2-3.5	**Do**: Safety harnesses are required when performing any elevation work.	The University of Texas at Austin, PETEX	www.utexas.edu/ce/petex
2-3.6	A rathole rig drills the first part of the hole.	The University of Texas at Austin, PETEX	www.utexas.edu/ce/petex
2-3.7	Workers are assembling a land rig in the U.S. Permian Basin of Texas.	Bret Boteler. Copyright © EnerMax, Inc. All rights reserved.	www.enermaxinc.com
2-3.8	The construction of rigs involves tasks that must be performed high above the ground, making safety a primary concern.	The University of Texas at Austin, PETEX	www.utexas.edu/ce/petex
2-3.9	Crewmembers lower the bit into a surface hole.	Bret Boteler. Copyright © EnerMax, Inc. All rights reserved.	www.enermaxinc.com
2-3.10	Safety is top priority; proper training and communication are key components of safe operations.	Copyright © Ensco International. All rights reserved.	www.enscous.com
3-1.1	Running a pipe to line the sides of a well and sealing off the outside of the pipe near pipe near the bottom prevented fluids from the formations near the surface from entering the well.	The University of Texas at Austin, PETEX	www.utexas.edu/ce/petex
3-1.2	Wooden barrels were the first containers containers for produced oil.	The University of Texas at Austin, PETEX	www.utexas.edu/ce/petex
3-1.3	Conductor, surface, intermediate, and production casing are cemented in the well.	The University of Texas at Austin, PETEX	www.utexas.edu/ce/petex
3-1.4	A production liner is cemented in place but hangs from the bottom of the intermediate casing rather than extending to the surface.	The University of Texas at Austin, PETEX	www.utexas.edu/ce/petex
3-1.5	An open-hole completion allows reservoir fluids to flow into an uncased hole.	The University of Texas at Austin, PETEX	www.utexas.edu/ce/petex
3-1.6	A perforating gun creates holes in the producing casing or liner, allowing fluids from the formation to enter the well.	The University of Texas at Austin, PETEX	www.utexas.edu/ce/petex
3-1.7	Tubing is smaller in diameter than casing.	The University of Texas at Austin, Department of Petroleum and Geosystems Engineering	www.pge.utexas.edu

Figure		Owner	Web site
3-1.8	A packer between the casing and tubing keeps well fluids out of the tubing-casing annulus.	The University of Texas at Austin, PETEX	www.utexas.edu/ce/petex
3-1.9	The slips grip the walls of the casing to hold the packer in place.	The University of Texas at Austin, PETEX	www.utexas.edu/ce/petex
3-1.10	A packer can have one sealing element or several separated by metal rings.	The University of Texas at Austin, Department of Petroleum and Geosystems Engineering	www.pge.utexas.edu
3-1.11	A multiple completion, such as this triple completion, usually has a separate tubing string and packer for each producing zone.	The University of Texas at Austin, PETEX	www.utexas.edu/ce/petex
3-1.12	Subsurface safety valve	Copyright © Schlumberger Ltd. All rights reserved. Source: Garner J, Martin K, McCalvin D and McDaniel D: "At the Ready: Subsurface Safety Valves," Oilfield Review 14, No. 4 (Winter 2002/2003): 52-64	www.slb.com
3-1.13	A wire-wrapped screen, or screen liner, is often combined with a gravel pack inside perforated casing.	The University of Texas at Austin, PETEX	www.utexas.edu/ce/petex
3-1.14	A gravel pack screen	The University of Texas at Austin, PETEX	www.utexas.edu/ce/petex
3-1.15	Valves on the Christmas tree control the flow of fluids from the well.	Copyright © Stream-Flo Industries Ltd. All rights reserved.	www.streamflo.com
3-1.16	This cutaway of a wellhead shows its inner workings.	The University of Texas at Austin, Department of Petroleum and Geosystems Engineering	www.pge.utexas.edu
3-1.17	High-pressure connector cutaway view	The University of Texas at Austin, Department of Petroleum and Geosystems Engineering	www.pge.utexas.edu
3-1.18	Subsea production tree	Copyright © TSC Offshore. All rights reserved.	www.tscoffshore.com
3-1-19a	Powerful truck-mounted pumps perform fracturing at the well site.	Bret Boteler. Copyright © EnerMax, Inc. All rights reserved.	www.enermaxinc.com
3-1.19b	Reservoir fluids flow into the fracture and the well.	The University of Texas at Austin, PETEX	www.utexas.edu/ce/petex
3-1.20	Sand is one proppant used to hold fractures open.	Copyright © CARBO. All rights reserved.	www.carboceramics.com
3-1.21	Acid enlarges existing channels or makes new ones.	The University of Texas at Austin, PETEX	www.utexas.edu/ce/petex
3-1.22	Beam pumping units like this one are a a common sight in certain areas where oil is present.	The University of Texas at Austin, PETEX	www.utexas.edu/ce/petex
3-1.23	A beam, or rod, pumping unit has many components.	The University of Texas at Austin, PETEX	www.utexas.edu/ce/petex
3-1.24	An electric submersible pump	The University of Texas at Austin, PETEX	www.utexas.edu/ce/petex

Figure		Owner	Web site
3-1.25	Hydraulic pumping system with components on the surface and in the well	The University of Texas at Austin, PETEX	www.utexas.edu/ce/petex
3-1.26	In a gas-cap drive reservoir, the free gas in the cap and the gas dissolved in the oil expand to move oil up to the surface.	The University of Texas at Austin, PETEX	www.utexas.edu/ce/petex
3-1.27	In a solution-gas drive reservoir, gas comes out of the oil, expands and lifts it to the surface.	The University of Texas at Austin, PETEX	www.utexas.edu/ce/petex
3-1.28	In a water-drive reservoir, saltwater under the oil pushes the oil to the surface.	The University of Texas at Austin, PETEX	www.utexas.edu/ce/petex
3-1.29	Water at the edges of the reservoir helps drive the oil into the wellbore.	The University of Texas at Austin, PETEX	www.utexas.edu/ce/petex
3-1.30	Eventually, the water level rises to the bottom of the well in a water-drive reservoir.	The University of Texas at Austin, PETEX	www.utexas.edu/ce/petex
3-1.31	In a gravity-drainage reservoir, the oil flows downhill to the well.	The University of Texas at Austin, PETEX	www.utexas.edu/ce/petex
3-1.32	In waterflooding, water is injected into wells around the producing well.	The University of Texas at Austin, PETEX	www.utexas.edu/ce/petex
3-1.33	Miscible gas injection	The University of Texas at Austin, PETEX	www.utexas.edu/ce/petex
3-1.34	Chemical flooding uses special chemicals in water to push oil out of the formation.	The University of Texas at Austin, PETEX	www.utexas.edu/ce/petex
3-1.35	Steam injection involves generating steam and forcing it down injection wells into the reservoir.	The University of Texas at Austin, PETEX	www.utexas.edu/ce/petex
3-1.36	In fireflooding, a fire is ignited in the reservoir.	The University of Texas at Austin, PETEX	www.utexas.edu/ce/petex
3-1.37	Steps are necessary to ready oil or gas for sale.	The University of Texas at Austin, PETEX	www.utexas.edu/ce/petex
3-1.38	Gravity is used to separate well fluids in a vertical separator.	The University of Texas at Austin, PETEX	www.utexas.edu/ce/petex
3-1.39	A horizontal separator	Copyright © KW International. All rights reserved.	www.kwintl.com
3-1.40	A horizontal, three-phase free-water knockout provides space for the free water to settle out and the gas to rise.	The University of Texas at Austin, PETEX	www.utexas.edu/ce/petex
3-1.41	An emulsion is made up of two liquids that will not mix together under normal conditions.	Copyright © N. Bremond/LCMD-ESCPI. All rights reserved.	www.focus.aps.org
3-1.42	A bottle test helps determine which chemical is the most efficient demulsifier for a particular emulsion.	Copyright © BJ Services. All rights reserved.	www.bjservices.com
3-1.43	A vertical heater-treater separates oil-water emulsions.	The University of Texas at Austin, PETEX	www.utexas.edu/ce/petex
3-1.44	Horizontal heater-treater	The University of Texas at Austin, PETEX	www.utexas.edu/ce/petex
3-1.45	A gas-hydrate plug taken from an offshore production line	Public Domain. U.S. Geological Survey. Photo by Bill Winters.	www.usgs.gov

Figure		Owner	Web site
3-1.46	Methanol or glycol is injected into the gas stream to prevent hydrate formation.	The University of Texas at Austin, PETEX	www.utexas.edu/ce/petex
3-1.47	An indirect heater warms the water bath, which in turn warms the gas flowing through the coil assembly.	The University of Texas at Austin, PETEX	www.utexas.edu/ce/petex
3-1.48	The glycol liquid-desiccant dehydrator unit is skid-mounted.	Copyright © DPS-Delta. All rights reserved.	www.dps-delta.com
3-1.49	This dehydration system uses liquid glycol as a desiccant.	The University of Texas at Austin, PETEX	www.utexas.edu/ce/petex
3-1.50	This sweetening unit uses an amine to remove carbon dioxide and sulfur compounds.	Copyright © DCP Midstream. All rights reserved.	www.dcpmidstream.com
3-1.51	A low-temperature separation unit separates NGLs produced from a gas well.	Photo by John Amatucci. Copyright © Gas Tech Engineering Corporation. All rights reserved.	www.gastecheng.com
3-1.52	A battery of stock tanks that temporarily store oil, natural gas liquids, and water after separation.	Copyright © Unit Liner Company. All rights reserved.	www.unitliner.com
3-1.53	The sampler lowers a thief to obtain an oil sample from a storage tank.	The University of Texas at Austin, PETEX	www.utexas.edu/ce/petex
3-1.54	A 1-quart beaker is used in bottle sampling.	Copyright © Channel Supplies. All rights reserved.	www.channelsupplies.com
3-1.55	A centrifuge test uses a graduated glass centrifuge tube that is placed in a high-speed centrifuge by which precise percentages of S&W can be read.	The University of Texas at Austin, PETEX	www.utexas.edu/ce/petex
3-1.56	A hydrometer test	The University of Texas at Austin, PETEX	www.utexas.edu/ce/petex
3-1.57	A skid-mounted LACT unit is an efficient system for measuring and testing oil.	The University of Texas at Austin, PETEX	www.utexas.edu/ce/petex
3-1.58	A sample container on a LACT unit holds oil samples automatically taken from the oil stream flowing through the unit.	The University of Texas at Austin, PETEX	www.utexas.edu/ce/petex
3-1.59	An orifice meter measures differential and static pressures of a stream of flowing gas.	The University of Texas at Austin, PETEX	www.utexas.edu/ce/petex
3-1.60	Typical well servicing and workover rig	The University of Texas at Austin, PETEX	www.utexas.edu/ce/petex
3-1.61	Reels of wireline mounted on the back of a truck used for completion and workover jobs	The University of Texas at Austin, PETEX	www.utexas.edu/ce/petex
3-1.62	Coiled tubing unit	Copyright © Stewart & Stevenson. All rights reserved.	www.ssss.com
3-1.63	A coiled-tubing unit runs tubing into the well using a large reel.	The University of Texas at Austin, PETEX	www.utexas.edu/ce/petex
3-1.64	This snubbing unit operates with a self-contained hydraulic system.	Copyright © Great White Pressure Control. All rights reserved.	www.greatwhitepressure control.com

651

Figure		Owner	Web site
3-1.65	Corroded sucker rods must be replaced to keep the pumping well in good condition.	Copyright © Weatherford International. All rights reserved.	www.weatherford.com
3-1.66	Abrasion damaged these sucker rods and their coupling.	The University of Texas at Austin, PETEX	www.utexas.edu/ce/petex
3-1.67	A paraffin scraper	The University of Texas at Austin, PETEX	www.utexas.edu/ce/petex
3-1.68	Macaroni tubing fits inside the production tubing to wash sand out.	The University of Texas at Austin, PETEX	www.utexas.edu/ce/petex
3-1.69	Coiled tubing also washes sand up the annulus between the production tubing and coiled tubing.	The University of Texas at Austin, PETEX	www.utexas.edu/ce/petex
3-1.70	One reason to place a cement plug is to shut off a lower producing zone to produce a formation nearer the surface.	The University of Texas at Austin, PETEX	www.utexas.edu/ce/petex
3-1.71	Squeezing cement through the lower perforations seals them.	The University of Texas at Austin, PETEX	www.utexas.edu/ce/petex
3-2.1	This self-contained platform, the Hibernia, houses all the drilling and production equipment and facilities for the crew.	Copyright © Hibernia Management and Development Company Ltd.	www.hibernia.ca
3-2.2	The hull of a jackup can be raised well above the water's surface.	The University of Texas at Austin, PETEX	www.photos.com
3-2.3	Helicopters and cranes are common sights around an offshore operation.	Photo by Jérome Deulin. Copyright © Eurocopter. All rights reserved.	www.eurocopter.com
3-2.4	Work boats transport crew and cargo between shore and platform.	Copyright © Reflex Marine Limited. All rights reserved.	www.reflexmarine.com
3-2.5	Example of a small, shallow water production platform	The University of Texas at Austin, PETEX	www.photos.com
3-2.6	In a wet subsea completion, valves and equipment to control the flow of hydrocarbons are placed on the seafloor.	Copyright © Cameron. All rights reserved.	www.c-a-m.com
3-2.7	A submerged production system connects satellite wells to the production platform for treating and then to a mooring buoy where tankers receive the oil.	The University of Texas at Austin, PETEX	www.utexas.edu/ce/petex
3-2.8	Arctic production must take into account areas of permafrost shown here in North America.	The University of Texas at Austin, PETEX	www.utexas.edu/ce/petex
3-2.9	The Alaska pipeline from the North Slope to Valdez harbor is an Arctic engineering masterpiece.	Copyright © Aleyska Pipeline Company. All rights reserved.	www.alyeska-pipe.com
3-3.1	Production worker controlling flow of fluids with valve	The University of Texas at Austin, PETEX	www.utexas.edu/ce/petex
3-3.2	Production personnel must fully understand all aspects of equipment and procedures to ensure safe operations.	The University of Texas at Austin, PETEX	www.utexas.edu/ce/petex
3-3.3	Driving vehicles and working around hazardous chemicals present dangers	The University of Texas at Austin, PETEX	www.photos.com

Figure		Owner	Web site
	for workers.		
3-3.4	High-pressure gas or liquid escaping from a valve can injure personnel.	The University of Texas at Austin, PETEX	www.photos.com
3-3.5	Workers must wear protective gear when exposed to chemicals.	The University of Texas at Austin, PETEX	www.utexas.edu/ce/petex
3-3.6	Many production lease activities are accompanied by inherent dangers while working with fluids.	The University of Texas at Austin, PETEX	www.utexas.edu/ce/petex
3-3.7	Caustic chemicals are commonplace on many worksites.	The University of Texas at Austin, PETEX	www.utexas.edu/ce/petex
3-3.8	Safety programs include group training to ensure all workers are aware of hazards.	The University of Texas at Austin, PETEX	www.utexas.edu/ce/petex
4-1.1	The transportation industry is responsible for moving millions of barrels of crude oil daily across land and water to reach processing facilities and consumers.	Public Domain: Photo by Mark Toigo.	www.seefloridago.com
4-1.2	The Oil Creek tributary of the Allegheny River in Pennsylvania (U.S.)	The University of Texas at Austin, PETEX	www.utexas.edu/ce/petex
4-1.3	Horse-drawn wagons and barges were initially used to move oil to rail and water shipping points.	The University of Texas at Austin, PETEX	www.utexas.edu/ce/petex
4-1.4	The Densmore brothers patented this early railway tank car design.	The University of Texas at Austin, PETEX	www.utexas.edu/ce/petex
4-1.5	When denied the right to cross a railroad, one pipeline company used tank wagons to transfer the oil from the pipeline to holding tanks on the other side and then back into the pipeline.	The University of Texas at Austin, PETEX	www.utexas.edu/ce/petex
4-1.6	An early pipeline pump station used steam power to build sufficient pressure to move the oil.	The University of Texas at Austin, PETEX	www.utexas.edu/ce/petex
4-1.7	Construction of the cross-country Big Inch pipeline	Public Domain. Library of Congress, LC-USW4-029616.	www.loc.gov/index.html
4-1.8	Using bamboo poles, the Chinese were among the first to pipe natural gas.	The University of Texas at Austin, PETEX	www.utexas.edu/ce/petex
4-1.9	True horsepower was used in early-day construction of gas pipelines and compressor stations.	The University of Texas at Austin, PETEX	www.utexas.edu/ce/petex
4-1.10	Hand tongs were used by early pipeline construction workers.	The University of Texas at Austin, PETEX	www.utexas.edu/ce/petex
4-1.11	The Gluckhauf was the first successful oceangoing tanker that carried oil in storage tanks built into its hull.	The University of Texas at Austin, PETEX	www.utexas.edu/ce/petex
4-1.12	An early tank truck hauls crude oil from the well's wooden storage tank.	The University of Texas at Austin, PETEX	www.utexas.edu/ce/petex
4-1.13	Tank cars are also used to ship crude oil and refined products to and from refineries.	Copyright © John McKey, 4rail.net. All rights reserved.	www.4rail.net

Figure		Owner	Web site
4-1.14	Railcar loading racks for loading and unloading products from tank cars	Copyright © Carbis, Inc. of Florence, South Carolina. All rights reserved.	www.carbis.net
4-1.15	General-purpose rail tank car	Copyright © Global Trans. All rights reserved.	www.globaltrans.com
4-1.16	Conventional tank cars are loaded and unloaded individually while interconnected tank cars can be handled from one loading rack.	The University of Texas at Austin, PETEX	www.utexas.edu/ce/petex
4-1.17	Interconnected hoses and valves allow the entire train to be loaded and unloaded in short time.	Copyright © BTB Refining. All rights reserved.	www.btbrefining.com
4-1.18	A general-purpose fuel tank truck	The University of Texas at Austin, PETEX	www.utexas.edu/ce/petex
4-1.19	Diamond-shaped placards are used to signal hazardous contents.	Redrawn. Public Domain.	Not available
4-1.20	Tank truck loading rack	Copyright © Carbis Inc. of Florence, South Carolina All rights reserved.	www.carbis.net
4-1.21	An LPG transport truck is used to carry propane to various LPG storage units.	Copyright © Richard Mohr. All rights reserved.	www.hankstuckpictures.com/mohr.htm
4-1.22	The draft marks on the side of a barge or ocean vessel indicate how full or empty the vessel is.	The University of Texas at Austin, PETEX	www.utexas.edu/ce/petex
4-1.23	A tugboat pulls a loaded barge out of the harbor.	The University of Texas at Austin, PETEX	www.photos.com
4-1.24	A towboat has large upright knees on its bow to facilitate pushing.	Copyright © Capt. John C. Farmer, NavCal Marine Services LLC. All rights reserved.	www.navcal.com
4-1.25	The Seawise Giant, an oceangoing super-tanker	Copyright © Auke Visser, Holland. All rights reserved.	www.aukeviser.nl
4-1.26	Tanker for transporting crude oil	The University of Texas at Austin, PETEX	www.photos.com
4-1.27	A double-ended tanker can plow through ice in reverse because of its hardened stern, and travel in open waters with its conventional bow.	Copyright © Aker Arctic Technology, Inc. All rights reserved.	www.akerarctic.fi
4-1.28	Azimuth thrusters allow ships to travel backwards with ease and enable steering and docking without the use of rudders.	Copyright © BOURBON. All rights reserved.	www.bourbon-online.com
4-1.29	The Arctic Princess, an LNG containment system of Kvaener-Moss design	Copyright © HÖEGH LNG. All rights reserved.	www.hoegh.com
4-1.30	An LNG ship: a Gaz Transport No. 96 membrane containment system	Copyright © Qatar Liquefied Gas Limited. All rights reserved.	www.qatargas.com
4-1.31	The Polar Eagle LNG ship IHI SPB containment system	Copyright © IHI Marine United Inc. All rights reserved.	www.ihi.co.jp/imc
4-1.32	A tanker shuttles down a U.S. coastal waterway.	The University of Texas at Austin, PETEX	www.photos.com
4-1.33	Tankers of various sizes transport North Slope crude oil from the Trans-Alaska Pipeline System at the Valdez Marine	Copyright © The Joint State-Federal Pipeline Office, Anchorage, Alaska. All rights reserved.	www.jpo.doi.gov

Figure		Owner	Web site
4-1.33 (cont.)	Terminal in southern Alaska and deliver it to ports in the lower 48 United States.		
4-1.34	Cycle of crude transport from the well-head to the lease tanks and to the consumer	The University of Texas at Austin, PETEX	www.utexas.edu/ce/petex
4-1.35	Pipeline pumps and motors	The University of Texas at Austin, PETEX	www.photos.com
4-1.36	Alaskan pipeline pump station	Copyright © The Joint State-Federal Pipeline Office, Anchorage, Alaska. All rights reserved.	www.jpo.doi.gov
4-1.37	A gauger measures the volume and draws samples to test before pumping begins.	The University of Texas at Austin, PETEX	www.photos.com
4-1.38	Booster pumps pull oil from storage tanks and move it to the suction of the trunkline pumps.	Larry Bennington	Not available
4-1.39	A tank farm is an integral component of a pipeline system.	Larry Bennington	Not available
4-1.40	The manifold at a pump station and tank farm permits routing of the oil stream to its destination.	Not available	Not available
4-1.41	Pipeline control room	Copyright © Kinder Morgan. All rights reserved.	www.kindermorgan.com
4-1.42	A products pipeline terminal supplies an area of high demand.	The University of Texas at Austin, PETEX	www.utexas.edu/ce/petex
4-1.43	A dispatcher controls product movement and monitors other operations from the main computer console.	Copyright © Kinder Morgan. All rights reserved.	www.kindermorgan.com
4-1.44	A products pipeline runs batches of different products in sequence, similar to this typical cycle.	The University of Texas at Austin, PETEX	www.utexas.edu/ce/petex
4-1.45	Major U.S. natural gas pipelines connect supply areas and demand centers.	Public Domain. Energy Information Administration, Office of Oil & Gas, Natural Gas Division, Gas Transportation Information System.	www.eia.doe.gov
4-1.46	A gas pipeline compressor station	Copyright © Siemens. All rights reserved.	www.siemens.com
4-1.47	A gas turbine used in gas compressor stations	The University of Texas at Austin, PETEX	www.utexas.edu/ce/petex
4-1.48	A control center using numerous auto-mated features monitors and controls the pipeline and keeps tabs on deliveries throughout a gas pipeline system.	Copyright © Kinder Morgan. All rights reserved.	www.kindermorgan.com
4-1.49	A clear pipeline right-of-way	The University of Texas at Austin, PETEX	www.utexas.edu/ce/petex
4-1.50	In this aboveground section of the Trans-Alaska Pipeline, the roadbed along the right-of-way supports working vehicles as well as the pipeline itself.	Copyright © The State of Alaska, Division of Oil and Gas. All rights reserved.	www.alaska.gov

Figure		Owner	Web site
4-1.51	A wheel ditcher leaves a neat spoil bank that aids in rapid backfilling.	The University of Texas at Austin, PETEX	www.utexas.edu/ce/petex
4-1.52	In aboveground construction, VSMs hold insulated pipe at various heights while special finned radiators and heat pipes draw heat away from the ground.	Source: Harvey Barrison	www.flickr.com/photo/hbarrison
4-1.53	The pipeline contractor strings pipe joints along the right-of-way so they are accessible but do not obstruct spread equipment and work crews.	The University of Texas at Austin, PETEX	www.utexas.edu/ce/petex
4-1.54	A pipe bending machine	The University of Texas at Austin, PETEX	www.utexas.edu/ce/petex
4-1.55	Preparing to weld	The University of Texas at Austin, PETEX	www.utexas.edu/ce/petex
4-1.56	Welders work on opposite sides of the pipe as they make the initial weld on two joints held together by an internal line-up clamp.	The University of Texas at Austin, PETEX	www.utexas.edu/ce/petex
4-1.57	Side-boom tractors with correctly spaced slings lower pipe into the ditch.	Copyright © Kinder Morgan. All rights reserved.	www.kindermorgan.com
4-1.58	Pipeline lowered in the trench.	The University of Texas at Austin, PETEX	www.utexas.edu/ce/petex
4-1.59	A boring machine pushes casing under a roadbed as its cutting head rotates just inside the front of the casing.	The University of Texas at Austin, PETEX	www.utexas.edu/ce/petex
4-1.60	Flotation devices support sections of pipe during a river crossing.	The University of Texas at Austin, PETEX	www.utexas.edu/ce/petex
4-1.61	After construction is completed, the pipeline is then backfilled using as much original dirt as possible, and the land is neatly restored so it can produce vegetation once again.	The University of Texas at Austin, PETEX	www.utexas.edu/ce/petex
4-1.62	Welding, coating, and inspection are handled at stations on the lay barge.	Copyright © Gulfstream Natural Gas System, LLC. All rights reserved.	www.gulfstreamgas.com
4-1.63	The completed pipeline is lowered into the water by way of an inclined ramp and astinger.	Copyright © CRC Evans. All rights reserved.	www.crc-evans.com
4-1.64	The stinger guides the pipeline safely to the seafloor.	The University of Texas at Austin, PETEX	www.utexas.edu/ce/petex
4-1.65	High-pressure jets of water from a jet sled dig a trench for a pipeline on the seafloor.	The University of Texas at Austin, PETEX	www.utexas.edu/ce/petex
4-1.66	A giant spool unreels continuous lengths of line pipe from a reel lay barge.	The University of Texas at Austin, PETEX	www.utexas.edu/ce/petex
4-1.67	Transportation modes are evident at this ship channel.	The University of Texas at Austin, PETEX	www.utexas.edu/ce/petex
4-1.68	Distribution of peak-shaving LNG facilities in the United States	Public Domain. Energy Information Administration, Office of Oil and Gas.	www.eia.doe.gov

Figure		Owner	Web site
4-1.69	Typical peak-shaving LNG facility	Copyright © Chicago Bridge and Iron Company. All rights reserved.	www.cbi.com
4-1.70	Projected scale of LNG industry	Stanley Huang	Not available
4-1.71	Components in LNG monetization chain	Redrawn with permission from KBR	www.kbr.com
4-1.72	Trinidad LNG plant where COPOC processes are performed	Copyright © ConocoPhillips. All rights reserved.	www.conocophillips.com
4-1.73	Three types of aboveground LNG tanks	Copyright © KBR. All rights reserved.	www.kbr.com
4-1.74	Artist drawing of the Sabine Pass LNG, L.P. Regasification Terminal, in western Cameron Parish, Louisiana.	Copyright © Cheniere Energy. All rights reserved.	www.cheniere.com
4-2.1	A refinery is an organized and coordinated arrangement of processes linked together with miles of pipe carrying crude oil in and products out.	Copyright © Valero Corporation. All rights reserved.	www.valero.com
4-2.2	Petroleum products are everywhere.	The University of Texas at Austin, PETEX	www.utexas.edu/ce/petex
4-2.3	World refineries by size	Source: Oil and Gas Journal	www.ogj.com
4-2.4a	Refineries upgrade crude oil to higher value products	Source: Valero Corporation	www.valero.com
4-2.4b	Refineries upgrade crude oil to higher value products	Source: Valero Corporation	www.valero.com
4-2.5	Hydrocarbon mix of gasoline.	Copyright © Valero Corporation. All rights reserved.	www.valero.com
4-2.6	Four types of hydrocarbon structures are paraffins, olefins, napthenes, and aromatics.	The University of Texas at Austin, PETEX	www.utexas.edu/ce/petex
4-2.7	A variety of processes is used to convert crude oil into many products, beginning with distillation.	The University of Texas at Austin, PETEX	www.utexas.edu/ce/petex
4-2.8	A simplified depiction of a refinery's key processes	Copyright © Valero Corporation. All rights reserved.	www.valero.com
4-2.9	An important job of refineries today is the conversion of oil at "the bottom of the barrel" into gasoline and other more marketable products.	Copyright © Valero Corporation. All rights reserved.	www.valero.com
4-2.10	Internal distilling process from atmospheric unit	The University of Texas at Austin, PETEX	www.utexas.edu/ce/petex
4-2.11	Basic refining concepts	Copyright © Valero Corporation. All rights reserved.	www.valero.com
4-2.12	Distillation curve chart showing the boil-off temperature of crude oil components	The University of Texas at Austin, PETEX	www.utexas.edu/ce/petex
4-2.13	Lines carry the distilled cuts from different heights to the distillation tower.	(a) The University of Texas at Austin, PETEX (b) Copyright © Chevron. All rights reserved.	www.photos.com www.chevron.com
4-2.14	Flexitrays	Copyright © Shaw Energy and Chemicals Group. All rights reserved.	www.shawgrp.com

Figure		Owner	Web site
4-2.15	Vapor passes through bubble caps and settles on trays in the distilling column.	The University of Texas at Austin, PETEX	www.utexas.edu/ce/petex
4-2.16	This Port Arthur refinery in Texas contains a vacuum distillation unit that fractionates residual oil into light vacuum gas oil, heavy vacuum gas oil, waxes and asphalt and other products.	Copyright © Valero Corporation. All rights reserved.	www.valero.com
4-2.17	Cat crackers break down gas oils into lighter, more useful products.	Copyright © Valero Corporation. All rights reserved.	www.valero.com
4-2.18	Texas City thermal cracking operations	Copyright © Valero Corporation. All rights reserved.	www.valero.com
4-2.19	An alkylation plant is capable of producing 9,200 barrels per day of alkylate	Copyright © Total Planète Energies. All rights reserved.	www.planete-energies.com
4-2.20	These tanks store n-butane, isobutene, and propane until they are needed as a feedstock or are sold.	Copyright © Valero Corporation. All rights reserved.	www.valero.com
4-2.21	Catalytic reforming boosts the octane rating of hydrotreated naphtha.	The University of Texas at Austin, PETEX	www.utexas.edu/ce/petex
4-2.22	Hydrodesulfurization is a catalytic chemical process widely used to remove sulfur from natural gas and from refined petroleum products.	Copyright © Valero Corporation. All rights reserved.	www.valero.com
4-2.23	Desalter vessel internals (TriGridmax unit)	Copyright © Cameron. All rights reserved.	www.c-a-m.com
4-2.24	Simplified hydrotreating reactor	The University of Texas at Austin, PETEX	www.utexas.edu/ce/petex
4-2.25	Hydrotreating process	The University of Texas at Austin, PETEX	www.utexas.edu/ce/petex
4-2.26	Operator looking at blending board.	Copyright © Valero Corporation. All rights reserved.	www.valero.com
4-2.27	A residual fuel hydrotreater	Copyright © Valero Corporation. All rights reserved.	www.valero.com
4-2.28	Petrochemicals satisfy the fundamental needs of modern life.	The University of Texas at Austin, PETEX	www.utexas.edu/ce/petex
4-2.29	Ethylene petrochemical plant	Copyright © Shaw Energy and Chemicals Group. All rights reserved.	www.shawgrp.com
4-2.30	Polyethylene is used to make a host of products.	Copyright © Rhewum GmbH. All rights reserved.	www.rhewum.com
4-2.31	This high-powered centrifugal compressoris an example of the huge yet precise equipment in a petrochemical plant.	Copyright © Elliot Company. All rights reserved.	www.elliott-turbo.com
4-2.32	Steam cracking is used to produce ethylene and propylene.	The University of Texas at Austin, PETEX	www.utexas.edu/ce/petex
4-2.33	Polypropylene is extruded into small bb-size pellets in its finished form.	Copyright © Plastic Options. All rights reserved.	www.plasticoptions.com

Figure		Owner	Web site
4-2.34	Water treatment and recycling to and from a petrochemical plant or oil refinery	Copyright © Eimco Water Technologies. All rights reserved.	www.eimcowater technologies.com
4-3.1	A typical gas processing plant	Copyright © Dominion. All rights reserved.	www.dom.com
4-3.2	Gas turbine-driven propane refrigeration compressor in a natural gas plant	Copyright © Elliot Company. All rights reserved.	www.elliott-turbo.com
4-3.3	The expander process is one way to recover NGLs cryogenically.	The University of Texas at Austin, PETEX	www.utexas.edu/ce/petex
4-3.4	An expander compressor used for cryogenic natural gas plants made for the El Wastani Field Development Project in Egypt	Copyright © Atlas Copco Mafi-Trench Company LLC. All rights reserved.	www.atlascopco-gap.com
4-3.5	The oil absorption process consists of NGL recovery, methane rejection, and separation of the absorbent.	The University of Texas at Austin, PETEX	www.utexas.edu/ce/petex
4-3.6	Example of a fractionation plant used to produce three products	Source: GPSA Engineering Data Book, 12th edition	http://gpsa.gasprocessors. com
4-3.7	Fractionation plant	Copyright © Linde Group. All rights reserved.	www.linde-engineering. com
5-1.1	Crude oil refinery	The University of Texas at Austin, PETEX	www.photos.com
5-1.2	Gas processing facility	Copyright © Shell Global Solutions. All rights reserved.	www.shell.com/global solutions
5-1.3	Graphical presentation of project cash flow	Source: Black Pool Energy, a W.R. Huff Company.	Not available
5-1.4	Prospect area map	The University of Texas at Austin, PETEX	www.utexas.edu/ce/petex
5-1.5	Typical jackup rig used to drill the proposed well off the Texas coast	The University of Texas at Austin, PETEX	www.photos.com
5-1.6	Well awaiting production and deck facilities	Copyright © Black Pool Energy, a W.R. Huff Company. All rights reserved.	Not available
5-1.7	Installing production deck and facilities	Copyright © Black Pool Energy, a W.R. Huff Company. All rights reserved.	Not available
5-1.8	Production deck and facilities installed	Copyright © Black Pool Energy, a W.R. Huff Company. All rights reserved.	Not available
5-1.9	Pipeline installation	Copyright © Black Pool Energy, a W.R. Huff Company. All rights reserved.	Not available
5-1.10	Structure map to demonstrate the prospect idea	The University of Texas at Austin, PETEX	www.utexas.edu/ce/petex
5-1.11	Subsurface structure map	Copyright © Black Pool Energy, a W.R. Huff Company. All rights reserved.	Not available

Figure		Owner	Web site
5-1.12	Seismic cross-section	Copyright © Black Pool Energy, a W.R. Huff Company. All rights reserved.	Not available
5-1.13	Calculating reservoir area	Copyright © Black Pool Energy, a W.R. Huff Company. All rights reserved.	Not available
5-1.14	Calculating thickness	Copyright © Black Pool Energy, a W.R. Huff Company. All rights reserved.	Not available
5-1.15	Production forecast	Source: Black Pool Energy, a W.R. Huff Company.	Not available
5-1.16	Natural gas price forecast	Source: Black Pool Energy, a W.R. Huff Company.	Not available
5-2.1	Recovery, transport, processing, and use of petroleum have potential hazards to human health and the Earth's ecology.	The University of Texas at Austin, PETEX	www.photos.com
5-2.2	Smokestacks are often used to cool the exhaust from combustion sources and to provide better air dispersion of emitted pollutants.	The University of Texas at Austin, PETEX	www.photos.com
5-2.3	Operators of offshore rigs must follow EPA regulations concerning any discharges of waste into water.	The University of Texas at Austin, PETEX	www.photos.com
5-2.4	An aquifer is a stratum of rock, sand, or gravel that holds enough water to supply wells or springs often used as a source of drinking water.	The University of Texas at Austin, PETEX	www.utexas.edu/ce/petex
5-2.5	The Outer Continental Shelf of the United States is leased to petroleum companies by the U.S. Department of the Interior.	The University of Texas at Austin, PETEX	www.utexas.edu/ce/petex
5-2.6	Waste disposal containers must be clearly labeled according to OSHA regulations.	Copyright © Saint Paul Ramsey County Department of Public Health. All rights reserved.	www.co.ramsey.mn.us/RamseyCounty
5-2.7	Water pits used for drilling fluids	Bret Boteler, Copyright © EnerMax, Inc. All rights reserved.	www.enermaxinc.com
5-2.8	Oil floating on top of drilling fluids that have been returned to the surface.	Bret Boteler, Copyright © EnerMax, Inc. All rights reserved.	www.enermaxinc.com
5-2.9	Mud chemicals to be used as additives	Bret Boteler, Copyright © EnerMax, Inc. All rights reserved.	www.enermaxinc.com
5-2.10	A derrickhand wearing personal protective equipment adds dry components to the mud.	The University of Texas at Austin, PETEX	www.utexas.edu/ce/petex
5-2.11	Water supply vessels combat the fire on the Deepwater Horizon while the U.S. Coast Guard searches for missing workers.	Public Domain. U.S. Coast Guard.	http://cgvi.uscg.mil/media
5-2.12	Pooled oil from the Exxon Valdez sitting between rocks on the shore.	Public Domain. National Oceanic and Atmospheric Administration, U.S. Department of Commerce.	www.noaa.gov

Figure		Owner	Web site
5-2.13	A boom is a flexible air-filled bag that prevents spilled oil from spreading further.	Public Domain. U.S. Coast Guard, photo by Petty Officer 1st Class John Masson.	www.uscg.mil
5-2.14	The skimmer and boom swing over the side of the boat to enclose and suck up the oil.	Public Domain. National Oceanic and Atmospheric Administration, U.S. Department of Commerce.	www.noaa.gov
5-2.15	Wildlife such as the birds can suffocate when covered with oil.	Copyright © State of Louisiana. All rights reserved.	www.la.gov
5-2.16	Health, Safety, and Environment workers were contracted to clean up oil on the beaches in Port Fourchon, Louisiana, in May 2010 following the Deepwater Horizon/BP oil spill.	Public Domain. U.S. Coast Guard, photo by Petty Officer 3rd Class Patrick Kelley.	www.uscg.mil
5-2.17	Detecting a leak in an underground pipeline.	Copyright © Tekscent Pipeline. All rights reserved.	www.tekscent.com
5-2.18	Accurately detecting leaks in pipelines canbe costly and difficult.	Public Domain	www.wikipedia.org
5-2.19	A bioreactor uses microorganisms to remove impurities from the water.	Copyright © Siemens Water Technologies Corp. All rights reserved.	www.water.siemens.com
5-2.20	A blower extracts the volatile components from soil contaminated with oil.	The University of Texas at Austin, PETEX	www.utexas.edu/ce/petex
5-2.21	Chemicals mixed with water and sprayed into the soil leach contaminants from the soil and into a recovery well.	The University of Texas at Austin, PETEX	www.utexas.edu/ce/petex
5-2.22	In biodegradation on site, groundwater is pumped to the surface, fertilizer is added, and then the groundwater is returned to the soil.	The University of Texas at Austin, PETEX	www.utexas.edu/ce/petex
5-2.23	Workers on oil rigs are exposed to numerous hazards.	Copyright © Ensco International. All rights reserved.	www.enscoplc.com
5-2.24	Proper signs help reinforce potential danger areas in the workplace.	Copyright © SignPro. All rights reserved.	www.signprofw.com
5-2.25	PPE helps prevent employee injuries or illnesses due to physical, chemical, electrical, or mechanical hazards.	Public Domain. Photo by MC2 Sandra M. Palumbo, U.S. Navy.	www.defenselink.mil
5-2.26	Checking the safety of electrical equipment	Copyright © Ensco International. All rights reserved.	www.enscoplc.com
5-2.27	Monitoring the control system to ensure safe operations of a facility	Copyright © Ensco International. All rights reserved.	www.enscoplc.com
5-2.28	All workers should receive training in safework practices.	The University of Texas at Austin, PETEX	www.utexas.edu/ce/petex
5-2.29	Procedures manuals and checklists assist in checking job site hazards.	Copyright © Optimum Safety. All rights reserved.	www.optimumsafety.co.za/Services.asp
5-2.30	Contractors must have well-documented, positive safety records to be considered to work on drilling and production operations.	The University of Texas at Austin, PETEX	www.photos.com

Figure		Owner	Web site
5-2.31	Training programs ensure employees maintain a safe workplace.	The University of Texas at Austin, PETEX	www.utexas.edu/ce/petex
5-2.32	Company safety meeting in progress	Copyright © Contek Solutions. All rights reserved.	www.contekllc.com
5-3.1	The global and United States energy mix is diverse, although fossil fuels satisfy more than 80% of the world's primary energy resources.	Public Domain. U.S. Department of Energy, Energy Information Administration.	www.eia.doe.gov
5-3.2	The fuels for electricity generation in the United States are diverse, with coal providing about half.	Public Domain. U.S. Department of Energy, Energy Information Administration.	www.eia.doe.gov
5-3.3	The percentage contribution to cumulative CO_2 emissions, 1850–2005, from different countries or regions reveals the United States to be the dominant historical contributor of CO_2 emissions to the atmosphere.	Source: T. Houser, et al.	Not available
5-3.4	High energy consumption causes impacts to the environment.	The University of Texas at Austin, PETEX	www.photos.com
5-3.5	To deliver electricity, power plants must draw significant resources to distribute energy.	The University of Texas at Austin, PETEX	www.photos.com
5-3.6	Gasoline prices directly impact households in terms of behavior.	The University of Texas at Austin, PETEX	www.photos.com
5-3.7	Projections reveal expectations for continued growth in overall energy consumption in the United States with little substantive change to the overall fuel mix, despite aggressive growth for renewable power.	Public Domain. U.S. Department of Energy, Energy Information Administration.	www.eia.doe.gov
5-3.8	Projections show expectations for continued growth in overall energy consumption.	Public Domain. U.S. Department of Energy, Energy Information Administration.	www.eia.doe.gov
5-3.9	The average daily petroleum imports in millions of barrels per day for the United States and China have shown similar patterns of growth over the last 12 years.	Public Domain. U.S. Department of Energy, Energy Information Administration.	www.eia.doe.gov
5-3.10	Paper or plastic?	The University of Texas at Austin, PETEX	www.photos.com
5-3.11	Three energy policy priorities: national security, economics and supply, and the environment.	The University of Texas at Austin, PETEX	www.utexas.edu/ce/petex
5-3.12	CO_2 from smokestacks and refineries can be captured and permanently injected in the ground.	The University of Texas at Austin, PETEX	www.photos.com
5-3.13	Carbon sequestration cycles	Public Domain. U.S. Department of Energy, Office of Fossil Energy.	www.fe.doe.gov
5-3.14	Map of population density of the United States by state.	Public Domain. U.S. Census Bureau.	www.census.gov

Figure		Owner	Web site
5-3.15	This map of wind resources at 50 miles above the Earth's surface in the United States shows that wind resources are generally located away from population centers.	Public Domain. U.S. Department of Energy, National Renewable Energy Laboratory.	www.nrel.gov
5-3.16	A map of solar photovoltaic insolation shows a phenomenon similar to that of wind in that solar resources are generally located away from population centers in the United States, with the exception of large southwest cities in Arizona, Nevada, and California.	Public Domain. U.S. Department of Energy, National Renewable Energy Laboratory.	www.nrel.gov
5-3.17	Wind and solar energy farms around the world help supply renewable energy options.	The University of Texas at Austin, PETEX	www.photos.com
5-3.18	Algae are resilient and easy to grow in both brackish and fresh water.	The University of Texas at Austin, PETEX	www.utexas.edu/ce/petex

Index